ACOUSTICAL MEASUREMENTS

REVISED EDITION

ACOUSTICAL MEASUREMENTS

REVISED EDITION

Leo L. Beranek, D.Sc.

1949 Edition: Acoustics Laboratory
Massachusetts Institute of Technology

1988 Edition: 975 Memorial Drive
Cambridge, MA 02138

**Published for the Acoustical Society of America
by the American Institute of Physics**

Library of Congress Catalog Card Number: 88-82582
International Standard Book Number: 0-88318-590-3

Printed in the United States of America

Preface to the Revised Edition

Forty years have passed since the manuscript for the first edition of *Acoustic Measurements* was completed. That era coincided with a vigorous expansion of theory, experiment, education, applications, and government support of acoustics throughout the world. The annual number of pages published in the Journal of the Acoustical Society of America has increased five-fold since 1948. Ten technical periodicals in the field, compared to one, are found in our libraries. Important acoustical research laboratories have been established in nearly every industrial country.

In the first edition, little space was devoted to the sound level meter, today's most basic sound measuring instrument. The sound level meter of the 1940s was usually equipped with a Rochelle salt crystal microphone, which was grossly sensitive to temperature and dissolved in high humidity and high temperature. Calibration of a sound level meter, even years after purchase, was seldom made and the user needed a strong back or a rolling table while taking data.

Analyzers were primarily laboratory research instruments and no high-fidelity apparatus for recording sound, except the optical track on movie film, was commercially available.

Nevertheless, one acoustical measurement device has, like the Rock of Gibraltar, stood unchanged since those days, namely, the National Bureau of Standards Type 9A coupler for measuring audiometric earphones. Other measuring equipment that have prevailed are condenser microphones, apparatus for reciprocity calibration of them, and graphic level recorders of the moving-coil-actuated type.

Today's sound and vibration level meters, analyzers, recorders, and computers are a triumph of solid-state electronics which permit a variety of accurate measurement functions. Microphones, vibration pickups and their associated amplifiers are highly stable and suited to widely varying ambient conditions. Sound, noise, and vibration generators assist every class of field and laboratory measurement. Recently, the intensity meter, which measures acoustic energy flow in any direction in complex noise fields, has come into use.

This revised edition of the original *Acoustic Measurements* attempts to cover many of these developments. Primarily owing to the lack of space, it does not deal with the design of digital equipment or with digital computer programs. References to these are given in the Appendix. The engineer must understand the basic physical laws of analog filters and signal processors to use digital equipment intelligently because both obey the same rules.

Over one-half of the pages in this edition are new, and twelve of the twenty chapters have been rewritten or revised in major ways. No attempt has been made to update the "History" section, mainly because of lack of time. Some of the more interesting earlier methods of sound measurement have been retained to illustrate the range of possibilities.

I wish to thank colleagues and equipment manufacturers who helped me with concepts and furnished me with drawings. My appreciation extends to Mary M. Smith in the Art Department of Bolt Beranek and Newman, Inc., for preparing many of the illustrations. It is my hope that the revised and renamed *Acoustical Measurements* will justify the confidence that the Acoustical Society of America has shown in producing a new edition.

Leo L. Beranek

Cambridge, Massachusetts
July 1988

Preface to the Original Edition

This book is intended primarily as a reference for graduate students and workers in the field of acoustics. I have attempted to cover the subject of acoustic measurements in such a way that the book will be an aid to five main groups of research workers: the acoustic physicist making fundamental laboratory measurements, the communications engineer measuring and evaluating the performance of audio communication systems, the psychologist performing measurements involving the human hearing mechanism, the otologist studying hearing defects, and, finally, the industrialist applying acoustic measuring techniques in manufacturing processes.

Acoustic measurements are sufficiently complex to require a knowledge of the fundamental factors involved in any given measurement and of the various apparatuses that will perform the measurement. This book gives the mathematical equations underlying each type of acoustic measurement; it describes and compares the relative advantages and disadvantages of alternative apparatuses. The resultant text is somewhat longer than that originally contemplated, but it is hoped that the increase in reading matter will effect a net saving in time for the experimenter.

I wish to express my indebtedness to many of my colleagues and fellow workers in the field of acoustics whose aid has been invaluable both in obtaining material and in reading and criticizing the manuscript. I am especially grateful to Dr. R. H. Nichols, Jr., of the Bell Telephone Laboratories, who, in addition to preparing the text for Chapters 8 and 14, devoted much time to editing and correcting the manuscript. Dr. James P. Egan of the University of Wisconsin gave kind permission to use material from one of his reports in Chapter 17.

I also wish to thank Clare Twardzik, who prepared the illustrations; Elizabeth H. Jones, who typed the manuscript; and Mr. Wilmer Bartholomew, who gave valuable assistance in editing the final manuscript.

The entire project was made possible through funds supplied by the Office of Naval Reserach, Navy Department, Washington,

D. C., under Contract No. N7onr-313.   In particular, I wish to acknowledge the assistance of Dr. Alan Waterman and Mr. Wilbert Annis in arranging for the contract and in supplying me with information from the documentary files of the Office of Naval Research.

Finally, I am grateful to my wife, Phyllis Knight Beranek, who assisted in the reading of the galley and page proof and who helped in many other ways.

I am aware that, in spite of every effort to the contrary, there will be errors in the following pages.   I assume responsibility for them, and I trust that my readers will be kind enough to point them out.

L. L. B.

Cambridge, Massachusetts
March, 1949

CONTENTS

1.

Introduction and Terminology

As in many of the other branches of science, major advances in acoustics have been preceded by empirical observation. It is not surprising that this should be true because the problems which require solution are likely to be very complicated and not readily amenable to theoretical treatment. Relatively few situations exist in which less than three dimensions need to be considered. Most acoustical phenomena such as speech, music, and noise are transient in nature. They occur in a medium which frequently is not at rest and which almost never is isotropic. Moreover, the boundary conditions to which a sound wave must adjust itself are irregularly located in space and require complex numbers for their complete specification. To complicate things further, audible sound contains components covering a range in frequency of ten octaves. Its intensity commonly varies between the two limits of hearing—the upper limit involving energies a million-million times the lower!

As a final deterrent to the theoretician, the speed of propagation of a sound wave is such that the lengths of sound waves in the audible region are neither large nor small compared with the obstacles forming the boundaries from which reflections ordinarily occur. Anyone who has taken a casual look at the equations which arise from the treatment of many relatively simple acoustical problems realizes why the scientist has frequently turned to his apparatus instead of his pencil. One such problem is the distribution of steady-state sound in a rectangular room, one wall of which has on it a few patches of acoustical material flush with the surface. The notation alone required in the solution of this problem amounts to more than 65 symbols! And even after the formulas have been evolved there is the difficulty of reducing them to numerical answers. As a result the mathematician is often forced to make a number of simplifying assumptions which restrict his treatment to a portion of the frequency range and to a limited choice of boundary conditions.

We must not conclude, however, that the theoretical physicist plays a less important part than the experimentalist in the advancement of acoustics. We need only to cite the tremendous influence which Lord Rayleigh and P. M. Morse exercised through the medium of their volumes, *The Theory of Sound* and *Vibration and Sound*, respectively, to prove this point. Furthermore, improved mathematical techniques are appearing. Significant developments in calculating devices are being made. And many institutions are employing groups of persons whose chief occupation is to convert formulas into charts or tables.

In addition to the mathematical and physical aspects of acoustics there is a third and equally important branch of knowledge which plays its role, namely, psychology. Many situations involving acoustics are as much psychological as physical. Music, speech, and noise more often than not are produced and controlled for the pleasure or displeasure of individuals. Hence, an important part of the understanding of the needs of an acoustic system is a knowledge of the way people react when subjected to the stimulus of a particular sound. Historically, the psychological aspects of acoustics have received considerable attention. Even the early literature concerns itself with determinations of the threshold of hearing and experiments on loudness and pitch. Nevertheless, progress in this field has been slow because of the inadequacies of measuring equipment, the scarcity of physicists acquainted with psychological methods, and the lack of psychologists familiar with the tools of physics.

The Bell Telephone Laboratories in this country has prosecuted an extended research program in psychoacoustics during the last 20 years. Also, several of the psychology departments in the universities of the United States and Europe performed intensive researches in speech and hearing before World War II. These researches have greatly advanced our understanding of methods of planning equipment and environments for the successful communication of speech and the enjoyment of music. Notable advances in psychoacoustics have arisen from the expenditures of the Office of Scientific Research and Development during World War II and of the Office of Naval Research since. In particular the work of the Psycho-Acoustic Laboratory at Harvard University has done much to advance the problems of speech and hearing in the presence of various types of masking noises.

The paragraphs above are presented to illustrate the difficulties which have plagued and will continue to plague the scientists in this field. Now we shall make a quick survey of the growth of the experimental aspects of acoustics before going on to the subject matter of this text.

We can always understand a subject better if we know something of its history. Furthermore, such a history points out which techniques are new and which are old and perhaps in need of revision. In compiling the history of acoustical measurements which follows, I have made no attempt to be exhaustive. The selections here may lack some worthwhile advances, and they probably include some developments which have not received much acclaim elsewhere.

1·1 History

Before 1800, scientific apparatus in acoustics was of the simplest kind. The pendulum had been used as a demonstration instrument by Galileo (1564–1642). Mersenne (1588–1648) had used it to time the speed of sound, arriving at the value of 1038 ft/sec. The first serious attempt to measure the speed of sound was made as part of the program of the *Accademia del Cimento* of Florence (*ca.* 1660). The value obtained was 1148 ft/sec. Still later, Flamsteed and Halley in England made careful experiments over a distance of about three miles from the Greenwich Observatory to Shooter's Hill. About 1708 they declared the speed to be 1142 ft/sec. The tuning fork had been invented in 1711 by John Shore, a trumpeter in the service of George I of England. He humorously referred to this instrument as a "pitch-fork." A variable standard of frequency was demonstrated by Stancari in 1706. His device was a direct copy of Robert Hooke's (1681) rotating serrated wheel against which a reed was pressed. Stancari demonstrated that the frequency could be calculated from the number of teeth and the speed of rotation. Later Savart (1830) used such a wheel for the determination of the frequency of a sound, and so the name Savart's wheel has arisen.

The speed of sound was again studied by a commission of the

French Academy of Sciences, and in 1738 they announced their result to be 1094 ft/sec at 0°C. No direct measurement of frequency had been devised, although John Robinson came close when he built a sort of siren to produce musical tones of varying frequency. Nor does it appear that a method for the measurement of the intensity of a sound field was available before 1800.

By comparison with the eighteenth century, progress in the nineteenth was tremendous, and it so appeared to Professor James Loudon[1] in 1901. He chose as his presidential address to the American Association for the Advancement of Science the subject, "A Century of Progress in Acoustics." We find his comments particularly interesting today.

"I am fully alive to the fact that this branch of science has been comparatively neglected by physicists for many years, and that consequently I cannot hope to arouse the interest which the choice of a more popular subject might demand. . . . Such a survey [over the century] will make it evident not only that the science of acoustics has made immense progress during that time, but also that many of the experimental methods in use in other branches of physical science were invented and first employed in the course of acoustical research. This latter fact . . . furnishes an illustration of the interdependence which exists between the various branches of physical science, and suggests the probability that the work of acoustical research in the future may be advanced by experimental methods specially designed for investigation in other fields. A revival will, of course, come in time for acoustics . . . and it ought to come all the sooner because of the cooperation which physicists may naturally look for from those who are cultivating the new fields of experimental psychology."

Professor Loudon believed that the first significant advance of the nineteenth century was the work of Chladni in 1802 in determining the wave patterns of vibrating bodies by means of sand figures. He also made elaborate investigations of the longitudinal and torsional vibrations of rods and strings and of the transverse vibrations of bars and plates. Those studies interested Wheatstone who, in 1833, developed a theory which showed that the existence of nodal lines was "due to the superposition of transversal vibrations, corresponding to sounds of the same pitch co-existing with respect to different directions in the plate."

[1] J. Loudon, "A century of progress in acoustics," *Science*, **14,** 987 (1901).

In 1807, Dr. Thomas Young described a graphical apparatus for accurate determination of frequency. It consisted of a rotating drum with a blackened surface. He described its purpose as follows: "By means of this instrument we may measure, without difficulty, the frequency of the vibrations of sounding bodies, by connecting them with a point which will describe an undulated path on the roller. These vibrations may also serve in a very simple manner for the measurement of the minutest intervals of time; . . . ."

Scott adapted the smoked surface technique to the measurement of air waves in 1858. Called the "phonautograph," it consisted of a horn terminated by a flexible diaphragm.[2] By means of a lever arrangement, a stylus was made to move in unison with the diaphragm motion and thus to trace out the to-and-fro motion (of the sound wave) on the smoked surface. This was the first use of a diaphragm to pick up sound. Since that time diaphragms have played an important role in all acoustic measurements.

About this same year, Leconte accidentally discovered the sensitive flame, which provided a crude means for determining the intensity of sound waves.[3] A sound-sensitive flame is produced by turning up a gas jet until the flame is just below its unstable point. The disturbance of the air around the jet produced by a sound wave breaks up the streamline motion of the air. A modification in the shape of the flame which is quite sensitive to changes in intensity of the wave results.

Between 1858 and 1862, Rudolph Koenig devoted himself specially to the perfecting of Scott's phonautograph and presented his results at the Exhibition in London in 1862 in the form of a large collection of "phonograms." Loudon says, "This collection in its seven sections comprises all the applications of the method which have so far been made in acoustics. . . . Parenthetically, I might remark that Edison's phonograph [1877] was doubtless suggested by Scott's phonautograph."

D. C. Miller became interested in the phonautograph and modified it to produce optically a greatly magnified trace of a sound wave (1909).[4] In essence his device, called the *phonodeik*, was the same as Scott's phonautograph, except that the stylus was

[2] L. Scott, *Cosmos*, **14**, 314 (1859); *Comptes rendus*, **53**, 108 (1861).

[3] J. Leconte, *Phil. Mag.*, **15**, 235 (1858).

[4] D. C. Miller, *The Science of Musical Sounds*, Macmillan (1916).

replaced by a rotatable mirror. A light beam, reflected from this mirror and properly focused, would move backward and forward across a film traveling in a vertical direction. The speed of his film was about 40 ft/sec, and the magnification of the diaphragm motion was about 40,000 times.

In 1827, Wheatstone invented the kaleidophone.[5] This device was based on a suggestion of Young in 1807 for an optical method of studying vibratory movements from curves constructed from the composition of two perpendicular vibratory movements. The kaleidophone consisted of two thin strips of metal each having dimensions of, say, 1 cm by 10 cm. One end of one strip was joined to one end of the other. The longitudinal axes of the two lay along a straight line. However, their flat surfaces were at right angles to each other. Consequently one strip would bend easily in the direction perpendicular to its flat surface, but the other would be very rigid in that direction. In use one strip was clamped in a vise, and a bright metallic bead was attached to the end of the other strip. If displaced in one particular direction both strips would oscillate. If displaced in a direction 90° to this only the unclamped strip would oscillate. If the system was given an initial displacement in a direction at an angle to these two directions, the bead would execute a motion compounded of two vibrations at right angles but of different periods. The bead was strongly illuminated and its motion projected on a screen. Loudon says, "The most important advance, however, in the development of this method was made by Lissajous, who published in 1857 his great paper entitled 'Mémoire sur l'étude optique des movement vibratoires.' . . . The chief merit of the method . . . lies in the fact that by this means we are able to determine with facility and with the utmost accuracy both the interval and the difference of phase between two vibratory movements. It is this fact which renders the optical comparator one of the most important instruments at the disposal of the acoustician."

An optical method for the determination of the strength of a sound wave was first described by Biot in 1820[6] and developed further by Kundt in 1864 and Mach in 1872.[7] With it the changes in density at the nodes of a sound wave inside a trans-

[5] A. Wood, *Acoustics*, p. 211, Interscience Publishers, Inc. (1941).

[6] J. B. Biot, *Physique*, **2**, 15 (1828).

[7] L. Mach, *Ann. d. Physik*, **146**, 315 (1872).

parent resonant tube could be exhibited when the nodal line was placed between the crossed mirrors of a polarization apparatus. During the continuance of the vibrations, the image would be highly illuminated in the analyzer, but it would become darkened when the vibrations stopped.

A second optical method was devised by Toepler and Boltzmann in 1870.[8] Their method consisted in producing interference bands by combining two rays of intermittent light originating from the same source, one of which passed through the air in its normal state, and the other through a nodal point of a vibrating air column. A vibrating movement of the interference bands resulted—a movement which could be made as slow as desirable by changing one of the path lengths. Thus it was possible to measure exactly by stroboscopic methods the movement of the air at the nodal point.

In 1862 Rudolph Koenig invented the method of manometric flames. By that method, illuminating gas was passed through a small chamber and thence into a regular burner tip. One side of the chamber was closed by a goldbeater's sheet, which, because of its thinness, vibrated in response to the pressure of a sound wave impinging on it. The changes in volume of the chamber caused by the motions of the thin diaphragm resulted in a "dancing" flame. This dancing flame was then reflected by a revolving mirror into the lens of a camera, and a photographic plate of pressure amplitude *vs.* time was obtainable for analysis.

The first use of stroboscopic disks for the purpose of observing very rapid periodic movements was made by Plateau in 1836. Many years later, Toepler made the method generally known when he published a number of his experiments in Poggendorff's *Annalen*, Volume 128.

Cagniard de la Tour in 1819 invented the siren, and it was he who gave it its name. The present form of the acoustic siren was constructed first by Seebeck (1841)[9] and improved on by Koenig in 1867. An account of a series of experiments using it was published by Koenig in 1881. It was the first instrument by which the frequency of a sound was directly determinable. Also, for many years, the acoustic siren was the principal source of continuously variable sound.

Last, but far from least, we mention the first practical, pre-

[8] A. Toepler and L. Boltzmann, *Ann. d. Physik*, **141**, 321 (1870).

[9] A. Seebeck, *Pogg. Ann.*, **35**, 417 (1841).

cision instrument for the measurement of the strength of a sound wave, the Rayleigh disk.   Invented by Lord Rayleigh in 1882,[10] it became, after Koenig's theoretical analysis of its performance in 1891,[11] a widely used instrument for the measurement of particle velocity in a sound wave.

Loudon concluded the first half of his summary of nineteenth century acoustics by saying, "The mere enumeration of the methods of acoustical research which have been devised since the days of Chladni is an indication of the enormous advances which have been made in this branch of science." Now, let us see where these instruments of measurement were used.

The principal advances of the nineteenth century involved four aspects of acoustical science: measurement of the velocity of sound, determination of frequency (called pitch), determination of particle velocity, and observations on timbre.   In particular, Loudon described the researches of Victor Regnault who, between 1860 and 1870, measured the velocity of sound by making use of electric signals and a graphical method to measure the time intervals between the starting of a signal and its reception at a distant point.   His tests were performed primarily in empty tubes, in lengths up to 4900 meters, which were to be part of the Paris sewer system.   The principal conclusions reached by Regnault were:

1. In a cylindrical tube the intensity of a sound wave varies, diminishing with distance.   The narrower the tube, the more rapid is the diminution.

2. The velocity of the sound decreases as the intensity diminishes.

3. The velocity approaches a limiting value, which increases with the diameter of the tube.   The mean value in dry air at 0°C in a tube of diameter 1.10 meter is 330.6 m/sec (1085 ft/sec).

4. The velocity in a gas is independent of the pressure.

5. The velocity is not affected by the method of producing the sound wave.

On the subject of pitch and frequency, Loudon described the work of Scheibler in 1834 as "most important."   Scheibler in 1834 invented a tonometer consisting of a series of 56 tuning forks going from *A* (440) to its octave *A* (880).   In 1862 during

[10] Lord Rayleigh, *Phil. Mag.*, **14**, 186 (1882).
[11] R. Koenig, *Wied. Ann.*, **43**, 43 (1891).

the London Exhibition Koenig drew attention to this instrument by displaying one of his own containing 65 forks going from C_3 (512) to C_4 (1024).[12]

The standard of pitch was decreed by the French Government in 1859 as $A = 435$ cps at 15°C. Lissajous prepared this standard, but it was later found to be too high by 0.45 cps. Koenig later standardized the familiar reference pitch of $C = 512$ cps at 20°C. Koenig then constructed a universal tonometer which he finished in 1897 after working a score of years. This tonometer had a range from 16 to 90,000 cps and consisted of:

1. 4 forks equipped with tuning sliders giving vibrations from 16 to 64 cps with increments at first of 0.25 cps and afterwards of 0.5 cps.

2. 132 large forks, equipped with tuning sliders, tuned to give (without the sliders) the 127 harmonics of C_1 (128). Of these C_2, C_3, C_4, C_5, and C_6 were in duplicate.

3. 40 resonators to reinforce the forks of (2).

4. 1 large resonator.

5. 18 forks for notes from C_7 to F_9.

6. 15 forks from G_9 to 90,000 cps.

This tonometer was then used as a source of sound by Koenig to determine the limits of audibility of the ear. He concluded that the limits are a function of the intensity of the sound and lie at about 13 cps and 17,500 cps, depending somewhat on the individual. Helmholtz showed that if the frequency of a sound is very low (the fundamental being accompanied by a series of harmonics), the fundamental may be quite inaudible by itself, while the harmonics are heard distinctly. In such a case the fundamental is often judged to be present.

With respect to the loudness of sounds, Loudon said, "With regard to the question of intensity [loudness] of sound, it is only necessary to say that there exists a great lacuna in our acoustical knowledge, as we do not yet possess a means of measuring the physiological intensity of sound."

When he came to summarize the studies of the nineteenth century on timbre, Loudon could do little except quote disagreements between Helmholtz and Koenig. Helmholtz is credited

[12] Helmholtz, *Sensations of Tone*, 3rd English edition, p. 443, Longmans, Green (1930).

with first stating that the timbre of a sound depends on the number and intensity of the harmonics accompanying the fundamental. The two disagreed, however, about the way the ear hears two tones and whether phase makes any difference. Helmholtz contended that timbre "depended only on the number and relative intensities of the harmonics which accompany the fundamental, and that it was not affected in any degree by differences in phases of these components." Koenig held "that differences of phase as regards harmonics exercise a very important influence on the timbre of the sound."[13] Loudon concluded by saying, "These experiments [by Koenig on the effects of the phase of harmonics on the timbre of the tone] may be said to be the last on this difficult subject in the years of the century which has just closed."

The most astonishing thing about Loudon's address is his complete disregard of the contributions of Lord Rayleigh. The Rayleigh disk was not even mentioned. He did this in spite of the fact that Rayleigh's treatise, *Theory of Sound*, was first published in 1877 and was immediately acknowledged by the scientific world as authoritative. Such disregard was not shown by W. H. Eccles, the retiring president of the Physical Society of London, who spoke on March 22, 1929, on the subject "The New Acoustics."[14] President W. H. Eccles paid Rayleigh the tribute he deserves by saying:

"It is just over fifty years since Lord Rayleigh published his *Theory of Sound*. Although it was mainly a mathematical treatment of the subject, it comprised much experimental matter and was undoubtedly the most comprehensive work on acoustics that had till then been published. It constituted a treatise of the whole physical theory and in it was arranged in logical order a great mass of material collected from all sources. Many old lacunae in the subject were filled by the author's own original work, experimental and mathematical; and as a consequence we may take it as representing the whole of physical acoustics of fifty years ago." However, Eccles said that the subject is carried "along in the traditional manner" and the books (including Volume II published eighteen years later) "show little indication of the change in treatment that has transformed acoustics within the past decade."

[13] R. Koenig, *Wied. Ann.*, **12**, 335 (1881).
[14] W. H. Eccles, *Proc. Phys. Soc.*, **41**, 231 (1929).

Eccles developed his speech around the premise that acoustics had advanced in the twentieth century primarily because of developments in electrical circuits and radio. He described the microphone, the vacuum tube amplifier, the production of sound waves by earphones and loudspeakers, the electrical wave filter, and, finally, the mathematical theory of electrical circuits and electromagnetic wave propagation as the building stones of modern acoustics. He spent considerable time discussing the advance of psychological acoustics until that time and stressed the importance of logarithmic frequency and intensity scales when dealing with sound in relation to the ear. Although it would be interesting to reproduce large parts of his talk it is probably more to the point to confine our efforts to tracing the history of the development of the measuring tools of acoustics during the present century.

Until 1916 only four methods had been advanced for the absolute determination of sound intensity: the Rayleigh disk method for determining particle velocity in a plane wave field;[10] the method of measuring the increased pressure at a reflecting wall according to the theory of Rayleigh and the experimental techniques of Altberg;[15] the method of measuring pressure changes at nodes of stationary waves by a manometer due to the work of Raps;[16] and, finally, several variations of the method making use of optical interference.[17]

Although the telephone was invented in 1876, it was not until 1908 that a report on the relative measurement of sound intensity by electronic equipment was published. G. W. Pierce in an experiment described in a paper entitled "A simple method of measuring the intensity of sound," used a Bell magneto-telephone receiver (also a carbon button) as a microphone, a tuning condenser, a step-up transformer, a molybdenite (MoS_2) rectifier, and a galvanometer.[18] With that apparatus he examined the sound intensity in different parts of various auditoriums, and he observed the whistle of a distant train on his galvanometer scale. Thus the first sound level meter was born. However, his meter did not enjoy immediate acceptance. In 1913, H. O. Taylor said

[15] W. Altberg, *Ann. d. Physik*, **11**, 405–420 (1903).

[16] A. Raps, *Ann. d. Physik*, **36**, 273 (1889).

[17] A. Raps, *Ann. d. Physik*, **50**, 44, 193 (1893); Sharpe, *Science*, **9**, 808 (1910, 1908).

[18] G. W. Pierce, *Proc. Am. Acad. Arts and Sci.*, **43**, 377 (1908).

that in a search for a method of measuring the intensity of sound he tested everything of any promise including "telephone receivers, strong and weak field galvanometers, molybdenite and silicon rectifiers," and that the Rayleigh disk was found to be "the most reliable and sensitive sound measuring instrument."[19]

The first effective attempts to introduce modern and precise measuring instruments into acoustics were those of Arnold and Crandall, and Wente of the American Telephone and Telegraph and Western Electric Laboratories in 1917. Arnold and Crandall's big contribution was the development of the thermophone.[20] This device is an electro-thermo-acoustical transducer which serves as an absolute standard of sound pressure. Its acoustic output in a closed cavity can be calculated from measurement of its physical properties and the electrical current passing through it. Wente's contribution was the development of an electrostatic microphone with a high diaphragm impedance, wide frequency range, and good stability, and the ability to be calibrated readily with the aid of a thermophone.[21] As Eccles pointed out, "it [the condenser microphone] would have been almost useless without that modern universal instrumentality, the triode amplifier. . . . Evidently, the combination of a sensitive microphone and a high [gain] amplifier solves the problem of converting even a feeble pressure variation in air into a measurable electrical current of equal frequency."

Early in the twentieth century the earphone was a relatively crude device. About 1912, the concept of motional impedance was introduced by Kennelly and Pierce,[22] and rapid improvement of the response characteristics of earphones soon followed. The development of suitable sound sources for acoustical experimentation came shortly after the development of these improved earphones. By 1920, "high fidelity" earphones, which were reasonably constant in response up to 4000 cps, were being used at the Bell Telephone Laboratories in investigations of speech and hearing. The coupling of these units to horns soon led to the loudspeaker, and another tool of tremendous value was available to the acoustical experimenter.

[19] H. O. Taylor, *Phys. Rev.*, **2**, 270 (1913).

[20] H. D. Arnold and I. B. Crandall, *Phys. Rev.*, **10**, 22 (1917).

[21] E. C. Wente, *Phys. Rev.*, **19**, 333 (1922).

[22] A. E. Kennelly and G. W. Pierce, *Proc. Am. Acad. Arts and Sci.*, **48**, 111 (1912).

Architectural acoustics was also receiving much needed attention at the turn of the century. Professor W. C. Sabine of Harvard, who practically constituted a one-man interest in the subject before World War I, brought forth the first real understanding of sound in auditoriums.[23] At the same time he introduced measuring techniques for determining the absorptivity and transmissivity of sound at the boundaries of rooms. The fact that in none of his published papers did this exceedingly conscientious scientist find an occasion to refer to an earlier paper shows that almost no work had been done before his entry into the field.

In summarizing the history of architectural acoustics, Dr. P. E. Sabine (a distant cousin of W. C. Sabine) wrote in 1939,[24] "Up until 1925, the stopwatch and ear method [of W. C. Sabine] was the only available means of timing reverberation with the old reliable organ pipe as the source of sound. . . . Later, the microphone, amplifier, and electrically operated timer replaced the ear and the stopwatch. At a still later date came the high speed level recorders giving a complete graph of the decay of reverberant sound." That is where the measurement of acoustical absorptivity remains today. Recently, a few experimenters have attempted to learn more about sound-absorbing materials by measuring the normal acoustic impedance of samples. A sizable literature is now building up around that technique.

The concept of acoustic impedance was advanced by Webster who, as Eccles says, "emphasized in 1914 the use of the concept of acoustic impedance for replacing by a single complex number all the quantities involved in the reaction of an acoustical system. He [Webster] proceeded to write down formulae for the typical impedances most frequently met with in pure acoustics, namely, those due to inertia, elasticity and the production of free waves. He then obtained expressions for the impedance of the open end of cylindrical and tapering tubes, and incidentally completed, by comparatively easy steps, Rayleigh's early discussion on the properties of horns."[25] In 1921 Kennelly and Kurokawa described a method for measuring acoustic impedance using the

[23] W. C. Sabine, *Collected Papers on Acoustics*, Harvard University Press (1927).

[24] P. E. Sabine, *Jour. Acous. Soc. Amer.*, **11**, 21 (1939).

[25] A. G. Webster, *Proc. Nat. Acad. Sci.*, **5**, 275 (1919).

principle of acoustic reaction on a vibrating diaphragm.[26] Shortly thereafter, other observers extended the method advanced by Taylor in 1913 for measuring absorption coefficients to the measurement of acoustic impedance. Because of these developments research on horns, loudspeakers, and acoustical materials has flourished.

Despite the strides in instrumentation just mentioned for both physical and psychological acoustics, many fundamental types of measurements received little or no attention until recently because of the lack of an environment suitable for the production of free progressive sound waves. It was not until 1935 that a "free-field" sound chamber suitable for precision measurements indoors was described in the literature by Bedell.[27] Although developments in Germany and in this country have led to improvements in sound chambers with non-reflective boundaries, the principal method today for measuring the response of a loudspeaker consists in taking it outdoors and pointing it in a direction where there are no reflecting surfaces—a method wherein ambient temperature, wind, and weather have free play. In part, the lack of precise measurements of sound pressure before the perfection of the thermophone was due to the difficulty of using the Rayleigh disk either outdoors, where there were uncontrollable drafts, or indoors, where there were undesirable standing waves.

The development of meters for the measurement of noise has been slow, despite the lead of Pierce in 1908 and the availability of the condenser microphone after 1917. With the development of rugged wide-band microphones (moving coil and crystal) requiring no polarizing voltage, portable noise meters made their appearance. It then became feasible to write American Standards covering the measurement and description of noise levels—a necessary action because calibrations of sound level meters of different manufacturers were made without a common reference level for the decibel scales.

World War II with the attendant German and Japanese submarine activity brought about an unprecedented amount of activity in applied acoustics[28] in the United States and Great

---

[26] A. E. Kennelly and K. Kurokawa, *Proc. Amer. Acad. Arts and Sci.*, **56**, 1 (1921).

[27] E. H. Bedell, *Jour. Acous. Soc. Amer.*, **8**, 118 (1936).

[28] J. P. Baxter, 3rd, *Scientists Against Time*, Little, Brown and Company (1946).

Britain. A number of large government-sponsored laboratories were formed in addition to already existing government and industrial groups for the investigation of acoustical problems associated with undersea warfare, the improvement of airborne voice-communicating equipment, the development of special types of sound sources and locating equipments, and the propagation of sound through the atmosphere. As this manuscript is being written numerous articles on these subjects are appearing in the journals.

In conclusion, we quote Eccles, "From this rapid review of the change that has come over the science of sound since the publication of Rayleigh's treatise . . . , it will be seen that the new acoustics is Baconian, that is to say, it is being prosecuted with a view to rendering services to mankind rather than from the motive of scientific curiosity." This observation still applies to large extent today, but, fortunately for its future as a fundamental science, there has been a revival of interest in acoustics by those possessing "scientific curiosity." With the new tools of quantum mathematics and of electronics we can hope for the solution of many of the complex problems of acoustics, for significant advances in speech communication, and for the maximum enjoyment of music and speech in our concert halls and homes.

1·2 Terminology

Absorption (see *Equivalent absorption*).

Absorption coefficient for a surface is the ratio of the sound energy absorbed by a surface of a medium (or material) exposed to a sound field (or to sound radiation) to the sound energy incident on the surface. The stated values of this ratio are to hold for an infinite area of the surface. The conditions under which measurements of absorption coefficients are made are to be stated explicitly.

Three types of absorption coefficients associated with three methods of measurement are:

CHAMBER ABSORPTION COEFFICIENT is obtained in a certain reverberation chamber. The conditions under which the coefficient is measured are to be stated explicitly.

FREE-WAVE ABSORPTION COEFFICIENT is obtained when a plane, progressive, sound wave is incident on the surface of the medium. The angle of incidence is to be stated explicitly. When the angle of incidence is normal to the surface, the coefficient is called *normal free-wave absorption coefficient*.

SABINE ABSORPTION COEFFICIENT is obtained when the sound is incident from all directions on the sample.

Acoustic compliance (see *Compliance*).

Acoustic impedance (see *Impedance*).

Acoustic mass (see *Mass*).

Acoustic ohm is the unit of acoustic resistance, acoustic reactance, and acoustic impedance. The magnitude of the acoustic ohm is unity when a sound pressure of 1 dyne/cm^2 produces a volume velocity of 1 cm^3/sec.

Acoustic reactance (see *Reactance*).

Acoustic resistance (see *Resistance*).

Acoustician is a person who is versed in the science of sound.

Acoustics is the science of sound (see *Sound*).

Air conduction is the conduction of sound to the middle and inner ear, through the air in the outer ear canal (see also *Bone conduction*).

American Standard pitch is based on the frequency 440 cps for tone *A* on the pianoforte keyboard. The word "pitch" here is used in place of the proper term "frequency."

Amplitude distortion (see *Distortion*).

Analyzer is an electrical, mechanical, or acoustical device capable of dividing a spectrum into a finite number of frequency regions (bands) and determining the relative magnitude of the energy in each region (band). Some analyzers also determine the relative phases of the components of a line spectrum.

Anechoic is an adjective meaning "echo-free." A chamber is said to be anechoic if a sound field can be established in it without objectionable interference from sound reflections at the boundaries. A common measure of satisfactoriness for many experiments is that the sound pressure in the chamber measured by a point microphone moving away from a point source decreases within ± 1.0 db of the theoretical inverse square law.

Antinodes are the loci (points, lines, or surfaces) in a standing (pseudo-stationary) wave system which have maximum amplitude of pressure or velocity.

Anti-resonance is the opposite of resonance (see *Resonance*).

Anti-resonant frequency is a frequency at which anti-resonance exists. The unit is the cycle per second. Where confusion may exist it is necessary to specify whether velocity or displacement anti-resonance is meant.

Articulation testing. ARTICULATION TEST is a procedure by which a quantitative measure of the intelligibility of speech is obtained.

ARTICULATION SCORE is the percentage of speech items correctly recorded by a group of listeners who are listening to sentences, words, or syllables read by a talker.

SENTENCE ARTICULATION SCORE is the articulation score obtained when sentences are read by a talker.

SOUND ARTICULATION SCORE is the percentage of the total number of fundamental speech sounds which are correctly recognized when the sounds are spoken in meaningless syllables.

SYLLABLE ARTICULATION SCORE is the articulation score obtained when syllables are read by a talker.

VOWEL, CONSONANT, INITIAL CONSONANT, OR FINAL CONSONANT ARTICULATION SCORE is the sound articulation score analyzed to show the percentage correctly recognized of the total number of vowels, consonants, initial consonants, or final consonants, respectively, used in the articulation test.

WORD ARTICULATION SCORE is the articulation score obtained when words are read by a talker.

Artificial ear is a device for the measurements of an earphone having an acoustical cavity whose impedance is intended to simulate the impedance of the average human ear; the cavity is equipped with a microphone for the measurement of sound pressures developed by the earphone.

Artificial voice is a small loudspeaker mounted in a shaped baffle which is proportioned to simulate the acoustical constants of the human head. It is used in calibrating microphones intended to be positioned in close proximity to the mouth.

Attenuation constant is the real part of the propagation constant. The unit is the neper per unit distance.

Audibility (range of) at a specified frequency is 20 times the logarithm to the base 10 of the ratio of the sound pressure level at the threshold of tickle to that at the threshold of audibility. The unit is the decibel.

Audible sound is sound containing frequency components lying between about 15 and 15,000 cps.

Audiogram is a graph showing hearing loss or percentage of hearing loss *vs.* frequency.

Auditory sensation area is the area enclosed by the curves defining the threshold of audibility and the threshold of tickle (or feeling).   It is generally plotted as decibels on a logarithmic scale of frequency.

Aural harmonic is a harmonic generated in the ear because of its non-linearity and assymetry.

Baffle is an acoustical shielding structure or partition.

Beats are the amplitude pulsations resulting from the addition of two or more component vibrations of different frequencies which are not harmonically related.

Bel is a fundamental division of a logarithmic scale for expressing the ratio of two amounts of power.   The number of bels denoting such a ratio is the logarithm to the base 10 of this ratio (see *Decibel*).

Bone conduction is the conduction of sound to the inner ear by the cranial bones (see *Air conduction*).

Cent is the interval between any two sound waves whose frequency ratio is the twelve-hundredth root of 2.   One hundred cents constitutes an equally tempered semi-tone.

$$\text{Number of cents} = 1200 \log_2 \frac{f_1}{f_2}$$

Characteristic impedance (see *Impedance*).

Compliance is that coefficient which, when multiplied by 2π times the frequency, gives the reciprocal of the magnitude of the imaginary part of the impedance.

ACOUSTIC COMPLIANCE is that compliance which results from the volume displacement per unit pressure.   The unit is the centimeter to the fifth power per dyne.

MECHANICAL COMPLIANCE is that compliance which results from the linear displacement per unit force.   The unit is the centimeter per dyne.

SPECIFIC ACOUSTIC COMPLIANCE is that compliance which results from the linear displacement per unit pressure.   The unit is the cubic centimeter per dyne.

Coupler is a cavity of predetermined shape used in the testing of earphones.   It couples the earphone to a microphone.

Dead room is a room which gives the subjective impression of having very little reverberation.

Decibel (*db*) is one-tenth of a bel.   The number of decibels denoting the ratio of two amounts of power is 10 times the logarithm to the base 10 of this ratio.   With W_1 and W_2 designating two amounts of power, or, in acoustics, two intensities, and n the number of decibels denoting their ratio,

$$n \text{ (in db)} = 10 \log_{10} \frac{W_1}{W_2}$$

When the impedances are such that ratios of currents, voltages, pressures, or particle velocities are the square roots of the corresponding power ratios or intensity ratios, the number of decibels by which the corresponding powers or intensities differ is expressed by

$$n = 20 \log_{10} \frac{I_1}{I_2} \quad \text{db}$$

$$n = 20 \log_{10} \frac{V_1}{V_2} \quad \text{db}$$

$$n = 20 \log_{10} \frac{v_1}{v_2} \quad \text{db}$$

$$n = 20 \log_{10} \frac{p_1}{p_2} \quad \text{db}$$

where I_1/I_2, V_1/V_2, v_1/v_2, and p_1/p_2 are the given current, voltage, velocity, and pressure ratios, respectively.

By extension, these relations between numbers of decibels and scalar ratios of currents, voltages, velocities, or pressures are often applied where these ratios are not the square roots of the corresponding power or intensity ratios. To avoid confusion, such usage should be accompanied by a specific statement of this application.

Diaphragm of an electroacoustic transducer is that portion which is actuated by sound pressures or from which sound is radiated.

Diffraction is the distortion of a wave front caused by the presence of an obstacle in the sound field (see *Scattering*).

Diffuse sound exists when the energy density is uniform in the region considered and when all directions of energy flux at all parts of the region are equally probable.

Directivity factor is the ratio of the mean-square pressure (or intensity) on a designated axis of a transducer at a stated distance to the mean-square pressure (or intensity) that would be produced at the same position by a spherical source if it were radiating the same total acoustic power. A free field is assumed as the environment for the measurement. The point of observation must be sufficiently remote from the transducer for spherical divergence to exist.

Directivity index is ten times the logarithm to the base 10 of the directivity factor. The unit is the decibel.

Dispersion is the variation of propagation velocity with frequency.

Distortion in a system used for transmission or reproduction of sound is a failure by the system to transmit or reproduce a received waveform with exactness.

AMPLITUDE DISTORTION is a distortion characterized by a lack of constancy of the ratio between the rms value of the response of the system and that of the stimulus at different amplitudes of the stimulus. Amplitude distortion is measured with the system operated under steady-state conditions by a stimulus of sinusoidal waveform and constant frequency. If overtones are present, the rms value of the response refers only to that at the fundamental frequency.

FREQUENCY DISTORTION is a distortion characterized by a lack of constancy of the ratio between the rms value of the response of the system and that of the stimulus at different frequencies of the stimulus. Frequency distortion is measured with the system operated under steady-state conditions by a stimulus of sinusoidal waveform and constant intensity. If overtones are present, the rms value of the response refers only to that at the fundamental frequency.

NON-LINEAR DISTORTION is a distortion resulting from a lack of constancy of the ratio between the instantaneous values of the response of the system and the corresponding instantaneous values of the stimulus. It is characterized by the production of harmonics when the system is driven under steady-state conditions by a stimulus of sinusoidal waveform of fixed amplitude and frequency.

TRANSIENT DISTORTION is a type of distortion which occurs only as the result of rapid fluctuation in amplitude or frequency of the stimulus or both. Transient distortion is frequently manifested as a duration of frequency components in the response in excess of the duration of the stimulus. This form of transient distortion may be measured as a rate of decay of the response consequent on the sudden removal of a steady stimulus.

Doppler effect is the phenomenon evidenced by the change in the observed frequency of a wave in a transmission system caused by a time rate of change in the length of the path of travel between a source and the point of observation.

Earphone is an electroacoustic transducer operating from an electrical system to an acoustical system and intended to be closely coupled acoustically to the ear. Earphones for telephones are often called telephone receivers.

Echo is a wave which has been reflected or otherwise returned with sufficient magnitude and delay to be perceived in some manner as a wave distinct from that directly transmitted.

FLUTTER ECHO is a special case of a multiple echo in which the reflected pulses resulting from the initial pulse occur in rapid succession. If the flutter echo is periodic and if the frequency is in the audible range it is called a musical echo.

MULTIPLE ECHO is a succession of separately distinguishable echoes arising from a single source. When the individual echoes occur in rapid succession this type of echo is often called a flutter echo.

Electrical impedance (see *Impedance*).

Electrostatic transducer (see *Transducer*).

Energy density is the sound energy per unit volume in a sound wave. The unit is the erg per cubic centimeter.

Energy flux of a sound field is the average, over one period or a time long compared to a period, of the rate of flow of sound energy through any specified area in a direction perpendicular to that area. The unit is the erg per second. Expressed mathematically, the sound energy flux J is

$$ J = \frac{1}{T} \int_0^T pav_a \, dt $$

where T is the period or a time long compared to a period

p is the instantaneous sound pressure over the area a

a is the area

v_a is the component of the instantaneous particle velocity in the direction normal to the area a, i.e., v_a equals $v \cos \theta$

v is the instantaneous particle velocity

θ is the angle between the direction of propagation of the sound and the normal to the area a.

In a gas of density ρ_0, for a plane or spherical free wave having a velocity of propagation c, the sound energy flux through the area a corresponding to an effective sound pressure p_e is

$$J = \frac{p_e^2 a}{\rho_0 c} \cos \theta \quad \text{ergs/sec}$$

Equivalent absorption of a room or of an object in the room is that area of a surface having a chamber coefficient of unity which would absorb sound energy at the same rate as the room or object.

In the case of a surface, the equivalent absorption is the product of the area of the surface and its chamber coefficient.

In the case of an object in the room, the equivalent absorption is the increase of the total equivalent absorption in the room brought about by the introduction of the object.

The unit of equivalent absorption is the absorption unit. When English units are used, the unit is the sabin.

Equivalent piston, a term often used in calculations to replace a diaphragm, is a surface vibrating at all parts with the same velocity as a specified point on the diaphragm and having such area that it constitutes a source of sound of the same strength as the diaphragm. The equivalent piston is imagined to take the place of the diaphragm for purposes of calculation of mechanical or acoustical impedance when non-uniformly distributed forces of action or reaction act on the diaphragm.

Flutter echo (see *Echo*).

Forced vibration is a vibration directly maintained in a system by a periodic force and having the frequency (or frequencies) of the force.

Free field is an isotropic, homogeneous, sound field free from bounding surfaces.

Free vibration is any vibration which exists in a system after all driving forces have been removed from the system (see also *Transient*).

Free wave (free progressive wave) is a sound wave propagated in a free field. A free wave can only be approximated in practice.

Frequency is the rate of repetition of the cycles of a periodic phenomenon. It is the reciprocal of the period. The unit is the cycle per second.

ANTI-RESONANT FREQUENCY is a frequency at which anti-ersonance exists.

DRIVING FREQUENCY is the frequency of the generator driving the system.

FUNDAMENTAL FREQUENCY is the lowest component frequency of a periodic quantity.

HARMONIC FREQUENCY is the frequency of a component of a periodic quantity and is an integral multiple of the fundamental frequency. For example, a component whose frequency is twice the fundamental frequency is called the second harmonic of that frequency (see PARTIAL below).

INHARMONIC FREQUENCIES are frequencies which are not rational multiples of each other.

NORMAL FREQUENCY (NATURAL FREQUENCY) is the frequency of a normal mode of vibration. The unit is the cycle per second.

OVERTONE (UPPER PARTIAL) is a partial having a frequency higher than that of the fundamental frequency (see PARTIAL below).

PARTIAL is a physical component of a complex sound. Its frequency may be either higher or lower than the fundamental or driving frequency and may or may not bear an integral relation to that frequency.

RESONANT FREQUENCY is a frequency at which resonance exists. The unit is the cycle per second.

When confusion might exist it is necessary to specify whether velocity or displacement resonance is meant.

SUBHARMONIC FREQUENCY is the frequency of a component of a compound sound which is an integral submultiple of the fundamental or driving frequency.

Frequency distortion (see *Distortion*).

Frequency level (see *Level*).

Hearing. HEARING LOSS (DEAFNESS) of an ear at a given frequency is the difference in decibels between the threshold of audibility for that ear and the normal threshold of audibility at the same frequency.

PERCENTAGE OF HEARING LOSS (PERCENTAGE OF DEAFNESS) at any given frequency is 100 times the ratio of the hearing loss in decibels to the number of decibels between the normal threshold levels of audibility and of tickle at that frequency.

Horn is a rigid, non-porous duct of which the cross-sectional area increases progressively from the small end (or throat) to the large end (or mouth).

Impedance of acoustic systems is specified in four different ways. The definition for acoustic impedance given below is that of the American Standards Association and is commonly used in applied acoustics. The specific acoustic impedance and the impedance ratio are those most often used in theoretical acoustics. Mechanical impedance is used when one wishes to mix acoustical impedances and mechanical impedances. No rigid rule for their use is offered because each type has certain advantages in the solution of specific problems. The type of impedance selected by the user must be carefully named.

The impedance concept in electrical systems is unambiguous and requires no discussion here.

ACOUSTIC IMPEDANCE (Z_a) of a sound medium on a given surface lying in a wave front is the complex quotient of the sound pressure (force per unit area) on that surface divided by the flux (volume velocity, or linear velocity multiplied by the area) through the surface. When concentrated rather than distributed impedances are considered, the impedance of a portion of the medium is defined by the complex quotient of the pressure difference effective in driving that portion divided by the flux (volume velocity). The unit is the acoustic ohm.

BLOCKED ELECTRICAL IMPEDANCE of a transducer is the impedance measured at the electrical terminals when the impedance of the output system is made infinite. For instance, in an electromechanical transducer the blocked electrical impedance is the impedance measured at the electrical terminals when the mechanical system is blocked or clamped.

CHARACTERISTIC IMPEDANCE of a medium in which sound waves are propagated is the specific acoustic impedance at a point in a progressive plane wave propagated in a free field. The unit is the rayl.

DRIVING-POINT IMPEDANCE is the complex ratio of the applied sinusoidal force to the resultant velocity at any one point in a mechanical system; or it is the complex ratio of the applied sinusoidal sound pressure to the resultant volume velocity at one part of an acoustical system.

ELECTRICAL IMPEDANCE is the complex ratio of the voltage across two terminals to the current flowing through them in an electrical system.

MECHANICAL IMPEDANCE (Z_m) of a sound medium on a given surface lying in a wave front is the complex quotient of the force on that surface divided by the linear velocity. When concentrated rather than distributed impedances are considered, the impedance of a portion of the medium is defined by the complex quotient of the difference in force effective in driving that portion by the linear velocity. The unit is the mechanical ohm.

MOTIONAL ELECTRICAL IMPEDANCE of a transducer is the vector difference between its blocked electrical impedance and the electrical impedance measured under a specified load.

NORMAL ELECTRICAL IMPEDANCE of a transducer is the electrical impedance measured at the input of the transducer when the mechanical (or acoustic) output is connected to its normal mechanical (or acoustical) load.

SPECIFIC ACOUSTIC IMPEDANCE (Z_s) (UNIT-AREA ACOUSTIC IMPEDANCE) of a sound medium on a given surface lying in a wave front is the complex quotient of the sound pressure (force per unit area) on that surface divided by the linear velocity. When concentrated rather than distributed impedances are considered, the impedance of a portion of the medium is defined by the complex quotient of the pressure difference effective in driving that portion by the linear velocity. The unit is the rayl.

SPECIFIC IMPEDANCE RATIO $(Z_s/\rho_0 c)$ is the ratio of specific acoustic impedance to the characteristic impedance of the medium, $\rho_0 c$. An impedance ratio of this type is dimensionless and is often said to be one of so many "$\rho_0 c$" units.

Infrasonic (infra-audible) sound is sound whose frequency is below the lower pitch limit, i.e., below about 15 cps.

Intelligibility of a sample of speech is the percentage of discrete speech units correctly recognized by a listener (see *Articulation testing*).

Intensity (sound) (I) (*sound energy flux per unit area*) in a specified direction at a point is the average rate of sound energy transmitted in the specified direction through a unit area normal to this direction at the point. The unit is the erg per second per square centimeter, but sound intensity may also be expressed in watts per square centimeter. It is also the sound energy flux through a unit area. Expressed mathematically, the sound intensity I is

$$I = \frac{1}{T} \int_0^T pv_a \, dt$$

where T is the period or a time long compared to a period

p is the instantaneous sound pressure at the point

v_a is the component of the instantaneous particle velocity in the specified direction, i.e., v_a equals $v \cos \theta$

v is the instantaneous particle velocity

θ is the angle between the direction of propagation of the sound and the specified direction.

In a gas of density ρ_0, for a plane or spherical free wave having a velocity of propagation c, the sound intensity corresponding to an effective sound pressure p_e is

$$I = \frac{p_e^2}{\rho_0 c} \cos \theta \quad \text{ergs/sec/cm}^2$$

Intensity level (see *Level*).

Interval between two tones is a measure of their difference in frequency and is usually represented numerically by the ratio of their frequencies or by the logarithm of their ratio.

Level. FREQUENCY LEVEL of a sound is a logarithm (base to be specified) of the ratio of the frequency of the sound to a reference frequency.

INTENSITY LEVEL, in decibels, of a sound is 10 times the logarithm to the base 10 of the ratio of the intensity I of this sound to the reference intensity I_0. The reference intensity I_0 shall be stated. A generally used value especially for air acoustics is 10^{-16} watt/cm^2.

Note: Conventional sound pressure meters and sound level meters do not measure intensity. Hence, the words "intensity level" should not be applied to data taken with them. Instead, the two expressions "sound level" and "sound pressure level" are used in this text as follows: (*a*) *sound level* is applied to data taken on instruments which meet the specifications for sound level meters drawn up by the American Standards Association; (*b*) *sound pressure level* is applied to data taken by a sound pressure meter with a "flat" response. In both cases the reference pressure is 0.0002 dyne/cm^2.

PRESSURE LEVEL, in decibels, of a sound is 20 times the logarithm to the base 10 of the ratio of the pressure p of this sound to the reference pressure $p_{ref.}$. The value of $p_{ref.}$ should always be stated. A common reference pressure used in connection with hearing and the specification of noise is 0.000200 dyne/cm^2. Another commonly used reference pressure is 1 dyne/cm^2. The two differ by exactly 74 db. It is to be noted that in many sound fields the sound pressure ratios are not proportional to the square root of corresponding power (intensity) ratios and hence cannot be expressed in decibels in the strict sense; however, it is common practice to extend the use of the decibel to these cases.

SPECTRUM LEVEL is a plot, as a function of frequency, of 20 times the logarithm to the base 10 of the ratio of the effective sound pressure for a bandwidth 1 cps wide to the reference sound pressure. The unit is the decibel.

Live room is any room which gives the subjective impression of having considerable reverberation.

Loudness is that aspect of auditory sensation in terms of which sounds may be ordered on a scale running from "soft" to "loud." Loudness is chiefly a function of the intensity of a sound, but it is also dependent on the frequency and the composition. The unit is the sone.

Loudness contours are curves of equal loudness for sinusoidal sound waves or narrow bands of noise plotted on a pressure level *vs.* frequency graph.

Loudness level of a sound is numerically equal to the sound pressure level in decibels of the 1000-cycle pure tone which is judged by the listeners to be equivalent in loudness. The 1000-cycle comparison tone shall be considered as a plane sinusoidal sound wave coming from a position directly in front of the observer. The listening is to be done with both ears, and the intensity level of the 1000-cycle comparison tone is to be measured in the free progressive wave. The reference sound pressure is 0.000200 dyne/cm^2. The unit is the phon.

Loudness unit (millisone) is one-thousandth of a sone, the unit of loudness (see *Sone*).

Loudspeaker is an electroacoustic transducer operating from an electrical system to an acoustical system and designed to radiate sound.

Lower pitch limit is the lowest pitch audible at a given intensity.

Masking is defined as the number of decibels by which a listener's threshold of audibility for a given tone is raised by the presence of another sound.

Masking audiogram is a graphical record of the masking due to a given sound as a function of the frequency of the masked tone (see *Audiogram*).

Mass (*inertance*). The acoustic mass of a sound medium is that coefficient which, when multiplied by 2π times the frequency, gives the magnitude of the imaginary part of the acoustic impedance resulting from the inertia or effective mass of the medium. The unit is the gram per centimeter to the fourth power, the gram per centimeter squared, or the gram, depending on the type of impedance being used.

Mean free path for sound waves in an enclosure is the average distance traveled by sound in the enclosure between successive reflections. The value in a room of conventional shape is approximately equal to the ratio of 4 times the volume to the total surface area.

Mechanical impedance (see *Impedance*).

Mechanical reactance (see *Reactance*).

Mechanical resistance (see *Resistance*).

Mel is the unit of pitch. It is so defined that a 1000-cycle tone 40 db above threshold has a pitch of 1000 mels. A curve of pitch *vs.* frequency is shown on p. 203.

Microbar (*dyne per square centimeter*) is the unit of sound pressure. One microbar equals 1 dyne/cm^2.

Microphone is an electroacoustic transducer which receives an acoustic signal and delivers a corresponding electric signal.

PRESSURE MICROPHONE is a microphone depending for its operation on the action of sound pressure on only one side of a diaphragm.

PRESSURE GRADIENT MICROPHONE (VELOCITY MICROPHONE) is a microphone depending for its operation on the resultant of sound pressures acting on both sides of a diaphragm which is sufficiently small to offer negligible obstruction to the passage of a sound wave.

THERMAL MICROPHONE is a microphone depending for its operation on the variations of the electric resistance of an electrically heated conductor or of the output of a thermocouple because of variations of its temperature caused by the passage of a sound wave.

Neper is a unit of the same nature as the decibel, which differs from it in magnitude. When used for expressing power ratios, the number of nepers N by which the power P exceeds the power P_0 is given by $N = \frac{1}{2} \log_e (P/P_0)$ or, if used for expressing the current, voltage, particle velocity, or pressure ratios when these are working into the same or equal impedances, by $N = \log_e (a_1/a_0)$, where a represents the corresponding variable. One neper is equivalent to 8.686 db.

Nodes are the points, lines, or surfaces (of pressure, velocity, or displacement) of a stationary wave system which have a zero amplitude (see *Partial nodes*).

Noise is any undesired sound.

RANDOM NOISE is a sound or electrical wave whose instantaneous amplitudes occur, as a function of time, according to a normal (Gaussian) distribution curve. A common thermal noise is that resulting from the random motion of the molecules of the air. Another type is produced by the random motion of electrons in an electrical resistance. Random noise need not have a uniform frequency spectrum.

WHITE NOISE is a sound or electrical wave whose spectrum is continuous and uniform as a function of frequency. White noise need not be random.

Noise audiogram (see *Masking audiogram*).

Non-linear distortion (see *Distortion*).

Normal frequency (see *Frequency*).

Normal mode of vibration (*free vibration*) is one of the possible ways in which a system will vibrate of its own accord as a result of a disturbance of the system. It will have a frequency depending solely on the properties of the system.

Octave is the interval between any two tones whose frequency ratio is 2:1.

Overtone (*upper partial*) is a partial having a frequency higher than that of the fundamental frequency.

Partial (see *Frequency*).

Partial nodes are the loci (points, lines, or surfaces) in a standing (pseudo-stationary) wave system which have minimum amplitude, pressure, or velocity differing from zero.

Particle velocity in a sound wave is the instantaneous velocity of a given infinitesimal part of the medium, with reference to the medium as a whole, due to the passage of the sound wave. The units are centimeters per second.

Period is the time interval of a single repetition of a varying quantity which repeats itself regularly.

Phase constant is the imaginary part of the propagation constant. The unit is the radian per unit distance.

Phon is the unit for measuring the loudness level of a tone. The number of phons is equal to the number of decibels a 1000-cycle tone is above the reference sound pressure when judged equal in loudness to the tone in question.

Pitch is that aspect of auditory sensation in terms of which sounds may be ordered in a scale running from "low" to "high." Pitch is chiefly a function of the frequency of a sound, but it is also dependent on the intensity and composition. The unit is the mel. For a graphical relationship between pitch in mels and frequency in cycles per second, see Fig. 5·17, p. 203.

Pitch limit (see *Upper pitch limit* and *Lower pitch limit*).

Point source (see *Simple source of sound*).

Pressure. AVERAGE SOUND PRESSURE is the time integral over a period or a time long compared to a period of a rectified sound wave. Either half- or full-wave rectification may be specified. The unit is the microbar (dyne per square centimeter).

BAROMETRIC PRESSURE (*static or ambient pressure*) is the pressure that would exist in the undisturbed medium. The unit is the microbar (dyne per square centimeter).

EFFECTIVE SOUND PRESSURE at a point is the root-mean-square value of the instantaneous sound pressure, taken over a complete cycle or a period long compared to a cycle, at that point. The unit is the microbar (dyne per square centimeter).

INSTANTANEOUS SOUND PRESSURE at a point is the total instantaneous pressure at that point minus the static pressure. This quantity is often called excess pressure. The unit is the microbar (dyne per square centimeter).

MAXIMUM SOUND PRESSURE for any given cycle is the maximum absolute value of the instantaneous sound pressure during that cycle without regard to sign. The unit is the microbar (dyne per square centimeter). In a sinusoidal sound wave this maximum sound pressure is also called the pressure amplitude.

MICROBAR (DYNE PER SQUARE CENTIMETER) is the unit of sound pressure. The use of the word *bar* instead of *microbar* to designate this quantity is disapproved.

PEAK SOUND PRESSURE for any specified time interval is the maximum absolute value of the instantaneous sound pressure in that interval without regard to sign. The unit is the microbar (dyne per square centimeter).

PRESSURE LEVEL (see *Level*).

PRESSURE METER (see *Sound pressure meter*).

Propagation constant of a plane sound wave in a homogeneous infinite medium is the natural logarithm of the ratio of the steady-state velocities or pressures at two points separated by unit distance in the medium. The ratio is determined by dividing the value of the velocity or pressure at the point nearer the transmitting end by the value of the velocity at the point more remote. Single frequency pressures and velocities are here supposed to be represented by complex numbers. Their ratio is therefore a complex number. The real and imaginary parts of the propagation constant are the *attenuation constant* and *phase constant*, respectively. The units of these two quantities are nepers and radians, respectively, per unit distance.

Radiation resistance at a surface vibrating in a medium is that portion of the total resistance which is due to the radiation of sound energy into the medium.

Random noise (see *Noise*).

Rate of decay is the time rate at which the sound field (amplitude of the sound pressure, or of the sound energy density) is decreasing at a given point and at a given time. Generally the rate is expressed in decibels per second.

Rayl. A specific acoustic resistance, reactance, or impedance is said to have a magnitude of 1 rayl when a sound pressure of 1 dyne/cm^2 produces a linear velocity of 1 cm/sec. This unit was named in honor of Lord Rayleigh.

Reactance of a sound medium is the imaginary component of the impedance. It is the component of the impedance which may result from the effective mass or from the compliance of the medium. The unit is the acoustic ohm, the rayl, or the mechanical ohm, depending on the type of impedance being used. (See *Impedance*.)

Resistance of a sound medium is the real component of the impedance. This is the component of the impedance which is responsible for the dissipation of energy. The unit is the acoustic ohm, the rayl, or the mechanical ohm, depending on the type of impedance being used. (See *Impedance*.)

Resonance. DISPLACEMENT RESONANCE exists between a body, or system, and an applied force if any small change in frequency of the applied force causes a decrease in the amplitude of displacement.

VELOCITY RESONANCE exists between a body, or system, and an applied force if any small change in the frequency of the applied force causes a decrease in velocity at the driving point; or if the frequency of the applied force is such that the absolute value of the driving-point impedance is a minimum.

Resonant frequency is the frequency at which resonance occurs.

Response is the ratio of some measure of the output of a device to some measure of the input under conditions which must be explicitly stated. The response characteristic, often presented graphically, gives the response as a function of some independent variable such as frequency.

Reverberation is the persistence of sound due to repeated reflections.

Reverberation chamber is an enclosure which has substantially complete sound reflection over all its boundaries.

Reverberation time for a given frequency is the time required for the time average of the sound energy density, initially in a steady state, to decrease, after the source is stopped, to one-millionth of its initial value. The unit is the second.

Reversible transducer is a transducer for which the magnitude of the electromechanical coupling terms in the impedance determinant are equal.

Root-mean-square (rms) value of a varying quantity is the square root of the mean value of the squares of the instantaneous values of the quantity. In periodic variation the mean is taken over one period.

Sabin is a unit of absorption equal to the absorption of 1 sq ft of surface which is totally sound absorbent.

Scattering is deflection of sound waves on encountering an obstacle or obstacles.

Sensation level (level above threshold) is the number of decibels the level of a tone is above its threshold of audibility for the particular subject or subjects at hand.

Sensitivity. AXIAL SENSITIVITY of a microphone about an axis perpendicular to the diaphragm is the free-field sensitivity when the sound is incident normally on the diaphragm.

FREE-FIELD SENSITIVITY of a microphone is the ratio of the electrical output, measured in a specified manner, to the sound pressure in a plane progressive wave into which the microphone is introduced at a specified angle.

RANDOM SENSITIVITY of a microphone is the average free-field sensitivity for all angles of incidence of the sound.

Simple source of sound is a spherical vibrating surface of dimensions small in comparison with the wavelength of the sound produced, the displacement having the same phase at all parts of the surface.

STRENGTH OF A SIMPLE SOURCE OF SOUND is the rate of volume displacement of the surface which constitutes the source. The unit is the cubic centimeter per second. The term "strength of a simple source" has often been restricted to the peak value of the rate of volume displacement.

Sone is a unit of loudness. It is defined as the loudness of a 1000-cycle tone 40 db above threshold. A millisone is one-thousandth of a sone and is often called the loudness unit.

Sound is an alteration in pressure, stress, particle displacement, or particle velocity which is propagated in an elastic material or the superposition of such propagated alterations.

Sound energy density (see *Energy density*).

Sound energy flux (see *Energy flux*).

Sound level is the reading of a sound level meter with the appropriate weighting network in the electrical circuit of the amplifier.

Sound level meter is an apparatus for estimating the equivalent loudness of noise by an objective method.

In the United States the acceptable performance of sound level meters has been standardized by the American Standards Association (American Standard for Sound Level Meters, Z24.3). Three alternate weighting networks are available in the electrical circuit to simulate the 40-db, 70-db and 100-db loudness contours of the human ear.

Sound pressure meter is an instrument comprising a microphone, amplifier, and indicating meter with a "flat" overall response as a function of frequency in the desired frequency range; it indicates the rms value of the sound pressure in a complex sound wave.

Sound probe is a microphone (or hydrophone) which permits exploration of the sound field in a small region in space without appreciable effect on the sound field generally.

Specific acoustic impedance (see *Impedance, Resistance,* and *Reactance*).

Spectrum in acoustics is the distribution of effective sound pressures or intensities measured as a function of frequency in specified frequency bands.

CONTINUOUS SPECTRUM is a spectrum which contains components of all frequencies within the specified frequency range.

LINE SPECTRUM is a spectrum which contains a finite number of components within the specified frequency range.

Spectrum level (see *Level*).

Speech level. EFFECTIVE SPEECH LEVEL is the effective (rms) sound pressure level being produced at a specified point by the speaker. The unit is the decibel.

INSTANTANEOUS SPEECH LEVEL is the sound pressure level being produced at a specified point by the speaker at any given instant. The unit is the decibel.

PEAK SPEECH LEVEL is the maximum value of the instantaneous speech level without regard to sign over the time interval considered. The unit is the decibel.

Speed (velocity) of propagation of a sinusoidal component of a progressive wave is the speed (velocity) at which a point in the wave must travel, in the direction of propagation, in order that no phase change shall occur at the point in the component concerned. It is equal to the product of the frequency times the length of the wave. The unit is the centimeter per second.

Standing waves constitute the wave system resulting from the interference of progressive waves of the same frequency and kind. They are characterized by the existence of nodes or partial nodes in the interference pattern. In order to obtain standing waves the interfering waves must have components traveling in opposite directions.

Steady state is said to have been reached by a system when the relevant variables of the system no longer change as a function of time.

Stiffness of a sound medium is that coefficient which, when divided by 2π times the frequency, gives the magnitude of the imaginary part of the acoustic impedance which results from the compliance of the medium. The unit is the dyne per centimeter to the fifth power, the dyne per centimeter to the third power, or the dyne per centimeter, depending on the type of impedance being used. (See *Compliance*.)

Streaming is the production of steady flow currents in a medium arising from the presence of sound waves. Streaming is possible only in media which have viscosity.

Subharmonic frequency (see *Frequency*).

Threshold. NORMAL THRESHOLD OF AUDIBILITY is the modal value of the threshold of audibility of a large number of normal ears. It is usually expressed in decibels *re* 0.000200 dyne/cm^2.

NORMAL THRESHOLDS OF DISCOMFORT, TICKLE, OR PAIN are modal values of the respective thresholds for a large number of normal ears. They are usually expressed in decibels *re* 0.000200 dyne/cm^2.

THRESHOLD OF AUDIBILITY at any specified frequency is the minimal value of the effective sound pressure of a sinusoidal wave of that frequency which evokes a response from the listener in the absence of any noise 50 percent of the time. The point in space at which the pressure is measured must be specified in every case. It is usually expressed in decibels *re* 0.000200 dyne/cm^2.

Note: For reasons unknown at this writing it seems that 6 to 10 db more sound pressure at the eardrum are necessary to produce audibility if the sound originates from an earphone (or small enclosure) than if it originates in a free field.

THRESHOLD OF (*a*) DISCOMFORT, (*b*) TICKLE, OR (*c*) PAIN at any specified frequency is the minimum value of the sound pressure of a sinusoidal wave of that frequency which evokes a response of (*a*) discomfort, (*b*) tickle, or (*c*) pain from the listener 50 percent of the time. The point in space at which the pressure is measured must be specified in every case. It is usually expressed in decibels *re* 0.000200 dyne/cm^2.

THRESHOLD OF FEELING is used generally to indicate the thresholds of discomfort, tickle, and pain. As published, it corresponds most closely with the threshold of discomfort.

Timbre is that aspect of tone quality principally correlated with waveform.

Tone is a sound giving a definite sensation of pitch, loudness, and timbre, and, therefore, lying between 15 and 15,000 cps.

COMBINATION TONE is a supplementary tone produced when two tones are sounded simultaneously. Combination tones are produced only in connection with non-linear devices, the ear being such a device.

DIFFERENCE TONE is the combination tone of which the frequency is the difference of the frequencies of the two generating tones.

PURE TONE is a sound produced by an instantaneous sound pressure which is a simple sinusoidal function of time.

SUMMATION TONE is the combination tone of which the frequency is the sum of the frequencies of the two generating tones.

WARBLE TONE is generally a pure tone, the frequency of which is continuously varying within fixed limits.

Transducer is a device designed to receive power from one or more systems and to supply power to one or more different systems.

ELECTROACOUSTIC TRANSDUCER is a transducer which is actuated by power from an electrical system and supplies power to an acoustical system or vice versa.

Transient is the phenomenon which takes place in a system owing to a sudden change of conditions and which persists for a relatively short time after the change has occurred.

Transient distortion (see *Distortion*).

Transmission coefficient is the ratio of the sound transmitted through an interface or septum between two media, exposed to the sound field, to the sound energy incident on the interface or septum.

Ultrasonic sound (*ultra-audible*) is sound whose frequency is above the upper pitch limit. The term supersonic is now disapproved because of its use in aerodynamics as a velocity greater than the velocity of sound. Unless otherwise stated, it will be assumed that the frequency of ultrasonic (ultra-audible) sound is greater than 15,000 cps.

Upper pitch limit is the highest pitch audible at a given intensity.

Velocity microphone (see *Microphone*).

Velocity of propagation (see *Speed of propagation*).

White noise (see *Noise*).

2.

The Medium

2·1 Introduction

We shall generally call the gas, liquid, or solid through which a sound wave is propagated *the medium*. In gases, the waves are propagated as *longitudinal* waves; that is, the oscillations of the particles are along a line parallel to the direction of propagation. Those waves for which the particle displacements are perpendicular to the direction of propagation we call transverse waves; light waves or surface waves in liquids are examples. One important difference between a longitudinal and a transverse wave is that the latter can be polarized. Light waves are polarized and scattered when they are reflected from small particles in a medium, but sound waves in air are only scattered. In contrast to waves on the surface of the water, longitudinal waves have no crests or peaks, but instead compressions and rarefactions are observed. Each type of wave is the result of particle displacements, the directions of the displacements being in planes perpendicular to each other in the two cases.

The propagation of sound is really quite simple to picture. A vibrating surface such as a loudspeaker diaphragm or the wooden case of a violin will move forward and backward alternately. As it moves forward it compresses the portion of the gas nearest it. Because of the forces developed by this compression, portions of the gas farther away will be set in motion progressively as the inertia of the air particles is overcome. When the diaphragm reverses its direction of motion, it produces a rarefaction of the gas near it, and a movement of the air particles farther away occurs progressively in the opposite direction. Each small volume of molecules, wherever located, oscillating backward and forward under the influence of the diaphragm, will

37

cause molecules farther on to oscillate at the same frequency. The inertia of the particles and the low elasticity of the gas cause the disturbance to travel at a slow rate relative to the speed of light. If the oscillations of the diaphragm persist, the disturbance will eventually cover a large region, the extent depending on the initial intensity of the sound, the dissipative losses in the gas, the presence of wind, turbulence, temperature gradients, and on bounding surfaces. All the air particles will oscillate with the same frequency, but only at certain multiples of a wavelength (if the wave front is nearly plane) will their motions be in phase.

We can express the phenomenon of sound propagation in the form of a wave equation obtained by combining three equations, one of them Newton's equation of motion and the other two representing two simple properties of the gas. One of these two properties is described by a restatement of the law of conservation of mass; that is, the increase in mass in a given packet of air in a given length of time is exactly equal to the net volume flow of mass through the side walls into the packet in that same length of time. The other property is described by the fundamental gas law, which relates the forces acting on the side walls of the packet to the change of density of the gas within due to compression of the packet.

We shall not attempt to derive those equations since Rayleigh,[1] Morse,[2] and others have done so for sound waves whose amplitude of vibration is small compared to a wavelength.

We should clearly recognize, however, that the customary wave equations exclude the possibility of dissipation in the gas due to viscosity and heat conduction, the loss of energy through heat exchange at the bounding surfaces in the medium, rotational motion of the air particles, and wind or temperature gradients. If we take those effects into account, a knowledge of all the basic properties of the medium must be at hand.

In the next few paragraphs values of the basic properties of air, some other gases, sea water, and a few other liquids and several solids will be listed in formula and chart form. We shall discuss means for calculating sound attenuation in air and conclude by discussing the propagation of sound waves of large amplitude in ideal gases.

[1]Lord Rayleigh, *Theory of Sound*, Macmillan (1929).

[2]P. M. Morse and K. U. Ingard, *Theoretical Acoustics*, McGraw-Hill (1968).

2·2 Properties of Gases

The fundamental properties of a gas[3] which determine its characteristics as an acoustic medium are given in Table 2·1. These include: density, pressure, temperature, specific heats, and the coefficients of viscosity and heat exchange. Let us now treat each of these and some combinations of them in detail.

TABLE 2·1 PROPERTIES OF A GASEOUS MEDIUM WHICH AFFECT THE PROPAGATION OF SOUND WAVES IN IT

Property	Symbol	Units	Function of	Formula
Density	ρ_0	g/cm^3	Pressure and temperature	$\rho_0 \propto \dfrac{P_0}{T}$
Pressure	P_0	$dynes/cm^2$	Temperature and altitude	(See Fig. 2·2.)
Temperature	T	°C	Altitude and many other factors	(See Fig. 2·2.)
Specific heat at constant volume	C_v	cal/(g-deg)	(See Table 2·4.)	
Specific heat at constant pressure	C_p	cal/(g-deg)	(See Table 2·4.)	
Ratio of specific heats	$\gamma = \dfrac{C_p}{C_v}$	None	(See Table 2·4)	
Coefficient of viscosity	η	$dyne\text{-}sec/cm^2$ or poises	Temperature	$\eta \propto T^n$ $0.6 < n < 1.0$
Kinematic coefficient of viscosity	$\nu = \eta/\rho_0$	cm^2/sec	Temperature and pressure	$\nu \propto \dfrac{T^{n+1}}{P_0}$ $0.6 < n < 1.0$
Coefficient of thermal conductivity	κ	cal/(cm-sec-deg)	Temperature	$\kappa \propto T^n C_p$ $0.6 < n < 1.0$
Coefficient of temperature exchange	$\alpha = \dfrac{\kappa}{\rho_0 C_v}$	cm^2/sec	Temperature and pressure	$\alpha \propto \dfrac{T^{n+1}}{P_0}$ $0.6 < n < 1.0$

A. Density

The density ρ_0 of a number of common gases is given in Table 2·2.[4] The variation of the density of air as a function of temperature and pressure is given in graphical form in Fig. 2·1,

---

[3]E. H. Kennard, *Kinetic Theory of Gases*, McGraw-Hill (1938).

[4]Table 2·2 and others in this book giving constants of gases, liquids, and solids are reprinted with permission from the *Handbook of Chemistry and Physics*, 67th edition (1986), CRC Press, Inc., Boca Raton, FL, and the *International Critical Tables*, McGraw-Hill (1926–1930), and Lange's *Handbook of Chemistry*, 11th ed., McGraw-Hill (1973).

where

$$\rho_0 = 0.001290 \left(\frac{P}{760}\right)\left(\frac{273}{T}\right).$$ (2·1)

TABLE 2·2 DENSITIES OF COMMON GASES (*CRC Handbook of Chemistry and Physics*, 67th ed., 1986)

Gas	Formula	Density, ρ_0 g/cm³ 0 °C, 760 mm
Air		0.0012920
Argon	A	0.0017837
Carbon dioxide	CO_2	0.0019769
Carbon monoxide	CO	0.0012504
Helium	He	0.00017847
Hydrogen	H_2	0.00008988
Neon	Ne	0.0008990
Nitric oxide	NO	0.0013402
Nitrogen	N_2	0.0012506
Nitrous oxide	N_2O	0.001977
Oxygen	O_2	0.0014290
Saturated steam (100°)	H_2O	0.000598

Here P is the barometric pressure in millimeters of mercury, and T is the absolute temperature in degrees Kelvin.

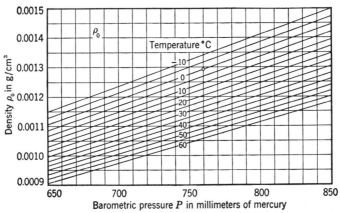

FIG. 2·1 Density of air as a function of barometric pressure and temperature. The equation from which this chart was derived is

$$\rho_0 = 0.001290(P/760)(273/T) \text{ g/cm}^3.$$

B. Pressure

Atmospheric pressure for a 760-mm column of mercury, with the temperature of the mercury at 0 °C, is 1.01325×10^6 dyne/

cm^2. The conversion factor between millimeters of mercury
and pressure is 10 mm of mercury at 0 °C equals a pressure of
0.01332×10^6 dyne/cm^2. If the observations are made on a barometer whose column of mercury is at a temperature other

TABLE 2·3 (EXCERPTS FROM U. S. STANDARD ATMOSPHERE, NATIONAL
OCEANOGRAPHIC AND ATMOSPHERIC AGENCY)

Geometric Altitude km	Miles	Temp. °C	Pressure Millibars 100 n/m²	Density kg/m³	Sound Speed m/s
20.0	12.4	− 56.500	55.293	0.088910	295.07
19.0	11.8	− 56.500	64.674	0.10400	295.07
18.0	11.2	− 56.500	75.652	0.12165	295.07
17.0	10.6	− 56.500	88.497	0.14230	295.07
16.0	9.9	− 56.500	103.52	0.16647	295.07
15.0	9.3	− 56.500	121.11	0.19476	295.07
14.0	8.7	− 56.500	141.70	0.22786	295.07
13.0	8.1	− 56.500	165.79	0.26660	295.07
12.0	7.5	− 56.500	193.99	0.31194	295.07
11.0	6.8	− 56.376	226.99	0.36480	295.15
10.0	6.2	− 49.898	264.99	0.41351	299.53
9.0	5.6	− 43.417	308.00	0.46706	303.85
8.0	5.0	− 36.935	356.51	0.52579	308.11
7.0	4.3	− 30.450	411.05	0.59002	312.31
6.0	3.7	− 23.963	472.17	0.66011	316.45
5.0	3.1	− 17.474	540.48	0.73643	320.55
4.0	2.5	− 10.984	616.60	0.81935	324.59
3.0	1.9	− 4.491	701.21	0.90925	328.58
2.5	1.6	− 1.244	746.91	0.95695	330.56
2.0	1.2	2.004	795.01	1.0066	332.53
1.5	0.9	5.252	845.59	1.0581	334.49
1.0	0.6	8.501	898.76	1.1117	336.43
0.5	0.3	11.750	954.61	1.1673	338.37
0.0	0.0	15.000	1013.25	1.2250	340.29

than 0 °C, corrections must be added to the readings if the conversion factor just stated is to be valid. Complete tables of conversion factors for barometers with brass or glass scales are to
be found in the *Handbook of Chemistry and Physics*. For example, if readings in the vicinity of 760 mm are taken on a brass
scale barometer whose temperature is 23 °C, then 2.84 mm
must be subtracted from the value read before the conversion
factor just stated can be used.

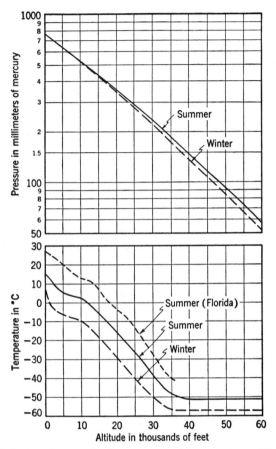

Fɪɢ. 2·2 Variation of atmospheric pressure and temperature with altitude.

The National Aeronautics and Space Administration has issued a document called "U.S. Standard Atmosphere, 1976
NOAA" (out of print), which gives the temperature, pressure,
density, and sound speed as a function of altitude, from which
Table 2·3 contains excerpts. Typical variations of pressure and
temperature for summer and winter, with one observation over
Pensacola, Florida, in August, are plotted in Fig. 2·2.[6]

[6]J. C. R. Licklider, K. D. Kryter *et al.*, "Articulation tests of standard and
modified interphones conducted during flight," Aircraft Radio Laboratory No.
149 and O.S.R.D. Report No. 1976, 1 July, 1944.

TABLE 2·4 SPECIFIC HEAT AT CONSTANT PRESSURE C_p AND THE RATIO γ OF C_p TO THE SPECIFIC HEAT AT CONSTANT VOLUME C_v

(*CRC Handbook of Chemistry and Physics*, 67th ed., 1986, the *International Critical Tables* and Lange's *Handbook of Chemistry*, 11th ed.)

| Gas | C_p, cal/g-deg | | $\gamma = C_p/C_v$ | |
	Temp., °C	C_p	Temp., °C	γ
Air	− 120(10 atm)	0.2719	− 118(1 atm)	1.415
	(20 atm)	0.3221		
	(40 atm)	0.4791		
	(70 atm)	0.7771	− 78(1 atm)	1.408
	− 50(10 atm)	0.2440	− 79(25 atm)	1.57
	(20 atm)	0.2521	− 79(100 atm)	2.20
	(40 atm)	0.2741		
	(70 atm)	0.3121		
	0(1 atm)	0.2400	0(1 atm)	1.3996
	(20 atm)	0.2490	0(25 atm)	1.47
	(60 atm)	0.2652	0(50 atm)	1.53
	50(20 atm)	0.2480	0(75 atm)	1.59
	(100 atm)	0.2719	17(1 atm)	1.403
	(220 atm)	0.2961	20(3 atm)	1.41
	100(1 atm)	0.2404	100(1 atm)	1.401
	(20 atm)	0.2471		
	(100 atm)	0.2600	200(1 atm)	1.398
	(220 atm)	0.2841		
	400(1 atm)	0.2430	400(1 atm)	1.393
	1000(1 atm)	0.2570	1000(1 atm)	1.365
	1400(1 atm)	0.2699	1400(1 atm)	1.341
	1800(1 atm)	0.2850	1800(1 atm)	1.316
Argon	15(1 atm)	0.1252	15(1 atm)	1.668
Carbon dioxide	15(1 atm)	0.1988	15(1 atm)	1.304
Carbon monoxide	15(1 atm)	0.2478	15(1 atm)	1.404
Helium	− 180(1 atm)	1.248	− 180(1 atm)	1.660
Hydrogen	15(1 atm)	3.388	15(1 atm)	1.410
Neon	...	...	19(1 atm)	1.64
Nitric oxide	15(1 atm)	0.2328	15(1 atm)	1.400
Nitrogen	15(1 atm)	0.2477	15(1 atm)	1.404
Nitrous oxide	15(1 atm)	0.2004	15(1 atm)	1.303
Oxygen	15(1 atm)	0.2177	15(1 atm)	1.401
Steam	100(1 atm)	0.4836	100(1 atm)	1.324

TABLE 2·5 COEFFICIENT OF VISCOSITY η FOR DIFFERENT GASES AS A FUNCTION
OF TEMPERATURE

(*CRC Handbook of Chemistry and Physics,* 67th ed., 1986)

Gas	Formula	Temp., °C	Viscosity, micropoises (dyne-sec/cm$^2 \times 10^{-6}$)
Air		− 31.6	153.9
		0	170.8
		18	182.7
		40	190.4
		54	195.8
		74	210.2
		100	217.5
		150	238.5
		229	263.8
		334	312.3
		409	341.3
		537	368.6
Argon	A	0	209.6
		20	221.7
Carbon dioxide	CO_2	0	139
		20	148.0
		40	157.0
Carbon monoxide	CO	0	166
		15	172
		100	210
Helium	He	0	186
		20	194.1
Hydrogen	H_2	0	83.5
		20.7	87.6
Neon	Ne	20	311.1
Nitric oxide	NO	0	178
		20	187.6
Nitrogen	N_2	27.4	178.1
Nitrous oxide	N_2O	0	135
Oxygen	O_2	0	189
		19.1	201.8
		127.7	256.8

C. Specific Heat

For a number of common gases, the values of C_p, the specific heat at constant pressure, and γ, the ratio of C_p to C_v, where C_v is the specific heat at constant volume, are given in Table 2·4. C_p is expressed in calories per gram. For air the specific heat at constant pressure at 0 °C and 1 atm is 0.2400 cal/g-deg, and γ is 1.3996.

D. Viscosity

The coefficient of viscosity η for a number of common gases is given in Table 2·5. The units of η are dyne-seconds per square centimeter or poises.

E. Thermal Conductivity

The thermal conductivity κ of a number of gases is given in Table 2·6. The units of κ are calories per centimeter-second-degree.

TABLE 2·6 THERMAL CONDUCTIVITY κ OF GASES AT 0 °C
(*CRC Handbook of Chemistry and Physics*, 67th ed., 1986)

Gas	Formula	Thermal Conductivity κ at 4.4 °C, cal/(cm-sec-deg)
Air		0.05831×10^{-3}
Argon	A	0.04009×10^{-3}
Carbon dioxide	CO_2	0.03562×10^{-4}
Helium	He	0.34342×10^{-3}
Hydrogen	H_2	0.41739×10^{-3}
Neon	Ne	0.10993×10^{-3}
Nitrogen	N_2	0.05827×10^{-3}
Oxygen	O_2	0.05943×10^{-3}
Steam (100 °C)	H_2O	0.0551×10^{-3} (100 °C)

F. Kinematic Coefficient of Viscosity

The quotient of the viscosity η to the density ρ_0 occurs frequently in formulas. For that reason it is denoted by a separate letter and is called the *kinematic coefficient of viscosity*

$$\nu = \frac{\eta}{\rho_0}. \tag{2·2}$$

ν has the dimensions of the product velocity times length, that is, square centimeters per second. For air, $\nu = 0.151$ cm^2/sec at 18 °C and 760 mm of mercury.

G. Coefficient of Temperature Exchange

The quantity α appears in heat conduction equations:

$$\alpha = \frac{\kappa}{\rho_0 C_v} \qquad (2\cdot3)$$

and we call it the coefficient of temperature exchange. The reciprocal of α is often called diffusivity. α has the dimensions of velocity times length, that is, cm^2/sec. For air, $\alpha = 0.27 \ cm^2/sec$ at 18 °C and 760 mm of mercury.

TABLE 2·7 SPEED (VELOCITY) OF SOUND IN GASES
(*CRC Handbook of Chemistry and Physics*, 67th ed., 1986 and *Journal of the Acoustical Society of America*)

Gas	Formula	Speed, m/sec at 0 °C	Speed, ft/sec at 0 °C
Air		331.30	1087.00
Ammonia	NH_3	415	1361
Argon	A	319	1046
Carbon monoxide	CO	338	1109
Carbon dioxide	CO_2	259.0 (low freq.)	850 (low freq.)
		268.6 (high freq.)[a]	881 (high freq.)[a]
Carbon disulfide	COS_2	189	606
Chlorine	Cl	206	676
Ethylene	C_2H_4	317	1040
Helium	He	965	3166
Hydrogen	H_2	1284	4213
Illuminating (coal) gas		453	1486
Methane	CH_4	430	1410
Neon	Ne	435	1427
Nitric oxide (10 °C)	NO	324	1063
Nitrous oxide	N_2O	263	863
Nitrogen	N_2	334	1096
Oxygen	O_2	316	1037
Steam (100 °C)	H_2O	404.8	1328

[a] "High frequencies" means that the acoustic period is so short that the periodic changes in the vibrational heat constant cannot remain in phase with the other periodic changes as the sound wave passes through the gas.

H. Speed (Velocity) of Propagation of Sound

The speed of sound in an ideal gas at a constant pressure is

$$c = \sqrt{\frac{\gamma R T_0}{M}} \doteq \sqrt{\frac{\gamma P_0}{\rho_0}}, \qquad (2\cdot4)$$

where R is the universal gas constant equal to 8314.48 J $kmol^{-1}K^{-1}$, $T_0 = 273.18$ °K, and M is the sum of the molar mass contributions, including that from water vapor.

For "standard" (dry) air, the molar fractions x_i are: $N_2 = 0.78084$; $O_2 = 0.209476$; $Ar = 0.00934$; $CO_2 = 0.000314$, and $Ne = 0.000018$, plus traces of other gases. The ratio of γ/M, where $\gamma = 1.3996$ for R.H. $= 0\%$ and $T = 0\,°C$, is given in Fig. 2·3a for various temperatures and relative humidities. Thus the value of c for standard air, under conditions (a) audible sound; (b) $0\,°C$ ($32\,°F$); and (c) 760 mm Hg (101.325 kPa), is

$$c = 33,130 \text{ cm/sec},$$
$$c = 1087.00 \text{ ft/sec}.$$

The speed of sound, c, at temperatures near 20° is

$$c = 33,150 + 58.4\theta \text{ cm/sec},$$
$$c = 1,053.5 + 1.067 \text{ F ft/sec},$$

where θ is degree centigrade and F is degrees Fahrenheit. If the value of θ differs much from 20° (68°) use

$$c = 33,130\sqrt{(273.2 + \theta)/273.2} \text{ cm/sec}.$$

The correction for pressure is usually negligible for air. It may not be for other gases.

Wave Number. The wave number k is the ratio of the circular frequency ω to the speed of sound c, i.e., ω/c.

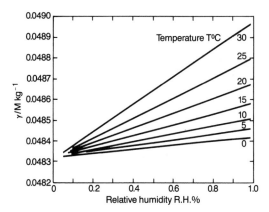

FIG. 2·3a γ/M *vs* relative humidity.[7]

[7]G. S. Wong and T. F. W. Embleton, "Variations of specific heats and of specific heat ratio in air with humidity" and "Variation of speed of sound in air with humidity and temperature," J. Acoust. Soc. Am. **76**, 555–559 (1984) and **77**, 1710–1712 (1985).

48   **The Medium**

I. Characteristic Impedance

The characteristic impedance is equal to the ratio of the sound pressure to the particle velocity in a plane wave traveling in an unbounded medium. It is equal to the density times the velocity of propagation, that is $\rho_0 c$. The variation of $\rho_0 c$ for air as a function of temperature and pressure is given in Fig. 2·3, as calculated from the formula

$$\rho_0 c = 42.80 \left(\frac{273}{°K}\right)^{1/2} \times \frac{H}{760} \text{ rayls,} \qquad (2·5)$$

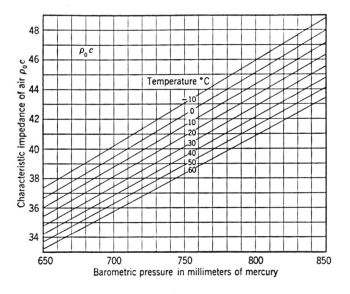

FIG. 2·3 Variation of the characteristic impedance $\rho_0 c$ of air as a function of barometric pressure and temperature. The unit is the rayl.

where °K is the temperature in degrees absolute and H is the barometric pressure in millimeters of mercury. The characteristic impedance of some other gases at °K = 273° and H = 760 is given in Table 2·8.

TABLE 2·8 CHARACTERISTIC IMPEDANCE $\rho_0 c$ OF COMMON GASES AT 0 °C (273 °K) TEMPERATURE AND 760 MILLIMETERS OF MERCURY BAROMETRIC PRESSURE

Gas	Formula	$\rho_0 c$ (dyne-sec/cm³), 0 °C, 760 mm Hg
Air		42.80
Argon	A	56.9
Carbon dioxide	CO_2	51.2
Carbon monoxide	CO	42.2
Helium	He	17.22
Hydrogen	H_2	11.54
Neon	Ne	39.1
Nitric oxide	NO	43.4
Nitrous oxide	N_2O	52.0
Nitrogen	N_2	41.8
Oxygen	O_2	45.2
Steam (100°)	HO_2	24.2

J. Wave Number for Thermal Diffusion Wave

The wave number for a thermal diffusion wave radiating outward from a boundary where heat exchange is taking place is equal to k_α:

$$k_\alpha = (1+j)\sqrt{\frac{\gamma\omega}{2\alpha}}, \tag{2·6}$$

where α is the coefficient of temperature exchange as defined in Table 2·1, γ is the ratio of specific heats, and ω is 2π times the frequency.

Evaluation of k_α for air yields $1.602(1+j)\sqrt{\omega}$ cm^{-1} at 18 °C and 760 mm of mercury. This wave travels with a velocity that is small compared to that of the regular compressional wave, and it diminishes rapidly as a function of distance traveled.

K. Wave Number for Frictional Wave

The wave number for a frictional wave radiating outward from a "rough" bounding surface is equal to k_ν:

$$k_\nu = (1+j)\sqrt{\frac{\omega}{2\nu}}, \tag{2·7}$$

where ν is the kinematic coefficient of viscosity as defined in Table 2·1. Evaluation of k_ν for air at 18 °C and 760 mm of mercury yields $1.82(1 + j)\sqrt{\omega}$. This wave travels with a velocity that is small compared to that of the regular compressional wave, and it diminishes rapidly as a function of distance traveled.

2·3 Some Properties of Liquids and Solids

This text is not primarily concerned with the propagation of sound in liquids and solids. However, some of the properties of fresh and sea water follow. Also we tabulate the speeds (velocities) of propagation of sound waves in a number of common liquids and solids.

A. Properties of Water

Density of Pure Water (1 atm pressure)

$T = \ \ 4$ °C	$\rho_0 = 0.99997$ g/cm^3
$T = 15$ °C	$\rho_0 = 0.99913$ g/cm^3
$T = 25$ °C	$\rho_0 = 0.99707$ g/cm^3
$T = 30$ °C	$\rho_0 = 0.99567$ g/cm^3

Density of Sea Water (1 atm pressure)

Standard medium $\begin{cases} T = 15 \text{ °C} \quad \rho_0 = 1.02338 \text{ g/cm}^3 \\ \text{Salinity} = 31.60 \text{ grams of salt per 1000 grams of water} \end{cases}$

Extremes for continental shelf sea water, temperate zone $\begin{cases} T = \ \ 5 \text{ °C} & \text{salinity} = 30 \text{ parts} & \rho_0 = 1.02375 \text{ g/cm}^3 \\ T = 25 \text{ °C} & \text{salinity} = 36 \text{ parts} & \rho_0 = 1.02412 \text{ g/cm}^3 \\ T = 15 \text{ °C} & \text{salinity} = 36 \text{ parts} & \rho_0 = 1.02677 \text{ g/cm}^3 \\ T = 20 \text{ °C} & \text{salinity} = 30 \text{ parts} & \rho_0 = 1.02099 \text{ g/cm}^3 \end{cases}$

Specific Heat of Pure Water

$T = \ \ 0$ °C	$C_p = 1.00874$ cal/(g-deg)
$T = 10$ °C	$C_p = 1.00184$ cal/(g-deg)
$T = 20$ °C	$C_p = 0.99859$ cal/(g-deg)
$T = 30$ °C	$C_p = 0.99745$ cal/(g-deg)
$T = 40$ °C	$C_p = 0.99761$ cal/(g-deg)
$T = 50$ °C	$C_p = 0.99829$ cal/(g-deg)
$T = 60$ °C	$C_p = 0.99934$ cal/(g-deg)

Viscosity of Pure Water

$T = 0\,°C$	$\eta = 0.01792$ dyne-sec/cm^2 (poises)
$T = 10\,°C$	$\eta = 0.01308$ dyne-sec/cm^2 (poises)
$T = 20\,°C$	$\eta = 0.01005$ dyne-sec/cm^2 (poises)
$T = 30\,°C$	$\eta = 0.00805$ dyne-sec/cm^2 (poises)
$T = 40\,°C$	$\eta = 0.00656$ dyne-sec/cm^2 (poises)
$T = 50\,°C$	$\eta = 0.00549$ dyne-sec/cm^2 (poises)

Thermal Conductivity of Pure Water

$T = 0\,°C$	$\kappa = 0.00120$ cal/(cm-sec-deg)
$T = 17\,°C$	$\kappa = 0.00131$ cal/(cm-sec-deg)
$T = 20\,°C$	$\kappa = 0.00143$ cal/(cm-sec-deg)

B. Speed (Velocity) of Sound in Water

Pure Water: The speed of sound as a function of T in °C is[8]

$$c = 1402.39 + 5.037T - 0.05808T^2 + 0.3342 \times 10^{-3}T^3$$
$$- 0.1478 \times 10^{-5}T^4 + 0.3146 \times 10^{-8}T^5 \text{ m/sec.} \quad (2 \cdot 8)$$

Typical values,

$T = 5\,°C$	1426.162 m/sec
$T = 10°$	1447.270
$= 15°$	1465.931
$= 20°$	1482.343
$= 30°$	1509.127

Sea Water: The speed of sound for depths up to 8000 m with a standard error of 0.070 m/sec is calculated from [8,9]

$$c = 1448.96 + 4.591T - 5.304 \times 10^{-2}T^2 + 2.374 \times 10^{-4}T^3$$
$$+ 1.340(S - 35) + 1.630 \times 10^{-2}D + 1.675 \times 10^{-7}D^2$$
$$- 1.025 \times 10^{-2}T(S - 35) - 7.139 \times 10^{-13}TD^3 \text{ m/sec,}$$
$$(2 \cdot 9)$$

where T = temperature in degrees centigrade, S = salinity in parts per thousand, and D = depth in meters.

---

[8]V. A. Del Grosso and C. W. Mader, "Speed of sound in pure water," J. Acoust. Soc. Am. **52**, 1442–1446 (1972) and "Speed of sound in sea water samples," **52**, 961–974 (1972).

[9]K. V. Mackenzie, "Nine term equation for sound speed in oceans," J. Acoust. Soc. Am. **70**, 807–812 (1981) and "Discussion of sea water sound-speed determinations," **70**, 801–806 (1981).

Equation (2·9) shows that speed increases (a) by about 0.2% per °C; (b) by about 0.2% per 100 fathoms (183 m); and by about 0.1% for each 0.1% increase in salinity, i.e., $c \propto (965 + S)$.

TYPICAL WORLDWIDE DOMAINS OF T, S AND D

$P, kg/cm^2$	$T,°C$	$S, \%$	D, m
0	0–30	30–40	0
50	0–20	32–40	487
100	0–16	32–40	972
200	0–16	32–39	1940
500	0–14	33–39	4810

Typical values of sound speeds in sea water,

$S = 32\%$	$P = 0$	$P = 50$	$P = 100$	$P = 200$ kg/m^2
$T = 5°$	1466.75	1474.73	1482.69	1499.00 m/sec
$= 10°$	1486.09	1494.07	1502.02	1518.33
$= 20°$	1518.06	1526.04	1534.04	1550.21
$S = 38\%$				
$T = 5°$	1474.48	1482.46	1490.42	1506.73 m/sec
$= 10°$	1493.51	1501.49	1509.44	1525.75
$= 20°$	1524.87	1532.85	1540.85	1557.02

C. Characteristic Impedance of Water, $\rho_0 c$

Pure Water: $T = 15°$ $\rho_0 c = 146,466$ rayls
Sea Water: $T = 15°$. $S = 35\%$, $P = 0$ $\rho_0 c = 153,800$ rayls

D. Speed (Velocity) of Sound in Liquids and Solids

The speeds of sound in a number of liquids and solids are given in Tables 2·9 and 2·10.[10]

The effective speed of sound in solids given in Table 2·9 is a reasonably complex function of the driving frequency and the shape of the vibrating element. The problem has not been well explored, but the following comments may be used as a guide in obtaining an approximate value of the effective speed in the elements of many vibrating systems.

For cylindrical elements of solids with approximately circular or square cross section, with free sides, the effective speed varies with the ratio of diameter to wavelength as illustrated by Fig. 2·4a, where V_3 is the bulk speed, V_1 is the long bar

[10]Reprinted with permission from *CRC Handbook of Chemistry and Physics*, 67th ed. (1986). Copyright CRC Press, Inc., Boca Raton, FL.

TABLE 2·9 SPEED (VELOCITY) OF SOUND IN LIQUIDS[10]

Liquid	Temperature, °C	Velocity, cm/sec
Alcohol, ethyl	12.5	1.24×10^5
	20	1.17×10^5
Benzene	25	1.295×10^5
Carbon disulfide	25	1.149×10^5
Chloroform	25	0.987×10^5
Ether, ethyl	20	1.01×10^5
Glycerin	20	1.92×10^5
Mercury	25	1.45×10^5
Pentaine	18	1.05×10^5
	20	1.02×10^5
Petroleum	15	1.33×10^5
Turpentine	3.5	1.37×10^5
	25	1.255×10^5

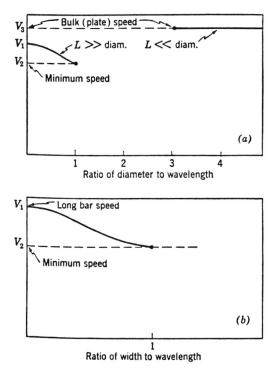

FIG. 2·4 Graphs showing the variation of the speed of sound in solids as a function of diameter or width to a wavelength. (a) Cylindrical elements with free sides. L is the length of the cylinder. (b) Rectangular elements with free sides and thicknesses less than the width.

TABLE 2·10 SPEED (VELOCITY) OF SOUND IN SOLIDS[10]

Material	Longitudinal Bar Velocity, cm/sec	Plate (Bulk) Velocity, cm/sec
Aluminum	5.00×10^5	6.42×10^5
Antimony	3.40×10^5	$\cdots$
Bismuth	1.79×10^5	2.18×10^5
Brass	3.48×10^5	4.70×10^5
Cadmium	2.40×10^5	2.78×10^5
Constantan	4.30×10^5	5.24×10^5
Copper (annealed)	3.81×10^5	4.76×10^5
German silver	3.58×10^5	4.76×10^5
Gold	2.03×10^5	3.24×10^5
Iridium	4.79×10^5	$\cdots$
Iron	5.20×10^5	5.96×10^5
Lead (annealed)	1.19×10^5	2.16×10^5
Magnesium	4.94×10^5	5.77×10^5
Manganese	3.83×10^5	4.66×10^5
Nickel	4.40×10^5	6.04×10^5
Platinum	2.80×10^5	3.26×10^5
Silver	2.68×10^5	3.65×10^5
Steel	5.18×10^5	5.94×10^5
Tantalum	3.35×10^5	$\cdots$
Tin	2.73×10^5	3.32×10^5
Tungsten (drawn)	4.31×10^5	5.41×10^5
Zinc	3.85×10^5	4.21×10^5
Cork	0.50×10^5	$\cdots$
Crystals		
Quartz X-cut	5.44×10^5	5.72×10^5
ADP($NH_4H_2PO_4$)		
45° Z-cut	3.28×10^5	4.92×10^5
Rochelle salt		
45° Y-cut	2.47×10^5	$\cdots$
45° X-cut	(See Fig. 2·5.)	(See Fig. 2·5.)
L-cut	$\cdots$	5.36×10^5
Tourmaline		
Z-cut	$\cdots$	7.54×10^5
CaF_2 (fluorite)		
X-cut	6.74×10^5	7.18×10^5
NaCl (rock salt)		
X-cut	4.51×10^5	4.78×10^5
NaBr		
X-cut	2.79×10^5	3.2×10^5
KCl (sylvite)		
X-cut	4.14×10^5	4.38×10^5
KBr		
X-cut	3.38×10^5	3.48×10^5
Glass		
Heavy flint	3.98×10^5	3.72×10^5
Extra light flint	4.55×10^5	4.80×10^5
Heaviest crown	4.71×10^5	5.26×10^5
Crown	5.30×10^5	5.66×10^5
Quartz	5.10×10^5	5.54×10^5

TABLE 2·10 (*Continued*)

Material	Longitudinal Bar Velocity, cm/sec	Plate (Bulk) Velocity, cm/sec
Granite	3.95×10^5	...
Ivory	3.01×10^5	...
Marble	...	3.81×10^5
Slate	4.51×10^5	...
Wood		...
Elm (along fiber)	...	4.12×10^5
Oak (along fiber)	...	$3.8 \ \times 10^5$

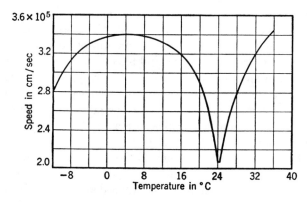

FIG. 2·5 Variation of the speed of sound in a 45°, X-cut Rochelle salt crystal with temperature.

speed, and V_2 is the minimum speed. For metals like aluminum, brass, or steel the ratio V_2/V_1 is about 0.65.

For rectangular elements with free sides whose thickness is less than the width, the effective speed for the element vibrating in extension (not thickness) varies with the ratio of width to wavelength as illustrated by Fig. 2·4b. Crystals are usually of such size that this curve is applicable. The ratio V_2/V_1 can be taken as equal to 0.8 for most of the cuts of crystals in general use.

Constraints on the sides of the cylindrical elements have the effect of increasing the ratio of diameter to wavelength. Similarly, constraining the sides of rectangular elements increases the effective ratio of width to wavelength.

The speed for a zero diameter-to-wavelength ratio is the long bar speed, and the speed for an infinite diameter-to-wavelength ratio is the bulk (plate) speed.

In Fig. 2·5, the speed of sound in Rochelle salt crystal is shown. In the vicinity of the curie point at 24.1°C the speed decreases rapidly.

2·4 Solutions to the Ordinary Wave Equation

The propagation of sound in a truly unbounded medium often is expressed by an equation which satisfies the wave equation in spherical coordinates. In that case, the losses due to heat conduction along the wave between points of compression and rarefaction are negligible in the audible and ultrasonic regions in comparison with absorption due to other reasons. Also, the correction to the adiabatic value of the velocity of sound, which is of second order, is so small as to be negligible. The losses due to viscosity and to molecular absorption are, however, of observable magnitude.

We shall discuss first solutions to the small signal wave equation with the damping constant δ inserted to take account of all types of losses which cause logarithmic decreases in the sound pressure as a function of distance. The values of δ will be discussed in the next part of this chapter.

We shall also consider here those cases in which propagation is unbounded in only one or two dimensions, and in which the bounding surfaces in the remaining one or two dimensions are separated by a distance small enough so that no wave motion occurs in a direction perpendicular to their surfaces.

A. Plane Waves

For the case of plane waves, that is, a medium bounded in two dimensions, the formula for the sound pressure as a function of distance x and time t is

$$p = A e^{j\omega[t-(x/c)]-\delta x} \qquad (2\cdot10)$$

where p is the instantaneous sound pressure, A is the maximum amplitude of the sound pressure, and ω is the circular frequency equal to 2π times the frequency f.

The particle velocity u (in the x direction, of course) is related to the pressure by the formula

$$u = -\frac{1}{j\omega\rho_0}\frac{\partial p}{\partial x} = \frac{A}{\rho_0 c}\left(1 - j\frac{\delta c}{\omega}\right)e^{j\omega(t-x/c)-\delta x} \qquad (2\cdot11)$$

Equation $(2\cdot11)$ says that the particle velocity is directly proportional to the pressure gradient $(\partial p/\partial x)$ and is inversely proportional to the frequency. Later we shall see that certain types of microphones are alternatively called velocity or pressure gradient microphones because they respond to the quantities expressed in Eq. $(2\cdot11)$.

The specific acoustic impedance Z_s, at any point x, is equal to the ratio of p to u:

$$Z_s = \frac{p}{u} = \frac{\rho_0 c}{\left(1 - j\frac{\delta c}{\omega}\right)} \doteq \rho_0 c \qquad (2\cdot12)$$

In other words, the pressure and particle velocity are nearly in phase and have the same ratio at all parts of the medium.

B. Cylindrical Waves

Let us assume now that we have a medium which is bounded in one dimension by a pair of walls whose separation is less than one-fourth wavelength. We can express the sound pressure at any point removed a distance r from a "line" source (or from the center of a circular cylinder whose radii expand and contract at all points in phase) by the formula

$$p = AH_0^{(2)}\left[\frac{\omega}{c}\left(1 - j\frac{\delta c}{\omega}\right)r\right] \qquad (2\cdot13)$$

where $H_0^{(2)}$ [ ] is a Hankel function of the zeroth order and second kind. Its value may be calculated from the equation

$$H_0^{(2)}(z) = J_0(z) - jN_0(z) \qquad (2\cdot14)$$

where J_0 and N_0 are Bessel and Neumann functions, respectively. Tables and charts of these two functions are published in many places.[2, 11] Graphs of J_0 and N_0 as a function of a *real* argument z, that is, for $(\delta c/\omega)^2 \ll 1$ and $(\omega r/c) = z$, are given

[11] E. Jahnke and F. Emde, *Tables of Functions with Formulae and Curves*, Dover Publications (1943).

in Figs. 2·6 and 2·7 for a range of values of z from 0 to 15.   For values of z greater than 15,

$$J_0(z) = \frac{\cos\left(z - \frac{\pi}{4}\right)}{\sqrt{\frac{\pi z}{2}}} \tag{2·15}$$

$$N_0(z) = \frac{\sin\left(z - \frac{\pi}{4}\right)}{\sqrt{\frac{\pi z}{2}}} \tag{2·16}$$

$$H_0^{(2)}(z) = \frac{e^{-j[z - (\pi/4)]}}{\sqrt{\frac{\pi z}{2}}} \tag{2·17}$$

Equations (2·13) to (2·17) show that in a complex wave each component is propagated with amplitude and phase different

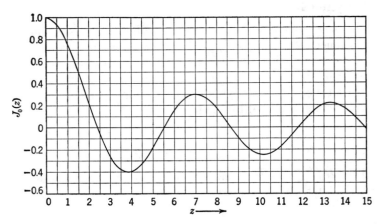

FIG. 2·6   Plot of Bessel's function of zero order $J_0(z)$ as a function of real argument z.

from those for each other component up to a distance where the approximate relations of (2·15) to (2·17) are valid.   Hence, complex cylindrical waves are propagated with a change of shape for z small.

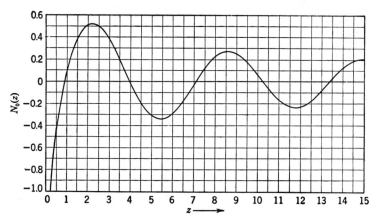

Fɪɢ. 2·7   Plot of Neumann's function of zero order $N_0(z)$ as a function of real argument z.

The particle velocity q (in the direction of r) is equal to

$$q = \frac{-1}{j\omega\rho_0}\frac{\partial p}{\partial r} = \frac{A\left(1 - j\dfrac{\delta c}{\omega}\right)}{j\rho_0 c} H_1^{(2)}\left[\frac{\omega}{c}\left(1 - j\frac{\delta c}{\omega}\right)r\right]e^{j\omega t} \quad (2\cdot18)$$

where $H_1^{(2)}$ [ ] is a Hankel function of the first order and second kind.   Its value may be calculated from the equation

$$H_1^{(2)}(z) = J_1(z) - jN_1(z) \quad (2\cdot19)$$

Graphs of the $J_1(z)$ and $N_1(z)$ as a function of a *real* argument of z are given in Figs. 2·8 and 2·9 for a range of values of z

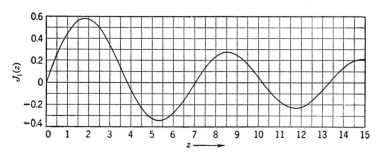

Fɪɢ. 2·8   Plot of Bessel's function of first-order $J_1(z)$ as a function of real argument z.

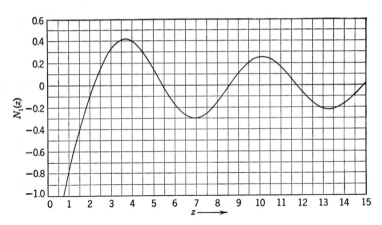

F𝐼G. 2·9   Plot of Neumann's function of first-order $N_1(z)$ as a function of real argument z.

from **0 to 15.**   For larger values of z use

$$J_1(z) = \frac{\cos\left(z - \dfrac{3\pi}{4}\right)}{\sqrt{\dfrac{\pi z}{2}}} \qquad (2\cdot20)$$

$$N_1(z) = \frac{\sin\left(z - \dfrac{3\pi}{4}\right)}{\sqrt{\dfrac{\pi z}{2}}} \qquad (2\cdot21)$$

$$H_1^{(2)}(z) = \frac{e^{-j\left(z - \dfrac{3\pi}{4}\right)}}{\sqrt{\dfrac{\pi z}{2}}} \qquad (2\cdot22)$$

The specific acoustic impedance Z_s at any point r in the medium is given by the ratio of p to q:

$$Z_s = \frac{p}{q} = \frac{j\rho_0 c}{\left(1 - j\dfrac{\delta c}{\omega}\right)} \frac{H_0^{(2)}\left[\dfrac{\omega}{c}\left(1 - j\dfrac{\delta c}{\omega}\right)r\right]}{H_1^{(2)}\left[\dfrac{\omega}{c}\left(1 - j\dfrac{\delta c}{\omega}\right)r\right]} = |Z_s|\angle\phi \quad (2\cdot23)$$

At large distances from the source $(r \rightarrow \infty)$,

$$Z_s = \frac{\rho_0 c}{1 - j\frac{\delta c}{\omega}} \doteq \rho_0 c \qquad (2 \cdot 24)$$

The values of the magnitude $|Z_s|/\rho_0 c$ and phase angle ϕ, as a function of r for a number of frequencies, are given in Figs.

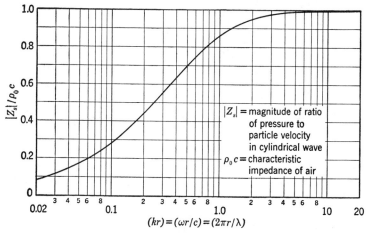

Fig. 2·10 Plot of the magnitude of the impedance ratio $Z_s/\rho_0 c$ in a cylindrical wave as a function of kr, where k is the wave number equal to ω/c or $2\pi/\lambda$, and r is the distance from the center of the cylindrical source.

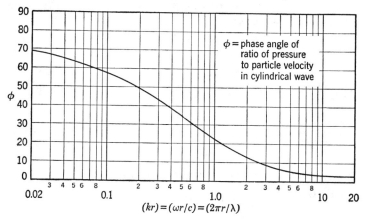

Fig. 2·11 Plot of the phase angle, in degrees, of the impedance ratio $Z_s/\rho_0 c$ in a cylindrical wave as a function of kr, where k is the wave number equal to ω/c or $2\pi/\lambda$, and r is the distance from the center of the cylindrical source.

2·10 and 2·11 for $(\delta c/\omega)^2 \ll 1$. It is seen that near the source or at low frequencies $\left| Z_s \right|$ becomes small and ϕ approaches 90°.

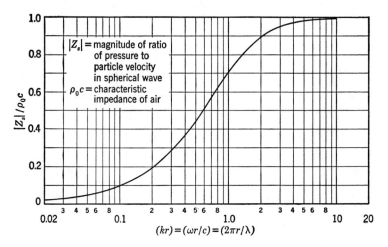

Fig. 2·12   Plot of the magnitude of the impedance ratio $Z_s/\rho_0 c$ in a spherical wave as a function of kr, where k is the wave number equal to ω/c or $2\pi/\lambda$, and r is the distance from the center of the spherical source.

C. Spherical Waves

In a completely unbounded medium, the equation for sound pressure at any point a distance r from a "point" source (or from the center of a sphere whose surface is pulsating the same at all points) is given by

$$p = \frac{A e^{j\omega[t-(r/c)]-\delta r}}{r} \qquad (2\cdot 25)$$

The particle velocity q is given by

$$q = \frac{-1}{j\omega\rho_0}\frac{\partial p}{\partial r} = \frac{A}{r}\left\{ \frac{\left(1-j\dfrac{\delta c}{\omega}\right)}{\rho_0 c} + \frac{1}{j\omega\rho_0 r} \right\} e^{j\omega[t-(r/c)]-\delta r} \qquad (2\cdot 26)$$

The specific acoustic impedance Z_s at any point r is given by the ratio of p to q:

$$Z_s = \frac{p}{q} = \frac{j\omega\rho_0 c r}{c + j\omega r\left(1-j\dfrac{\delta c}{\omega}\right)} \qquad (2\cdot 27)$$

or, for $(\delta c/\omega)^2 \ll 1$,

$$Z_s = |Z_s| \underline{/\phi} = \frac{kr\rho_0 c}{\sqrt{1 + k^2 r^2}} \underline{/\tan^{-1}\frac{1}{kr}} \qquad (2\cdot 28)$$

where $k = \omega/c$ is the wave number. For large values of r, $Z_s \doteq \rho_0 c$.

The values of the magnitude $|Z_s|/\rho_0 c$ and phase angle ϕ plotted as a function of r for a number of frequencies are given

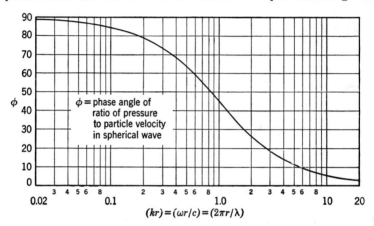

FIG. 2·13 Plot of the phase angle, in degrees, of the impedance ratio $Z_s/\rho_0 c$ in a spherical wave as a function of kr, where k is the wave number equal to ω/c or $2\pi/\lambda$, and r is the distance from the center of the spherical source.

in Figs. 2·12 and 2·13; it is assumed that $(\delta c/\omega)^2 \ll 1$. The quantity $\rho_0 c/Z_s$ expressed in decibels, is plotted in Fig. 14·2.

D. Three-Dimensional Bounded Media

The mathematical representation of the propagation of sound in a bounded three-dimensional medium is necessarily complex. The first requirement is that the Laplacian, $\nabla^2\phi$, which appears in the wave equation

$$\nabla^2 p - \frac{1}{c^2}\frac{\partial^2 p}{\partial t^2} = 0 \qquad (2\cdot 29)$$

is best expressed in a coordinate system suitable to the configuration of the boundaries. For a sound field in a rectangular enclosure, rectangular coordinates are the best; for the sound field around a sphere, spherical coordinates may be used, and so on. There are eleven coordinate systems which may be used in the solution of the steady-state wave equation (scalar Helmholtz equation). The following eight have been investigated: (1) *cylindrical coordinate systems*—(a) rectangular, (b) polar, (c) parabolic, (d) elliptic; (2) *rotational coordinate systems*—(a) spherical, (b) prolate spheroidal, (c) oblate spheroidal, (d) paraboloidal. We cannot hope to discuss these different coordinate systems adequately in this chapter. Reference should be made to Morse[2] and to other suitable texts of mathematical physics for solutions in some of the above coordinate systems.

2·5 Attenuation of Sound in Air

A. Quiet Isotropic Air

Sound absorption in quiet isotropic air is caused by two processes. First, energy is extracted from a sound wave by losses arising from heat conduction and viscosity in the air, expressed by the attenuation coefficient m'. This so-called classical absorption, which is proportional to frequency squared, is, of itself, only predominant at very low frequencies. Second, energy is extracted from a sound wave by rotational and vibration relaxation of the oxygen molecules in the air. The vapor content of the air determines the time constant of the vibration relaxation, which is more important than rotational relaxation. In addition, this molecular absorption, expressed by m'', depends in a major way on temperature.

The attenuation of the intensity of a sound wave is given by,

$$I(x) = I_0 e^{-(m' + m'')x} = I_0 e^{-mx} \qquad (2.30)$$

from which the attenuation in decibels per 100 meters is

$$dB/100 \text{ m} = 100 \times 4.434 \text{ m.} \qquad (2·31)$$

The combined absorption from both processes for sound in standard air has been determined theoretically, and in the laboratory, at between 50 and 12,500 Hz.[12] References 12 contain over 30 citations as bases for the results, which are taken directly from ANSI S1.26-1978.

[12]American National Standard, ANSI S1.26-1978, "Absorption of sound by the atmosphere," Acoustical Society of America. C. M. Harris, "Absorption of sound in air versus humidity and temperature," J. Acoust. Soc. Am. **40**, 148–159 (1966).

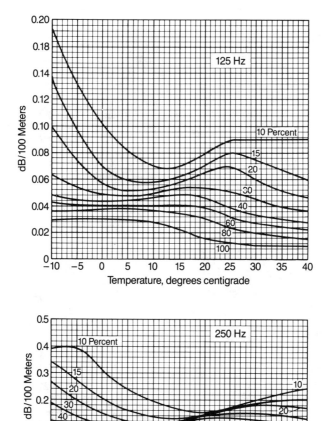

FIG. 2·14 Attenuation of sound in air in dB/100 m at 125 and 250 Hz.

The Medium

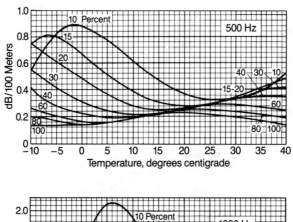

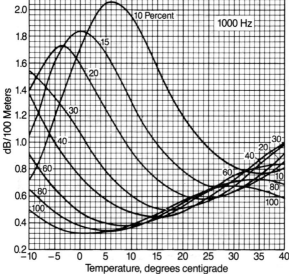

FIG. 2·15 Attenuation of sound in air in dB/100 m at 500 and 1000 Hz.

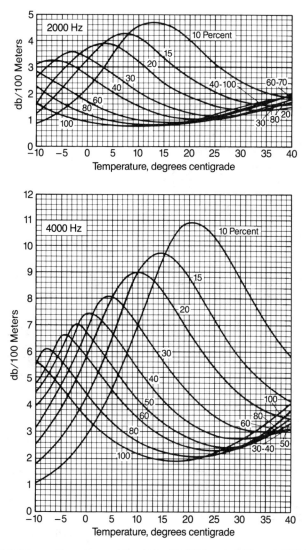

FIG. 2·16 Attenuation of sound in air in dB/100 m at 2000 and 4000 Hz.

Figures 2·14 through 2·17 show the attenuations in dB per 100 meters. In Fig. 2·17 the attenuation at higher frequencies is shown vs relative humidity at 20° with frequency as parameter.

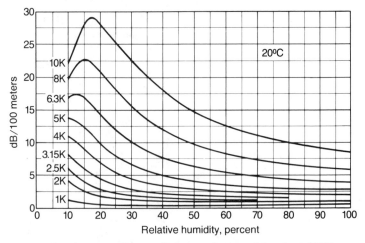

FIG. 2·17 Total attenuation coefficient m for sound in air at 20 °C, versus relative humidity with frequency as parameter, between 1 and 12.5 kHz in ⅓ octave bands.

The aircraft industry has produced standardized charts for estimating the sound attenuation in normal quiet air for noise traveling from an airplane to ground. Their charts are shown in Figs. 2·18a and 2·18b.[13]

For engineers interested in measuring continuous-spectrum, random-noise outdoors in quiet air using an American Standard Sound Level Meter set to A-weighting, the chart of Fig. 2·19 is useful.

Special Note: References 12–24 in the first edition have been deleted. Those references and new material on attenuation of sound in air are derived from Refs. 12 and 13 and their citations.

[13]Aerospace Recommended Practice, ARP 866, "Standard values of atmospheric absorption as a function of temperature and humidity for use in evaluating aircraft flyover noise," March 15, 1975, Society of Automotive Engineers, 485 Lexington Ave, New York, NY. (Mathematical representations suitable for machine computation and interpolation are included.)

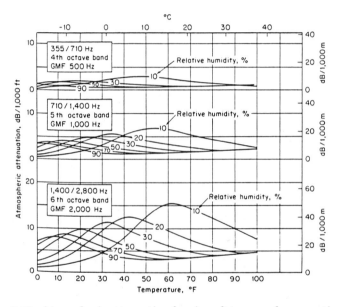

FIG. 2·18a Atmospheric attenuation for aircraft-to-ground propagation in dB/1000 ft (or dB/1000 m) for octave bands with center (geometric-mean) frequencies at 500, 1000, and 2000 Hz.

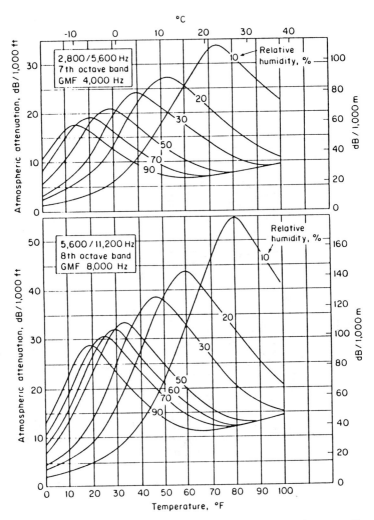

FIG. 2·18*b* Atmospheric attenuation for aircraft-to-ground propagation in dB/1000 ft (or dB/1000 m) for octave bands with center frequencies at 4000 and 8000 Hz.

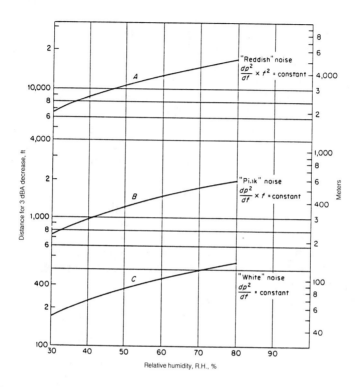

FIG. 2·19 Means for determining the distance that a continuous-spectrum random noise must travel to be attenuated 3 dB(A) as measured on the A scale of an American Standard sound-level meter. The abscissa is relative humidity (R.H.) in percent. Curve A is for a noise with a spectrum that when measured with a set of constant-percentage bands (e.g., octave or one-third-octave bands, "flat" response instrument) falls 3 dB for each doubling of band mid-frequency. Curve B is for a noise that, when measured the same way, has a spectrum that remains constant with band mid-frequency. Curve C is for a noise that has a spectrum that rises 3 dB for each doubling of band mid-frequency.

B. Tubes

Tubes are frequently employed as a means of producing and guiding plane waves. Examples are: wave guides for the measurement of acoustic impedance; attachments to microphones or sound sources to serve as sound probes or point sources; stethoscopes; and acoustic delay lines. Because of thermal and viscous losses at the walls of the tube, the sound is attenuated as it travels along the length. Several investigations of this attenuation have been reported in the literature.[25-29] Tischner, Waetzmann and Wenke, and Beranek report that the attenuation in nepers per centimeter for smooth metal or hardwood tubes is about 15 percent greater than that predicted by Kirchhoff,[30] but that otherwise his formula satisfactorily predicts the attenuation. Kirchhoff's formula for the attenuation constant in circular tubes is

$$\zeta = \frac{1.02}{c} \left(\frac{f^{1/2}}{R} \right) \text{ nepers/cm.} \qquad (2 \cdot 32)$$

This quantity appears in the exponent of the wave in the pressure equation. f is the frequency in cycles per second, R is the radius of the tube in centimeters, and c is the speed of sound in centimeters per second.

Fay,[27] investigating sound transmission in a tube using dried air and with the tube walls packed in sand, found that Kirchhoff's formula was valid within a very small percentage, but that an added linear term in frequency was necessary to explain his results. His expression for a tube with a bore of 0.749 in. reads

[25]H. Tischner, "On the propagation of sound in tubes," *Elektr. Nachr.-Tech.*, **7**, 192–202 (1930) (in German).

[26]E. Waetzmann and W. Wenke, "Sound damping in rigid and elastic walled tubes," *Akus. Zeits.*, **4**, 1 (1939) (in German); English translation: L. L. Beranek, *Jour. Acous. Soc. Amer.*, **11**, 154–155 (1939).

[27]R. D. Fay, "Attenuation of sound in tubes," *Jour. Acous. Soc. Amer.*, **12**, 62–67 (1940).

[28]L. L. Beranek, "Precision measurement of acoustic impedance," *Jour. Acous. Soc. Amer.*, **12**, 3–13 (1940).

[29]W. P. Mason, "The propagation characteristics of sound tubes and acoustic filters," *Phys. Rev.*, **31**, 283–295 (1928).

[30]Lord Rayleigh, *Theory of Sound*, Macmillan (1929), Vol. II, pp. 312ff.

$$\zeta = 2.92 \times 10^{-5} f^{1/2} + 6.75 \times 10^{-8} f \text{ nepers/cm,} \qquad (2\cdot33)$$

where f is the frequency in cycles.

When we attempt to compare Fay's formula with the data of the other experimenters, we find that at higher frequencies the calculated values are higher than the measurements by 10 to 20 percent. Fay states that the linear frequency term appears to be attributable to the gas itself and not to the tube, but that the absorption obtained is much greater than that attributable to molecular or viscous absorption in the gas as discussed in the previous paragraphs of this chapter. He also finds that Mason's[29] data satisfy a formula similar to that of Eq. (2·33).

Until the problem has been explored further, it appears that, for normal (undried) air where the attenuation in the gas is small compared to that at the side walls of the tube (with the walls of the tube exposed to the outer space), Eq. (2·32) times 1.08 should be used to predict the attenuation. Kirchhoff's equation *increased in magnitude by 8 percent* and expressed in nepers per foot or per centimeter becomes

$$\zeta = 38.2 \times 10^{-5} (f^{1/2}/R_i) \text{ ft}^{-1}, \qquad (2\cdot34)$$

$$\zeta = 3.18 \times 10^{-5} (f^{1/2}/R) \text{ cm}^{-1}, \qquad (2\cdot35)$$

where f is the frequency in cycles per second, R is the radius of the tube in centimeters, and R_i is the radius in inches.

For tubes or ducts which are nearly square, ζ may be calculated by multiplying (2·34) or (2·35) by the ratio of (P/A for the rectangular duct) to (P/A for the circular duct), where P is the perimeter, and A is the cross-sectional area. For example, to determine ζ for a square duct, multiply (2·34) or (2·35) by $2R/d$, where d is an inside dimension of the square duct in inches or centimeters, respectively.

For the total attenuation due to losses at the side walls and to losses in the gas, the values of δ_A discussed earlier must be added to the values of ζ computed from (2·34) or (2·35).

Waetzmann and Wenke measured the attenuation in a number of tubes not having smooth and rigid walls. For one set of these data they used two tubes made from wood and steel and compared the attenuation for them with that of two similar tubes whose inner walls were made rough. The diameter of the tubes was 19 mm; the wall thickness of the steel tubes, 2 mm; and the wall thickness of the wood tubes, somewhat greater than 2 mm. A graph of their results is given in Fig. 2·20.

Waetzmann and Wenke also investigated the attenuation of sound in several types of elastic tubes. Typical data are shown in Fig. 2·21

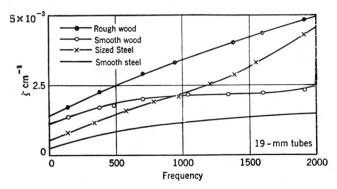

FIG. 2·20 Attenuation as a function of frequency of a plane wave propagated down tubes, 19 mm in diameter, made of rough wood, smooth wood, sized steel, and smooth steel. The numbers on the ordinate should be multiplied by 10^{-3} as indicated. (After Waetzmann and Wenke.[26])

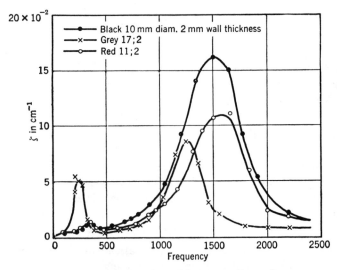

FIG. 2·21 Attenuation as a function of frequency for a plane wave propagated down several kinds of rubber tubing. The numbers on the ordinate should be multiplied by 10^{-2} as indicated. (After Waetzmann and Wenke.[26])

where the colors listed refer to hot vulcanized red rubber, gray technical rubber, and very soft black rubber manufactured at low temperatures. For use as a stethoscope they found that a red rubber hose 6 mm
in diameter with a wall thickness of 1.5 mm was almost as good as a
length of rigid metal tubing.

2·6 Attenuation of Sound in Water

A. Fresh Water

The attenuation of sound in water is very difficult to measure
at low frequencies. Recent data taken at high frequencies yield
the values shown in the upper part of Fig. 2·22.[31] The long-
dashed line is extended to lower frequencies from the measured
values. It is to be noted that the measured values lie above the
theoretical values by roughly a factor of two.

B. Salt Water

The attenuation of sound in salt water is the same at high
frequencies as that in pure water. At low frequencies, however,
the attenuation is greater because of the salinity of the liquid.[31]
It is possible that this increased absorption arises from molecular interaction similar to the phenomenon of intermolecular
absorption in air.

2·7 Diffraction and Scattering

A. Wind and Temperature Gradients

Appreciable vertical temperature and wind gradients almost
always exist over open level ground; the former because of heat
exchange between ground and atmosphere, the latter because
of friction between the moving air and ground. Because of these
gradients, the speed of sound varies with height above the
ground and sound waves are refracted, that is to say, bent upward or downward. Under such conditions, it is possible to have
a "shadow zone" into which no direct sound can penetrate or,

[31]F. E. Fox, "Ultrasonic interferometry for liquid media," *Phys. Rev.*, **52**, 973–
981 (1937); F. E. Fox and G. D. Rock, "Ultrasonic absorption in water," *Jour.
Acous. Soc. Amer.*, **12**, 505–510 (1941); *U. C. D. W. R. Reports* U307, U394, U422,
"The influence of thermal conditions on the transmission of 24-kc sound," Pts. I–
III (1945–46); L. N. Lieberman, "Frequency dependent properties of liquids,"
Marine Physical Laboratory Quarterly Report, July–Sept., pp. 3–4 (1947); R. W.
Leonard, unpublished data, University of California at Los Angeles (1948).

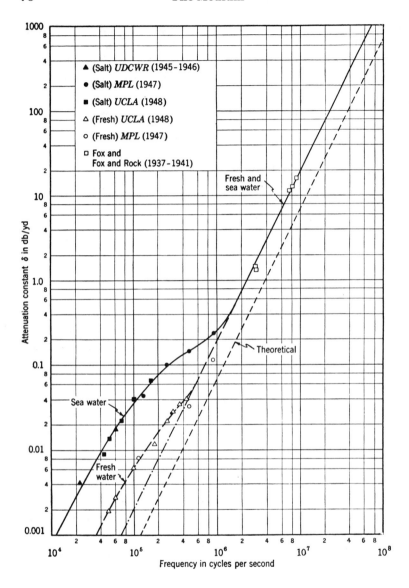

FIG. 2·22 Attenuation of sound in fresh and sea water. The short-dashed curve is the theoretical value. The long-dashed curve is extrapolated from measured values at high frequencies for fresh water. The solid curve is formed from measured values for salt water at low frequencies and both salt and fresh water at high frequencies. The deviation of the fresh water curve at low frequencies is probably due to small impurities.

conversely, propagate over unusually long distances.[32,33] Shadow zones are never sharp in the sense of light because acoustical diffraction effects are associated with much longer wavelengths and, in addition, sound energy is scattered into the shadow zone by turbulence.

Wind gradients near the ground are nearly always positive; that is, the windspeed increases with height. As a result, a shadow zone is most commonly encountered upwind from a source. Downwind, the sound rays are bent downward, and no shadow zone is produced. Crosswind, there is a zone of transition.

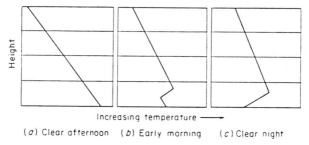

(a) Clear afternoon   (b) Early morning   (c) Clear night

FIG. 2·23 Example of temperature profiles at three times of day: (a) normal lapse; (b) high inversions with normal lapse above and below; and (c) ground inversion with normal lapse above.

Temperature-induced sound refraction tends to be symmetrical about the source. A shadow may completely encircle a source in the presence of a strong negative temperature gradient (large temperature lapse, as shown in Fig. 2·23a) and low windspeed, such as may be expected on a calm, clear afternoon. On the other hand, there will be no shadow at all, within a mile or two of the source, in the presence of a strong positive temperature gradient (large temperature inversion, as shown in Fig. 2·23c) and low windspeed, such as may be expected on a clear calm night. A double gradient, such as shown in Fig. 2·23b), may cause a channeling of sound, with slowly diminishing level over a long distance.

[32]U. Ingard, "On Sound-transmission Anomalies in the Atmosphere," *J. Acoust. Soc. Am.,* vol. 45, pp. 1038–1039, 1969.

[33]U. Ingard, "A Review of the Influence of Meteorological Conditions on Sound Propagation," *J. Acoust. Soc. Am.,* vol. 25, pp. 405–411, 1953.

B. Excess Attenuation over Ground—No Shadow Zone

Two anomalies are commonly observed.[32] The first is an excess sound attenuation at comparatively low frequencies, say 300 to 600 Hz, which often may be *greater* by 10 to 50 dB than the value predicted from geometrical spreading and air absorption of sound. The second is at high frequencies, say at 6000 Hz, where the sound attenuation may be 10 to 50 dB *less* than that predicted.

The low-frequency excess attenuation is probably caused[32] by interference between the direct sound (say from a source 3 m above the ground) and the reflected sounds that reach the receiver. The amplitude and phase of the reflected sounds are determined by the acoustic impedance of the ground, which may be regarded as a very deep porous medium. Because the impedance of the ground varies with frequency, the condition for destructive interference is met only in a narrow frequency band in the range of 300–600 Hz.

The high-frequency unusually low attenuation compared to that calculated for the average air humidity over a range of heights above the ground, or for the humidity obtaining at ground level, is often caused by the fact that both temperature and water-vapor content usually vary with position, particularly with height above the ground. The acoustic transmissivity, therefore, is different for different paths between the source and the receiver. Exceptionally low attenuation results from the occurrence of a path, or "channel," of unusually high transmissivity.

To help quantify the anomalous excess attenuation, a series of 159 measurements were made in the Leningrad region[34] over a 3-year period, during all seasons, at night and during the day, over seven distinct stretches of terrain, at distances ranging from 1.5 to 5 km (1 to 3 miles), and at frequencies up to 2000 Hz. Atmospheric measurements of temperature, humidity, wind velocity, and temperature and wind gradients were made at heights up to 250 m (800 ft). By calculation, the attenuation owing to geometric spreading and molecular absorption was subtracted out to yield the *anomalous excess attenuation*.

---

[34]I. A. Dneprovskaya, V. K. Iofe, and F. I. Levitas, "On the Attenuation of Sound as It Propagates through the Atmosphere," *Soviet Phys.-Acoust.*, vol. 8, pp. 235–239, 1963.

The results are illustrated in Fig. 2·24. In (a) the excess attenuation in dB/km (dB/3280 ft) is shown for four measurement distances and is seen to be a strongly nonlinear function of distance. In (b) the anomalous excess attenuation is shown for the seven different propagation paths. In (c) it is shown that the anomalous excess attenuation is greater in daytime than at

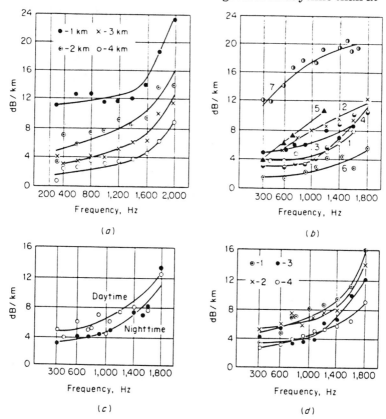

FIG. 2·24 Values of excess attenuation measured near Leningrad over a period of three years: (a) excess attenuation in dB/km (dB/3280 ft), in the absence of acoustic shadowing, for four path lengths: (b) excess attenuation for (1) straight highway, (2) field covered with sparse shrubbery, (3) open road in forest, (4) open field, (5) field with jagged and broken profile, (6) lake, and (7) very dense pine forest with treetops higher than 6 m (20 ft); (c) excess attenuation for daytime and nighttime; and (d) excess attenuation for (1) summer, (2) spring, (3) autumn, and (4) winter. It is apparent from (a) that one cannot speak of anomalous excess attenuation in decibels per unit distance, because the rate of attenuation is greater for short distance than long probably owing to atmospheric scattering.

night. From (*d*), we see that the anomalous excess attenuation is greater in summer (1), decreases in spring and fall, (2) and (3), and is least in winter (4). The graphs also show that the anomalous excess attenuation increases sharply above 1000 Hz. No correlation between anomalous excess attenuation and wind velocity or direction was found.

Figure 2·25 shows an empirical design chart, based on all available data in the literature, that gives the excess attenuation for sound propagation in the *non-shadow zone* (downwind) over open level terrain with low ground cover and for frequencies in the range of about 300 to 5000 Hz and distances of 2–4 km (1.25–2.5 miles). Afternoon and average season conditions are assumed. The abscissa is plotted in terms of the product $f_m r$, where r is the distance from the source to the reciever (lower scale in feet; upper scale in meters) and f_m is the center frequency of the band in question in hertz. For shorter or longer distances, and for other conditions, these values of excess attenuation may be modified by estimates determined from Fig. 2·24.

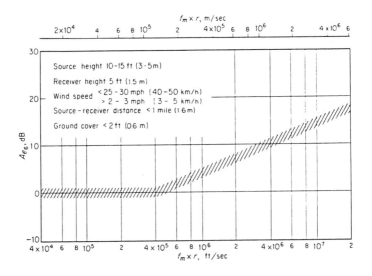

FIG. 2·25 Design chart for estimating the excess attenuation for non-shadow-zone (downwind) propagation over open level terrain (subject to confirmation at the very low and very high audio frequencies). (Courtesy U. Kurze.)

C. Excess Attenuation over Ground—Shadow Zone, A_{gs}.

Consider Fig. 2·26 where a source and receiver are shown a distance r apart. The average direction from which the wind is blowing is indicated by a wind vane; that is, the wind blows from the upwind sector to the downwind sector. The angle between the direction of the wind vane and the line connecting the source and receiver is called ϕ. There will generally be a shadow zone (shaded region) produced on the upwind side of the source because the sound waves that travel upwind tend to be bent upward by the wind. Oftentimes the air near the ground is warmer than that farther up, so that, in addition, there is a tendency for the sound waves to be refracted upward on all sides of the sound source. However, any wind present tends to bend the sound waves downward in the downwind direction. At some critical angle ϕ_c the effects of wind and temperature gradients may cancel each other and the shadow zone vanishes. As a result the plane is divided into an upwind sector $2\phi_c$ and a downwind sector $360° - 2\phi_c$.

Experiments have shown that the excess attenuation is frequently radically different upwind and downwind, with a gradual transition at the boundaries $\phi = \pm \phi_c$. On a sunny day, with moderate winds, the excess attenuation upwind inside the shadow zone, at distances in excess of $2X_0$ from the source, is typically 20 to 50 dB higher than that for the same distance downwind. For very low frequencies, it can be assumed that A_{gs} = 0 to 3 dB upwind, crosswind, and downwind up to distances of about 0.5 mile from the source.

Figure 2·27 shows a design chart, giving values of A_{gs}, for straight upwind propagation. The abscissa is plotted in terms of source-receiver distance, normalized to the minimum distance to the shadow zone X_0. The distance X_0 can be obtained either by direct measurement in the field or estimated from Table 2·11.

It should be noted that Figs. 2·25 and 2·27 do not necessarily apply for source and receiver heights appreciably different from those shown. This is especially true for upwind propagation, since the distance X_0 to the shadow zone increases with both source and receiver height.

D. Turbulence

Unstable turbulent atmosphere, which is more likely at daytime than at nighttime, mainly causes fluctuations of the received sound propagated along the ground. The excess attenuation by turbulence is of minor importance. In keeping with conservative estimates, assume that this attenuation is zero.

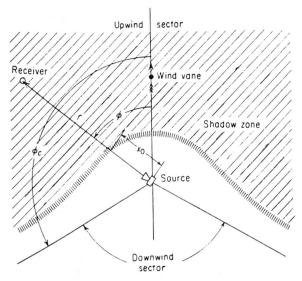

x_0 Distance from source to shadow zone
ϕ Angle between wind and sound
ϕ_c Critical angle

FIG. 2·26 Geometry of sound propagation over open level terrain (plan view). Average daytime conditions are shown. The wind blows from the upwind sector toward the downwind sector.

2·8 Propagation of Sound over Hilly Terrain

Experiments where sound is propagated from hilltop to hilltop across a valley indicate that wind direction, temperature, and wind gradients play a much smaller role than if sound propaga-

TABLE 2·11 ESTIMATES OF X_0 UPWIND, 300–5000 Hz, $\phi = 0$ (SOURCE HEIGHT 10–15 FT. RECEIVER HEIGHT 5 FT)

Time		Sky		Temperature profile			Wind	X_0
Day	Night	Clear	Overcast	Lapse	Neutral	Inversion	mph	ft
	X	X				X	2–4	2000
X			X		X		10–15	400
X		X		X			10–18	250

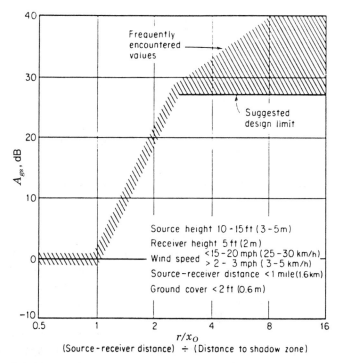

FIG. 2·27 Design chart for estimating the excess attenuation upwind over open level terrain (subject to error at the very low and very high audio frequencies). (Courtesy U. Kurze.)

tion had taken place over level terrain. After accounting for the excess attenuation resulting from molecular absorption (see Sec. 2·5), the experimental data show a residual excess attenuation that is roughly independent of frequency.[35] Residual attenuations of 10–20 dB have been measured in the frequency range of about 400 to 2000 Hz for distances of 1–1.5 miles (1.5–2.5 km). This residual attenuation is possibly due to turbulence in the air. For conservative engineering estimates and until more systematic data are available, it seems best to disregard an excess attenuation A_{gs} in sound-control problems involving propagation over hilly terrain.

3.

Disturbance of Plane Sound Waves by Obstacles and by Finite Baffles

---

3·1 Introduction

In the previous chapter we discussed the medium itself. We saw that sound propagation in an unbounded medium can easily be calculated provided the many assumptions made in deriving the equations are satisfied. Among those assumptions is that no obstacles are present in the medium. Such a condition can hardly be expected to hold in practice. Even in an anechoic sound chamber where it is possible to absorb *ca.* 99.8 percent of the energy from a wave on a single reflection from any wall, one finds that reflections occur from facilities such as rods, cables, or monorails necessary to the support of equipment and the experimenter.

It is not easy to find in the literature information in explicit form on the way in which spheres, cylinders, and plates disturb a plane wave sound field, yet no measurement is made without the use of such obstacles as part of the supporting framework for the equipment under test. In this chapter we attempt to show in the form of graphs how the sound pressure deviates from the value which it will have in a free field as several types of obstacles are approached. Also, because of its importance in many kinds of measurement, we discuss the disturbing effect of a finite-sized baffle on the radiation pattern of a loudspeaker.

3·2 Disturbance by a Sphere

When a spherical obstacle is inserted into an otherwise unbounded medium, the disturbing effect which it produces can be either measured directly by means of a probe microphone or calculated exactly. Although the exact solution might be interesting, the experimenter generally is interested only in the approximate magnitude of the disturbing effect, so he can more accurately assess his experimental error. A few papers have appeared in the literature which yield equations that can be adapted directly to that purpose. Rayleigh[1] developed the complete solution for the sound field around a rigid sphere exposed to an incident plane wave. Schwarz[2] made extensive calculations of the complex sound pressure at all points on the surface of a sphere for various values of kr_0 and θ, where k is the wave number (ω/c), r_0 is the radius of the sphere, and θ is the angle between the radius connecting the point on the surface of the sphere and the radius lying in the direction of the source of the plane wave. Wiener[3] plots Schwarz's calculations on a decibel scale and presents data confirming the theory. Wiener's graphs are given in Figs. 3·1 and 3·2. These figures show $|\,p/p_0\,|$ vs. θ, and $|\,p/p_0\,|$ and ϕ vs. kr_0, respectively. Here $|\,p/p_0\,|$ is the magnitude of the ratio of the sound pressure on the surface of the sphere to the pressure in the plane wave before the sphere is introduced into the sound field, and ϕ is the phase shift (in degrees or radians as indicated) between the pressure on the surface of the sphere and the pressure in the undisturbed plane wave field.

Stenzel[4] has treated the case of the distortion of a sound field at points somewhat removed from the surface of the sphere. He gives the equation

$$\frac{p \text{ (with sphere)}}{p_0 \text{ (free field)}} = 1 - e^{-jkr(1+\cos\theta)} \frac{r_0}{r} Y_s(kr_0; \theta) \quad (3\cdot1a)$$

where Y_s is a complex quantity which we shall call the *reflection factor* and is related to the wave number $k = \omega/c = 2\pi/\lambda$, the radius of the sphere r_0, and the angle θ with respect to the direction of travel of the incident wave. The distance between the center of the sphere and the point of measurement is r. As usual $j = \sqrt{-1}$. It is assumed that $kr_0 = \omega r_0/c$ is large enough

[1] Lord Rayleigh, "On the bending of waves round a spherical obstacle," *Proc. Roy. Soc., London*, **A72**, 40–41 (1903); also, *Collected Scientific Papers*, Vol. V, pp. 112, 149, Cambridge University Press (1912).

[2] L. Schwarz, "Theory of the diffraction of a plane sound wave by a sphere," *Akust. Zeits.*, **8**, 91–117 (1943) (in German).

[3] F. M. Wiener, "Sound diffraction by rigid spheres and circular cylinders," *Jour. Acous. Soc. Amer.*, **19**, 444–451 (1947).

[4] H. Stenzel, "On the distortion of a sound field brought about by a rigid sphere," *Elektr. Nachr.-Tech.*, **15**, 71–78 (1938) (in German).

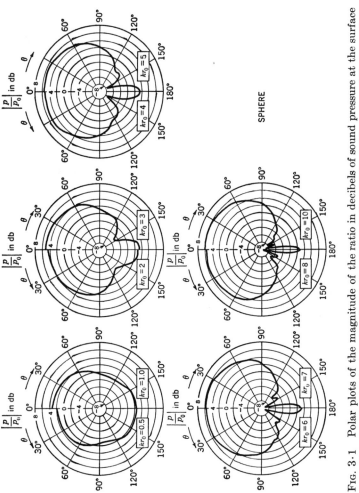

Fig. 3·1 Polar plots of the magnitude of the ratio in decibels of sound pressure at the surface of a sphere to that in the free sound field for various values of kr_0. Note that different values of kr_0 appear on each half of a polar plot. For any given value of kr_0, the plots are symmetrical about the 0°–180° line. (After Wiener.[3])

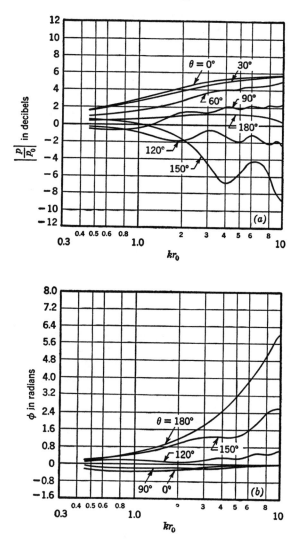

FIG. 3·2 (a) Graphs of the magnitude of the ratio in decibels of sound pressure at the surface of a sphere to that in the free sound field as a function of kr_0 with θ as a parameter. (b) Graphs of the phase shift ϕ in radians between the pressure at the surface of a sphere and that at its center before its introduction, as a function of kr_0 with θ as parameter. A positive phase angle denotes a time lag of the pressure at the obstacle with respect to the free-field pressure. (After Wiener.[3])

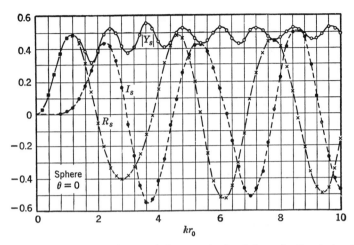

FIG. 3·3   Graphs, for spheres, of the magnitude of the reflection factor Y_s and its components R_s, the real part, and I_s, the imaginary part, as a function of kr_0 for $\theta = 0$.   The assumption is made that kr is greater than 2. (After Stenzel.[4])

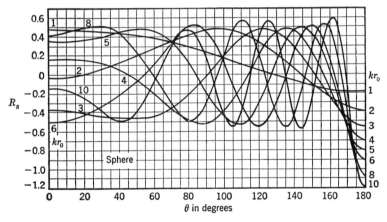

FIG. 3·4   Graph, for spheres, of the real part R_s of the reflection factor Y_s as a function of θ for $kr_0 = 1, 2, 3, 4, 5, 6, 8, 10$.   (After Stenzel.[4])

to allow the spherical functions to be replaced by their asymptotic values.   This means that the equation is approximately valid for $kr > 2$.   The magnitude and the real (R_s) and imaginary (I_s) parts of Y_s are plotted in Fig. 3·3 as a function of $kr_0 = \omega r_0/c$ for the special case of $\theta = 0°$.   Values of the real and imaginary parts of Y_s for other angles of incidence θ with $kr_0 =$

$fr_0(1.827 \times 10^{-4})$ as parameter are plotted in Figs. 3·4 and 3·5. The velocity of sound was assumed to be 34,400 cm/sec so that kr_0 could be replaced by fr_0, where f is the frequency in cycles. In Fig. 3·6 is given the magnitude $|Y_s|$ of the reflection factor as a function of the angle θ. $|Y_s|$ is proportional to the scattered pressure at large distances from the sphere. Scattering cross

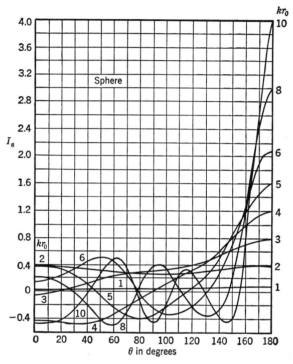

FIG. 3·5 Graph, for spheres, of the imaginary part I_s of the reflection factor Y_s as a function of θ for $kr_0 = 1, 2, 3, 4, 5, 6, 8, 10$. (After Stenzel.[4])

sections, familiar to physicists, can also be calculated from these data.

We are interested in the disturbance of a plane sound field which a sphere produces at various distances and frequencies. Although we may calculate this disturbance accurately from Eq. (3·1a), it is probably more helpful to know the maximum disturbance of the sound field in decibels which one might expect because of the introduction of the sphere. The equation for the boundary above which maximum disturbances of the sound field

in decibels (without regard to sign) cannot occur is $-20 \log_{10}$
$|p/p_0|_{\min}$, where

$$\left| \frac{p}{p_0} \right|_{\min} = 1 - \frac{r_0}{r} |Y_s| \qquad (3 \cdot 1b)$$

A graph of Eq. $(3 \cdot 1a)$ in decibels for the particular case of $r/r_0 =$
4 and $\theta = 0$ is shown in Fig. $3 \cdot 7$. The quantity $-20 \log_{10}$
$|p/p_0|_{\min}$ for this case is plotted as the dotted line in the same

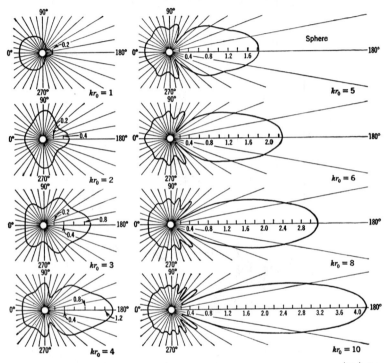

FIG. $3 \cdot 6$ Polar plots of the magnitude of the reflection factor $|Y_s|$ for
spheres, for $kr_0 = 1, 2, 3, 4, 5, 6, 8, 10$. (After Stenzel.[4])

figure. The phase angle of Eq. $(3 \cdot 1a)$ for $r/r_0 = 4$ and $\theta = 0$ is
shown in Fig. $3 \cdot 8$. Y_s from Fig. $3 \cdot 3$ was used in the preparation
of these graphs.

Graphs of the maximum deviations in decibels to be expected
for values of r/r_0 from 1 to 40 and fr_0 from 2000 to 100,000 are
shown in Figs. $3 \cdot 9$ and $3 \cdot 10$ for $\theta = 0°$ and $\theta = 180°$, respectively.
These curves are plots of the expression $-20 \log_{10} |p/p_0|_{\min}$
where $|p/p_0|_{\min}$ is given by Eq. $(3 \cdot 1b)$.

It is seen that the disturbing effect of the sphere's presence at low frequencies and for small spheres is greater in front of the sphere, but less behind it. At high frequencies quite the opposite is true because of the shadow which is cast behind the sphere.

As an example, let us consider the distortion of a sound field at a frequency of 1000 cps when a spherical microphone whose

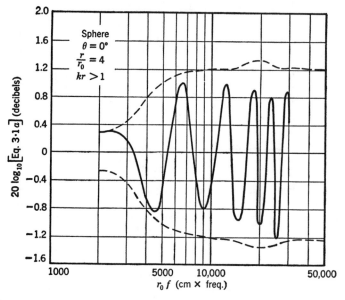

FIG. 3·7 Deviation in decibels of magnitude of sound pressure at a distance $r = 4r_0$ from the center of a sphere of radius r_0 as a function of r_0 times the frequency f. Here the point at which the pressure is measured is on the same side of the sphere as the source; i.e., $\theta = 0°$. The solid line is calculated from the expression $20 \log_{10}$ [Eq. (3·1a)]. The dotted lines are calculated from the expression $-20 \log_{10}$ [Eq. (3·1b)].

radius is 3 cm is inserted into it. Before the observable distortion of the field in front of the microphone becomes less than 0.1 db, one must move away a distance of 60 cm (2 ft). These curves also show that at that frequency (1000 cps) less distortion is observed behind the microphone than in front. At about 6000 cps and 60 cm the disturbing effect is the same in front and behind. Above that frequency the difference between the distortion at the two locations is very pronounced, being much greater in the shadow.

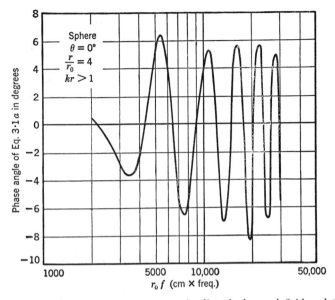

FIG. 3·8   Phase shift between pressure in disturbed sound field and that in free sound field; i.e., ϕ (disturbed) minus ϕ (free-field) for the particular case of $r/r_0 = 4$. Here the microphone is on the same side of the sphere as the source; i.e., $\theta = 0°$.

3·3   Disturbance by a Cylinder

The diffraction of sound by cylinders is of even greater significance than the diffraction by spheres because most supporting rods are cylindrical in shape. Lowan, Morse, Feshbach, and Lax[5] have prepared tables of amplitudes and phase angles for the different components of scattering and radiation from cylindrical objects. Wiener[3] compared data computed from their tables with the measured values of the sound pressure on the surface of a circular cylinder as a function of θ and kr_0. These data are plotted in two forms in Figs. 3·11 and 3·12.

From the tables of Lowan, Morse, et al.[5] we can write the following equation for values of kr which are larger than about 2:

---

[5] A. Lowan, P. Morse, H. Feshbach, and M. Lax, "Scattering and radiation from circular cylinders and spheres," Mathematical Tables Project (NBS) and M. I. T. Underwater Sound Laboratory, U. S. Navy Department, Office of Naval Research, Washington, D.C., July, 1946.

$$\frac{p \text{ (with cylinder)}}{p_0 \text{ (free field)}} = 1 - e^{-jkr(1+\cos\theta)} \sqrt{\frac{r_0}{r}}\, Y_c(kr_0;\theta) \quad (3\cdot 2a)$$

and

$$\left|\frac{p}{p_0}\right|_{\min} = 1 - \sqrt{\frac{r_0}{r}}\, |\, Y_c(kr_0;\theta)\, | \quad (3\cdot 2b)$$

where Y_c is a complex quantity called the *reflection factor for*

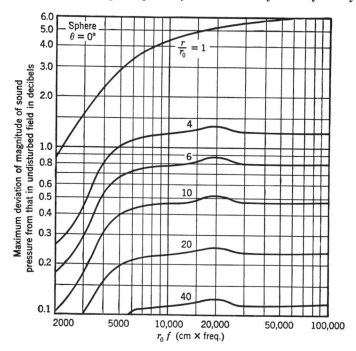

FIG. 3·9 Maximum expected deviation in decibels of magnitude of sound pressure at a distance r from the center of a sphere of radius r_0 as a function of r_0 times the frequency f. Here the microphone is on the same side of the sphere as the source; i.e., $\theta = 0°$.

cylinders; $k = \omega/c$ is the wave number; r_0 is the radius of the cylinder; r is the radius connecting the center of the cylinder to the point of observation; c is the velocity of sound; and θ is the angle formed by the radius r with a radius pointing toward the source of the plane wave.

Graphs of the magnitude and of the real and imaginary parts of Y_c as a function of kr_0 for $\theta = 0°$ and $\theta = 180°$ are given in Figs. 3·13 and 3·14.

In the same manner as for the sphere, graphs of the distortion in decibels and the phase angle in degrees that will occur for various frequencies and r_0's at different r's are plotted for $\theta = 0°$ and $\theta = 180°$ in Figs. 3·15 to 3·18.

It is obvious, from a comparison of the figures for spheres and cylinders with $\theta = 0°$, that the disturbing effect of a cylinder is

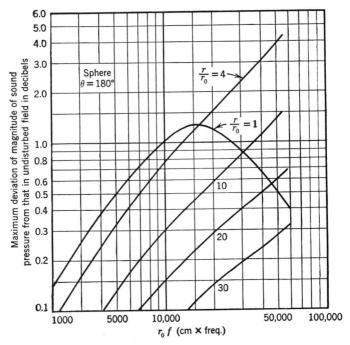

FIG. 3·10 Maximum expected deviation in decibels of magnitude of sound pressure at a distance r from the center of a sphere of radius r_0 as a function of r_0 times the frequency f. Here the microphone is on the opposite side of the sphere from the source; i.e., $\theta = 180°$.

greater than that of a sphere and that the disturbance drops off much more slowly as one moves away from a cylinder than from a sphere. For $\theta = 180°$, the disturbance behind a cylinder appears from theory to be quite small. Experimental confirmation of this prediction has not been reported in the literature.

3·4 Disturbance by a Circular Disk

Interest has been shown in the diffraction of sound by a thin, opaque circular disk in a plane sound field. Qualitatively, the

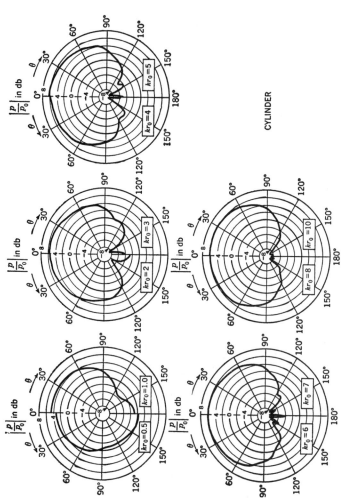

FIG. 3·11 Polar plots of the magnitude of the ratio of sound pressure at the surface of a cylinder to that in a free sound field for various values of kr_0. Note that different values of kr_0 appear on each half of the polar plot. For any given value of kr_0, the plots are symmetrical about the 0°–180° line. (After Wiener.[3])

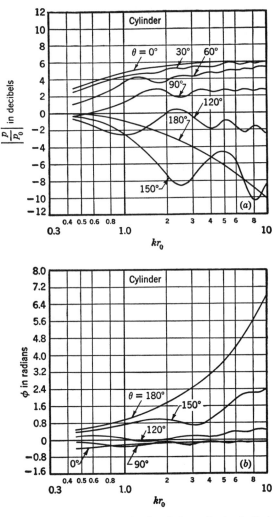

FIG. 3·12 (*a*) Graphs of the magnitude of the ratio in decibels of sound pressure at the surface of a cylinder to that in a free field as a function of kr_0 with θ as a parameter. (*b*) Graphs of the phase shift ϕ in radians between the pressure at the surface of a cylinder and that at its center before its introduction, as a function of kr_0 with θ as parameter. A positive phase angle denotes a time lag of the pressure at the obstacle with respect to the free-field pressure. (After Wiener.[3])

observed results show that for normal incidence, $\theta = 0$, there is a "bright spot" behind the disk surrounding an axial line passing through the center of the disk and the source. The pressure in that bright spot is approximately equal to the undisturbed pressure, and the diameter of the affected region is of the order of a

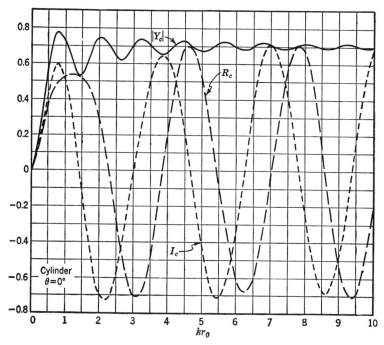

Fig. 3·13 Graphs, for cylinders, of the magnitude of the reflection factor Y_c and its components R_c, the real part, and I_c, the imaginary part, as a function of kr_0 for $\theta = 0°$. The assumption is made that kr is greater than 2.

wavelength immediately behind the disk, and increases in diameter with increasing distance from it. Around this bright spot there is an axially symmetric region in which the sound intensity is, on the whole, low. Primakoff, Klein, Keller, and Carstensen[6] call this the "physical shadow" region as distinguished from the "geometrical shadow," which is an infinite cylinder whose base is the disk. The sound intensity in the physical shadow undergoes periodic variations ("bright" and "dark" rings) with

[6] H. Primakoff, M. J. Klein, J. B. Keller, and E. L. Carstensen, "Diffraction of sound around a circular disk," *Jour. Acous. Soc. Amer.*, **19**, 132–142 (1947).

increasing distance from the axis. The physical shadow is bounded on the outside by another region of high sound intensity. The cross section of this outer region of high intensity between the physical and geometrical shadow boundaries, called the

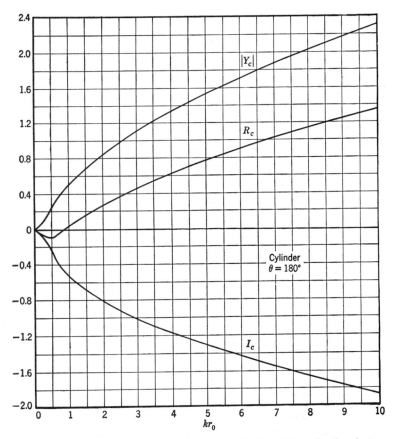

FIG. 3·14   Graphs, for cylinders, of the magnitude of the reflection factor Y_c and its components R_c, the real part, and I_c, the imaginary part, as a function of kr_0 for $\theta = 180°$. The assumption is made that kr is greater than 2.

annular ring, also increases in width with increasing distance behind the baffle. At a distance behind the disk approximately equal to a^2/λ, where a is the disk radius and λ is wavelength of sound, the bright spot and the annular ring meet, and the physical shadow ceases to exist.

Experimental data taken by Primakoff *et al.* in water are shown in Figs. 3·20 to 3·22. The experimental conditions are sketched in Fig. 3·19. At 10,000 cps, the r_0 for their disk and λ are almost equal, as their measurements were made under water where the wavelengths are roughly five times as long as those in air. Their

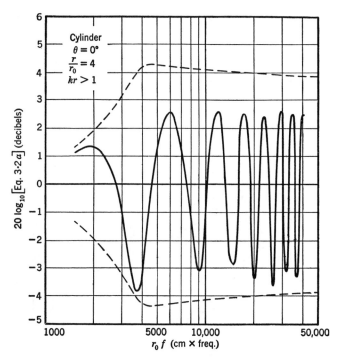

Fig. 3·15 Deviation in decibels of the magnitude of sound pressure at a distance r from the center of a cylinder of radius r_0 as a function of r_0 times the frequency f for the particular case of $r/r_0 = 4$. Here the microphone is on the same side of the cylinder as the source; i.e., $\theta = 0°$. The solid line is calculated from the expression $20 \log_{10}$ [Eq. 3·2a]. The dotted lines are calculated from the expression $-20 \log_{10}$ [Eq. 3·2b].

data confirm the qualitative observations stated above, and a theoretical treatment predicting the results of their measurement is presented.

3·5 Disturbance by a Semi-infinite Plane Screen

The erection of a plane screen in an anechoic chamber with the edges extending to three of the boundaries of the room should produce a sizable disturbance of a sound field.   Sivian and O'Neil[7] treated this problem theoretically and presented in their paper a number of curves showing the pressure variation over the faces of the screen and at various points in space.   Of these curves, one set is of interest to us in connection with the experimental condition shown in Fig. 3·23.   In this case, we shall use k = wave

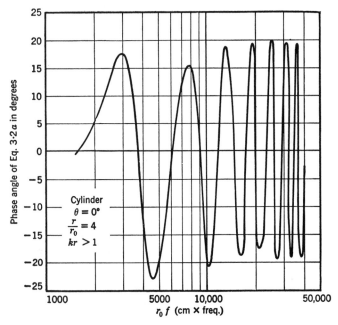

FIG. 3·16   Phase shift between pressure in disturbed sound field and that in free field; i.e., ϕ (disturbed) minus ϕ (free field) for the special case of $r/r_0 = 4$.   Here the microphone is on the same side of the cylinder as the source; i.e., $\theta = 0°$.

number = ω/c, c = velocity of sound, and r = radial distance from the edge of the screen.   The direction of propagation of the sound wave is along the axis, $\theta = 0$.   A graph showing the distortion of the sound field in decibels is shown in Fig. 3·24. These curves indicate that no disturbance of the plane wave field occurs in the plane of the screen ($\theta = 90°$).   The amplitude of the sound field in front of the screen, however, oscillates with

[7] L. J. Sivian and H. T. O'Neil, "On sound diffraction caused by rigid circular plate, square plate and semi-infinite screen," *Jour. Acous. Soc. Amer.*, **3**, 483–510 (1932).

a period of $kr \doteq 3.2$, while that behind the screen falls off monotonically.

3·6 Diffraction around the Human Body

The human body is occasionally a necessary part of an acoustical experiment. It is an irregularly shaped, diffracting object,

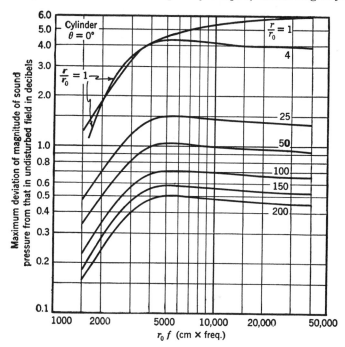

FIG. 3·17   Maximum expected deviation in decibels of the magnitude of sound pressure at a distance r from the center of a cylinder of radius r_0 as a function of r_0 times the frequency f. Here the microphone is on the same side of the cylinder as the source; i.e., $\theta = 0°$.

the acoustic impedance of which measured at the surface is not infinite. Two regions of the body have received attention from acousticians in the past, namely, the head and the region around the chest. A knowledge of the diffracton of sound by the head is of interest to those studying the psychological aspects of hearing, that is, loudness, threshold of hearing, and localization.

Wiener[8] has measured, as a function of frequency and angle of

[8] F. M. Wiener, "On the diffraction of a progressive sound wave by the human head," *Jour. Acous. Soc. Amer.*, **19**, 143–146 (1947).

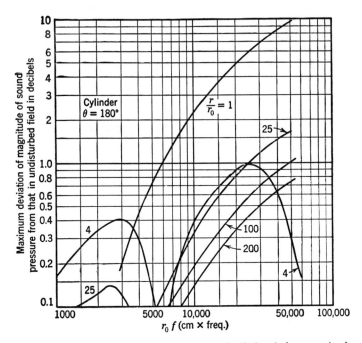

FIG. 3·18 Maximum expected deviation in decibels of the magnitude of sound pressure at a distance r from the center of a cylinder of radius r_0 as a function of r_0 times the frequency f. Here the microphone is on the opposite side of the cylinder from the source; i.e., $\theta = 180°$. There is no experimental evidence to support the low values of disturbance shown here for $r/r_0 > 1$.

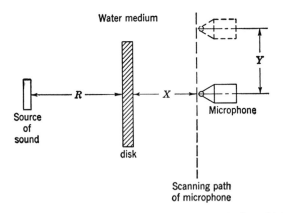

FIG. 3·19 Experimental arrangement used by Primakoff *et al.*[6] to obtain the sound field around a metal disk in water.

incidence, the magnitude of the sound pressures at the left and
right ears of a number of observers exposed to a progressive sound
wave with a vertical front.   Some of Wiener's data are plotted
in Chapter 5.   Briefly, he found that the distribution of the
pressure in the auditory canal is essentially independent of the
orientation of the observer with respect to the source of sound.

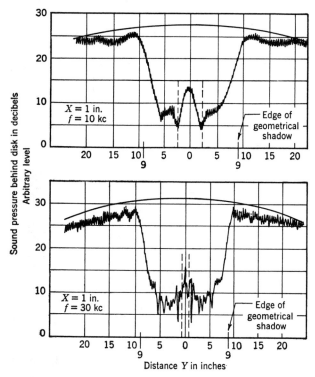

FIG. 3·20   Variation of sound pressure behind an 18-in. circular disk as a
function of perpendicular distance off the axis of the disk. $X = 1$ in. and
$f = 10$ kc and 30 kc.   (After Primakoff *et al.*[6])

Because of diffraction around the head there is a pressure increase
relative to the free-field pressure at all frequencies for azimuths
up to about 90°.   At negative azimuths a marked shadow is cast
by the pinna and by the head itself, especially at the high
frequencies.

    Data on the diffraction of sound around the chest of humans
ɹave been taken by several experimenters interested in calculat-

ing the response of hearing aids.[9, 10] They determined the response of hearing aids suspended in open air and mounted against the chest of a wearer. Great variability of results was obtained according to the type of hearing aid being tested and the kind of clothing worn. A rough idea of the type of results which they found may be obtained from Fig. 3·25. In that

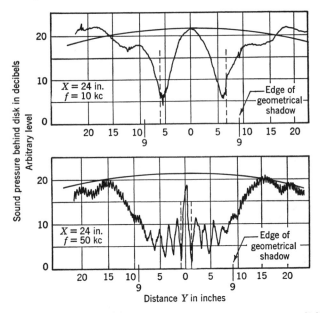

Fɪɢ. 3·21   Variation of sound pressure behind an 18-in. circular disk as a function of perpendicular distance off the axis of the disk. $X = 24$ in. and $f = 10$ kc and 50 kc. (After Primakoff *et al.*[6])

figure a plot is made of the ratio of the output of the hearing aid under the two conditions named above and for normally incident sound. Hanson calculated a curve resembling the one shown in Fig. 3·25 under the assumptions that the human body is a flat baffle of dimensions 0.5 x 19.5 x 26 in. and that the sound is normally incident on it. However, the extreme variability of the baffle effect from one person to another and for different

[9] W. W. Hanson, "The baffle effect of the human body on the response of a hearing aid," *Jour. Acous. Soc. Amer.*, **16**, 60–62 (1944).

[10] R. H. Nichols, Jr., R. J. Marquis, W. G. Wiklund, A. S. Filler, C. V. Hudgins, and G. E. Peterson, "The influence of body-baffle effects on the performance of hearing aids," *Jour. Acous. Soc. Amer.*, **19**, 943–951 (1947).

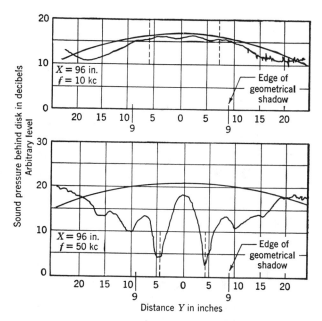

FIG. 3·22 Variation of sound pressure behind an 18-in. circular disk as a function of perpendicular distance off the axis of the disk. $X = 96$ in. and $f = 10$ kc and 50 kc. (After Primakoff *et al.*[6])

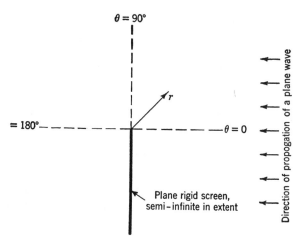

FIG. 3·23 Geometry of the problem of sound propagation around a rigid, semi-infinite plane screen.

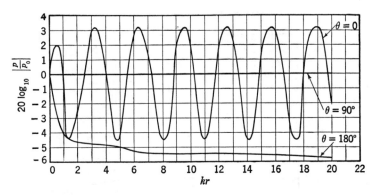

FIG. 3·24   Graph of disturbance of a plane wave sound field by a plane screen in decibels for $\theta = 0°$, $90°$, and $180°$.   (After Sivian and O'Neil.[7])

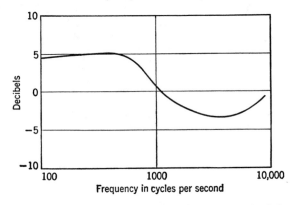

FIG. 3·25   Typical curve showing the ratio, expressed in decibels, of sound pressure at the chest of a person to that in a free sound field with the person facing the source.

spacings of the microphone from the baffle precludes the use of a single curve to represent the phenomenon.

3·7   Sources in Finite Baffles

A commonly used sound source for test purposes is a loud-speaker with a closed back.   Such a loudspeaker usually is contained in a case whose lateral dimensions are about twice the diameter of the radiating cone.   The familiar existing theories for the propagation of sound from a finite piston assume an infinite baffle.   Nichols[11] has studied the effect of finite baffles

[11] R. H. Nichols, Jr., "Effects of finite baffles on response of source with back enclosed," *Jour. Acous. Soc. Amer.*, **18**, 151–154 (1946).

of various diameters on the sound pressure produced at a point in an anechoic chamber by a sound source whose diameter was ¾ in. The experiment was first suggested by an observation of Nichols that, as a microphone is moved perpendicularly away from a point source (in a 16-in. circular baffle) in an anechoic chamber, the pressure does not decrease linearly on a decibel *vs.* log distance plot, but rather that it fluctuates with an amplitude of as much as ±5 db about a mean. At first it appeared that those irregularities in response are caused by standing waves in the room, but an investigation of the standing wave pattern, in which a very small source and a probe microphone were used, proved, in his case, that they are not. Nichols' results, which are summarized here, also point out the fallacy of the customary assumption that, at frequencies where the dimensions of the baffle are large in comparison with the wavelength, a finite baffle is effectively an infinite baffle. In fact, it appears from his studies that the size of the baffle needs to approach

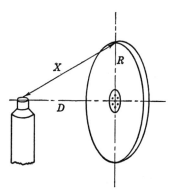

Fig. 3·26 Geometry of the problem of sound radiation from an enclosed loudspeaker in a baffle of finite diameter.

enormous proportions before such an assumption is justified.

The problem which Nichols investigated is sketched in Fig. 3·26. A small condenser microphone is placed a distance D in front of a circular baffle of radius R at the center of which is mounted the source with a diameter of ¾ in. For various values of D, the sound pressure is measured as a function of frequency. In Fig. 3·27 four curves are given for different values of D. The ordinate is the ratio of the pressure developed by the source mounted in a 16-in. baffle to the pressure developed when mounted in a 2-in. baffle. It is observed that peaks (or valleys) occur at harmonically related frequencies for a given value of D. Moreover, the magnitudes and characteristic frequencies of the peaks and valleys increase with increasing values of D. One should be able to predict the results for large D by reciprocity from results of plane wave diffraction by a disk, measured on the surface where the source is located. For small values of D, the problem is more difficult.

Qualitatively, the wave motion is that shown in Fig. 3·28. When the wave leaving the center of the baffle strikes the edge,

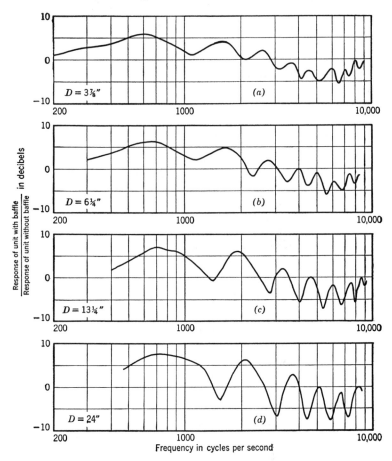

FIG. 3·27 Graphs of ratio in decibels of sound pressure produced by a small source at the center of a 16-in. baffle relative to that produced in a 2-in. baffle as a function of frequency for various distances D. (After Nichols.[11])

it will be diffracted and will set up a new wave with its source at the edge. That new wave will travel outward, and its amplitude will add vectorially with that of the directly radiated wave. The line P indicates one locus of points at which the pressure

from the two sources are always in phase. However, along most
paths the pressure will alternately increase and decrease as
$R + X - D$ approaches and passes beyond an integral multiple
of one-half wavelengths. Along the axis perpendicular to the

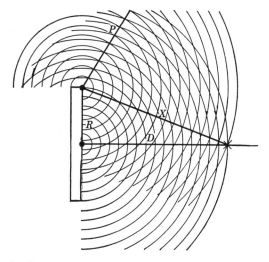

Fig. 3·28 Qualitative sketch showing how a direct and a diffracted sound
wave combine to produce a non-uniform sound field in front of a source
located in a finite baffle.

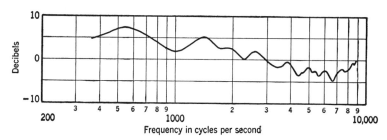

Fig. 3·29 Graphs of ratio in decibels of sound pressure produced by a small
source off center in a 16-in. square baffle to that produced in a 2-in. baffle
as a function of frequency. (After Nichols.[11])

center, the diffracted waves from the edge of a *circular* baffle
achieve their maximum effect and yield the curves already discussed in connection with Fig. 3·27. Whenever $R + X - D \doteq$
$n\lambda/2$, a point of low or high pressure will be achieved; the former
if n is an odd integer, the latter if n is an even integer.

This phenomenon is not nearly so pronounced if the edges of the baffle are not equidistant from the center of the source. Curves are shown in Figs. 3·29 and 3·30 for a 16-in. square baffle and for a 16-in. circular baffle with the sound source mounted off center. The measured response characteristic is much less irregular than those shown in Fig. 3·27.

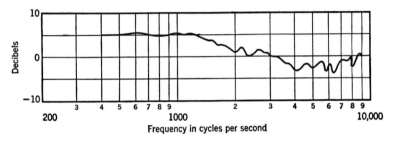

FIG. 3·30   Graphs of ratio in decibels of sound pressure produced by a small source off center in a circular baffle 16 in. in diameter to that produced in a 2-in. baffle as a function of frequency.   (After Nichols.[11])

In conclusion, finite baffles will not yield sound fields which can be represented by the theory of radiation from a rigid piston set in an infinite baffle, even when the diameter of the baffle is many times that of the wavelength.   The deviations of the actual from the theoretical case can be minimized, but not eliminated, by the use of large irregularly shaped baffles with the source located off the geometrical center.

4.

Primary Techniques for the Measurement of Sound Pressure and Particle Velocity and for the Absolute Calibration of Microphones

---

4·1 Introduction

In any laboratory where acoustic measurements are made, there is need for an accurately calibrated standard microphone for the measurement of the strength of a sound field. This standard may itself be used to yield accurate measurements of acoustic quantities in a given experiment, or it may be used for the calibration of other microphones. Before the recent development of the reciprocity technique, the calibration of such a standard microphone could be accomplished only by placing it in a sound field produced by a source of known (measured or computed) distribution and strength and measuring the microphone's electrical output. The characteristics of the source were determined by observation—say, by means of the Rayleigh disk—of some physical property of the wave related to intensity, or by use of a generator whose characteristics could be computed theoretically, the pistonphone or the thermophone for example. This chapter, therefore, includes the two somewhat unrelated topics listed in the heading.

A plane, progressive sound wave possesses a number of characteristics, any one or several of which may be measured to yield a knowledge of its "strength." These characteristics include:

1. Sound pressure at a point in space.
2. Particle velocity at a point in space.
3. Particle displacement at a point in space.
4. Gradient of the sound pressure between two points separated in space an infinitesimal distance.

5. Density variation at a point in space (usually observed optically).

6. Temperature variation at a point in space.

7. Intensity at a point in space.

8. Static pressure increase at a reflecting surface.

Various researches have been performed to determine the feasibility of measuring the various quantities listed above. For many purposes, the most fundamental property of a sound wave seems to be its *intensity*, defined as the flow of energy per unit time in a specified direction through a unit area perpendicular to that direction. Since about 1980 commercial equipment has become available for the measurement of sound intensity, based on a combination of 1 and 4 above.[1] Methods for the measurement of increase of static pressure at a reflecting surface and for the measurement of periodic changes in density or temperature at a point in space are very difficult and usually inaccurate. There are then, sound intensity, sound pressure, pressure gradient, particle velocity, and particle displacement.

It appears that sound pressure is the easiest quantity of the four to measure, and much effort has been spent in developing techniques for measuring it accurately. Particle velocity and displacement have been measured directly through observation of the motion of microscopic particles suspended in the gas through which the wave is traveling. However, in the measurement of particle velocity, it is more common to employ detecting devices which respond to differences in pressure on either side of a lightweight membrane because the particle velocity is nearly directly proportional to the pressure gradient.

In this chapter, only those techniques of calibration are described which at the present time have been developed sufficiently to qualify as absolute techniques. Other methods less well developed or more difficult to execute are not discussed here but are listed in the references. We shall first discuss the reciprocity method, then methods for measuring particle velocity and amplitude, and, finally, methods for producing known sound pressures by other than reciprocity techniques.

[1]C. W. Clapp and F. A. Firestone, "The acoustic wattmeter, an instrument for measuring sound energy flow," J. Acoust. Soc. Am. **13**, 124–136 (1941); J. H. Enns and F. A. Firestone, "Sound power density fields," J. Acoust. Soc. Am. **14**, 24–31 (1942).

4·2 Reciprocity Technique of Calibration

A. General Theory

Of the principal methods for calibrating microphones, the reciprocity technique is the most accurate, at least for all frequencies where the wavelength is not much shorter than the maximum dimension of the sensitive microphone element. The concept of reciprocity for dynamical systems in general was described early by Rayleigh.[2] Schottky[3] derived a universal relationship between the action of a transducer as a microphone and as a loudspeaker. Ballantine[4] significantly advanced the method by his excellent discussion of its application to a wide variety of systems. MacLean and Dubois both promoted it as a means for the absolute measurement of sound fields, although MacLean's contribution was more general.[5]

In contrast to the other methods, the reciprocity technique can be used in either liquids or gases, it imposes no fundamental restriction on the frequency range, and it requires the measurement of electrical quantities only, with the exception of one measurement of distance (or volume) and, in gases, a measurement of the barometric pressure. Furthermore, the theoretical treatment is sufficiently straightforward to avoid undue simplifying assumptions. In addition, only ordinary laboratory transducers are required. Microphones to be used as working standards may be calibrated directly by reciprocity techniques, thus eliminating the need for a secondary comparison calibration of the standard microphone.

Cook[6] successfully demonstrated the utility of the method by calibrating a variety of microphones with different types of

[2]Lord Rayleigh, *The Theory of Sound* (Macmillan, London, 1877), Vol. II, Sec. 108.

[3]W. Schottky, "The concept of reciprocity in acoustics and electro-acoustics," Z. Phys. **36**, 689–736 (1926) (in German).

[4]S. Ballantine, "Reciprocity in electromagnetic, mechanical, acoustical and interconnected systems," Proc. Inst. Radio Eng. **17**, 929–951 (1929).

[5]W. R. MacLean, "Absolute measurement of sound without a primary standard," J. Acoust. Soc. Am. **12**, 140–146 (1940); R. Dubois, "Electrical methods permitting completely the study of reversible microphones in air and in water," Rev. Acoust. **2**, 253–287 (1932); **3**, 27–46 (1933) (in French).

[6]R. K. Cook, "Absolute pressure calibration of microphones," J. Res. Nat. Bur. Std. **25**, 489–505 (1940); also J. Acoust. Soc. Am. **12**, 415–420 (1941).

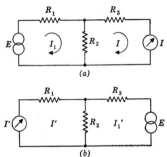

FIG. 4·1 Circuit diagrams illustrating the reciprocity principle for linear, electrical networks. (a) A voltage E produces a current I. (b) On interchanging the voltage generator and the ammeter, if they have the same resistance, a voltage E will produce a current I' which will equal I in (a).

transduction and favorably comparing the results with other primary methods of calibration, including the electrostatic actuator, pistonphone, and Rayleigh disk methods. The technique was refined in World War II by the Electro-Acoustic Laboratory at Harvard. Wong and Embleton have further refined the equipment used in the calibration.[7] It is now commonly used for the calibration of acoustic standards in air and in liquids.[7a]

The concept of reciprocity is based on principles familiar to communication engineers. In electrical circuit theory, if a voltage E from a generator (with a certain impedance), acting in any part of a linear, passive circuit, produces in another part of the circuit a current I in an ammeter (with the same impedance as the generator), the same current I will flow in the ammeter if the positions of the two are reversed. Consider the simple two-mesh, four-terminal network of Fig. 4·1a.

The mesh equations for this system are

$$(R_1 + R_2) I_1 - R_2 I = E,$$
$$-R_2 I_1 + (R_2 + R_3) I = 0.$$

(4·1)

Solving for I gives

$$I = \frac{ER_2}{\begin{vmatrix} (R_1 + R_2) & -R_2 \\ -R_2 & (R_2 + R_3) \end{vmatrix}} = EZ.$$

(4·2)

Reversing the ammeter and generator (see Fig. 4·1b) and solving for the current I' gives

[7]G. S. Wong and T. F. W. Embleton, "Arrangement for precision reciprocity calibration of condenser microphones," J. Acoust. Soc. Am. **66**, 1275–1280 (1979).

[7a]American National Standard ANSI S1.10-1966 (R1976), "Method for calibration of microphones"; International Standard IEC 327-1971, "Precision method for pressure calibration of microphones."

$$I' = \frac{ER_2}{\begin{vmatrix} (R_2 + R_3) & -R_2 \\ -R_2 & (R_1 + R_2) \end{vmatrix}} = EZ' \qquad (4 \cdot 3)$$

Because the two determinants of Eqs. (4·2) and (4·3) can be made identical by performing an even number of interchanges of rows or columns, $Z \equiv Z'$, $I \equiv I'$, and the circuit is said to be reciprocal. The equality of Z and Z' can be shown for linear, passive four-terminal networks of any complexity by the same process.

The principle of reciprocity applies to most linear, passive electromechanical or electroacoustical systems[8] in magnitude because the electromechanical constants can be faithfully represented as impedance elements of a four-terminal electrical network. In such a network, the impedance determinant is always symmetrical. However, the reciprocal relationship will not necessarily be the same in sign (i.e., $Z = \pm Z'$). It may be stated[9] that transducers possessing (a) electrostatic coupling only or (b) electromagnetic coupling only obey the reciprocity relations provided the polarizability, the susceptibility, the Hooke's law, and the conductivity tensors are symmetric. On the other hand, transducers possessing (c) piezoelectric coupling only or (d) magnetostrictive coupling only demand in addition the equality of the direct and inverse piezoelectric and magnetostrictive coupling tensors. The symmetry and equality of the tensors is always satisfied at sufficiently low frequencies. Whether or not such is true in general depends on the medium and on its electroacoustic coupling. In particular, if dissipative phenomena of the "relaxation" type are present, the symmetry and equality of the tensors are destroyed.

Individual transducers with a combination of couplings mentioned above do not in general obey the laws of reciprocity[8] unless all couplings are dissipationless. This is also true of combinations of individual transducers when each obeys the reciprocity relations and when they are connected

---

[8]E. McMillan, "Violation of the reciprocity theorem in linear, passive electromechanical systems," J. Acoust. Soc. Am. **18**, 344–347 (1946).

[9]L. L. Foldy and H. Primakoff, "A general theory of passive linear electroacoustic transducers and the electroacoustics reciprocity theorem," J. Acoust. Soc. Am. **17**, 109–120 (1945), and **19**, 50–58 (1947).

otherwise than all in tandem. All the last cases, though interesting theoretically, are perhaps not of great practical importance.

The general treatment of the electroacoustic reciprocity theorem given by Foldy and Primakoff[9] covers completely the various phases of radiation and reception of sound by electroacoustic transducers when coupled to each other by an acoustic medium. The formulas in this chapter will be somewhat less generalized.

B. Free-Field Method

Following MacLean[5] in our choice of terminology, we write

A = transformation constant, in square centimeters

d = distance between source and microphone, in centimeters

D = diffraction constant = ratio of blocked diaphragm pressure to free-field pressure

e = electrical generator voltage, in abvolts*

e_{oc} = open-circuit voltage produced by a transducer, in abvolts

f = frequency, in cycles

i_{ss} = short-circuit current produced by a transducer in abamperes

i_T = constant current supplied to a transducer when operated as a source of sound, in abamperes

$j = \sqrt{-1}$

λ = wavelength, in centimeters

$M_o = e_{oc}/p_{ff}$ = ratio of the open-circuit voltage produced by a transducer in a plane wave sound field to the sound pressure present before the microphone was inserted

L = largest dimension of a transducer

$M_s = i_{ss}/p_{ff}$ = ratio of the short-circuit current produced by a transducer in a plane wave sound field to the free-field pressure

p_{ff} = free-field sound pressure present before insertion of the microphone in the field

* If the voltage is in practical volts and you wish to know the number of abvolts, multiply the number of practical volts by 10^8. Multiply the number of practical amperes by 10^{-1} to get the number of abamperes. Multiply the number of practical ohms by 10^9 to get the number of abohms. If mks units are used, all electrical quantities may remain in practical units.

p_d = sound pressure averaged over the diaphragm of a transducer

S_0 = p_d/i_T = ratio of the sound pressure averaged over the diaphragm of a transducer to the driving current i_T at its terminals (Its units are dynes-cm^{-2} per abampere.)

S_s = p_d/e_T = ratio of the sound pressure averaged over the diaphragm to the driving voltage e_T at its terminals (Its units are dynes-cm^{-2} per abvolt.)

T = symbol for a transducer

τ = coupling coefficient, which for electromagnetic transducers is equal to Bl, the product of the flux density times the length of the conductor (Its units are abvolts per cm-sec^{-1}.)

U = volume velocity of air, in cm^3-sec^{-1}

v = linear velocity of diaphragm, in cm-sec^{-1}

Z_e = blocked diaphragm electrical impedance, in abohms

Z_L = electrical load (or generator) impedance, in abohms

Z_M = open-circuit mechanical impedance, in mechanical ohms (dyne-sec-cm^{-1})

Z_r = acoustic radiation impedance, in acoustic ohms (dyne-sec-cm^{-5})

ω = $2\pi f$

"x" = pertaining to reversible transducer

"$'$" = pertaining to auxiliary microphone

A simple, linear, reciprocal transducer may be represented by either of the analogous circuits shown in Fig. 4·2.

For the general case of simultaneous electric and acoustic excitation, we may write

$$(Z_r A^2 + Z_M)v \; (\pm)^* \tau i = ADp_{ff} \tag{4·4}$$

$$\tau v + (Z_e + Z_L)i = e$$

The open-circuit voltage produced by the transducer when it is placed in a free field is

$$e_{oc} = -\tau v = \frac{-\tau A D p_{ff}}{Z_r A^2 + Z_M} \tag{4·5}$$

---

* The sign of τ in the first equation will be positive for crystal or condenser transducers and negative for electrodynamic or magnetic transducers. The positive sign will be carried in the discussion immediately following.

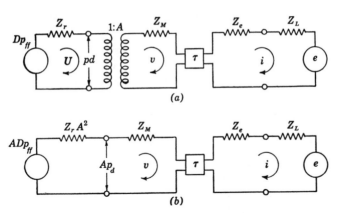

FIG. . 4·2 Equivalent circuits of a reversible transducer in a free field. Z_r is the acoustic radiation impedance; Z_M is the mechanical impedance of the diaphragm; τ is the electromechanical coupling constant; Z_e is the blocked electrical impedance; and Z_L is the electrical load resistance.

or

$$M_o = \frac{-\tau A D}{Z_r A^2 + Z_M} \qquad (4 \cdot 6)$$

The short-circuit current produced by the transducer when it is placed in a free field is

$$i_{ss} = \frac{-\tau A p_{ff} D}{(Z_r A^2 + Z_M)Z_e - \tau^2} \qquad (4 \cdot 7)$$

or

$$M_s = \frac{-\tau A D}{(Z_r A^2 + Z_M)Z_e - \tau^2} \qquad (4 \cdot 8)$$

The pressure at the diaphragm produced by the transducer when it is driven by a constant electrical current, i_T, is

$$p_d = \frac{-\tau Z_r A}{Z_r A^2 + Z_m} i_T \qquad (4 \cdot 9)$$

or

$$S_o = \frac{-\tau Z_r A}{Z_r A^2 + Z_M} \qquad (4 \cdot 10)$$

Finally, the pressure produced at the diaphragm, when the transducer is driven with a constant voltage across its terminals, is

$$p_d = \frac{-\tau Z_r A e_T}{(Z_r A^2 + Z_M)Z_e - \tau^2} \tag{4.11}$$

or

$$S_s = \frac{-\tau Z_r A}{(Z_r A^2 + Z_M)Z_e - \tau^2} \tag{4.12}$$

We see immediately that

$$\frac{M_0}{S_0} = \frac{D}{Z_r} = \frac{M_s}{S_s} \equiv J_0 \tag{4.13}$$

where J_0 is called the reciprocity parameter. Such a parameter could not be written if τ in the first equation of (4.4) were not equal to τ in the second equation.

It has been shown that the directivity pattern (diffraction constant D) is the same whether the unit is operated as a microphone or as a loudspeaker.[9] Now let us determine the pressure p_0 which the transducer will produce at a distance d from the diaphragm, where d is assumed to be large compared to the largest dimension L of the transducer, $(d \gg L)$. Then,

$$p_0 \doteq \frac{a p_d D}{d} e^{-j(2\pi d/\lambda)} \tag{4.14}$$

where we have replaced the transducer by a sphere of equivalent radius a. The transducer is now assumed to be indistinguishable from a small spherical radiator as long as we confine our observations along a radial line extending from the acoustic center of the transducer. We know that for a small spherical source, where $a \ll \lambda$,

$$Z_r \doteq j \frac{\rho c}{2a\lambda} \tag{4.15}$$

where λ is the wavelength of the sound wave and ρc is the characteristic impedance of the medium.

Hence, the reciprocity factor J, for a small transducer producing a sound pressure p_0 at a distance d from the diaphragm, is

$$J = \frac{J_0 d}{aD} e^{j(2\pi d/\lambda)} = \frac{2d\lambda}{\rho c} e^{j[(-\pi/2)+(2\pi d/\lambda)]} \qquad (4\cdot16)$$

Now let us apply these results to the free-field calibration of a reversible transducer. Three transducers with the following designations are required for the experiment.

T^x is a reversible transducer.

T' is a microphone.

T is a source which produces a sound field that is spherical over the region to be occupied by T' and T^x. Its presence must not change the radiation impedance Z_r of either T^x or T', and its radiative properties must not be affected by the introduction of T' or T^x into the sound field. To satisfy these conditions, $L \ll d$ and $L^2/\lambda \ll d$, where L is the largest dimension of T, T', or T^x.

When calibrating the transducer T^x, two steps are required to obtain the desired answer, $M_0{}^x$:

STEP 1. With T as a source, expose successively T^x and T' at a distance d and determine the open-circuit voltages $e_{oc}{}^x$ and $e_{oc}{}'$. These voltages form the ratio

$$\frac{M_0{}^x}{M_0{}'} = \frac{e_{oc}{}^x}{e_{oc}{}'} \qquad (4\cdot17)$$

STEP 2. Drive T^x with a constant current $i_T{}^x$. Place T' a distance d from it. Measure the open-circuit voltage $E_{oc}{}'$ produced by the microphone T'. These quantities form the ratio

$$\left[\frac{E_{oc}{}'}{i_T{}^x}\right] = \frac{M_0{}' S_0{}^x aD}{d} e^{-j(2\pi d/\lambda)} \qquad (4\cdot18)$$

By the principle of reciprocity,

$$S_0{}^x = \frac{M_0{}^x}{J_0{}^x} = \frac{Z_r{}^x M_0{}^x}{D} \qquad (4\cdot19)$$

Combining (4·15), (4·17), (4·18), and (4·19), we get

$$M_0{}^x = \sqrt{\left[\frac{E_{oc}{}'}{i_T{}^x}\right] \cdot \left[\frac{e_{oc}{}^x}{e_{oc}{}'}\right] \frac{2d\lambda}{\rho c}} \; e^{\jmath\left(\frac{-\pi}{4}+\frac{\pi d}{\lambda}\right)} \qquad (4·20)$$

Converting to practical units and considering the magnitude only,

$$\boxed{\; \left| M_0{}^x \right| = \sqrt{\left[\frac{E_{oc}{}'}{i_T{}^x}\right] \cdot \left[\frac{e_{oc}{}^x}{e_{oc}{}'}\right] \frac{2d\lambda}{\rho c} \times 10^{-7}} \;} \qquad (4·21)$$

It is apparent that with the aid of Eq. (4·17) we can also obtain M_0'. This means that the microphone to be calibrated need not be the reversible one.

The formula above can be applied to the calibration of any type of microphone (dynamic, ribbon, etc.) if performed in a free sound field. Recent progress in the design of anechoic (echofree) chambers[10] has made this experiment more feasible, the principal remaining difficulty being the lack of small-sized reversible transducers with high acoustic output. The calibration of pressure gradient microphones is a function of the curvature of the sound field. Hence, it is necessary either that the source of sound (T or T^x when acting as a loudspeaker) be far from the microphone or else that $M_0{}^x$ calculated from Eq. (4·21) be multiplied by the factor $[1 + (c/\omega d)^2]^{-\frac{1}{2}}$ if a plane wave calibration is desired.

In selecting a source, great care should be used to choose one which behaves as a spherical source in the desired frequency range. That is to say, it should produce a sound pressure field that decreases inversely with distance in the range of d used in the experiment. (See Chapter 3.[11]) To test this, plots of sound pressure level (in decibels) should be made as a function of the logarithm of the separation of a "point" microphone from the source. If a straight line is drawn on the graph, with a negative slope of 6 db per doubling of distance, the deviations of the points from it will be a test of the suitability of both the source and the chamber in which the test is being conducted. The ratio of the

[10] L. L. Beranek and H. P. Sleeper, Jr., "Design and construction of anechoic sound chambers," *Jour. Acous. Soc. Amer.*, **18**, 140–150 (1946).

[11] R. H. Nichols, Jr., "Effects of finite baffles on response of source with back enclosed," *Jour. Acous. Soc. Amer.*, **18**, 151–154 (1946).

responses obtained by alternately placing the transducers in the sound field of T will be accurately obtained in the following cases: (a) if T' and T^x have identical shapes and are placed in exactly the same place; or (b) if the deviation of the sound pressure level of T from the desired straight line is a slowly varying function of distance, so that the maximum dimensions of T' and T^x are small compared to the extent of the deviations in space. The acoustic center of the source may be determined by extrapolating a curve of p_0 vs. distance back toward zero distance.

When a calibration is about to be performed, arbitrary centers on, in, or near T, T^x and T' are chosen. Also, three axes are arbitrarily chosen. The axis for the source T should be that at which its directivity pattern is a maximum, whereas that for the microphone T^x or T' under test will depend on the manner in which the microphone will be used in future experimentation.

The most difficult part of the experiment is to determine accurately the separation distance d between T^x and T' during step 2. Generally, d cannot be made very large because the output of the reversible transducer is small. One procedure for doing this is to measure and plot the quantity $[E_{oc}'/e_T{}^x]$ as a function of the distance between the arbitrary centers on T^x and T'. A hyperbolic curve fitted to these data would extrapolate to zero if the centers on T^x and T' happened to be located accurately. The amount by which the extrapolation misses zero can be used to relocate the arbitrary centers so that the distance between them yields d accurately.

The choice of terminals for the reversible transducer should be those for which the calibration of the microphone is desired and should be kept the same in both tests in which the microphone is involved. The terminals may be selected at the output of a preamplifier associated with the microphone, or at the end of a fixed length of cable, or directly at the output terminals of the microphone itself. The essential point is, however, that the current input into the transducer when it is operating as a loudspeaker be measured at the same pair of terminals at which the open-circuit voltage is measured when the transducer is operating as a microphone. So far as the auxiliary transducer is concerned, the choice of terminals is ordinarily made at the output of the transducer element itself. However, the choice is to a large extent arbitrary (if linear networks only are involved) and may be selected for greatest convenience in making the tests.

C. Closed Chamber Method

Theory

A convenient application of the reciprocity technique is in the calibration of microphones which can be enclosed in a small cavity or "coupler." For this measurement no expensive and bulky anechoic chamber is required. Such a calibration is generally called a *pressure calibration* because the results are expressed in terms of open-circuit voltages for a constant sound pressure which is uniform over the diaphragm. Obviously, diffraction effects and cavity resonances are not included in this measurement and must be taken into account if the microphone is to be used subsequently for free-field measurements.

When the coupler method is used, there are two cases which must be considered. The first of these cases is that in which wave motion cannot be avoided in the cavity so that its effects must be taken into account explicitly. Little has been said about this case in the literature, and it will be treated here first. The second case is that in which it is possible to introduce into the cavity a gas other than air, such as hydrogen, to extend the range of calibration to a sufficiently high frequency before the transit time of the sound in the cavity becomes appreciable. Of course, if calibrations are desired only at low audio frequencies and if the dimensions of the microphone are small, it may not be necessary to introduce a special gas into the cavity. The second case, with hydrogen in the cavity, is that employed by most calibrating laboratories in the United States.

The terminology for this section is the same as that used in the previous section (see p. 116) plus

A_c = cross-sectional area of the cavity

$C_{eT}{}^x$ = electrical capacitance of transducer "x" when operated as a source of sound, in abfarads

d_{33} and d_{31} = respectively, the piezoelectric modulus for normal pressures on the faces of a tourmaline crystal perpendicular to the principal axis, and the piezoelectric modulus for normal pressures on any two faces which are parallel to the principal axis and to each other

e_T = applied voltage across terminals of a transducer used as source, in abvolts

γ = ratio of the specific heats of the gas in the cavity

M = magnitude of the electric moment per cubic centimeter acting on the crystal

$M_0 = e_{oc}/p$ = ratio of the open-circuit voltage produced by the microphone to the Thévenin generator sound pressure p^* (The units are abvolts per dyne-cm^{-2}.)

$M_s = i_{ss}/p$ = ratio of the short-circuit current produced by the microphone to the Thévenin generator sound pressure p^* (The units are abamperes per dyne-cm^{-2}.)

μ = viscosity of the gas, in poises

p = sound pressure, in dyne-cm^{-2}, that would be produced at the diaphragm of a transducer if its diaphragm impedance were infinite.

p_d = sound pressure actually produced at the diaphragm, in dyne-cm^{-2}

P_0 = Ambient pressure, in dyne-cm^{-2}

$\rho_m = e_{oc}/p_d$ = open-circuit pressure calibration of a transducer, in abvolts per dyne-cm^{-2}

$\rho_s = i_{ss}/p_d$ = short-circuit pressure calibration of a transducer, in abamperes per dyne-cm^{-2}

ρ_0 = density of the gas, in grams-cm^{-2}

$S_0 = p_d/i_T$ = ratio of the sound pressure at the diaphragm of a transducer, when that transducer is driven by a constant current i_T (The units are dyne-cm^{-2}-abamp^{-1}.)

$S_s = p_d/e_T$ = ratio of the sound pressure at the diaphragm of a transducer to a constant voltage e_T driving that transducer (The units are dyne-cm^{-2}-abvolt^{-1}.)

U = volume velocity, in cm^3-sec^{-1}

v = linear velocity of the diaphragm, in cm-sec^{-1}

Z_c = acoustic impedance of the cavity in acoustic ohms as viewed from the surface of the diaphragm of the

---

* A Thévenin generator in acoustics is analogous to a Thévenin generator in electric circuit theory. We assume that a generator of sound driving a diaphragm can be replaced by a series sound pressure generator and a mechanical impedance. The mechanical impedance is equal to the impedance seen by the diaphragm when the sound source is suppressed; i.e., it is the radiation impedance of the diaphragm with the sound source in the field. The Thévenin generator sound pressure is that pressure which would exist at the diaphragm if its velocity were zero (open-circuit); i.e., it is the pressure at the diaphragm when its motion is blocked.

microphone T' when the transducer T^x is acting as a loudspeaker   (The units are dyne-sec-cm^{-5}.)

Z_k = acoustic impedance of the cavity in acoustic ohms as viewed from the surface of the diaphragm of the transducers T' or T^x when T is acting as a loudspeaker   (The units are dyne-sec-cm^{-5}.)

The experimental arrangement of two of the three transducers T, T^x, and T' is shown in Fig. 4·3.   The cavity is assumed to

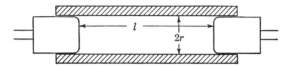

FIG. 4·3   Cross-sectional sketch of a cavity for calibrating two reversible transducers.

have a length l and a radius r.   To facilitate calculation of wave motion, the microphone diaphragms ideally have the same diameter as the cavity, but if there are differences they may be accounted for by assumption of an impedance transformation equal to the ratios of the areas of the diaphragm and cavity. For cases when wave motion is not a factor, only the volume of the cavity is important.

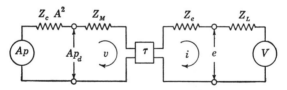

FIG. 4·4   Equivalent circuit of a reversible transducer in a closed chamber. Z_c is the acoustic impedance of the chamber as presented to the diaphragm; Z_M is the mechanical impedance of the diaphragm; τ is the electromechanical coupling constant; Z_e is the electrical impedance; and Z_L is the electrical load impedance.

A reversible transducer operating in such a setup can be represented by the analogous circuit of Fig. 4·4.   For this case,

$$(Z_cA^2 + Z_M)v - \tau i = Ap$$
$$\tau v + (Z_e + Z_L)i = V$$

$$(4·22)$$

As before,

$$\frac{M_0}{S_0} = -\frac{1}{Z_c} = \frac{M_s}{S_s} \equiv J_0 \qquad (4\cdot23)$$

where J_0 is the reciprocity parameter.

For the pressure calibration we desire to obtain the quantity $p_m{}^x$, where the x designates the reversible transducer. As before, two steps in the calibration are required.

STEP 1. Insert T in one end of the cavity and apply a constant current to it. Then successively insert T^x and T' in the cavity and determine their open-circuit voltages $e_{oc}{}^x$ and e_{oc}'. From these we may form the ratio

$$\left[\frac{e_{oc}{}^x}{e_{oc}'}\right] = \frac{p_m{}^x}{p_m'} \times \frac{p_d{}^x}{p_d'} = \frac{p_m{}^x}{p_m'} \times K \qquad (4\cdot24)$$

where $K \equiv p_d{}^x/p_d'$.

If we replace the cavity and the transducer T by an acoustic Thévenin generator with an open-circuit pressure p and an impedance Z_k, we can easily see that

$$K = \frac{Z_d{}^x(Z_d' + Z)}{Z_d'(Z_d{}^x + Z_k)} \qquad (4\cdot25)$$

where[12]

$$Z_k = \frac{\rho c}{A_c} \coth\left[j\frac{\omega}{c}l + \psi_0\right]$$

$$\psi_0 = \coth^{-1}\frac{Z_d A_c}{\rho c} \qquad (4\cdot26)$$

and Z_d, $Z_d{}^x$, and Z_d' are the acoustic impedances of the diaphragms of the three transducers.

As a simple example, let us consider that the acoustic impedances of these diaphragms are pure compliances. This is the case for crystal and condenser transducers below the first reso-

[12]P. M. Morse, *Vibration and Sound*, Chapter 6, McGraw-Hill (1936); reprinted by Acoustical Society of America (1981).

nance frequency. Then we can replace the three impedances by

$$Z_d = -j \frac{\rho c^2}{\omega l_1 A_c}$$

$$Z_d{}^x = -j \frac{\rho c^2}{\omega l^x A_c} \qquad (4 \cdot 27)$$

$$Z_d{}' = -j \frac{\rho c^2}{\omega l' A_c}$$

where l_1, l^x, and l' are the depths of air cavities having the same acoustic compliances as the three diaphragms, respectively. If these impedances are not pure compliances, their exact value must be inserted in Eq. (4·26).

Furthermore, if $(l + l_1)$ is less than $\lambda/8$, we can write that

$$Z = -j \frac{\rho c^2}{\omega(l + l_1) A_c} \qquad (4 \cdot 28)$$

which gives

$$\boxed{K \doteq 1 + \frac{l' - l^x}{l + l_1 + l^x}} \qquad (4 \cdot 29)$$

Rearranging (4·24) gives

$$\boxed{\rho_m{}' = \rho_m{}^x \left[\frac{e_{oc}{}'}{e_{oc}{}^x} \right] K} \qquad (4 \cdot 30)$$

STEP 2. Replace T with T^x and close the opposite end of the cavity with the transducer T'. Drive T^x with a constant current $i_T{}^x$ and measure an open-circuit voltage $E_{oc}{}'$.

Now $E_{oc}{}' = \rho_m{}' p_d{}'$. Let

$$K_1 = \frac{p_d{}'}{p_d{}^x} \qquad (4 \cdot 31)$$

Then,

$$E_{oc}{}' = \rho_m{}' p_d{}^x K_1$$

and

$$p_d{}^x = S_0{}^x i_T{}^x$$

Hence

$$E_{oc}{}' = \rho_m{}' S_0{}^x i_T{}^x K_1 \qquad (4 \cdot 32)$$

From Eq. (4·23) we have $S_0{}^x = -M_0{}^x Z_c{}^x$.

Combining this with (4·30) and (4·32) gives

$$\left[\frac{E_{oc}'}{i_T{}^x} \right] = -\rho_m{}^x M_0{}^x \left[\frac{e_{oc}'}{e_{oc}{}^x} \right] K Z_c{}^x K_1 \qquad (4\cdot33)$$

Now,

$$K_1 M_0{}^x = \rho_m{}^x \frac{p_d'}{p^x} = \rho_m{}^x K_2 \qquad (4\cdot34)$$

where $K_2 \equiv p_d'/p^x$.

Substituting (4·34) in (4·33) and rearranging gives, in practical units (volts-dynes^{-1}-cm^2),

$$\rho_m{}^x = j \sqrt{\left[\frac{E_{oc}'}{i_T{}^x} \right] \left[\frac{e_{oc}{}^x}{e_{oc}'} \right] \cdot \frac{10^{-7}}{Z_c{}^x K K_2}} \qquad (4\cdot35)$$

In order to obtain the desired calibration, we must evaluate $Z_c{}^x K_2$. Here, $Z_c{}^x$ is the acoustic impedance of the cavity viewed from the reversible transducer when it is acting as a source, and K_2 is the ratio of p_d' to p^x, where p^x is a Thévenin pressure and is related to $p_d{}^x$ by the equation (see Fig. 4·4)

$$\frac{p^x}{p_d{}^x} = \left[1 + \frac{Z_c{}^x}{Z_d{}^x} \right] \qquad (4\cdot36)$$

The impedance of a cavity of length l terminated by an impedance Z_d' is

$$Z_c{}^x = \frac{\rho c}{A_c} \coth \left[j \frac{\omega}{c} l + \psi_0 \right] \qquad (4\cdot37)$$

where

$$\psi_0 = \coth^{-1} \left[\frac{Z_d' A_c}{\rho c} \right] \qquad (4\cdot38)$$

and

$$p_d{}^x = p_d' \frac{\cosh \left[j \frac{\omega}{c} l + \psi_0 \right]}{\cosh \psi_0} \qquad (4\cdot39)$$

Combining (4·36) and (4·39), we get

$$\frac{1}{K_2} = \frac{p^x}{p_d{}^x} \times \frac{p_d{}^x}{p_d'} = \frac{\cosh \left[j \frac{\omega}{c} l + \psi_0 \right]}{\cosh \psi_0} \left[1 + \frac{Z_c{}^x}{Z_d{}^x} \right] \qquad (4\cdot40)$$

Hence,

$$\frac{1}{K_2 Z_c{}^x} = \frac{A_c \sinh\left[j\dfrac{\omega}{c}l + \psi_0\right]}{\rho c \cosh \psi_0}\left[1 + \frac{Z_c{}^x}{Z_d{}^x}\right] \qquad (4\cdot41)$$

Equation (4·41) is the exact answer when wave motion is taken into account and when the diameters of the diaphragms are the same as that of the cavity. For other diameters appropriate impedance transformations should be made. Generally, the diaphragm impedance of crystal and condenser microphones is high enough that the following approximations can be made:

$$\psi_0 \doteq \frac{\rho c}{Z_d' A_c} \qquad (4\cdot42)$$

$$\cosh \psi_0 \doteq 1$$

So that

$$\boxed{\frac{1}{K_2 Z_c{}^x} = \frac{A_c}{\rho c} \sinh\left[j\frac{\omega}{c}l + \frac{\rho c}{Z_d' A_c}\right]\left[1 + \frac{Z_c{}^x}{Z^x}\right]} \qquad (4\cdot43)$$

At low frequencies, where $l \ll \lambda$, that is to say, when the transit time is negligible, we can further simplify the results to yield

$$\frac{1}{K_2 Z_c{}^x} = \left[j\omega \frac{A_c l}{\rho c^2} + \frac{1}{Z_d'}\right]\left[1 - j\frac{\rho c^2}{Z_d{}^x \omega A_c(l + l')}\right] \qquad (4\cdot44)$$

In some instances, it is justifiable to assume that the diaphragm impedances vary as a pure compliant reactance, so that we may replace Z_d' and $Z_d{}^x$ by the values of Eq. (4·27). Then,

$$\boxed{\frac{1}{K_2 Z_c{}^x} \doteq j\omega\left[\frac{A_c(l + l' + l^x)}{\rho c^2}\right] = j\omega C_a} \qquad (4\cdot45)$$

where C_a is an acoustical compliance, and $\rho c^2 = \gamma P_0$.

Finally, we also observe that for most condenser and crystal microphones

$$\frac{e_T{}^x}{i_T{}^x} = \frac{1}{j\omega C_{eT}{}^x} \qquad (4\cdot46)$$

where $C_{eT}{}^x$ is the electrical capacitance of the reversible transducer when its diaphragm is terminated in $Z_c{}^x$. This gives the usual equation for ρm, in practical units (volts-dyne^{-2}-cm^2),

$$\rho_m{}^x = j \sqrt{\left[\frac{E_{oc}{}'}{e_T{}^x}\right]\left[\frac{e_{oc}{}^x}{e_{oc}{}'}\right]\frac{C_a \cdot 10^{-7}}{C_{eT}K}} \tag{4·47}$$

where

$$K \doteq 1 + \frac{l^x - l'}{l + l_1 + l'} \tag{4·47a}$$

For odd-shaped cavities where the wavelength is large enough that the effects of wave motion do not exist,

$$K \equiv 1 + \frac{V^x - V'}{V + V_1 + V'} \tag{4·47b}$$

where V is the volume of the cavity and V_1, V^x, and V' are the equivalent volumes of the diaphragms of T, T^x, and T'.

If the diaphragm compliances of T^x and T' are nearly equal, or if the ratio of the difference of their compliances to the compliance of the cavity is small, then $K \doteq 1$. An attempt is generally made to select T^x and T' with nearly the same compliances and to make l as large as possible without violating the assumption that $l + l' + l^x < \lambda/8$.

Equation (4·47) constitutes the desired result for condenser microphones when wave motion in the cavity can be neglected and when the diaphragm impedances can be replaced by equivalent increases in the length of the coupling chamber. If these approximations cannot be made, then, for accurate results, Eqs. (4·35), (4·25), and (4·41) must be employed. The value of K will reduce to unity under the conditions mentioned above. K_2 will reduce to unity only if T^x and T' have such high diaphragm impedances that they do not affect significantly the impedance which the cavity has when the microphones are replaced by rigid plugs.

Wong and Embleton[7] and Bruel and Kjaer[14] have described variations in their apparatus from the equipment that is described on the pages immediately following. Wong and Embleton determine the equivalent volume of their cavity acoustically by taking three sets of measurements using the voltage

[14]Bruel & Kjaer, "Reciprocity calibration apparatus," 185 Forest St., Marlborough, MA 01752.

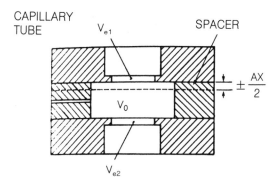

FIG. 4·4a Arrangement for determining the equivalent cavity volume—i.e., cavity volume, gas density, capillaries, and heat conduction—in one measurement.

output from one of the microphones (Fig. 4·4a). One of the measurements is made using the nominal cavity volume V_0, the second, using $V_0 + A \cdot x/2$, and the third, using $V_0 - A \cdot x/2$, where, $\pm x/2$ is produced with spacers as shown in the sketch below. With this procedure, repeated at each frequency of interest, correction factors for heat-conduction, capillarity, and diaphragm compliances are rendered unnecessary. The size of openings necessary for the nominal one-inch condenser microphones used in the calibration is shown in Fig. 4·15. They estimate that the maximum possible error in their calibration results was 0.004 dB.

Bruel and Kjaer give the accuracy of their apparatus as ± 0.05 dB at middle and low frequencies, decreasing to 0.1 dB at 10,000 Hz.

Practical Considerations

Transducers with high diaphragm impedance and a well-defined diaphragm plane, such as condenser and crystal microphones, are ideally suited to calibration in small chambers by the reciprocity technique.[14a] As a practical matter we shall confine ourselves to the simple case when wave motion in the cavity can be neglected. This means that the cavity will usually

---

[14a] A. L. DiMattia and F. M. Wiener, "On the absolute pressure calibration of condenser microphones by the reciprocity method," J. Acoust. Soc. Am. 18, 341–344 (1946) and G. S. Wong and T. F. W. Embleton, "Arrangement for precision reciprocity calibration of condenser microphones," *ibid.* 66, 1275–1280 (1979).

be filled with a gas in which the speed of sound is high. Also, we assume that the diaphragm impedance is a simple compliance. Hence, the formulas applicable to the discussion here are (4·47).

A suitable acoustical coupling element is a closed, rigid cavity, of known physical dimensions, filled with a gas of a known ratio of specific heats and at a known ambient pressure. Since the calibration of a condenser microphone depends on its polarizing voltage, it is necessary, for practical reasons, to determine this voltage in absolute terms.

Electrical circuits. Because of the very high electrical impedance of crystal and condenser microphones, it is not possible to measure their open-circuit voltage with ordinary instruments. To avoid this difficulty, the insert resistor method, described in Chapter 13, is employed. The circuit applicable to our present case is shown in Fig. 4·5.

The open circuit voltage and internal capacitance of the microphone are shown as e_{oc} and C_{eT}, respectively. The guard ring is shown shielding the high input terminal of the amplifier from the insert resistor. C_s is the amplifier input capacitance, contributed by the guard ring, circuit wiring, and interelectrode capacitance of the tube.

The basic circuit of one well-designed experimental setup is shown in Fig. 4·6. The voltage ratio measurement for step 1 is made in two operations. In the first operation, the transfer switch is thrown to the upper position. This energizes the source by impressing the oscillator voltage across its terminals. The microphone, being coupled acoustically to the source by means of the cavity, is thereby also energized, its amplified output producing a deflection on the output meter. Practically, the gain of the voltage amplifier is adjusted to give any convenient deflection of the output meter. This completes the first operation.

In the second operation, the transfer switch is thrown to the lower position, impressing a voltage across the insert resistor. The calibrated attenuator is adjusted until the deflection of the output meter equals the deflection obtained in the first operation, with the gain of the voltage amplifier remaining unchanged after the initial adjustment. The setting of the variable attenuator in conjunction with the fixed attenuation pad of 40.0 db across its output terminals gives directly $[E_{oc}/e_T]$ in decibels.

A variable band-pass filter is used between the voltage amplifier and the output meter to reduce the effect of noise.

This figure also shows the method of supplying both condenser microphones with their proper polarizing voltage. A potentiometer across a small part of the supply battery permits adjustment of the polarizing voltage within very close limits. A voltmeter accurate to within ± 0.3 percent should be used to measure the bias voltage of 200 volts. The 1-megohm resistor and 1-μf condenser located in the polarizing supply circuit of the source are necessary to decouple the source from the microphone.

The preamplifier should have low internal noise and be free

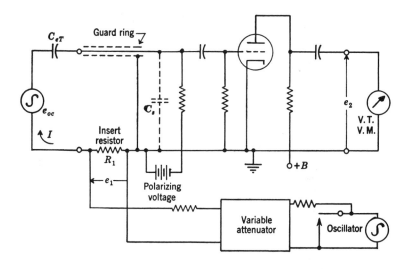

FIG. 4·5 Electrical circuit diagram for the reciprocity calibration of a condenser microphone.

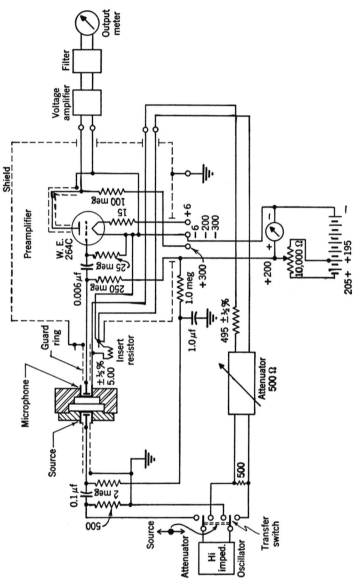

FIG. 4·6 Circuit diagram for the measurement of the voltage ratios E_{oc}/e_T for condenser microphones. (After DiMattia and Wiener.[13])

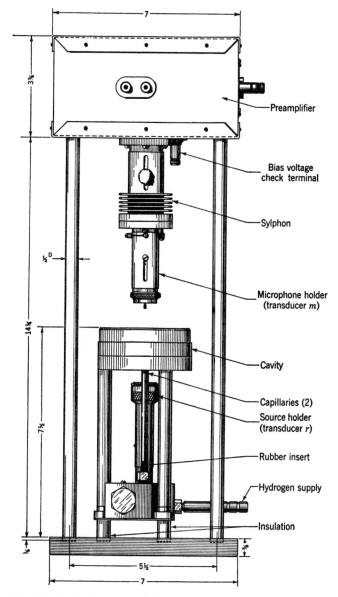

FIG. 4·7 Mechanical features of the cavity assembly. (After Wiener and DiMattia.[13])

from microphonics.   Stability of gain is a requirement only for the very short interval of time needed for making the voltage-ratio measurement described above.

It is important that the correct voltage appear across the insert resistor.   This voltage, for the particular choice of the fixed attenuation pad in Fig. 4·6, is 40.0 db below the voltage appearing across the attenuator output terminals.   This is achieved by bringing out both ends of the insert resistor to the attenuator and the 500-ohm series resistor.   Note also that, with the switch in the "attenuator" position, the circuit is grounded at one point only, namely, the shield enclosing the preamplifier and connected to the low side of the insert resistor.   When in the "source" position, the oscillator is grounded separately.   Note that the two end plates of the cavity are not in electrical contact. The influence of stray capacitances on the measured open-circuit voltage of the microphone is removed by using the guard ring mentioned above extending to the center terminal of the microphone.

The attenuator used for the voltage-ratio measurements must be calibrated accurately so that all readings can be corrected to within 0.05 db, since the ratios $[E_{oc}/e_T]$ are read directly as differences in attenuator readings, as has been explained previously. The attenuator should have a flat frequency characteristic over the range being covered.

Cavity Assembly.   One possible cavity assembly is shown by the drawing in Fig. 4·7.   The *preamplifier* is housed in the metal box at the top of the assembly.   Care must be taken to maintain high insulation resistance of the input grid terminal since leakage will drop the "effective" d-c polarizing voltage existing at the microphone terminals below the value read by the d-c voltmeter. This results from the high value of the polarizing coupling resistor used.   It is important that the effective polarizing voltage be accurately known, since the microphone calibration depends on this voltage.

Two *test cavities* suitable for use with miniature condenser microphones are shown in Fig. 4·8.   Each consists of two heavy end plates of brass separated by a bakelite spacer which insulates the two microphones electrically.   The dimensions of the cavities shown in Fig. 4·8 are critical and are those for an optimum or near-optimum coupler with a useful frequency range extending to about 12,000 cps with hydrogen in the cavity.

To make the cavities hydrogen-tight a small amount of

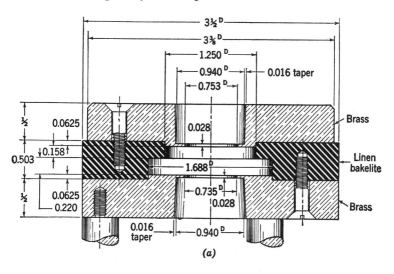

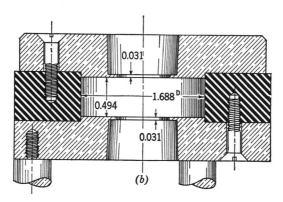

FIG. 4·8   Test cavities for reciprocity calibration of condenser microphones.
(a) Cavity developed by DiMattia and Wiener.[13]   (b) Cavity used at
National Bureau of Standards.

vacuum (low-vapor-pressure) grease is used on the end plates
and elsewhere when the unit is assembled.   The two transducers
are seated in two tapered wells with flat bottoms.   A seal is
achieved by a small amount of vacuum grease applied to the
front rim of the microphones.

Hydrogen is introduced into the cavity by means of the two
metal capillaries shown in Fig. 4·7.   Their acoustic impedance
is very high compared with the impedance of the cavity.   How-

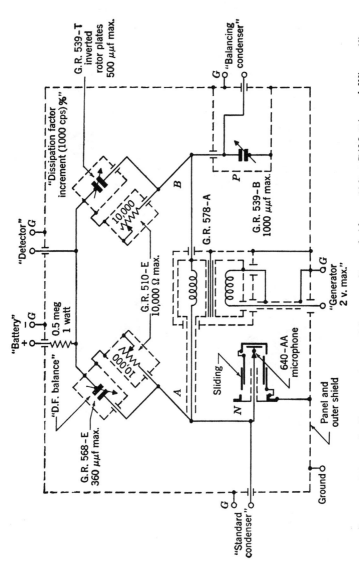

FIG. 4·9   Schematic diagram of a precision capacitance bridge.   (After DiMattia and Wiener.[13])

ever, in accurate work, the presence of the capillaries cannot quite be neglected, since practical considerations limit the length and the fineness of the bore.

In the design of the cavities care must be taken to avoid any appreciable transfer of mechanical energy from the source transducer to the solid structure and thence to the microphone. Such energy, reaching the microphone, will give rise to unusable values of E_{oc}/e_T. The hydrogen is introduced into the cavity in such a way as to make the steady pressure of the gas in the cavity equal to the ambient pressure outside the cavity. However, only approximate equalization of pressure in the cavity may be achieved by this bridge arrangement. Hence, after proper hydrogen concentration has been obtained, the hydrogen flow is stopped and the cavity is opened through a fine capillary system to the atmosphere.

Capacitance Bridge. The quantity $C_{eT}*$ in Eqs. (4·47) must be understood to be the electrical capacitance of the reversible transducer at its terminals when loaded by the same hydrogen-filled cavity used in measuring the voltage ratios, although failure to load the cavity in this way may not affect the results in the greater part of the frequency range.

A suitable capacitance bridge which has been used is shown schematically in Fig. 4·9. It is a modified Schering type of bridge with facilities for applying the correct polarizing voltage to the microphone under test. Cook[14b] describes a bridge which can have the same type of guard ring as the microphone holder in the cavity assembly described above. Such a bridge makes use of a Wagner ground and is called a three-terminal bridge.

Since C_{eT} is a function of frequency the capacitance measurements must be carried out over the whole frequency range for which the calibration is desired. The frequencies are chosen conveniently to coincide with the frequencies for which the voltage ratios are measured. Measurements are made by the substitution method, a precision variable capacitor being used as a standard of capacitance. A typical curve of C_{eT} *vs.* frequency for a WE 640-AA microphone is given in Fig. 4·10. The data

* $1/j\omega C_{eT}$ has been used in the derivation of Eqs. (4·47) instead of the total electrical impedance. This is permissible even for highly accurate work, since the microphone electrical impedance is almost a pure capacitance.

[14b] R. K. Cook, "Theory of Wagner ground balance for alternating current bridges," *Jour. of Research, National Bureau of Standards*, **40**, 245–249 (1948).

show also the small difference between C_{eT} for termination in open air and in a hydrogen-filled cavity of 12.7 cc volume.

Cavity Performance and Design. The diaphragm impedance of condenser microphones is a function of frequency, and it varies from instrument to instrument. A few calculations show that it is not possible to make the cavity volume large enough so that the diaphragm impedances can be altogether neglected for highly accurate work and still have a cavity without appreciable wave motion up to about 10,000 cps. Since it is highly desirable to extend the calibrations at least to that frequency, one must

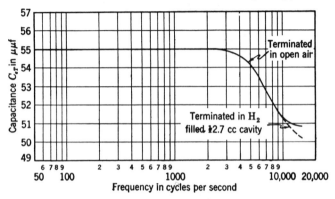

FIG. 4·10   Typical capacitance curve for a Western Electric 640-AA condenser microphone.   (After DiMattia and Wiener.[13])

be satisfied with chamber volumes ranging from 10 to 20 cc and must make corrections for the finite diaphragm impedances.

Suppose two series of measurements of the voltage ratio $[E_{oc}'/e_T{}^x]$ are made as a function of frequency for a given cavity and combination of transducers. First the coupler is filled with hydrogen, then with air. Since the velocity of propagation of sound in hydrogen is about 3.8 times that in air, a similar condition of wave motion will occur in the hydrogen-filled coupler at a frequency higher by the same factor.

Dividing the two voltage ratios so obtained gives,

$$\frac{\left[\dfrac{E_{oc}'}{e_T{}^x}\right]_{\text{air}}}{\left[\dfrac{E_{oc}'}{e_T{}^x}\right]_{H_2}} = F \qquad (4.52)^*$$

*In the revised edition Equations 4·48 through 4·51 are omitted.

or

$$20 \log F = 20 \log \left[\frac{E_{oc}{}'}{e_T{}^x} \right]_{\text{air}} - 20 \log \left[\frac{E_{oc}{}'}{e_T{}^x} \right]_{\text{H}_2} \quad (4 \cdot 53)$$

$20 \log F$ is called "pattern factor" for want of a better term. Since γ for air and hydrogen are very nearly equal, $20 \log F = 0$ for low frequencies where no wave motion exists. Any deviation of the transmission from zero will indicate wave motion in air and thus provide a useful performance index for cavities.

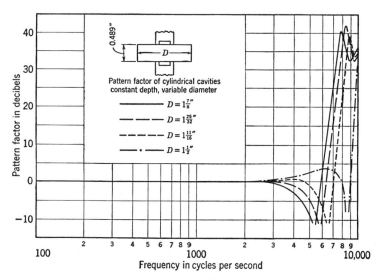

Fɪɢ. 4·11   Pattern factor characteristics of cylindrical cavities.   (After DiMattia and Wiener.[13])

Data on cylindrical cavities of various sizes and shapes are shown in Figs. 4·11 and 4·12 in the form of a plot of $20 \log F$ as a function of frequency.

At low frequencies $20 \log F = 0$, as expected.   For configurations where the diameter is much larger than the depth, an anti-resonance exists.   This is followed by a resonance in the vicinity of 9000 cps, which is the second transverse mode of vibration. The first longitudinal mode occurs between 12,000 and 14,000 cps. For couplers in which the diameter is not very much greater than the depth, no anti-resonance occurs (see Fig. 4·12).   The best design will be achieved if the transmission curve continues horizontally as far as possible along the $20 \log F = 0$ line.   This should be achieved for the greatest volume possible.* Of the cavities shown in Fig. 4·12 a configuration with a depth of 0.489 in. and a diameter lying between $1^{11}/_{16}$ and $1^{25}/_{32}$ in. is the optimum. As a general statement, it can be said that the ratio of diameter to length for any size of cavity should be 3.5 to 1.

In making measurements of $[E_{oc}'/e_T{}^x]$ it is good practice to start with the high frequencies when the hydrogen concentration is still high (after the flow has been shut off). As the frequency decreases, full hydrogen concentration becomes less and less important.

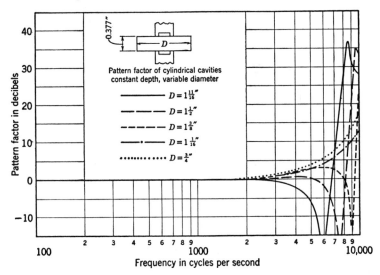

FIG. 4·12 Pattern factor characteristics of cylindrical cavities. (After DiMattia and Wiener.[14a])

Systematic Errors. The following sources of systematic errors must be taken into account:

(1) Finite diaphragm impedance of the microphone and source transducer.

(2) Losses caused by heat conduction by the cavity walls.

(3) Losses caused by finite acoustic impedance of the capillaries.

(4) Wave motion in the cavity at high frequencies.

*The "total volume" of a practical coupler consists of the following: (1) the cavities in front of the microphones, (2) the metal flanges against which the microphones are sealed, and (3) the cavity proper.

Since the diaphragm impedance of condenser microphones at low and medium frequencies is almost a pure stiffness reactance, it can be conveniently expressed as an "equivalent volume" $A_c(l' + l^x)$, as discussed in connection with Eqs. (4·45) and (4·47).

The errors caused by heat conduction and leakage through the capillaries become a concern only at low frequencies, and both act to decrease the sound pressure from the calculated value.

To take into account *leakage through the capillary ducts* the following procedure is necessary. Assume that there are two ducts for the supply of hydrogen, of length d and area S, and

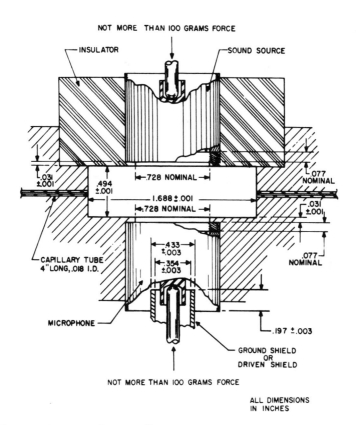

FIG. 4·13 American Standard[15] recommended coupler for reciprocity calibration of condenser microphones. $D/L = 3.417$.

that these ducts are terminated at the remote end by a system of tubing of such large diameter as to offer negligible acoustic resistance. The unit-area acoustic impedance of *each* capillary tube (looking from the enclosure) is approximately

$$SZ = \frac{p}{u} = \frac{8\mu d\pi}{S} + j\,\frac{4}{3}\,\omega\rho_0 d \text{ rayls} \qquad (4\cdot54)$$

where μ is the coefficient of viscosity in poises.

This impedance is equivalent to a softening of the wall in which the tubes are contained and, in relation to the cavity, it must be multiplied by the ratio $A_c/2S$, where A_c is the area of the wall of the cavity, and a factor 2 is introduced because there are two tubes. Hence,

$$Z\bigg]_{\substack{\text{over}\\ \text{wall}\\ \text{area}}} = \frac{4\pi\mu d}{S^2} + j\,\frac{2}{3}\,\omega\rho_0\,\frac{d}{S} \equiv R + jX \text{ acoustic ohms.} \quad (4\cdot55)$$

The acoustic impedance of the volume of air is

$$Z_a = \frac{\gamma p_0}{j\omega V_c}$$

where l is the depth of the cavity, and $V_c = A_c l$.

The total impedance of the cavity then becomes $Z_a Z/(Z_a + Z) = Z_T$; that is,

$$Z_T = \frac{\gamma p_0}{j\omega V_c}\left[\frac{R + jX}{R + j\left[X - \dfrac{\gamma p_0}{\omega V_c}\right]}\right]. \qquad (4\cdot56)$$

If

$$\frac{\omega^2 \rho_0 d V_c}{15\gamma p_0 S} > 1 \qquad (4\cdot57)$$

then

$$Z_T \doteq \frac{\gamma p_0}{j\omega V_c}.$$

For frequencies below that point, Z_T will become smaller, and corrections to the formula will be necessary. As an example, if the capillary tubes have an area S of 2×10^{-5} cm^2 and a length

---

[15]American National Standard, ANSI S1.10-1966, "Method for the calibration of microphones," Acoustical Society of America.

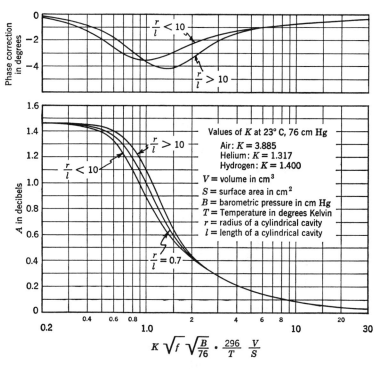

FIG. 4·14 Corrections for change in effective cavity volume because of heat conduction at the boundaries. The number of decibels on the ordinate should be added to $20 \log_{10 \, pm}$ (in decibels) calculated from Eq. (4·47). (After Daniels.[16])

of 10 cm each, then, for air, the lowest frequency at which the cavity can be used without correction is

$$f = \frac{187}{2\pi} V_c^{-1/2} \doteq 30 V_c^{-1/2} \quad \text{(air)} \tag{4·58}$$

for a 10-cc cavity, $f \doteq 10$ cps.

For hydrogen, this formula becomes

$$f \doteq 114 V_c^{-1/2} \quad \text{(hydrogen)} \tag{4·59}$$

For a 10-cc cavity, $f \doteq 40$ cps.

The effects of *heat conduction* at the side walls will be more important than those due to the leakage through capillaries with radius and length on of the order of 0.0026 cm and 10 cm,

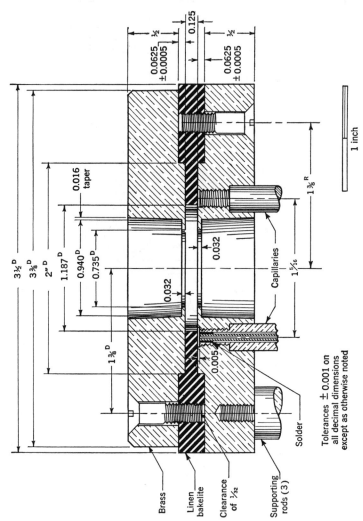

Fig. 4·15 Cavity for the calibration of condenser microphones in the range of 5000 to 21,000 cps. (After DiMattia and Wiener.[13])

respectively. Correction curves for cylindrical cavities with three ratios of radius to length and either air, hydrogen, or helium are given in Fig. 4·14. These curves are taken from Daniels.[16] Note that the constant K is different for each of the three gases and that the ordinate is simply K times the square root of the frequency times the ratio of the volume to the surface area of the cavity, if $T \doteq 23°C$ and if the barometric pressure is 760 mm.

D. Ultrasonic Frequency Range

The upper frequency limit of the 12.7-cc coupler is about 12,000 cps, in hydrogen. Calibrations at higher frequencies may

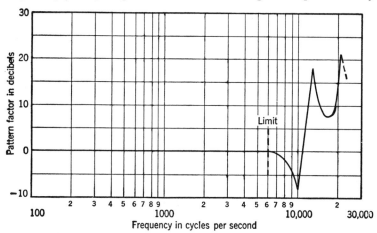

FIG. 4·16   Pattern factor characteristic of high frequency coupler developed by DiMattia and Wiener.[13]

be obtained by means of one or more additional couplers having smaller volume. The error due to the equivalent volume of the microphone diaphragms will be larger because of the decreased volume. However, if it is known, corrections for this equivalent volume can be taken into account. Capillary losses are not a concern, since small cavities are not ordinarily used at low frequencies.

A possible coupler for extending the frequency range with condenser microphones to about 21 kc (using hydrogen) is shown in the drawing in Fig. 4·15. The total volume of the coupler is 3.77 cc.

[16] F. B. Daniels, "Acoustical impedance of enclosures," *Jour. Acous. Soc. Amer.*, **19**, 569–571 (1947).

A pattern factor curve of the high frequency coupler is given in Fig. 4·16. The limiting frequency for zero wave motion in air is about 6000 cps, in hydrogen about 21,000 cps. A practical upper frequency limit is usually set by inadequate signal-to-noise ratios in the $[E_{oc}'/e_T^x]$ measurement, as the microphone sensitivity decreases rapidly with frequency in the ultrasonic range.

Rudnick[17] has extended the free-field reciprocity technique successfully up to 100,000 cps by using a miniature condenser microphone as the reversible transducer. He reports accuracies of ± 1.0 db in that frequency range.

4·3 Wave Measurements

A. Particle Velocity—Rayleigh Disk

The Rayleigh disk has long been used as a primary means for measuring the magnitude of the particle velocity in a plane wave sound field. Lord Rayleigh[18] first observed that under some circumstances a torque is exerted on a thin disk suspended by a fine fiber in a stream of air, and he recognized in this phenomenon a means for measuring the intensity of sound.

Koenig[19] developed the following relationship between the torque and the stream velocity:

$$L = \tfrac{4}{3}\rho_0 a^3 u^2 \sin 2\alpha \qquad (4·60)$$

the terms of which are defined below Eq. (4·61). The assumptions underlying Eq. (4·60) are that the fluid is incompressible, that the disk is an infinitely thin ellipsoid and is rigidly held, that the scattered sound can be neglected, and that there are no forces due to viscosity, heat conduction, or discontinuities of flow at the edge of the disk. In view of these assumptions, the method cannot be considered an absolute one, and the validity of Eq. (4·60) must be determined by test.

As employed in practice, a Rayleigh disk is *freely suspended*, in which circumstance it performs (in addition to its primary

[17] I. Rudnick, "Atmospheric physics and sound propagation," Progress Report No. 19, Penn State College, October 20, 1947.

[18] Lord Rayleigh, "On an instrument capable of measuring the intensity of aerial vibrations," *Phil. Mag.*, **14**, 186–187 (1882).

[19] W. Koenig, "Theory of the Rayleigh Disk," *Wied. Ann.*, **43**, 43–60 (1891) (in German).

rotation) small oscillations along a line drawn normal to its surface, under the influence of the first-order radiation pressure, as well as angular oscillations about the axis of suspension. In other words, it cannot be assumed that the disk is rigidly held. The first effect may be appreciable, especially when employed to measure the intensity of sound in liquids. The second effect is of less importance in disks of circumference small compared with the wavelength.

King[20] set out to derive an equation for the disk in which he took into account the diffraction of the incident sound field when the direction of propagation was at an angle α to the normal of the disk. He made use of cylindrical wave functions and allowed for second-order movements of the disk. Although his analysis does not include the effects of viscosity and heat conduction, the results are believed to be accurate.[21]

The time average of the torque on a Rayleigh disk as King finally derived it is given in Eq. (4·61) for a *plane progressive wave* whose rms particle velocity is u. This equation includes the effects of inertia and diffraction and is correct to the second order in (ka). The diameter of the disk is assumed to be small compared to a wavelength.

$$L = -\frac{4}{3}\rho_0 a^3 \sin 2\alpha \, u^2 \left[\frac{m_1\{1 + \frac{2}{5}(ka)^2 \cos^2 \alpha\}}{m_1 + m_0 \{1 + \frac{1}{5}(ka^2)\}} \right.$$
$$\left. - \frac{2}{15}(ka)^2 \frac{I_1}{I_1 + I_0} \cos 2\alpha \right] \quad (4\cdot61)$$

where a = radius of the disk, in centimeters
$\quad\quad$ α = angle which the sound wave makes with a line drawn normal to the surface of the disk, in radians
$\quad\quad$ I_1 = moment of inertia of disk = $(\frac{1}{4})m_1 a^2$, in gram-cm^2
$\quad\quad$ I_0 = hydrodynamic moment of inertia of disk = $(\frac{2}{15})m_0 a^2$, in gram-cm^2
$\quad\quad$ k = wave number = ω/c
$\quad\quad$ L = time average of the torque tending to rotate the disk about its vertical axis, in dyne-centimeters

[20] L. V. King, "On the theory of the inertia and diffraction corrections for the Rayleigh disc," *Proc. Royal Soc. London,* **A153,** 17–40 (1935).
[21] R. A. Scott, "An investigation of the performance of the Rayleigh disk," *Proc. Royal Soc. London,* **A183,** 296–316 (1945).

m_1 = mass of disk = $\pi a^2 \rho_1 t_1$, in grams

m_0 = hydrodynamic mass of disk = $(\frac{8}{3})\rho_0 a^3$, in grams

ρ_1 = density of disk, in gram-cm^{-3}

ρ_0 = density of the air, in gram-cm^{-3}

t_1 = uniform thickness of disk, in centimeters

T = period of oscillation, in seconds, of a heavy disk hung on the suspending fiber

τ = torsional constant of the suspending fiber = $-L/\theta$, in dyne-cm-radian^{-1}

θ = angular rotation of the disk about its vertical axis, in radians

u = rms particle velocity in the wave, in cm-sec^{-1}

This equation is valid in gases. However, if measurements are made in a high density medium such as water, m_1 must be replaced by $m_1 - m_w$ and I_1 by $I_1 - I_w$, where m_w and I_w are the mass and the moment of inertia of a disk of the same dimensions and a density equal to that of the medium.

The torque on a Rayleigh disk placed in a *plane standing wave* is

$$L = -\frac{4}{3}\rho_0 a^3 \sin 2\alpha \, u^2 \left[\sin^2 kh \frac{m_1\{1 + \frac{2}{5}(ka)^2 \cos^2 \alpha\}}{m_1 + m_0\{1 + \frac{1}{5}(ka)^2\}} \right.$$
$$\left. - \frac{2}{15}(\cos^2 kh)(ka)^2 \frac{I_1}{I_1 + I_0}\cos 2\alpha \right] \quad (4\cdot62)$$

where h is the perpendicular distance from the reflecting plane to the center of the disk.

At the velocity *loops* of the system of standing waves, $\sin^2 kh = 1$; therefore

$$(L)_{\text{loops}} = -\frac{4}{3}\rho_0 a^3 \sin 2\alpha \, u^2 \left[\frac{m_1\{1 + \frac{2}{5}(ka)^2 \cos^2 \alpha\}}{m_1 + m_0\{1 + \frac{1}{5}(ka)^2\}} \right] \quad (4\cdot63)$$

In these circumstances there are no angular oscillations of the disk.

At the velocity *nodes* of the standing waves, there are no linear oscillations of the disk, $\cos^2 kh = 1$, and

$$(L)_{\text{nodes}} = \frac{4}{45}\rho_0 a^3 \sin 4\alpha \,(ka)^2 u^2 \frac{I_1}{I_1 + I_0} \quad (4\cdot64)$$

The couple on a small disk for which $ka \ll 1$, situated at a node, is thus of a much smaller order of magnitude than that exerted on it at a loop, and it is of opposite sign. The stable positions of the disk in the range $0 < \alpha < \pi/2$ are those corresponding to $\alpha = \pi/8$ and $\alpha = 3\pi/8$.

In the measurement of the intensity of sound, a Rayleigh disk is sometimes mounted in a resonator at the loop of a system of standing waves. Formula (4·63) is valid for this case.

Disk with Optimum Sensitivity. If a disk is chosen small enough so that the terms containing $(ka)^2$ can be neglected and if it is placed in a progressive wave whose particle velocity is u, or at the loops of a stationary wave of the same velocity, the torque tending to set the disk broadside to the wave normal is given by

$$L \doteq -\frac{4}{3} \rho_0 a^3 u^2 \sin 2\alpha \left[\frac{m_1}{m_1 + m_0} \right] \qquad (4 \cdot 65)$$

In practice, the disk is hung from a fine glass or metal fiber. It is first set to some angle α, preferably $\alpha = 45°$ because that is the angle for which the greatest sensitivity is obtained. Then the sound field is turned on and the disk rotates to a new angle α. Finally, the fiber on which the disk is suspended is rotated through an angle θ until the disk returns to its original position.

If the torsional constant of the fiber is denoted by τ, the torque necessary to rotate the disk through an angle θ is given by

$$L = -\tau\theta$$

Hence,

$$u^2 = \frac{2}{\sin 2\alpha} \frac{m_1 + m_0}{m_1 m_0} \tau\theta \qquad (4 \cdot 66)$$

where $(\tfrac{8}{3})\rho_0 a^3$ was replaced by m_0.

The torsional constant τ is most easily determined in terms of the time of the free oscillations of a heavy disk in air by the equation

$$T = 2\pi \left\{ \frac{I_1 + I_0}{\tau} \right\}^{1/2} \qquad (4 \cdot 67)$$

where T is the period of the oscillations.

Substituting the value for τ in the earlier equation leads to the *working* equation for the Rayleigh disk:

$$u^2 = \frac{8\pi^2}{T^2} \frac{1}{\sin 2\alpha} \frac{(I_1 + I_0)(m_1 + m_0)}{m_1 m_0} \theta \qquad (4 \cdot 68)$$

in which all quantities are measurable.

If Eq. 4·68 is maximized so that θ is a maximum for a given u, King has shown that

$$\boxed{\frac{t_1}{a} = 0.620 \frac{\rho_0}{\rho_1}} \qquad (4 \cdot 69)$$

where t_1 and ρ_1 are the thickness and density of the disk of radius a, respectively. If this relation is substituted into the working formula and if $\alpha = 45°$, we get u^2 for an optimum disk:

$$\boxed{u^2 = \frac{8\pi^2}{T^2} \times 0.748 a^2 \theta} \qquad (4 \cdot 70)$$

These formulas clearly show that, for a maximum deflection of the disk, a and t_1 must be very small and T must be very long.

It is easy to show that even if T exceeds 10 sec and a is less than 1 mm (conditions hard to attain in practice) it is difficult to measure a sound pressure level of less than 50 db (*re* 0.0002 dyne/cm^2) in air, or 85 db in water using the disk without a resonator. This calculation assumes that the angular deflection of the disk is measured by means of a galvanometer lamp and scale and that the minimum deflection desired is one of 1 mm on a scale 1 meter distant.

Viscosity, Heat Conduction, and Vortices. The remaining assumption in Eq. (4·61) is that no torque due to viscosity, heat conduction, or vortex motion in the vicinity of the disk is exerted on the disk. Merrington and Oatley[22] investigated the influence of these factors experimentally and arrived at the conclusion that the viscous effects cannot account for more than about 2 percent of the total couple at atmospheric pressure.

Heat conduction and vortex motion combine to produce much greater errors than that just indicated, vortex motion being the greater in importance. The results of Merrington and Oatley

[22] A. C. Merrington and C. W. Oatley, "An investigation of the accuracy of König's formula for the Rayleigh Disk," *Proc. Roy. Soc. London*, **A171**, 505–524 (1939).

show that the total couple exerted by these factors for air at atmospheric pressure is of the order of 10 percent at frequencies of 9 to 22 cps. Earlier experimenters did not find errors of this order of magnitude, and Merrington and Oatley explain this by saying that the earlier observers used the torsional oscillations of the Rayleigh disk itself to determine the torsional constant of the fiber. That method introduces an error due to the added inertia of the air, which can be minimized by using large, heavy disks

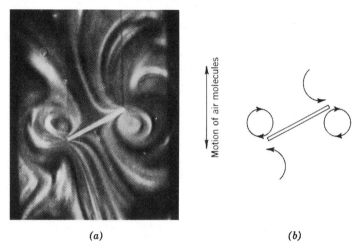

(a)   (b)

FIG. 4·17   Vortex motion around a Rayleigh disk. (a) Photograph of smoke particles. (b) Sketch showing direction of vortex motion. (After Merrington and Oatley.[22])

for the determination of τ. It so happens that the effect due to the added inertia of the air is, for small, light disks, in the right direction and of about the right magnitude to mask the discrepancy between theory and experiment brought about by the presence of vortices.

A photograph of the vortex motion as indicated by particles of cigarette smoke appears in Fig. 4·17a, and a sketch showing the directions of vortex rotation appears in Fig. 4·17b. An attempt was made by Merrington and Oatley and by Scott[21] to determine whether there was a critical velocity above which an onset of vortex motion might be expected. No such critical velocity was observable, but vortex motion did exist for all particle velocities which they could measure down to 0.5 cm/sec.

To take account of vortices, Merrington and Oatley deduced

from their measurements near 15 cps that Eq. (4·61) should be multiplied by a factor of 1.10 to give correct predictions. Scott, however, found that a constant correction factor is not indicated, and he presents an empirical curve of the correction factor needed *vs.* frequency. His data at very low frequencies are in satisfactory agreement with those of Merrington and Oatley. The results are given in Fig. 4·18.

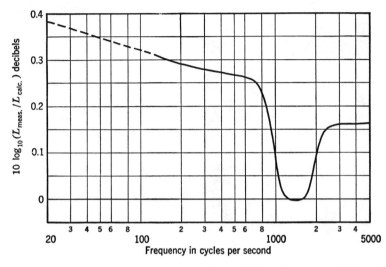

FIG. 4·18 Empirical correction curve to be applied to the torque calculated by the exact King formula. The ordinate gives 10 $\log_{10}$ (L_{meas}/L_{calc}), where L_{meas} is the torque which actually operates to rotate the disk and L_{calc} is that calculated from the King formula, Eq. (4·61), or, to a cruder approximation, Eq. (4·65). (After Scott.[21])

Disk Resonances. The Rayleigh disk when mounted on its suspension is capable of vibrating almost like a free plate. Barnes and West[23] showed that except for very small disks a principal resonance falls in the audio-frequency range and it may produce errors of as much as 15 percent in the determination of particle velocity at frequencies in the vicinity of the resonance. In particular, they studied two disks whose dimensions were: diameter, 6.18 and 1.6 cm; thickness, 0.013 and 0.0045 cm. The former had a resonance at 560 cps and the latter at 1800 cps. The effect extended over a range of ±10 percent on either side

[23] E. Barnes and W. West, "The calibration and performance of the Rayleigh Disk," *Jour. Inst. Elec. Engrs.*, **65**, 871 (1927).

of the resonant frequency. Cementing a small mirror to the center of the disk greatly reduced this effect.

Effect of Diameter and Thickness. Scott[21] assembled a group of disks ranging in diameter from 0.6284 to 1.914 cm and determined the values of torque produced by them when placed in the same sound field. His results showed that the torque varies as the cube of the radius of the disk provided corrections were made for the finite thickness and for the lack of infinite inertia. It appears, therefore, that the diameter of the disk is fully taken into account in the basic formula. The thickness of the disk is of considerable importance, however. Scott measured the torque

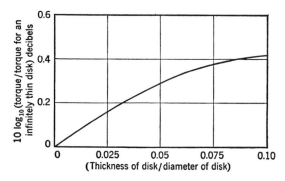

FIG. 4·19 Graph showing effect of thickness of Rayleigh disk on the torque produced. The ordinate gives the ratio of the torque actually acting on the disk to that calculated for an infinitesimally thin disk. (After Scott.[21])

developed by a series of disks ranging in thickness from 0.0064 to 0.1219 cm and having a diameter of 1.159 cm. His derived correction factors for disks of different thicknesses are plotted in Fig. 4·19. King's formula was used to correct for the variations in mass.

Practical Design and Calibration. Practical sizes of disks which have been used with success are given in Table 4·1. These disks appear to be too thick to meet the optimal requirements outlined in the theoretical section. When attached to a fiber having a torsional constant τ of 0.0017 dyne-cm/radian, the smallest of the disks in Table 4·1 is capable of measuring velocities only down to about 0.25 cm/sec (95 db).

To measure the deflection of the disk, Ballantine and others attached a small glass mirror about 0.1 cm square and weighing about 0.0005 gram to the face of the disk. This mirror is cut from No. 1 microcoverglass which has been silvered, and it reflects a beam of light onto a galvanometer scale. Tests indicate that the addition of the mirror does not affect the accuracy of the Rayleigh disk. Delsasso* makes the disk itself serve as the reflecting mirror. To form the disk he punches a pellet 0.08 cm in diameter from a sheet of aluminum 0.045 cm thick. This pellet is then laid on a quarter diopter convex glass lens and a drop of oil is put on it. Next, a punch with a concave tip,

TABLE 4·1

Disk	Mass, grams	Radius, cm	Thickness, cm	Resonant Frequencies, kc	Reference
Microcoverglass	0.0501	0.6345	0.016		Merrington and Oatley
Microcoverglass		0.3142	0.0162	21.2	Scott
Microcoverglass		0.5792	0.0135	5.2–8.2	Scott
Mica	0.0060	0.497	0.003		Merrington and Oatley
Mica	0.002	0.400	0.0025		Ballantine and Barnes and West
Copper		0.5809	0.0200	5.6–8.8	Scott
Molybdenum		0.5792	0.0032	2.5–3.9	Scott
Aluminum		0.5	0.0004		Scott

slightly more curved than the convex lens, is brought against the pellet to fix it in position on the glass. The punch is then backed off and a lead sheet, 0.02 cm thick, is placed above the pellet. Then the punch is again lowered and applied at large pressure to the lead sheet and pellet until an aluminum disk is formed with a diameter of about 0.25 cm. This means that the final disk will have a thickness of about 0.0046 cm. By placing the scale at the focal point of the mirror, bright spots of light are obtained.

The suspension can be made of quartz, soft (soda) glass thread, or a phosphor bronze wire. Quartz or glass fibers may be formed[24] by first drawing a long fine tip on a piece of quartz rod. Then the flame is adjusted on an oxygen burner to a height of about 1 ft. Next the fine tip is inserted into the hot part of the

* Communicated privately to the author by Leo P. Delsasso, University of California at Los Angeles.

[24] J. Strong *et al.*, *Procedures in Experimental Physics*, Prentice-Hall (1945).

flame, and the rising heated air draws a fiber and carries it upward. Then a meter or so of the fiber is caught against a soft cloth. The fibers are generally used in lengths of 20 to 50 cm.

Phosphor bronze suspensions should be about 0.025 cm in diameter. A wire of this material must be annealed before use to insure that it will hang straight when stretched by the very small weight of the disk. This annealing is accomplished by suspending a small weight by means of a long loop of the wire whose ends are fastened to two rods which pass through a rubber stopper. The weight is then lowered into a brass tube, the top end of which is closed with the rubber stopper. The tube is evacuated and a current passed through the wire for a few seconds to raise it to a temperature just below red heat. After this treatment it should hang perfectly straight. However, glass or quartz fibers should be used when great sensitivity and a long-time stability are desired.

The torsional constant of a suspension fiber is determined by finding the period of oscillation of a small brass disk attached to the bottom of the fiber. A short piece of wire, 0.5 mm in diameter, is attached to the disk along a diameter and projects beyond the edge. The fiber can be joined conveniently to this projection. The calibrating disk is weighed and measured and its moment of inertia about a diameter is calculated. Then solder is used to attach the short piece of wire. A spot of shellac is melted onto the projecting end of the wire, and the suspension fiber is laid out with its free edge touching the shellac and in proper alignment. A hot iron brought near the shellac will soften it sufficiently to grab the wire. The suspended calibrating disk is next placed in a draft-free enclosure. Several readings of its time of swing T are made, and the average is taken. The value of τ can then be calculated from Eq. (4·67). Finally, the calibrating disk is removed from the suspension by the application of an iron near the shellac, and the Rayleigh disk is attached by the same means. For precise results the torsional constant should be measured before and after using a fiber in an experiment to make sure that it has not been damaged.

If the disk is to be used in a circular enclosure its diameter should be less than one-half that of the enclosure if errors of less than 0.2 db are desired.

One of the most troublesome manipulative features of the Rayleigh disk is its sensitivity to drafts. To alleviate this diffi-

culty, the disk should be enclosed in a screen made up of open-
mesh silk or other fabric.   A high quality, closely woven cheese-
cloth such as used for dental napkins is quite suitable.   The
loss of sound through such material is almost negligible and certainly less than 5 percent up to 10,000 cps.   Such loss can be
determined by mounting a microphone in the enclosure and
measuring its output, when subject to a plane sound wave, with
and without the draft screen around it.   As an indication of the
degree to which drafts must be eliminated, Devik and Dahl[25]
prepared the information shown in Table 4·2.   That table gives
the maximum permissible air currents at any given sound level
being measured, if it is assumed that the air current is less than
one-tenth of the particle velocity.

To adjust a disk so that its axis lies at 45° to the direction of
motion of the air particles, the suspension head is turned until
the axis of the disk is parallel to the direction of motion.   This
setting can be made with great accuracy, since the scale reading
of the spot of light reflected from the disk is the same whether
the sound field is on or off.   When the setting has been made,
the torsion head is turned through 45°.

Table 4·2

RMS Sound Pressure, $dyne/cm^2$	Sound Pressure Level, db	RMS Velocity u, cm/sec	Permissible Air Current, cm/sec	mi/hr
1	74	0.024	0.0024	5.37×10^{-5}
10	94	0.24	0.024	5.37×10^{-4}
100	114	2.4	0.24	5.37×10^{-3}
1,000	134	24	2.4	0.0537
10,000	154	240	24	0.537

If the technique of setting the disk back to $\alpha = 45°$ after it
has been displaced by the sound is not used, but instead direct
readings of the displacement angle are made on a scale, a flat
scale should be used.   The reason is that the error involved in
assuming that the displacement of the spot is proportional to
the angular deflection of the disk almost cancels that due to the
assumption that the axis of the disk is always at an angle of 45°
to the direction of particle motion.

For every run, the barometric pressure and the room temperature must be measured and recorded.

[25] O. Devik and H. Dahl, "Acoustical output of air sound senders,"
Jour. Acous. Soc. Amer., **10**, 50–62(1938).

B. Particle Amplitude

Few methods have been advanced for the direct measurement of particle amplitude in a sound wave. Of these the best depends on the determination of the particle amplitude from the length of the traces of smoke particles suspended in the sound field. This procedure was first advanced by Carrière[26] and later used by Andrade and by Andrade and Parker.[27] The accuracy of the method depends on how well the theory predicts the degree to which the motion of the molecules is taken up by the smoke particles. Andrade presented a formula due to Stokes and others for computing the motion of a spherical particle in a fluid. If w_0 and v_0 are the amplitudes of motion of the sphere and of the surrounding medium in centimeters, respectively, ρ is the static density of the medium in g cm^{-3}, ρ_0 is the density of the sphere in g cm^{-3}, r is the radius of the sphere in centimeters, f is the frequency, ν is the kinematic coefficient of viscosity in cm^2-sec^{-1}, then

$$\frac{w_0}{v_0} = \left[\frac{1 + 3a + \frac{9}{4}(2a^2 + 2a^3 + a^4)}{b^2 + 3ab + \frac{9}{4}(2a^2 + 2a^3 + a^4)} \right]^{1/2} \quad (4\cdot71)$$

where

$$a = \frac{1}{r}\sqrt{\frac{\nu}{\pi f}} \quad \text{and} \quad b = \frac{1}{3} + \frac{2\rho_0}{3\rho} \quad (4\cdot72)$$

Scott,[21] reporting on this technique, produced smoke particles of magnesium oxide by igniting 20 mg of magnesium ribbon in a 2.5-liter flask. Observations, under an electron microscope, of particles which had settled 20 minutes after the smoke had formed, indicated that the particles were cubes with edges between 0.1 and 0.2μ long. Andrade and Parker estimated that the effective radius of particles made by this technique is 0.3 μ. Cigarette smoke particles are about one-half that diameter but are less visible.

Calculations of w_0/v_0 made with Eq. (4·71) and on the assumption that $r = 0.3$ μ are shown in Table 4·3.

[26] M. Z. Carrière, "Ultra-microscopic analyses of aerial vibrations," *J. phys. et radium*, **10**, 198–208 (1929) (in French).

[27] E. N. C. Andrade, "On the circulations caused by the vibration of air in a tube," *Proc. Roy. Soc. London*, **A134**, 445–470 (1931); E. N. C. Andrade and R. C. Parker, "A standard source of sound and the measurement of minimum audibility," *Proc. Roy. Soc. London*, **A159**, 507–526 (1937).

TABLE 4·3 AMPLITUDE OF SMOKE PARTICLES RELATIVE TO AMPLITUDE OF
AIR PARTICLES

Frequency, cps	Ratio, $\dfrac{\text{amplitude of smoke particle}}{\text{amplitude of air particle}}$
250	0.99996
1250	0.99916
2250	0.9975
3250	0.9947
4250	0.9913
5250	0.9868

It appears from the experiments of Scott and of Andrade and Parker that the smoke particle technique provides a measurement of sound amplitude which, without correction by Table 4·3, is accurate to within 1 percent up to a frequency of 400 cps, and to within 2 percent up to 5000 cps.

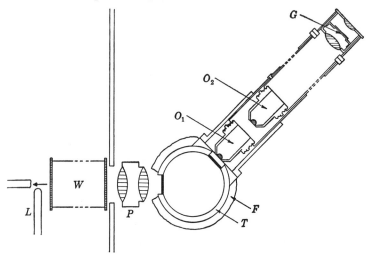

FIG. 4·20 Cross-sectional sketch of a cylindrical tube, fitted for smoke particle measurement. L is an arc light; W is a water bath; P is a condenser lens; T is a tube 4.43 cm in diameter; F is felt damping; O_1 and O_2 are microscope objectives; and G is an eyepiece graticule. (After Scott.[21])

A cross-sectional sketch of the apparatus used by Scott is shown in Fig. 4·20. T is a tube 4.44 cm in diameter surrounded by a layer of vibration damping felt F and furnished with two windows. The particles are illuminated from an arc lamp L, and a large-aperture projection lens P. A composite objective with a focal length of about 2.5 cm, an n.a. of 0.11, and a sufficiently large working distance (about 2.5 cm) is constructed to permit measurements to be made of the particle amplitude at various distances from the axis of the tube.

The lengths of the smoke particle traces are determined by fitting to the eyepiece a glass graticule G consisting of two accurately spaced parallel lines. The intensity of the sound in the tube is adjusted until the ends of a trace, as seen through the microscope, appear just to touch the lines. A series of graticules is used for determining various particle amplitudes.

4·4 Primary Sources of Sound

A. The Thermophone

In 1907 a Russian engineer, Gwozdz, made various experiments in a small village in the neighborhood of Lodz, in Poland, with a wire heated by electricity as a source of sound. Although his device was quite inefficient and never of practical utility, it did arouse the interest of de Lange[28] who in 1914 announced the invention of a thermophone with substantial acoustical output which made use of fine wires. Arnold and Crandall[29] then treated the subject analytically, and their paper served to establish the thermophone as a primary source of sound for use over a wide frequency range, a position which it has held since that date. They attributed the invention of the thermophone to F. Braun[30] who found that acoustic effects could be produced by passing alternating currents through a bolometer in which the usual direct current was also maintained.

Corrections to the theory of Arnold and Crandall have been offered by Wente,[31] Sivian,[32] Ballantine,[33] Geffcken and Keibs,[34] and Cook.[35]

[28] P. de Lange, "On thermophones," *Proc. Royal Soc. London*, **A91**, 239–241 (1915).

[29] H. D. Arnold and I. B. Crandall, "The thermophone as a precision source of sound," *Phys. Rev.*, **10**, 22–38 (1917).

[30] F. Braun, "Note on thermophonics," *Ann. d. Physik*, **65**, 358–360 (1898) (in German).

[31] E. C. Wente, "The thermophone," *Phys. Rev.*, **19**, 333–345 (1922).

[32] L. J. Sivian, "Absolute calibration of condenser transmitters," *Bell System Technical Jour.*, **10**, 96–115 (1931).

[33] S. Ballantine, "Technique of microphone calibration," *Jour. Acous. Soc. Amer.*, **3**, 319–360 (1932).

[34] W. Geffcken and L. Keibs, "The thermophone and its application as an acoustical measuring instrument," *Ann. d. Physik*, **16**, 404–430 (1933) (in German).

[35] R. K. Cook, "Absolute pressure calibrations of microphones," *Jour. of Research, National Bureau of Standards*, **25**, 489–505 (1940).

Theoretical Considerations.   The formulas given here are drawn largely from Geffcken and Keibs, although the work of the other observers is incorporated where necessary. The terminology follows.

a = radius of the circular wire, in centimeters

b = depth of the steady temperature layer surrounding the wire

B = depth of the steady temperature layer surrounding the foil

β = specific heat of the foil per unit area

β' = specific heat of the wire per unit length

c_p = specific heat of the gas at constant pressure, in cal deg^{-1}

c_v = specific heat of the gas at constant volume, in cal deg^{-1}

γ = ratio of specific heats = c_p/c_v

I_0 = steady current in the conductor, in amperes

I_1 = maximum amplitude of the alternating current, in amperes

K_0 = heat conductivity of gas at 0°C

K_θ = heat conductivity of gas at temperature θ

K_{θ_0} = heat conductivity of gas at temperature of conductor θ_0

l = length of the circular wire, in centimeters

ω = angular frequency = $2\pi f$.

P_0 = ambient pressure of gas

p_1 = maximum amplitude of sound pressure, in dyne-cm^{-2}

r = radial distance measured from the center of the wire, in centimeters

R = foil or wire resistance measured in its heated state, in ohms

ρ_0 = density of gas at 0°C, in gram-cm^{-3}

ρ_1 = maximum amplitude of the excess density, in gram-cm^{-3}

ρ_T = density of gas at temperature T

S = area of the foil, in square centimeters

T_a = temperature of the side walls of the cavity, in degrees Kelvin (°K)

T_0 = steady temperature of the gas in the volume surrounding the conductor, in centigrade degrees (°C)

T_{1m} = mean amplitude of the alternating temperature in the volume of gas surrounding the conductor, in centigrade degrees (°C)

θ_0 = temperature of the conductor when heated with a current I_0, in degrees Kelvin (°K)

θ_1 = maximum amplitude of the alternating temperature in wire, in centigrade degrees (°C)

V_0 = volume of chamber surrounding the conductor, in cubic centimeters

x = distance measured perpendicular to the surface of the metal foil, in centimeters

An alternating current passing through a thin strip of metal (foil) or circular wire will produce heating effects which cause the

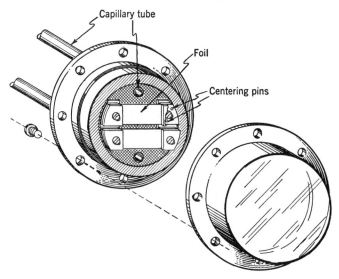

FIG. 4·21 Sketch showing the general appearance of a foil thermophone. Two capillary tubes supply hydrogen or helium to the cavity to extend the frequency range.

temperature of the conductor to increase and decrease with respect to the surrounding medium. These variations will be propagated as a heat diffusion wave from the conductor. That wave is rapidly attenuated, but it gives rise to an acoustic wave whose amplitude is proportional to the increase and decrease of the temperature near the foil. Assume now that the foil or wire is mounted in a cavity which is acoustically rigid, as shown in Fig. 4·21. In practice, a steady current I_0 is passed through the conductor along with the alternating current $I_1 e^{j\omega t}$. Because the heat generated by the conductor is proportional to the square of the current passing through it, three terms appear in the heat equation:

$$\text{Heat (cal/sec)} = 0.239R(I_0{}^2 + 2I_0I_1e^{j\omega t} + I_1{}^2e^{j2\omega t}) \quad (4\cdot73)$$

where R is the resistance of the conductor.   If pressure variations whose fundamental frequency is ω are desired, a direct current I_0 is necessary.   If a negligible amount of the second harmonic is to appear, $I_0{}^2 \gg I_1{}^2$.

The assumptions made in the derivation of the sound pressure developed in the cavity are:

1. If a thin foil is used as the source of heat it must be wide so that edge effects are negligible and so that the temperature wave is propagated outward with its front parallel to the surface of the foil.

2. In setting up the boundary conditions for the steady-state temperature, both the conduction of heat through the gas and the convection currents must be taken into account.   The convection currents operate in such a way that in the steady state the temperature of the gas is the same as that of the cavity walls up to the edge of a thin layer of gas surrounding the conductor. It can be assumed that inside that layer the temperature rises uniformly to its maximum value at the surface of the conductor. The thickness of this layer is independent of the temperature of the conductor, but it is a function of the thermal properties of the gas.[36]

For an "infinitely" wide foil (no edge effects) the depth of this layer on either side is, for air, equal to $B = 0.215$ cm.   For wire in air it has been shown empirically to be given by $b \ln (b/a) = 0.43$ cm, where b is the radius of the outer edge of this layer around the wire and a is the radius of the wire.

Inserting one of these facts as a boundary condition in the solution of the heat conduction equation (for the steady temperature) yields the formulas

For wide foils:

$$T_0 = \left[\frac{0.239 \times 3 \times \sqrt{273}}{4} \frac{RI_0{}^2}{SK_0} (B - x) + T_a{}^{3/2} \right]^{2/3} \quad (4\cdot74)$$

[36] J. Langmuir, "Convection and conduction of heat in gases," *Phys. Rev.*, **34**, 401–422, (1912).

For circular wires:

$$T_0 = \left[\frac{0.239 \times 3 \times \sqrt{273}}{4\pi} \frac{RI_0{}^2}{lK_0} \ln\left(\frac{b}{r}\right) + T_a{}^{3/2} \right]^{2/3} \quad (4\cdot75)$$

These two equations when plotted give the curves shown in Fig. 4·22.

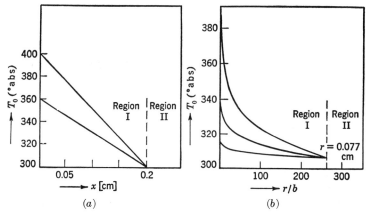

FIG. 4·22 Graphical representation of the formulas for the stationary temperature distribution; (a) near a thin foil, and (b) near a fine wire. (After Geffcken and Keibs.[34])

The final equation relating p_1 in the cavity whose volume is V_0 to the current flowing in a *thin metal foil* whose total area is $2S$ is

$$p_1 = \frac{\sqrt{2}\,P_0\gamma}{V_0 T_a \alpha_{\theta_0}} \times \frac{0.478RI_0I_1}{[(\beta\omega)^2 + 4(\beta\omega)(\alpha_{\theta_0}K_{\theta_0}) + 8(K_{\theta_0}\alpha_{\theta_0})^2]^{1/2}} \quad (4\cdot76)$$

where

$$K_{\theta_0} = K_0 \left[\frac{\theta_0}{273} \right]^{1/2} \quad (4\cdot77)$$

and

$$\alpha_{\theta_0} = \sqrt{\frac{\rho_0 c_p \omega}{2K_0}} \left(\frac{273}{\theta_0} \right)^{3/4} \quad (4\cdot78)$$

As will be discussed later, Geffcken and Keibs concluded from their experimental data, which was obtained by comparing the sound pressures generated by two types of wire thermophone with one type of foil thermophone, that α_{θ_0} should be replaced by

$$\alpha_{T_a} = \sqrt{\frac{\rho_0 c_p \omega}{2 K_0}} \left(\frac{273}{T_a}\right)^{3/4} \tag{4.79}$$

Their justification for making a change in α_{θ_0} to some quantity at least nearer α_{T_a} is that the thermal wave emitted from the surface of the foil is actually not plane, as it was assumed to be in the derivation. Certainly, at the edges of the foil, the wave front becomes nearly cylindrical. A substantially plane wave at other parts can be achieved only if the breadth of the foil is made very large. The foil must not come too close to the boundaries of the chamber, or the theory breaks down. On the other hand, the smaller the foil is made, the greater is the influence of the boundary in determining the mean temperature distribution in the volume.

For *wires of small diameter*, if frequencies in the audible range and a cavity whose dimensions are small compared to a wavelength of sound are assumed,

$$p_1 = \frac{0.956 P_0 \gamma K_0 \alpha_{T_a}}{4\pi^2 \rho_{T_a} T_a c_p V_0 \beta'} \left(\frac{T_a}{273}\right)^{3/2} \frac{I_0 R}{\phi(f)} I_1 \tag{4.80}$$

where

$$\phi(f) = f^2 \left[\left(\frac{L}{\pi}\right)^2 + \left(\frac{2K}{\omega\beta'}\right)^2 + \frac{K}{\omega\beta'} + \frac{1}{16}\right]^{1/2} \tag{4.81}$$

and

$$L = 0.577 + \ln\left(\alpha_{T_a}\frac{a}{\sqrt{2}}\right) \tag{4.82}$$

and

$$K = K_{\theta_0} \tag{4.83}$$

The factor $\phi(f)$ is dependent on frequency and its values for two diameters of wire; that is, 6μ and 10μ (cm $\times$ 10^{-6}) are given as a function of frequency in Fig. 4·23. Typical values of p_1 *vs.* frequency for foil and wire thermophones are shown in Fig. 4·24.

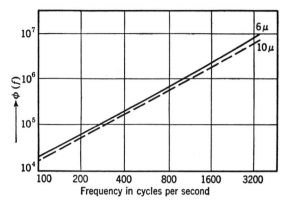

FIG. 4·23 Plot of the factor $\phi(f)$ as a function of frequency.

The Wente formula for foils in the notation of this text with negligibly small terms omitted is

$$p_1 = \frac{0.478RI_0I_1}{\dfrac{V_0T_a\alpha_{\theta_0}}{\sqrt{2}\,P_0}\left(1 - \dfrac{\gamma-1}{\gamma}\dfrac{\theta_0}{T_a}\right)[(\beta\omega)^2 + 8(\alpha_{\theta_0}K_{\theta_0})^2 + 4(\beta\omega)(\alpha_{\theta_0}K_{\theta_0}]^{\frac{1}{2}}}$$

(4·84)

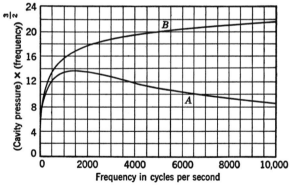

FIG. 4·24 Frequency characteristics of thermophones; (A) fine wire, (B) thin foil. (After Wente.[31])

Wente gives a first-order correction term for the case of zero temperature at the side walls by which Eq. (4·84) is to be multiplied.   The term is

$$\sqrt{1 - \frac{S_w}{V_0 \alpha_{\theta_0}} + \frac{S_w^2}{2 V_0^2 \alpha_{\theta_0}^2}} \qquad (4 \cdot 85)$$

where S_w is the total area of the side walls.

A comparison of Eq. (4·76) with the uncorrected formula of Wente shows one difference, namely, that the factor $1 - (\gamma - 1)(\theta_0/T_a\gamma)$ in the Wente formula has been replaced by $1/\gamma$. This difference comes about because Wente did not take into account the convection effects in the chamber; therefore his region I extended out to the boundaries of the chamber where the ambient temperature was assumed to be T_a. Moreover, he assumed that the oscillating temperature at the bounding walls was the same as that which would have existed if the walls had the same heat impedance as an infinite thickness of gas. The proper boundary condition at the walls is $T_1 = 0$.

The effect of the difference in the factors $1/\gamma$ and $1 - (\gamma - 1)$ $(\theta_0/T_a\gamma)$ reveals itself primarily when the temperature of the conductor is much higher than that of the side walls of the chamber. Geffcken and Keibs showed that, with a wire whose radius is 10μ, the results of the two formulas are the same for currents of less than 0.015 amp, and with a wire of radius 6μ the value is 0.005 amp. Above those values of current, the calculated curves show an increase in p_1/I_0 with increasing θ_0, while the measurements show that the quantity remains constant. With Eq. (4·80) that difficulty is removed.

Experimental Setup. A sketch of the active element of a foil thermophone was shown in Fig. 4·21. The metal foil is generally constructed to have a thickness between 1 and 10×10^{-6} cm and an area of $S = 5$ to 10 sq cm. The material of the foil is usually either gold or platinum. The wire thermophone is constructed in the same manner, except that very small supporting posts are possible. Wollaston* wire is generally used in diameters between 5×10^{-6} and 100×10^{-6} cm. The silver coating on Wollaston wire should be removed by an electrolytic process[37] and the wire then washed many times in hot water and

---

* Wollaston wire is a very fine wire made of platinum and first used by Wollaston for cross hairs in telescope eyepieces.

[37] E. Woetzman, M. Gnielinski, and H. Heisig, "Wollaston wires and foils and their application as resistance thermometers," *Zeits. f. Physik*, **58**, 449–469 (1929) (in German).

alcohol. If the foil of a foil thermophone is prepared from rolled Wollaston wire, final annealing appears to be advantageous in order to remove completely the layer of moisture which remains over its relatively large surface after the washing.

The clamping members which secure the ends of the gold foil should be provided with pins which are engaged by holes in the supporting blocks to avoid tearing of the foil by movement of the clamping members when the screws are tightened. These pins may be made from the ends of ordinary sewing needles. The use of insulating supporting blocks and clamping members to reduce the conduction of heat from the foil or the wires into the side walls of the cavity is recommended.

The dimensions of the cavity, the electrical circuit, the means for introducing gases into the cavity, and the general experimental precautions to be taken are the same as those outlined for the reciprocity method preceding.

Calibration and Use. One of the first things which must be determined is the temperature of the conductor. Two different methods may be used. For either method, the first step is to pass a direct current I_0 through the conductor and to measure the resistance R, using a Wheatstone bridge for a range of values of I_0. For wires whose diameters are of the order of 5 to 10 $\times$ 10^{-6} cm, the current will be of the order of 0.01 to 0.2 amp. For foils, however, the current will need to be roughly 50 times that value, and a compensation type of apparatus for measuring the resistance is recommended. The next step is to obtain a relation between the resistance R and the temperature of the conductor θ_0.

For the first method, the thermophone is placed in an oven whose temperature is accurately known. The resistance of the wire is determined with the aid of a Wheatstone bridge if the wire is used, or a Thompson bridge if a foil is used. Very small alternating currents are used in order not to increase the temperature of the wire measurably. The oven temperature is varied, and a plot of R *vs.* θ_0 is obtained. From the two sets of curves the function θ_0 *vs.* I_0 is determinable.

By the second method the temperature of the conductor is calculated from a knowledge of the temperature coefficient of the metal. The chief difficulty of this type of measurement is that, if the coefficient of the metal is not known, a chemical assay of the metal must be obtained, and whether the temperature coeffi-

cient for a thin foil is the same as that for the solid metal must
be known.

If the above determination of θ_0 *vs.* I_0 has been carried out in
air and if the current required to produce a given conductor
temperature in, say, hydrogen is desired, it can readily be computed as follows: Let ΔT_1 and ΔT_2 represent, for air and hydrogen,
respectively, the difference in temperatures of the strip and the
enclosure walls. Let I_{01} and I_{02} represent the corresponding
steady currents. Then, since ΔT is proportional to I_0^2/κ,

$$\frac{I_{01}^2}{I_{02}^2} = \frac{\Delta T_1}{\Delta T_2} = \frac{\kappa_1}{\kappa_2}$$

$$I_{02} = I_{01}\sqrt{\frac{\kappa_2}{\kappa_1}}$$

(4·86)

where κ is the coefficient of thermal conductivity of the gas (see
Chapter 2).

At high frequencies, when the amplitude of the a-c component
of the current I_1 may be made large, it is necessary to remember
that the total heating effect is proportional to $I_0^2 + (I_1^2/2)$,
and to vary I_0 to keep this quantity and T_{s0} and T_a constant.
The second harmonic component will become large if I_1 is not
negligible compared to I_0.

Accuracy. Cook[35] and Franke[38] have reported on the accuracy of the thermophone. Cook used the formula given by Ballantine[33] to compute his results, whereas Franke used that of
Geffcken and Keibs; see Eqs. (4·76) and (4·80). Cook's calculations give a pressure which is greater by 1.5 to 2.0 db for hydrogen
and 2.0 to 2.5 db for air than that which he observed by a reciprocity method. Those differences are substantially independent
of frequency and much greater than the estimated probable error
of individual points (±0.2 db). The calculations for helium were
even farther removed from the reciprocity observations, the
figure being 2.3 to 2.8 db.

Franke's results were somewhat different. He used a thermophone with a Wollaston wire 5.6×10^{-6} cm in diameter, a cavity
volume of 13.6 cm³, and a current of 18 ma. He measured the
pressure in the cavity by a statically calibrated microphone. By

[38] E. Franke, "Experimental verification of the thermophone theory,"
Ann. d. Physik, **20**, 780–782 (1934) (in German).

this process of calibration the force acting on the diaphragm due to the sound was compensated for by means of an opposing, measurable electric force. When the forces were made equal, the diaphragm was at rest, and its impedance was infinitely large. The pressure in the cavity was calculated to be *less* than that measured by about 0.7 db, and the difference was substantially independent of frequency.

The reasons for these differences can be found by taking the ratio of the pressure as calculated for wires by the Geffcken and Keibs formula to that calculated by the Wente formula. The result is

$$\frac{p_G}{p_w} = \frac{\gamma \rho_0 (1 - 0.001\theta_0)}{\rho T_a} \left(\frac{T_a}{\theta_0} \right) \qquad (4 \cdot 87)$$

If it is assumed that the ambient temperature is approximately 300°K and that the temperature of the wire is approximately 400°K,

$$\frac{p_G}{p_w} = 0.6 = -4.4 \text{ db}$$

For foils the ratio of the pressures calculated by the Geffcken and Keibs formula to that calculated by the Wente formula is

$$\frac{p_G}{p_w} = \left[\gamma - (\gamma - 1) \frac{\theta_0}{T_a} \right] \left[\frac{T_a}{\theta_0} \right]^{3/4} \qquad (4 \cdot 88)$$

If it is assumed that the temperature of the foil θ_0 is 350°K and the ambient temperature T_a is 300°K,

$$\frac{p_G}{p_w} = 0.836 = -1.55 \quad \text{db}$$

This difference is about the order of magnitude of that found by Cook. Hence, Eqs. $(4 \cdot 76)$ to $(4 \cdot 83)$ should yield results very nearly correct.

In summary, it appears that the formula of Geffcken and Keibs yields results nearer to fact (reciprocity and Rayleigh disk determinations) than do the formulas of Wente and Ballantine. On the basis of the data available from Cook, it appears that, in air, the pressure generated is *less* than that calculated by the Wente formula by 1.0 to 3.0 db, whereas it is *greater* than that calculated by the Geffcken and Keibs formula by 0 to 1.0 db.

B. Pistonphone

The pistonphone was extensively used for the absolute calibration of condenser and crystal types of microphones at low
frequencies before the advent of the reciprocity technique.[39]
Today it is used widely for field calibrations.[40,41]

In its essentials, the pistonphone consists of a rigid-walled
chamber, terminated on one side by the microphone under test
and connected to a small cylinder on the opposite side. In this
cylinder, a piston moves in and out with a sinusoidal motion. If
the rms amplitude of motion of the piston on either side of its
mean position is d, the rms sound pressure produced in the
cavity will be

$$p = \frac{dA_p\, P_0\gamma}{V} \qquad (4\cdot89)$$

where $V =$ effective volume of the enclosure with the piston
in its mean position. (The effective volume includes the volume of the cavity plus the equivalent volume of the microphone diaphragm.)

$P_0 =$ atmospheric pressure
$\gamma =$ ratio of specific heats for the gas
$A_p =$ area of piston
$d =$ rms amplitude of motion of piston, where a positive sign indicates an inward movement of the
piston.

It is assumed in the above equation that $A_p d \ll V$. Equation
(4·89) may also be written

$$p = UZ_a = (j\omega dA_p)\left(\frac{1}{j\omega\left(\dfrac{V}{\gamma P_0}\right)}\right) = \frac{dA_p}{C_a} \qquad (4\cdot90)$$

where $C_a = \dfrac{V}{\gamma P_0} =$ acoustic compliance

$U =$ volume velocity, in $cm^3\ sec^{-1}$
$Z_a =$ acoustic impedance, in dynes sec cm^{-5}.

[39]G. W. C. Kaye, "Acoustical work of the National Physical Laboratory," J.
Acoust. Soc. Am. **7**, 167–177 (1936).

[40]"Pistonphone for acoustic calibration," Type 4220, Bruel & Kjaer, 185 Forest Street, Marlborough, MA 01752.

[41]American National Standard, "Specification for Acoustical Calibrators,"
ANSI S1.40-1984, Acoustical Society of America.

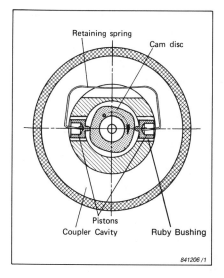

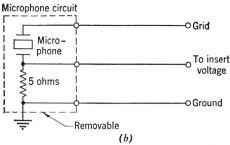

FIG. 4·25 Sketch of electromagnetically driven pistonphone.[40]

As in the reciprocity technique, the value of C_a must be corrected to account for heat conduction at the walls of the cavity. Corrections have been given in Fig. 4·14. The device shown in Fig. 4·25 consists of two small pistons, driven in opposite directions by a precision cam. For a fixed frequency controlled by a tachometer, the sound pressure is accurate to within ± 0.15 dB.

C. Electrostatic Actuator

At very high frequencies, pressure calibrations of microphones using a coupler and the reciprocity technique or a vibrating piston are not feasible because of wave motion in the

cavity. Today, many laboratories are using an earlier apparatus, the electrostatic actuator,[33] for obtaining pressure calibrations of miniature condenser microphones. The electrostatic actuator consists of a fixed slotted plate mounted very near the
diaphragm of the microphone. An alternating plus a steady
potential are applied between the slotted plate and the diaphragm. The electrostatic potential developed between two solid plates under these conditions is given by

$$p(t) = \frac{1}{8\pi d^2} \left(E_0{}^2 + \frac{E_1{}^2}{2} \right) + \frac{1}{4\pi d^2} E_0 E_1 \sin \omega t$$
$$- \frac{1}{16\pi d^2} E_1{}^2 \cos 2\omega t \qquad (4\cdot91)$$

where E_0 = steady potential, in electrostatic volts
$E_1 \sin \omega t$ = alternating potential, in electrostatic volts
   d = separation of the solid plates from the dia-
         phragm, in centimeters
   ω = angular frequency, in cycles.

Note: The ratio of the number of practical volts to the number of
electrostatic volts is 300.

   In actual practice, this equation must be modified to take account of
the slots in the driving plate. These slots are introduced to minimize
the acoustic loading on the diaphragm. Let us consider the cross-
sectional sketch of the actuator in Fig. 4·26. The grill sections have a
width W and the slots a width S. If the slots are deep compared to S, it
is theoretically permissible when speaking electrically to replace the

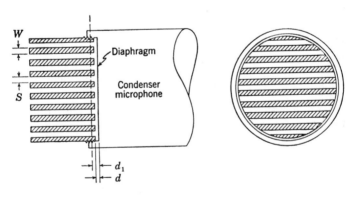

FIG. 4·26 Cross-sectional sketch of an electrostatic actuator mounted in
front of the diaphragm of a condenser microphone.

grill by a solid plate with a new spacing d_1.[33] For a grill of the type shown in Fig. 4·26, the ratio d_1/d has been computed for various values of W/S and W/d. These results are shown in Fig. 4·27.[42] If we replace d by d_1 and make $E_1 \ll E_0$, then Eq. (4·91) becomes, in practical units,

$$p = \frac{8.85E_0e}{d_1{}^2} 10^{-7} \tag{4·92}$$

where p = rms pressure, in dyne cm^{-2}
          E_0 = direct polarizing potential, in volts
          e = rms alternating potential, in volts.

The accuracy of the ratio d_1/d given in Fig. 4·27 with reference to any particular application may be checked by the reciprocity method at low frequencies. If a discrepancy is found, a constant correction factor may be employed over the entire frequency range.

The important advantage of this method is that a uniform pressure is obtained over the surface of the diaphragm, independent of frequen-

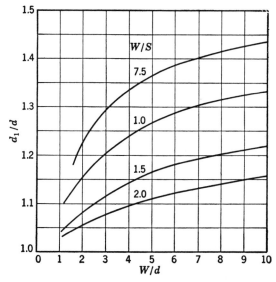

FIG. 4·27 Values of d_1/d vs W/d, where d is the actual separation between the actuator and the disphragm, d_1 is the separation of a hypothetical actuator with no slots, W is the width of each metal plate, and S is the width of the slots between the plates.

[42]H. F. Olson and F. Massa, *Applied Acoustics*, Blakiston's Son & Co. (1939).

cy, atmospheric pressure, and density and ratio of specific heats of the gas. In addition, because no new electrical circuitry is required, the method is a logical extension of the highly accurate reciprocity technique to ultrasonic frequencies.

As the distance between the microphone diaphragm and the actuator must be small and the sound pressure varies inversely to the square of that separation, accurate calibrations are difficult. If the calibration of the microphone at a low frequency is made with another primary method, the electrostatic actuator is valuable in determining the relative pressure response as a function of frequency.

5.

Microphones and Ears

5·1 Introduction

Every investigator setting out to make sound measurements is aware that a microphone is a device which translates acoustic energy into electric energy. Nearly always there is a membrane of some sort which responds either to the pressure or to the particle velocity of the sound wave. The motion of this membrane or the force it transmits is converted into alternating electromotive force or electric current by some kind of transducing element.

A. Function

Since a microphone is essentially a transducing device it is usually desirable that its electrical output be a faithful undistorted image of the sound pressure or particle velocity acting on it. Furthermore, the factor of proportionality between the electric output and the acoustic input (the response) should remain constant from one time to another. Practical microphones may fall short of ideal performance in several ways. Noise or induced signals may be present when no acoustic signal is applied. Nonlinear distortion can generate harmonics from a pure tone and cause the appearance of sum and difference frequencies when two or more pure tones are involved. Frequency distortion may suppress or accentuate some frequencies. Phase distortion, which delays the response of a microphone to different frequencies by different amounts, is likely to be present. The sensitivity of the microphone may change as a result of temperature, humidity, or ambient pressure changes, rough usage, or age.

Much can be done to reduce these imperfections in a particular microphone if their nature and magnitude are known. It is easy to cancel changes in sensitivity by compensatory changes in attenuation or amplification of the electric signal. When phase and frequency distortion are not too violent they can be canceled, over a limited frequency range, by electric equalizing networks. Induced signals may be excluded by shielding or shortening leads. Nevertheless, the choice of the proper microphone for a specific application is not a trivial matter, and a discussion of the behavior to be expected from specific types is worthwhile.

Microphones may be divided into classes according to the service for which they are intended. In speech communication systems of telephone quality, more·nonlinearity, frequency discrimination, and internal noise can be tolerated than in motion picture recording, sound recording, or radio broadcasting. On the other hand, the radio broadcaster can tolerate sensitivity changes which would not please the man who makes absolute measurements. Microphones suitable for underwater use, for studies of explosion shock waves, for detecting a single frequency, for ultrasonic use have been constructed. Such instruments are often adapted to a specific purpose only at the sacrifice of other desirable properties.[1]

B. Variables

When choosing a microphone for a specific purpose one should consider the nature of the sound field, the important characteristics of the sounds which are to be measured, and the environmental conditions under which the microphone will be operated. Table 5·1 contains a list of factors the importance of which should at least be estimated.

C. Purpose of Chapter

This chapter is designed to show the experimenter how to select that microphone which best fits his requirements. Having listed some criteria for judging quality, we consider in the next section some specific properties which are common to all ordinary microphones, and which explain their interaction with the sound field. After discussing free-field effects we relate the acoustic impedance of the microphone diaphragm to the role it plays in chamber measurements.

In Section 5·3 we discuss another property common to all

---

[1] L. L. Beranek, *Acoustics* (McGraw-Hill, New York, 1954, 2nd ed. by Acoustical Society of America, 1986).

microphones, namely, self-noise. Self-noise arises from thermal agitation in the resistive component of the internal impedance of the microphone, or it may arise from random motion of the air molecules which actuate the microphone.

Then in Section 5·4, without attempting to describe all microphones, we give a more detailed description and discussion of examples of the more common types, prefacing these with a discussion of the human ear. Sectional views, typical circuits, and acoustical properties of five principal types, including carbon, condenser, dynamic, ribbon, and crystal, are presented.

Section 5·5 deals in a general way with directional arrays of microphones. Section 5·6 describes some microphone housings suitable for measurements in medium and high velocity winds. Finally, Section 5·7 describes a method for measuring sound intensity.

TABLE 5·1 SOME FACTORS TO CONSIDER IN CHOOSING A MICROPHONE

A. Expected properties of sound field
    1. Free field or closed chamber
    2. Density and wave velocity in the medium
    3. Important range of sound pressure level
    4. Important frequency range.

B. Desired precision of measurement
    1. Sensitivity tolerance
    2. Frequency distortion tolerance
    3. Phase distortion tolerance
    4. Non-linear distortion tolerance
    5. Self-noise tolerance

C. Environmental conditions of measurement
    1. Background noise level
    2. Temperature
    3. Humidity
    4. Atmospheric pressure
    5. Wind
    6. Strong electromagnetic fields
    7. Mechanical shock
    8. Weight and space limitations

The experimental procedures for determining the various characteristics discussed in this chapter are described in detail in Chapters 13, 14, and 16.

5·2 Microphones in Sound Fields

Air is a very light material. In the absence of confining walls it has a characteristic acoustic impedance of about 41 rayls (see Chapter 2). All the common microphone diaphragms have a comparatively high acoustic impedance. Even the ribbon pressure gradient microphone has a specific acoustic impedance above 200 rayls. We are therefore justified in looking on any microphone as a rigid body, at least for the purpose of predicting its interaction with sound waves in a free field.

A. Free Field

The maximum dimensions as well as the minimum dimensions of most microphones are in the range of 0.25 to 1 in. This size is selected for various reasons, not the least of which are mechanical manufacturing tolerances. When considering the size of a microphone we have to include the housing for any auxiliary amplifier or transformer which is intimately associated with the actual pickup device. In air the speed of sound is approximately 13,000 in./sec; therefore, at some frequency below 20,000 cps within the audible range, the dimensions of a microphone become comparable with the dimensions of sound waves.

Diffraction. When the impinging sound waves are comparable to the dimensions of the microphone, a kind of external resonance effect takes place. The sound pressure distribution on the surface of the microphone is dependent upon the combination of the reflected (scattered) wave with the incident wave. The manner in which the sound pressure varies over the surfaces of spheres and cylinders has been discussed in Chapter 3. Naturally the distribution of this reflected or scattered wave, known as the diffraction pattern, depends both on the shape of the microphone housing and on the direction from which the incident sound comes. Sometimes it is possible to separate this complex effect into relatively simple components.[2] Many microphones, particularly among the older types, have flat diaphragms recessed in a shallow cavity. Rigorously this cavity should be considered part of the microphone housing, but it is suggestive to think of it as a very short open-ended resonator tube. Above the fundamental resonant condition of this cavity

---

[2]H. C. Harrison and P. B. Flanders, "An efficient miniature condenser microphone system," Bell Syst. Tech. J. 11, 451–461 (1932).

there is a sucession of higher resonances which reinforce or cancel the incident wave. It is not uncommon to adjust this cavity resonance to compensate for resonances in the diaphragm or internal mechanical structure of a microphone.

At very high frequencies a microphone may be several wavelengths in diameter. Under these circumstances it acts like a reflecting wall; that is to say, it returns a wave nearly equal in magnitude to the incident wave, but oppositely directed. The sum of the pressure amplitudes of these two waves at the microphone is twice the pressure amplitude of the incident wave, and this phenomenon gives rise to the so-called pressure-doubling effect.

The importance of these two phases of diffraction in practical microphones may be judged from Fig. 5·1 where data are plotted from experimental measurements. Pressure doubling, or

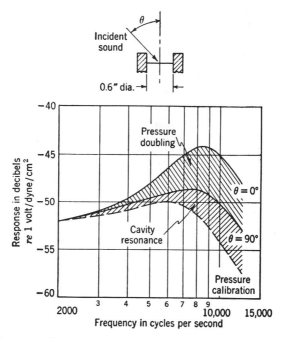

FIG. 5·1 Response of a pressure-actuated microphone with a recessed diaphragm at two angles of incidence. The lower curve is the response with a constant sound pressure at the face of the diaphragm. The $\theta = 90°$ curve is the response to a plane sound wave at grazing incidence to the diaphragm. The $\theta = 0°$ curve is the response to a plane sound wave at normal incidence to the diaphragm.

even tripling, present when the wave is incident on the diaphragm perpendicularly in a free field, is missing in the curve for grazing incidence ($\theta = 90°$). Cavity resonance is missing when the diaphragm is electrostatically driven, or when the microphone is calibrated by the closed chamber reciprocity method described in the previous chapter; hence we obtain the so-called pressure calibration.

When the dimensions of a microphone housing are comparable with the wavelength of an incident sound, the back of the housing plays an important role. It is important that the housing of the microphone, or at least that part of it which reflects sound, should be small so that diffraction effects will be confined to the higher frequency part of the sound spectrum.

All these external resonances affect the response of a microphone to incident sound, accentuating certain frequencies and suppressing others. It is very difficult, except for the simplest

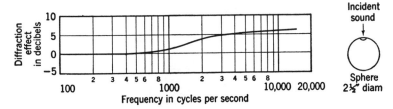

FIG. 5·2 Ratio of sound pressure at the point indicated on a sphere 2.5 in. in diameter to the free-field sound pressure. More general curves are presented in Chap. 3.

shapes of housing, to get a complete analytical picture of the diffraction pattern. Perhaps this is one reason why many modern microphones are externally simple in shape. The analytical approach consists in adding in proper manner a series of solutions of the wave equation. The process, however, is useful only for a few simple shapes such as spheres and cylinders, which were discussed in Chapter 3.

However, it is not hard to estimate the frequency range in which this source of frequency distortion is important. For example, we see in Fig. 5·2 the calculated diffraction effects[3] for a

[3]R. N. Marshall and F. F. Romanow, "A non-directional microphone," Bell Syst. Tech. J. **15**, 405–423 (1936); F. M. Wiener, "Sound diffraction by rigid spheres and circular cylinders," J. Acoust. Soc. Am. **19**, 444–451 (1947).

spherical microphone. We can roughly approximate any compact housing shape by an equivalent sphere. The first frequency at which the diffraction effects reach a maximum, that is, the fundamental resonance frequency of diffraction, is related to the diameter of this sphere and can be estimated from Fig. 5·3. We must remember, however, that this method does not give the details of the frequency response curve at higher frequencies, since they depend on the details of the housing shape.

When microphones are used under ordinary conditions it is often sufficient to rely on the average frequency response

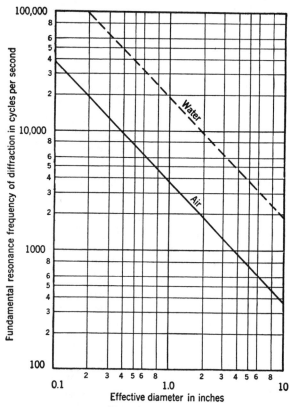

FIG. 5·3 Graph of the first frequency (approximate) at which diffraction effects reach a maximum as a function of the effective diameter, in inches.

curves supplied in the literature of the manufacturer. These curves generally include diffraction effects along with the effects of diaphragm and internal resonances and built-in acous-

tic networks. The latter three effects vary in production; consequently, when precise experiments are to be made, individual
calibrations are necessary. Also, in media other than air or at
temperatures quite far from normal ambient temperatures we
find that the diffraction effects shift along the frequency scale.
In gases this shift is a matter of the speed of sound alone. The
speed of sound is given by $(\gamma P_0 / \rho_0)^{1/2}$ (see p. **39**). However, P_0 / ρ_0
is proportional to variation in absolute temperature only.
Hence, the speed of sound is independent of pressure. Table 2·7
(Chap. 2) gives the speed of sound for several different gaseous
media. We must remember, however, that it may be incorrect
to shift the whole frequency response curve to adjust it to dras-
tic changes in sound speed, because internal effects which were
adjusted to cancel diffraction effects partially do not change
with sound speed.

A different approach must be taken for microphones used in
liquid or solid media. There the diaphragm impedance is no
longer large, and it may even be small compared to the impedance of the medium. From the standpoint of analysis, the problem remains the same, but the boundary conditions in the equations are somewhat more complex. Thus we can still derive the
fundamental resonance frequency of diffraction from the dimensions of the pickup housing in terms of wavelengths in the
liquid; but now the amplitude of the diffraction effect depends
on a different set of characteristics of the medium than is the
case with gases. Fortunately, however, sound speeds in liquids
are high enough so that, for audio frequencies, microphones
(called hydrophones) are small compared to a wavelength. Most
sound sources in the lower ultrasonic range generate pressures
great enough so that very small pickups, like the one shown in
Fig. 5·4, are sufficiently sensitive.

Directionality. Diffraction also causes preferential response
to sounds coming from certain directions. A pressure microphone is generally intended to measure the pressure which
would exist in the sound field if the microphone were not there.
Ideally, it should be equally sensitive to waves from all directions. Most pressure microphones are small enough so that
they do not affect the sound pressure in low frequency waves.
At very high frequencies where their dimensions are many
wavelengths, they cast an "optical" shadow. But in the upper
audio range, where wavelengths and housing dimensions are

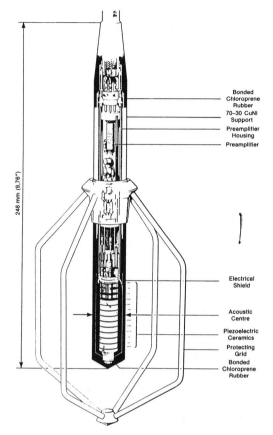

Bonded
Chloroprene
Rubber
70-30 CuNi
Support
Preamplifier
Housing
Preamplifier

Electrical
Shield

Acoustic
Centre

Piezoelectric
Ceramics
Protecting
Grid
Bonded
Chloroprene
Rubber

248 mm (9.76')

Fɪɢ. 5·4 Cross-sectional sketch of a B&K type 8101 hydrophone. In water it is sufficiently small to be entirely free from diffraction effects up to about 30,000 cps. (Courtesy Bruel & Kjaer.)

comparable, many directional effects occur which are not immediately obvious.

Again it is possible to find the directional pattern of simple shapes by mathematical analysis of the boundary problem, but it is usually done by experiment. Since most microphones are almost symmetrical, only the angle which the sound wave makes with the axis of symmetry need be given. As an example of a directional characteristic we give a polar plot (Fig. 5·5) for a German[4] dynamic pressure microphone basically spherical in

[4]W. Baer, "A new dynamic microphone," Akust. Z. **8**, 127–135 (1943) (in German).

shape. Data like these are often given as a series of frequency response curves at various specific angles of incidence.

Pressure gradient microphones, which measure essentially the difference between pressures at two points close to each other, suffer less from diffraction effects. They are essentially bidirectional at all frequencies, but at high frequencies the response along the principal axis is decreased by diffraction effects.

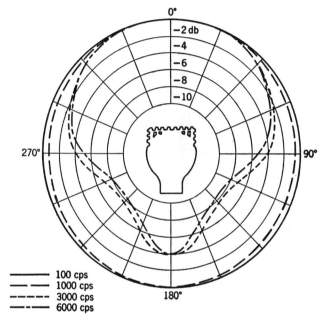

FIG. 5·5   Directional characteristics for a spherical microphone with protective grid. (After Baer.[4])

B. Chamber Measurements

One should clearly understand that all the preceding discussion, in so far as the diaphragm impedance is considered very large, applies only to free-field conditions. In chamber or impedance tube measurements, where the microphone diaphragm forms one wall of the chamber, the diaphragm impedance can no longer be neglected. Furthermore, the chamber itself, if it is small, controls the distribution of the sound field, and diffraction effects from the microphone cannot be treated independently.

Diaphragm Microphones. In chamber measurements, the source produces a small alternating change in the volume of the chamber, which in turn produces an alternating change in pressure throughout the chamber. Air at atmospheric pressure confined in a small volume is quite stiff. A stiffness-controlled (compliant) diaphragm forming part of a wall of a small chamber substantially reduces the pressure rise which accompanies a given volume change. In this sense the compliant diaphragm acts like an extra volume of air; therefore impedance is often expressed in terms of cubic centimeters of air at atmospheric pressure. Resistance-controlled and mass-controlled diaphragms have impedances which can also be expressed in cubic centimeters of standard air, but the number of cubic centimeters for these diaphragms is inversely proportional to the first or second power of the frequency, whereas for stiffness-controlled diaphragms the number of cubic centimeters is independent of frequency.

Probe Microphones. In many acoustic measurements, it is necessary that a very small microphone be used in order not to disturb the sound field appreciably. Such microphones are generally constructed by adding a small probe tube to a larger sized microphone. As one looks into the end of such a probe tube the acoustic impedance will be equal to that calculated for the tube terminated by the impedance of the microphone and its coupling chamber.

A typical arrangement for a probe tube[5] is shown in the upper part of Fig. 16·15 on p. 721. There a probe tube of 0.025-in. inside diameter is connected with a W.E. 640-AA condenser microphone whose characteristics are given in Section 5·4C. As can be seen from the calibration curve of Fig. 5·6 suggestions of resonances appear at several frequencies. If the bore of the tube were larger, these resonances would become more pronounced. For tubes wherein the diameter is small enough that the resonances are suppressed, the *added* attenuation produced by an increment in length may be estimated from the formulas which follow.

Rayleigh[6] gives the following formula for the real part of the

[5] R. H. Nichols, Jr., R. J. Marquis, W. G. Wiklund, A. S. Filler, D. B. Feer, and P. S. Veneklasen, "Electro-acoustical characteristics of hearing aids," Section I, O.S.R.D. Report 4666, Harvard University, Cambridge, Massachusetts. This report is not available to the public.

[6] Lord Rayleigh, *Theory of Sound*, §350, Vol. 2, p. 325, Macmillan and Company, Ltd. (1940).

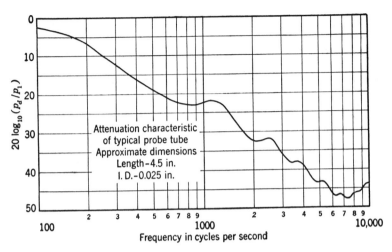

$20 \log_{10} (p_d/p_1)$

Attenuation characteristic
of typical probe tube
Approximate dimensions
Length–4.5 in.
I. D.–0.025 in.

Frequency in cycles per second

Fig. 5·6 Calibration curve for probe tube of the upper part of Fig. 16·15,
p. 733, to be subtracted from basic calibration curve for W.E. 640-AA
microphone.   (Courtesy R. H. Nichols, Jr.)

propagation constant for tubes which are not too small in
diameter:

$$\text{Attenuation constant} = \frac{\sqrt{2\omega}}{cd}\left[\sqrt{\nu} + (\gamma - 1)\sqrt{\frac{\alpha}{\gamma}}\right]$$

$$= \frac{A}{\sqrt{\lambda}\, d} \quad \text{nepers/cm} \quad (5\cdot1)$$

where d = diameter of tube, in centimeters
   λ = wavelength of sound, in centimeters
   ν = kinematic coefficient of viscosity, in square centi-
       meters per second (see Chapter 2)
   c = velocity of sound, in centimeters per second
   γ = ratio of specific heats for air = 1.4
   α = coefficient of temperature exchange, in square centi-
       meters per second (see Chapter 2)
   ω = angular frequency = $2\pi f$
   A = constant for the particular gas, ambient pressure, and
       temperature existing; for air at 17°C, A = 0.0108.

For very small capillary tubes, Rayleigh gives

$$\text{Attenuation constant} = \frac{4\sqrt{\nu\omega\gamma}}{cd} = \frac{B}{\sqrt{\lambda}\, d} \quad \text{nepers/cm} \quad (5\cdot2)$$

For air at 17°C, the constant $B = 0.0248$. This equation should be used when $\sqrt{4\pi\nu/f}$ is comparable to the radius of the tube. For air at 17°C this quantity simplifies to $1.4/\sqrt{f}$. To convert to decibels per centimeter the above equations should be multiplied by 8.69.

May[7] gives experimental data on the attenuation of sound in capillary tubes at ultrasonic frequencies. His results are tabu-

TABLE 5·2

Frequency, kc	Tube Radius, cm	Temp., °C	Attenuation	
			nepers/cm	db/cm
39.1	0.073	16.7	0.18	1.56
	0.0585	14.7	0.22	1.91
	0.0295	17.2	0.52	4.5
58.0	0.073	14.5	0.27	2.3
	0.0585	14.7	0.33	2.9
	0.0317	14.4	0.55	4.8
90.0	0.073	19.8	0.32	2.8
	0.0317	19.6	0.60	5.2
115	0.073	18.3	0.25	2.2
	0.0585	18.1	0.38	3.3
	0.0317	18.0	0.73	6.3

lated in Table 5·2. These values are found to be about three times as great as those calculated from Eq. (5·1). Equation (5·1) should be valid for the frequency range and size of tubes which he used. Other experimenters have obtained similar results.

5·3 Self-Noise

Even if it were possible to place a microphone in an environment in which there is absolute quiet, a randomly fluctuating voltage would be produced at its output. The voltage arises from the thermal agitation in the resistive part of the electrical impedance as measured at the terminals of the microphone. For this measurement the microphone would need to be located

[7] J. May, "The propagation of supersonics in capillary tubes," *Proc. Phys. Soc.*, **50**, 553–560 (1938).

in an acoustic environment presenting the customary acoustic impedance to the diaphragm and free of ambient noise except for that noise caused by thermal agitation of the air molecules.

The ambient noise voltage at the electrical terminals of the microphone is composed of three parts: that from the electrical resistance measured with the diaphragm blocked; that from the motional component of the resistance due to the real part of the mechanical admittance; and that from the motional component of the resistance due to the real part of the acoustic admittance.

Schottky,[8] Johnson and Llewellyn,[9] and many others have discussed this problem.   Mathematically, the self-noise produced by a microphone is given by

$$e_{tot.} = \sqrt{4kT \int_{f_1}^{f_2} R(f)\, df} \qquad (5 \cdot 3)$$

where $e_{tot.}$ = rms open-circuit voltage in the total band between f_1 and f_2 cps

$\quad k$ = Boltzmann gas constant equal to 1.37×10^{-23} joule/°K

$\quad T$ = absolute temperature, in degrees Kelvin

$\quad R(f)$ = resistive component of the electrical impedance of the microphone, in ohms; in general, a function of frequency

$\quad f_1, f_2$ = the limiting frequencies of the pass band.

Often, we express the rms voltage as a function of frequency for a band 1 cycle wide.   Then

$$e = \sqrt{4kTR(f)} \qquad (5 \cdot 4)$$

If the microphone has a terminal impedance whose resistive component R is constant with frequency, the total rms open-circuit voltage produced between the frequency limits f_1 and f_2 is

$$e_{tot.} = \sqrt{4kTR(f_2 - f_1)} \qquad (5 \cdot 5)$$

At a temperature of 23°C, this expression becomes

$$e_{tot.} = 1.27 \times 10^{-10} \sqrt{R(f_2 - f_1)} \qquad (5 \cdot 6)$$

This equation is valid for the calculation of open-circuit self-

[8] W. Schottky, "On spontaneous current fluctuations in various electric conductors," *Ann. d. Physik.*, **57**, 541–567 (1918) (in German).

[9] J. B. Johnson and F. B. Llewellyn, "Limits to amplification," *Bell System Technical Jour.*, **14**, 85–96 (1935).

noise produced by dynamic and ribbon microphones wherein the resistance is largely that of the voice coil or ribbon and is constant.

Crystal and condenser microphones can be replaced by an equivalent parallel resistor-condenser circuit such as that shown

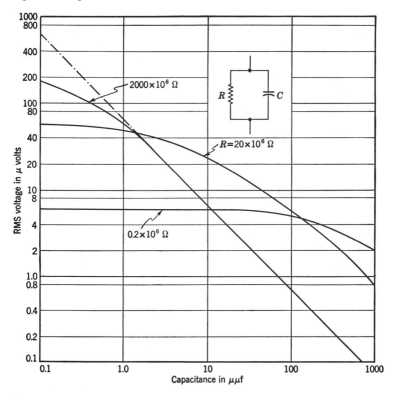

Fig. 5·7 Open-circuit rms voltage produced by thermal agitation in the real component of the impedance of a parallel resistor and condenser. For small capacitances, the noise voltage approaches the value that would obtain for the resistor alone. The frequency range considered extends from 10 to 10,000 cps. (After Weber.[10])

in Fig. 5·7. In this case, the value of $R(f)$ will be equal to

$$R(f) = \frac{R}{1 + (\omega C R)^2} \tag{5·7}$$

where $\omega = 2\pi$ times the frequency f.

Let us calculate the value of self-noise that will be produced by microphones of the crystal or condenser type in the audio-frequency range. Substitution of Eq. (5·7) in Eq. (5·3) and integration yields

$$e_{\text{tot.}} = \sqrt{\frac{2kt}{\pi c}} \sqrt{\tan^{-1}(\omega_2 CR) - \tan^{-1}(\omega_1 CR)} \qquad (5 \cdot 8)$$

For the frequency range 20 to 10,000 cps, this equation is plotted in Fig. 5·7 for three values of resistance and for a capacitance range of 0.1 to 1000 $\mu\mu$f.[10] For a bandwidth 1 cycle wide centered on a frequency f, this equation is plotted in Fig. 5·32 as a function of f. It is apparent that a high pass filter should be used with these types of microphones to eliminate the large low frequency noise wherever possible. If a high pass filter is used, or if the amplifier naturally cuts off the low frequencies, less noise is often obtained when a *higher* grid resistor is used. (See Fig. 5·32.)

5·4 Specific Devices

The foregoing discussion should help to make the reader aware that the accuracy of the measurements is influenced by the external shape and dimensions of sound-detecting equipment and by the presence of unwanted self-noise. We shall now discuss details of some types of microphones and show how their mechanism fits them for some kinds of use and makes them unfit for others.

A. The Ear

A logical beginning on sound-detecting devices is a discussion of the human ear, for it is an instrument which most of us use constantly. The human hearing mechanism is more than a microphone. It is at one and the same time a highly selective frequency analyzer, a sound localizer, and an indicator of the loudness, the pitch, and the timbre of sounds. The range of frequencies of sounds which it can perceive covers about ten octaves. Sound pressures one million times as great as the minimum detectable or threshold sound pressure can be endured safely. At the most favorable pitch an ordinary ear can detect sound pressures smaller than 10^{-10} of normal atmospheric pressure. At this low sound pressure the eardrum moves less than 10^{-9} cm, which is one

---

[10] W. Weber, "Random noise in high fidelity microphones," *Akust Zeits.*, **8**, 121–127 (1943).

hundred-thousandth of the wavelength of light or one-tenth the diameter of the smallest atom![11]

Knowledge of the psychological and physiological aspects of hearing has increased as the electronic art has grown, and now a substantial literature exists. Suitable reference texts are available.[12, 13] In this section we shall discuss the more common aspects of hearing in so far as they bear on acoustic measuring

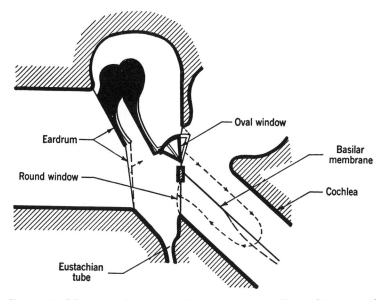

FIG. 5·8 Schematic diagram of the human ear. (From Stevens and Davis.[12])

practices. Many of the results quoted are from recent research built on the excellent groundwork laid by earlier investigators.

Structure. From a physiological standpoint, the ear can be represented by the schematic diagram of Fig. 5·8. The external ear canal is about 2.5 cm long and 0.7 cm in diameter. Sound traveling down it strikes a tight membrane called the eardrum which terminates the canal. Motion of the eardrum is transmitted by the small bones of the middle ear to the oval

[11] A. Wilska, "A method for determining the vibrating amplitude of the eardrum for various frequencies," *Skand. Arch. f. Physiol.*, **72**, 161 (1935).

[12] S. S. Stevens and H. Davis, *Hearing, Its Psychology and Physiology*, Wiley (1938).

[13] H. Davis, *Hearing and Deafness*, Murray Hill Books (1947).

window. The oval window, in turn, transmits a pressure to a tapered canal filled with liquid. The basilar membrane divides this channel lengthwise. The tapered canal, and the long structure housing it, form the cochlea, so named because it is coiled like a snail shell. The weight and strength of the eardrum are more than enough to prevent the loudest sounds in nature from rupturing it. Simple calculations show that the relative areas of the eardrum and the oval window plus the mechanical advantage of the ossicles are ideally proportioned for an impedance match to transmit sound energy into the cochlea.

It has been known for some time that the nerve endings which detect the pitch and loudness of a sound are distributed along the basilar membrane. Apparently the disturbance produced in the cochlea by sound of a particular pitch is localized at a small region of the basilar membrane. The location of points of maximum stimulation with frequency is shown in Fig. 5·9.[14] deRosa[15] suggests that this kind of effect could be the result of superposing two waves traveling at different speeds,

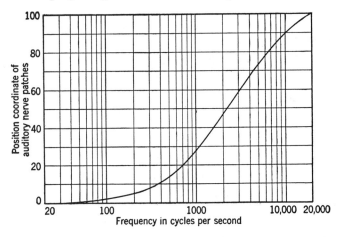

FIG. 5·9 Curve showing the relation between the frequency of excitation and the position on the basilar membrane of the nerve patch maximally excited. The position coordinate is given in percentage of the length of the basilar membrane, with the 100% point lying nearest the oval window. (After Fletcher.[14])

[14]H. Fletcher, "Auditory patterns," Rev. Mod. Phys. 12, 47–65 (1940).

[15]L. A. deRosa, "A theory of the scala tympani in hearing," J. Acoust. Soc. Am. 19, 623–628 (1947).

one in the basilar membrane and one in the cochlear liquid, although this physical picture has not been confirmed by physiological measurement.

Threshold of Audibility. The lowest sound pressure level of a particular frequency which can be heard by one or two ears is an individual characteristic which depends on the listener as well as his age. When expressed as the minimum audible sound pressure level *re* a specified reference level we call it the threshold of audibility.

Average thresholds of audibility as functions of various factors are shown in Figs. 5·10,[16] 5·11,[21] and 5·12.[18] In Fig. 5·10

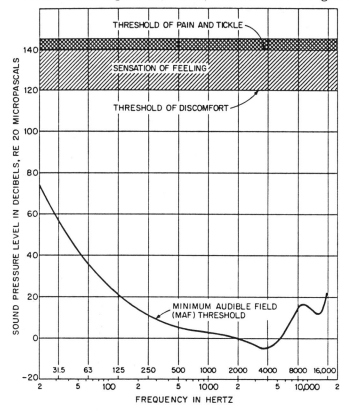

FIG. 5·10 The auditory sensation area. Upper limits are set by the thresholds of discomfort, feeling, pain, and tickle. Lower limit is minimum audible field (MAF) threshold for young adults.[16]

[16]R. S. Gales, "Hearing Characteristics," *Handbook of Noise Control*, edited by C. M. Harris (McGraw-Hill, New York, 1975). Reprinted with permission from McGraw-Hill Book Company.

the auditory sensation region in which useful sounds fall is shown.[16] At the bottom is the threshold of audibility for pure tone sounds for a large sample of young people (ages 18 to 25) without hearing defects. The *minimum audible field* (MAF) threshold curve was determined with the listeners facing the sound source in an anechoic chamber. The sound pressure level was determined, without the listener present, at the position of

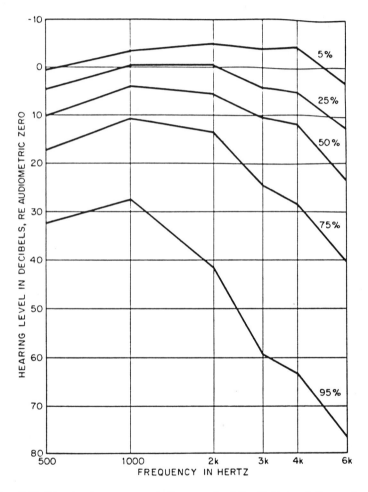

FIG. 5·11 Hearing in a representative sample of the U. S. A. adult population. Curves show percentage of persons with hearing level in better ear equal to or better than ordinate. Audiometer reference zero level is ANSI-1969 shown in Table 8.1. (*Data from USPHS.*[21])

'the center of the head. The wavy appearance of the curve is caused by diffraction of the sound around the listener's head and by resonances in the ear canal.[17-19]

At the top, three thresholds are associated with loud sounds. The threshold of discomfort occurs when the listener first says, "That sound is too loud, turn it down." Between 120 and 140 dB discomfort increases, with a sense that the sound is "felt" in the ear. After 140 dB, the ear experiences pain.

In Fig. 5·11 a set of curves is presented showing the deviation of people's hearing as determined from a large-scale public survey made by the U. S. Public Health Service in 1959–62.[20,21] The audiometric zero measured under an earphone is given in Table 8.1. The curves show the percentage of persons with hearing level at each frequency in their better ear is equal to or better than the number on the ordinate. For example, only about 10% of the population hears as well as the MAF threshold curve of Fig. 5·10. Otologists normally say that a person does not have a hearing handicap until the average of the hearing level at 500, 1000, and 2000 Hz exceeds 25 dB. About 15% of the adult population has a hearing handicap.

High altitude data taken by Rudmose *et al.*[22] indicate that there is no measureable change in the average threshold of hearing between sea level and 35,000 ft, provided the static pressures on the two sides of the eardrum are equalized.

Thresholds of Feeling. At the other extreme of the hearing range, we want to know the maximum level of a pure tone or continuous spectrum sound which the ear can tolerate without discomfort or injury. In Fig. 5·10, a threshold of discomfort is

[17]F. M. Wiener, "On the diffraction of a progressive sound wave by the human head," J. Acoust. Soc. Am. **19**, 143–146 (1947).

[18]F. M. Wiener and D. A. Ross, "Pressure distribution in the auditory canal," J. Acoust. Soc. Am. **18**, 401–408 (1946).

[19]L. L. Beranek, "The design of speech communication systems," Proc. Inst. Radio Eng. **35**, 880–890 (1947).

[20]*Hearing Study Series*, a series of bulletins from the National Institute of Health.

[21]U. S. Public Health Service, "Hearing levels of adults by sex and age," Bulletin No. 1000, Series 11, No. 11, U. S. Government Printing Office, Washington, D.C., October 1965.

[22]H. W. Rudmose, K. C. Clark, F. D. Carlson, J. C. Eisenstein, and R. A. Walker, "The effects of high altitude on speech," J. Acoust. Soc. Am. **20**, 776–786 (1948).

shown for pure tones at sound levels of 120 dB. Above it is a region called "sensation of feeling" which is bounded on the top at 140 dB by an area that is called "threshold of pain and tickle."

Diffraction and Resonance. Spherically shaped objects exhibit a diffraction resonance, and the human head is no exception. Furthermore, the ear canal is a small resonant tube. Wiener[17] and Wiener and Ross[18] have investigated the effects of these two factors on the sound delivered to the eardrum. Their results are summarized in Fig. 5·12. Curve (a) gives the ratio of the sound pressure at the eardrum to the pressure at the entrance of the ear canal for a free sound field. Curve (b) gives the ratio of the sound pressure at the eardrum to the pressure immediately beneath a dynamic earphone with a close-fitting cushion. Curve (c) gives the ratio of the sound pressure at the eardrum to that measured in a diffuse sound field before the person entered it. Curve (d) gives the average ratio of the sound pressure at the entrance to the ear canal to that measured in a plane wave sound field before the person entered it. The person faced the source of the plane wave when the pressure was being measured. The results for cases when the listener does not face the source of sound are shown in Fig. 5·13 for a plane wave.

Loudness and Loudness Level. Loudness is a subjective quantity. It is defined as that aspect of auditory sensation in terms of

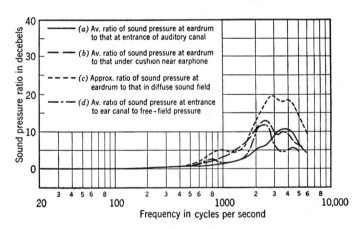

FIG. 5·12 Curves showing the ratios of sound pressures measured in and around the ear. Curve (b) is based on meager data. Curve (c) is calculated. (Courtesy F. M. Wiener.)

which sounds may be ordered on a scale running from "soft" to "loud." Loudness is chiefly a function of the sound pressure level, but it is also dependent on the frequency and the composition of the sound. The range of loudness is divided subjectively into equal-unit steps called *sones*.

The loudness of a sound at a given sound pressure level at one frequency may be quite different from the loudness of a sound of the same level at a different frequency. Nevertheless, listeners can adjust the level of one tone to match the loudness of another, and fair agreement among observers is usually obtained. Such experiments provide a useful objective scale of

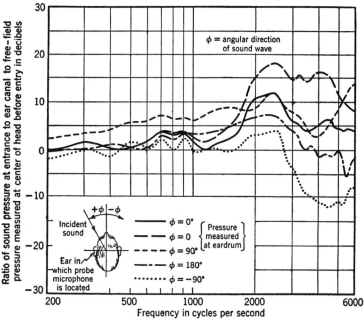

FIG. 5·13 Ratio of sound pressure at entrance to ear canal to free-field sound pressure. (After Wiener and Ross.[18])

loudness, called loudness level. *Loudness level* of a tone in *phons* is numerically equal to the sound pressure level of a 1000-cps tone which sounds equally loud. Equal loudness contours for pure tones are shown in Fig. 5·14. The numbers on the contours indicate the loudness levels in phons. These curves were obtained under free-field conditions, and the ordinate of the curve is free-field sound pressure level. Another set of equal

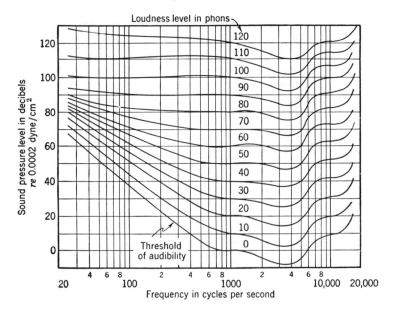

FIG. 5·14 Normal equal loudness contours for pure tones.[23] The levels were measured after the listener left the free plane-wave sound field. [International Standard ISO R226-1961].

loudness contours expressed in terms of sound pressure level at the eardrum could be made up from existing information[18,24] and Fig. 5·13. The waviness at high frequencies is caused by diffraction around the head, as can be seen from the long-dash curve (pressure measured at eardrum) in Fig. 5·13. The subjects were young persons, age 18 to 25 years, with normal hearing. The loudness in sones (S) has been related to the loudness level in phons (P) by the formula $S = 2[\exp(P - 40)/10]$.

Pitch. The subjective quality of sound most closely associated with frequency is *pitch*. Pitch is defined as that aspect of auditory sensation in terms of which sounds may be ordered on a scale running from "low" to "high." Pitch is chiefly a function of the frequency of a sound, but it also depends on the intensity and composition. The unit is the *mel*.

From careful experiments[12] it appears that the auditory sensation of pitch is directly related to the distance along the basi-

---

[23]*Acoustic Noise Measurements* (Bruel & Kjaer, 185 Forest Street, Marlborough, MA 01752, 280 pp., 1979).

[24]Y. Ando, *Concert Hall Acoustics* (Springer, Berlin, 1985), pp. 25 and 26.

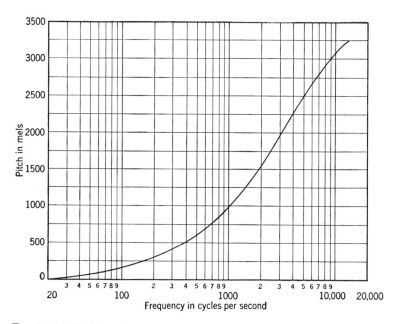

FIG. 5·15 Relationship between subjective pitch expressed in mels and frequency. (After Stevens and Volkman.[25])

lar membrane at which the corresponding pressure resonance occurs (see Fig. 5·9). This means that equal intervals of pitch correspond to equal intervals along the basilar membrane. Hence, the relation between pitch and frequency is not precisely linear, as Fig. 5.15[25] shows. The loudness level for which this curve is valid is 40 phons.

Masking. One question which often confronts the acoustical engineer is, "To what level do I need to reduce a tone so that it will become inaudible in the presence of background noise?" In airplanes, for example, noise from auxiliary generators and servos, which could not economically be eliminated, might conceivably be reduced until it is lost in the general noise of motors, propellers, and turbulent air. To set standards for noises in the presence of other noises we need to know what extent one sound hides or masks another.

Quantitatively, *masking* is defined as the number of decibels

[25]S. S. Stevens and J. Volkman, "The relation of pitch to frequency: a revised scale," Am. J. Psychol. **53**, 329 (1940).

by which a listener's threshold of audibility for a given pure tone is raised by the presence of another sound.

When a pure tone is sounded in the presence of a random noise, only the noise in a narrow frequency band on either side of it serves to mask it. In other words, the ear performs as though it were an analyzer composed of a group of narrow, contiguous filter bands. The widths of these ear "filter bands" expressed both in cycles per second and in decibel units (equal to ten times the logarithm to the base 10 of the bandwidths) are given in Fig. 5·16. Fletcher[14] has shown that the width of one of these *critical bands* (in decibel units) is equal to the number of decibels that a pure tone must be elevated above the spectrum level of a random noise to make it just audible. Hence, the answer to the question posed above is given by the data of this figure. For example, a 1000-cps tone will be inaudible whenever the level of that tone is less than 16.5 dB above the *spectrum level* of the general noise. Spectrum level is defined in Chapter 1.

B. Carbon Microphone

Structure. The carbon microphone is fundamentally a very simple device. As Fig. 5·17 shows, there is a diaphragm which

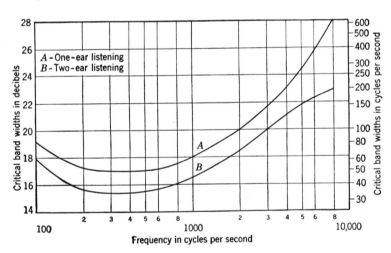

Fig. 5·16 Critical bands for listening. (*A*) One-ear listening. (*B*) Two-ear listening. The left-hand ordinate is in dB = $10 \log_{10} \Delta f$. The right-hand ordinate is Δf in cycles per second. (After French and Steinberg.) (*A*) is used in ANSI S3.26-1981 Audiometric Bone Vibrators.

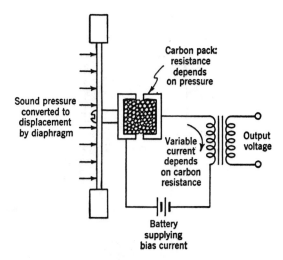

Fig. 5·17 Simplified diagram of the structure of a carbon microphone.

converts sound pressure into mechanical force. This diaphragm
compresses a loose pack of carbon granules. Pressing these
granules together increases their area of contact and decreases
the electric resistance of the pack. When the force is released
the area of contact is diminished, and the resistance of the pack
returns to its initial value. When a constant current passes
through the carbon granules, the potential drop across the
pack is inversely related to the instantaneous sound pressure.
Since the carbon acts as a valve rather than a generator, a
given amount of acoustic power striking the diaphragm can
produce a fairly large audio-frequency signal in the electric
output circuit.

Carbon microphones are used extensively in telephone systems. Figure 5·18 is a cross section of a type designed for use in
oxygen masks and manufactured by the Western Electric Company. It is similar to the telephone microphone described by
Jones.[26] The diaphragm is behind several protective obstacles
which guard it from mechanical damage and corrosive moisture. The center of the diaphragm is formed into a deep cup
which provides mechanical rigidity and forms one wall of the
carbon chamber. A very small puncture permits the static pres-

[26]W. C. Jones, "Instruments for the new telephone sets," Bell Syst. Tech. J. **17**,
338–357 (1938).

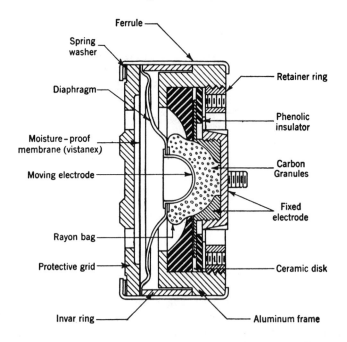

FIG. 5·18 Cross-sectional sketch of an ANB-MC-1 carbon microphone used by the Armed Services during World War II and manufactured by the Western Electric Company.

sure behind the diaphragm to follow slow changes of the pressure outside. The carbon granules are retained by a cloth bag which is attached to the back of the diaphragm. The diaphragm itself forms one electric terminal of the carbon pack. The other terminal is mounted on the base of the microphone housing.

Many other carbon-button microphones have been designed to achieve higher frequency range, larger output, lower distortion, smaller size, lower biasing current. All carbon microphones require some biasing current. The circuit of Fig. 5·19 specifically developed for telephone microphones, is also a reasonable first trial circuit for most other carbon-button microphones.

Internal Properties. Although carbon microphones are simple and have high sensitivity they leave something to be desired in almost every other respect. The carbon pack itself is distinctly a non-linear device which produces amplitude distortion, so that any two tones cross-modulate each other. The fre-

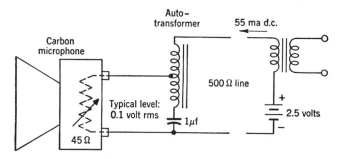

FIG. 5·19 Typical electrical circuit in which to operate a carbon microphone. (After Jones.[26])

quency range is limited by the properties of the carbon pack as well as the properties of the diaphragm and it is influenced also by the size and shape of the microphone housing.

In Fig. 5·20 are shown a number of the properties of the carbon microphone for use in an oxygen mask shown in Fig. 5·18.[27] This microphone has low sensitivity at low frequencies to compensate for the reinforcing acoustical properties of the mask. In (a) of Fig. 5·20, frequency response curves are shown for various sound pressure levels. If this microphone were linear, these curves would be parallel instead of tightly compressed at high output levels. Diffraction effects do not appear in these curves because the tests were made by holding the sound pressure constant over the face of the microphone. In (b) the variation in frequency response for three carbon currents is shown. Except for very low currents, the response is reasonably independent of this variable. The carbon microphone has an essentially pure internal resistance. The curves of (c) show large percentage of intermodulation distortion which may occur when environmental noise makes it necessary for the user to speak in a loud voice.

Carbon microphones produce rather large amounts of self-noise, particularly in the low frequency range.[28] The sources of

[27]F. M. Wiener et al., Response characteristics of interphone equipment, O. S. R. D. Report 3105, Jan. 1, 1944. This report may be procured in photostatic or microfilm form from the Office of Technical Services, Department of Commerce, Washington, D.C. Ask for P. B. 22889.

[28]C. J. Christensen and G. L. Pearson, "Spontaneous resistance fluctuations in carbon microphones and other granular resistances," Bell Syst. Tech. J. **15**, 197–223 (1936).

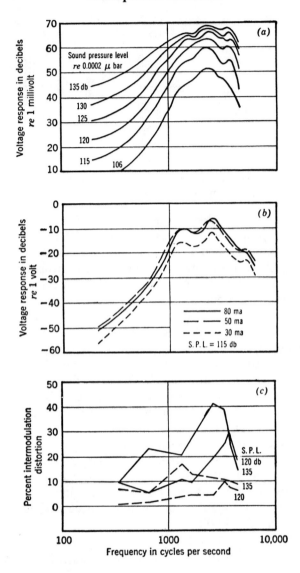

FIG. 5·20 (a) (b) (c) Performance characteristics of an ANB-MC-1 carbon microphone for use in oxygen masks. (a) Variation of response with signal level. (b) Effect of carbon current. (c) Percentage intermodulation distortion as a function of frequency and level. The solid lines are the first-order components, and the dashed lines are the second-order components. (After Wiener *et al.*[27])

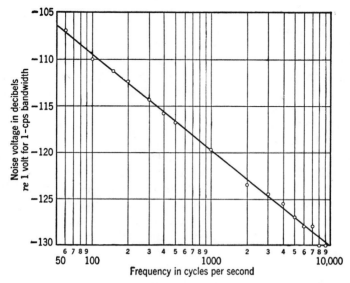

Fig. 5·21 Noise spectrum level as a function of frequency for a well-designed carbon microphone. (After Christensen and Pearson.[28])

this noise are not well understood, though it seems to be caused by the passage of the biasing current. A typical curve, shown in Fig. 5·21, indicates that the noise level decreases with increasing frequency.

There is another kind of variation in carbon resistance at very low frequency.[29] Thermal effects in the microphone produce a cyclic process which causes a very low frequency pulsing. The cycle is as follows: The current through the carbon granules warms their housing. The housing expands, reducing the pressure on the carbon, and, hence, the current. This produces cooling, and the housing contracts. Then the cycle is repeated. This pulsing, called "breathing," although not audible, may modulate audio-frequency signals.

Noise sets a limit to the weakest sounds that a carbon microphone can detect at about 9.8×10^{-5} volt in the 200–3000-cps region. This number is, however, a function of a great many variables and may be greater in some cases.

Environmental Influences. Carbon microphones are subject to a number of environmental influences which are partially

[29]E. Waetzmann and G. Kretschmer, "On spontaneous resistance fluctuations in carbon microphones," Akust. Z. **2**, 57–61 (1937).

suppressed in modern telephone designs. In early carbon buttons the granules had a tendency to pack when subjected to shock, either mechanical or acoustic. This packing may reduce the resistance of the carbon. Proper design of the carbon chamber makes these packing effects small. Other microphones were built with carbon chambers that allowed the granules to separate from the rear electrode when the microphone was operated in a "facedown" position. The chamber design of Fig. 5·18 eliminates this difficulty. Excessive humidity or temperature tends to deteriorate the carbon granules. The carbon granules do erode, even when precautions are taken to prevent it, perhaps largely as a result of the action of the polarizing current. After three years of telephone use, the sensitivity of a microphone is likely to be down 2 or 3 dB. The best granules are prepared from the highest grade anthracite, and they go through a complicated heat treatment.

C. Condenser Microphone

Structure. The condenser microphone[30] has found widespread use because it has a "flat" frequency-response characteristic and reasonably low self-noise. As shown in Fig. 5·22, the diaphragm of the microphone is a thin, stretched membrane which acts as one plate of a condenser. A second or "back" electrode serves as the other plate. When positive sound pressure deflects this diaphragm inward, the capacitance of this condenser increases. Since the resistor R is very large (20 megohms) the charge on the condenser remains constant except at very low frequencies. Hence, the potential across the condenser drops because it is equal to the charge divided by the capacitance. When the cycle reverses and a negative pressure is applied to the diaphragm, the potential across the condenser increases. The output voltage, therefore, is proportional to the displacement of the diaphragm.

Two possible electrical circuits for use with the condenser microphone are shown in Figs. 5·22 and 5·23a.[27,31] The microphone itself is equivalent to a series generator and capacitance.

[30]American National Standard, "Specification for laboratory standard microphones," ANSI S1.12-1967, Acoustical Society of America.

[31]P. S. Veneklasen, "Instrumentation for the measurement of sound pressure level with the W. E. 640-AA condenser microphone," J. Acoust. Soc. Am. **20**, 807–817 (1948).

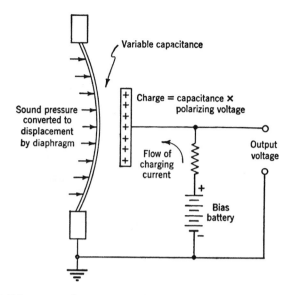

FIG. 5·22 Diagrammatic representation of the operation of a condenser microphone.

In Fig. 5·23a it is connected between grid and ground of a "cathode follower" type of vacuum tube circuit. The value of R_g is made very high. The voltage drop across R_1 is made sufficient to bias the grid of the tube. The drop across R_2, which supplies the direct potential to the condenser microphone, is several hundred volts. The alternating output voltage appears across the load resistance R' and may be measured with a vacuum tube voltmeter.

The part of the circuit diagram containing the insert resistor and attenuator is a means for measuring the open-circuit voltage produced by the microphone during laboratory experiments (see Chap. 13). It is not required for studio use.

The cathode follower circuit (excluding the microphone) has the following desirable properties: (1) At all audio frequencies the input impedance from grid to ground becomes very high (200 megohms) in comparison with the microphone impedance due to the inverse feedback; (2) the output impedance from cathode to ground is very low at all audio frequencies in comparison with the input resistance of the vacuum tube voltmeter; and (3) the voltage amplification e_2/e' is very close to

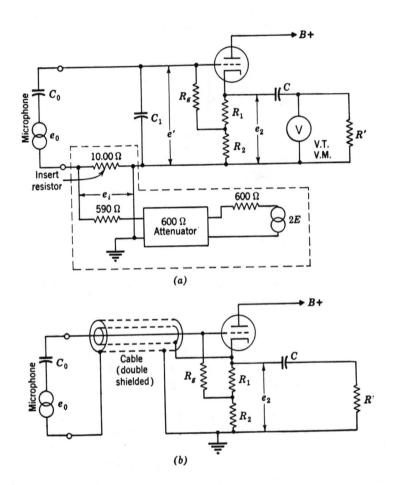

FIG. 5·23 (a) Cathode follower circuit for transforming the voltage e' produced at high impedance at the microphone to the voltage e_2 at low impedance. e_2 is nearly equal to e'. Practical values of components for a 1620-type vacuum tube are $C = 0.5$ µf, $R_g = 20$ megohms, $R_1 = 200$ ohms, and $R_2 = 100,000$ ohms. The effective grid-to-ground impedance (with 6J7) is 3×10^8 ohms, and the effective cathode-to-ground impedance is 600 ohms. (b) A similar circuit, except that a double-shielded cable is used to permit separation of the microphone from the amplifying stage. (Courtesy F. M. Wiener, R. L. Wallace, Jr., and P. S. Veneklasen.)

unity, independent of ordinary variations in tube parameters, and independent of frequency in the audio range.

The principal disadvantage of this circuit is that the amplifier tube must be mounted very near the condenser microphone to keep the value of C_1 (stray capacitance) small. One circuit suitable for eliminating the effects of C_1 and permitting the use of a cable several feet in length is shown schematically in Fig. 5·23b. The significant difference is the addition of a double shielded cable. The capacitance between cathode and grid is reduced to a very small value because of the inverse-feedback action of the tube. The capacitance across the cathode resistors has no effect because the inverse feedback has reduced the cathode-to-ground impedance to a few hundred ohms.

It should be noted from Fig. 5·23 that the noise voltage produced in the resistance R_g does not appear without amplification across $R_1 + R_2$, but rather the noise voltage is amplified in a normal manner by the vacuum tube.

For the measurement of sound pressures at very low frequencies (down to 0.1 cps), a special circuit employing a condenser microphone has been developed. This circuit as further developed by Hull is shown in Fig. 5·24.[32] Here, the condenser C_1 is varied until the carrier voltage e_1 has a value 0.8 of that which it has at resonance; see (b). Variations in C_0 [see (b)] produced by the sound field acting on the condenser microphone produce corresponding variations in the amplitude of the carrier. This signal is then rectified and filtered to obtain a wave with the form and frequency of the sound wave. The lower part of Fig. 5·24a shows a means for partially suppressing the carrier in the output so that a higher percentage modulation will be obtained. The elements R_3, R_4 and C_2 serve to adjust the amplitude and the phase of the canceling signal so that cancellation is achieved. Hull advocates three settings of the tap on R_5, permitting 10 percent modulation for sound fields of 10, 100, and 1000 microbars. An advantage of this circuit is a reduction in self-noise below that produced by the resistor R_g of Fig. 5·22.

This circuit will operate at frequencies down to as low as zero provided the diaphragm displacement remains proportional to the applied pressure. In many condenser microphones, how-

[32]G. F. Hull, "Resonant circuit modulator for broad band acoustic measurements," J. Appl. Phys. **17**, 1066–1075 (1946).

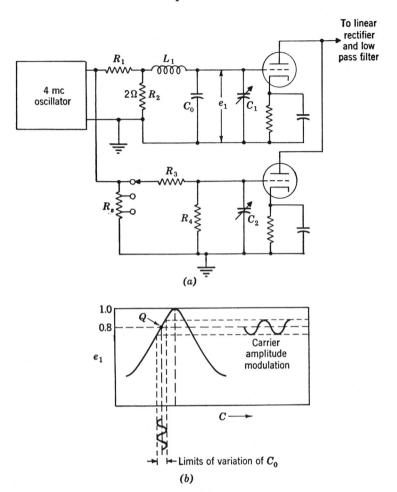

FIG. 5·24 (a) Circuit using a condenser microphone (C_0) to modulate a 4-megacycle carrier. (b) Principle of operation of the circuit. (After Hull.[32])

ever, a static pressure release is incorporated which effectively reduces their output at frequencies below a few cycles per second. Hull devised an acoustic filter for attachment to the base of the W. E. 640-AA condenser microphone which held its response nearly constant to 0.1 cps.

Electret Prepolarized Microphone

The major disadvantage of the conventional condenser microphone is the necessity for a 100 to 200 volt polarizing vol-

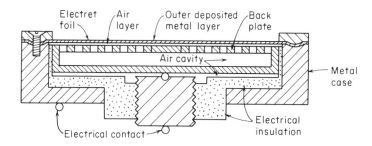

FIG. 5·25 Construction of electret microphone. (*After Sessler and West.*)

tage. Sessler and West[33] developed a prepolarized condenser microphone, which they named "electret." Their construction (Fig. 5·25) comprises (a) a polymer film sheet (electret foil), less than 0.002 cm thick, in which an electric charge is bonded to the molecules, the outer surface of which is coated with a thin metallic layer that forms the grounded plate of the condenser, (b) a perforated backplate, and (c) an air cavity. The backplate acts as an acoustic resistance that connects to an acoustic compliance (airspace).

An alternate design is shown in Fig. 5·26. Here the electret foil is stretched over raised points on the backplate, which assures precision spacing between the two plates of the condenser. However, the stability of diaphragm tension for a polymer sheet, of which the foil is made, is less than the stability of the electric charge in the foil. With time, the tension of the foil will drop owing to stretching. A decrease in diaphragm tension will increase the sensitivity at lower frequencies and lower the upper cut-off frequency a small amount. This change is of little importance in sound level meters, where recalibration is performed on each use, but it is critical in laboratory secondary standard microphones.

Another alternate model (Fig. 5·27) uses a conventional diaphragm made of nickel with a protective quartz film on the outside, for which the long-term stability is very high. In this model, the charge-carrying element is attached to the surface of the backplate. The material used for the electret element is

[33]G. M. Sessler and J. E. West, "Electret Microphones," a series of papers, J. Acoust. Soc. Am. **35**, 1354–1357 (1963); **40**, 1433–1440 (1966); **46**, 1081–1086 (1969); and **58**, 273–278 (1975).

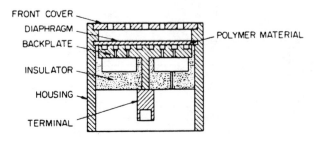

FIG. 5·26 Simplified diagram showing the basic elements of an electret microphone with supported diaphragm. (Courtesy GenRad.)

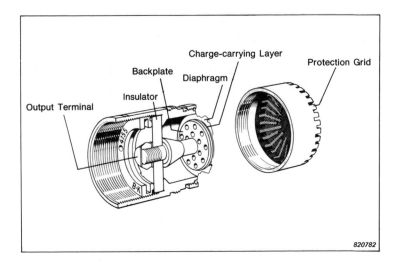

FIG. 5·27 Cross-section view of a prepolarized (electret) microphone, one-half inch in diameter. (Courtesy Bruel & Kjaer.)

polytetrafluorethylene[33A], which has very low conductivity and which carries the inserted electrical space charges. High stability results because inserted space charges are trapped in positions from which they are not able to move unless they are activated by an external source of energy, for example, heat.

[33a] E. Frederiksen, N. Eirby, and H. Matheasen, "Prepolarized condenser microphones for measurement purposes," Technical Report No. 4 (1979), Bruel and Kjaer, 185 Forest Street, Marlborough, MA 01752 and S. van Turnhout, *Thermally Stimulated Discharge of Polymer Electrets.*

The electret material is stabilized by cycling it up to 200 ℃, which causes the less well bonded charges to be released.

The advantages of the electret construction are freedom from a power supply, 10 to 12 dB greater sensitivity than same diameter dc-polarized microphones, and lower internal noise in high humidity. The greater sensitivity is achieved by using a lower diaphragm tension, which is possible because there is no danger of arcing.

The backplate as well as the main housing is made of corrosion resistant high nickel alloy. The insulator is silicon treated synthetic sapphire, which gives good electrical insulation and long-term dimensional stability. The protecting grid is fitted with an internal gauze filter.

The manufacturer of the microphone of Fig. 5·27 states that the change in sensitivity is about $+ 0.1$ dB per 10° decrease in temperature and, long term, about 1 dB in 400 years at room temperature.

A design of dc-polarized condenser microphone which meets an American standard specification[34] is shown in Fig. 5·28. The elaborate construction, slotted back-plate and airspace, behind the diaphragm is used to damp its first resonant mode of vibration which occurs at about 7000 cps. Movements of the diaphragm force air in and out through the slots in the back plate. The resulting combination of thermodynamic and viscous effects damps the diaphragm resonance. The capacitance of the diaphragm and back plate is 50 to 70 $\mu\mu$f. This particular instrument is ordinarily used with a polarizing potential of 200 volts.

Internal Properties. There are two effects which tend to limit the dynamic range over which a condenser microphone can reproduce sounds linearly. In the first place, it is non-linear in principle, for the potential across the condenser is not directly but inversely proportional to its capacitance. The percentage of second harmonic distortion produced by this effect is given approximately by the relationship

---

[34]ANSI S 1.12-1967, "Specifications for laboratory standard microphones," American National Standards Institute, 1430 Broadway, New York, NY 10018; IEC 655 (1979), "Values for the difference between free-field and pressure sensitivity levels for one-inch standard condenser microphones," International electrotechnical Commission, 3 Rue de Varembe, Geneva, Switzerland.

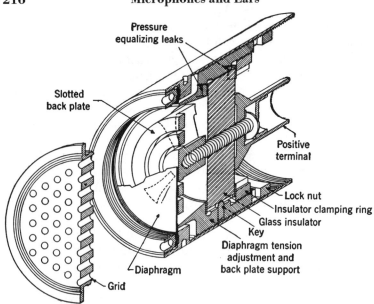

FIG. 5·28 Cross-sectional drawing of the W. E. 640-AA condenser microphone. The slotted back plate serves both as the second terminal of the
condenser and as a means for damping the principal resonant mode of the
diaphragm. Small pressure-equalizing leaks are provided. (Sketch prepared by author from X-rays of the instrument and from a drawing supplied
by the Bell Telephone Laboratories.)

$$\text{Percentage of distortion} = 5\,\frac{\hat{e}}{E_0} \qquad (5\cdot9)$$

where $\hat{e}$ is the peak open-circuit alternating voltage being produced by the microphone and E_0 is the steady bias voltage applied to it. A second limitation is that the deflection of the diaphragm, which causes the change of capacitance, is not
proportional to pressure except at very small deflections. However, the distortion produced by this effect is generally very
small compared to the first, so that either a dc-polarized or a
prepolarized condenser microphone in conjunction with a
preamplifier, exhibits about 3% second harmonic distortion at
sound pressure levels 135 dB above 0.0002 dyne/cm^2.

Condenser microphones can be made to cover the audio-frequency range quite well. Figure 5·29 indicates the frequency

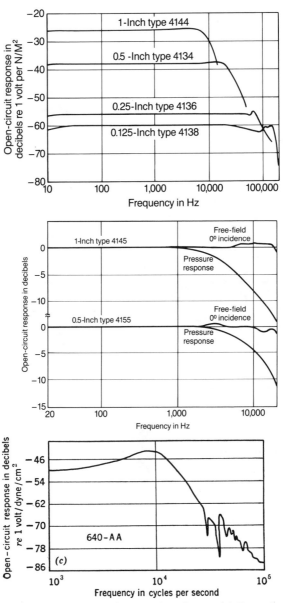

FIG. 5·29 Typical data for condenser microphones. (*a*) Open-circuit pressure response (constant sound pressure at the diaphragm) of dc-polarized types. (*b*) Pressure and Free-field responses of 1-inch dc-polarized and 0.5-inch pre-polarized types. (*c*) Open-circuit pressure response of one-inch dc-polarized type at sultrasonic frequencies.

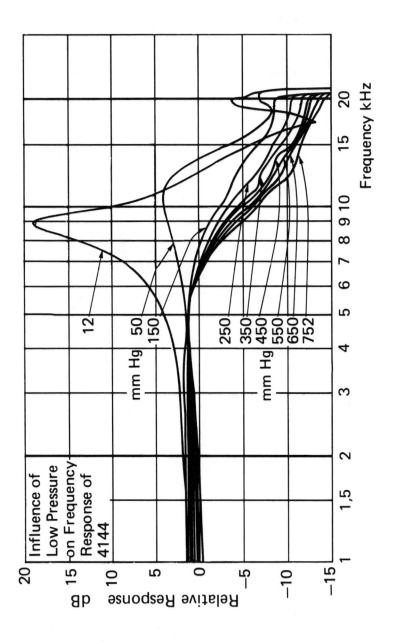

FIG. 5·30 Typical data for B&K 4145 condenser microphones, showing effects of ambient pressure and temperature. (Courtesy of Bruel & Kjaer.)

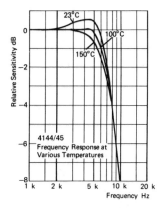

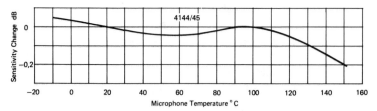

FIG. 5·30 (con't). Typical data for B&K 4145 condenser microphones, showing effects of ambient pressure and temperature. The lowest graph is for a frequency of 250 Hz. (Courtesy of Bruel & Kjaer.)

response of typical microphones for a constant sound pressure at the diaphragm.[27] If the response is desired for a free plane wave sound field, the appropriate curve from Fig. 5·32 should be added to that of Fig. 5·29. The algebraic sum of a curve in 5·29 and one in 5·32 gives a curve which includes diffraction, mechanical resonance, and the influence of internal acoustic networks.

At high frequencies, the frequency response drops off at a rate of 12 dB per octave, as can be seen in Fig. 5·29c. This microphone is still quite usable in the range up to 100 kHz. The response is a function of both ambient pressure and temperature, as Fig. 5.30 shows.

The phase characteristic is of concern when the microphone is to be used to measure transient sounds. Phase data on two microphones are shown in Fig. 5·32. Here is shown the difference in phase between the open-circuit output voltage produced by the microphone and the alternating pressure in the sound field before insertion of the microphone. The slope of the phase characteristic is called the envelope delay and is expressed in seconds. Listening tests reported by the Bell Telephone Laboratories[35] indicate that delay distortion rather than phase distortion is most readily noticed by listeners, and that about 8 msec is permissible at high frequencies and about 15 msec at 100 cycles, both referred to 1000 cps as reference frequency.

Reference to Fig. 5·29(a) shows three pressure (electrostatic actuator) response curves for microphones that are currently available. The types shown here have a nearly-flat response curve for sound at perpendicular wave incidence ($\theta = 0°$). Another type, not shown here, (e.g., 640-AA) has a nearly flat response curve at high frequencies for sound waves impinging on the microphone at incidence parallel to the plane of the diaphragm ($\theta = 90°$). The latter is commonly used in America; the former in many other countries. Users must determine which orientation of each particular microphone to use in order to avoid errors of up to 12 dB in making measurements at higher frequencies (see Chap. 20).

Typical directional characteristics for one-inch, half-inch and fourth-inch microphones are shown in Fig. 5·32 (a) through (d) with protective grids over the diaphragm in place.[35,36]

The noise level of condenser microphones is caused primarily by thermal fluctuations of electrons in the load resistor and in the insulating material between the back plate and the diaphragm. The microphone capacity acts as a shunting circuit which reduces this thermal noise at high frequencies. The noise generated by a parallel combination of a resistor and condenser has been discussed in Section 5·3. Figure 5·31 shows how the thermal noise for a typical microphone with two values of load resistance varies as a function of frequency. The circuit of Fig. 5·22 is assumed. The total rms voltage in the frequency range between 10 and 10,000 cps may be seen from Fig. 5·7.

With the circuit of Fig. 5·24, the noise voltage is reduced to a lower value in relation to the signals produced by the sound field. Other noise voltages may arise from electrical leakage

[35]*Measuring Microphones*, Bruel & Kajaer, DK-2850 Naerum, Denmark (1972).

[36]*Condenser Microphones and Preamplifiers*, Bruel & Kjaer, DK-2850, Naerum, Denmark. See also, M. Brock, "Wind and Turbulence noise of turbulence screen, nose cone, and sound intensity probe with wind screen." (Same address.)

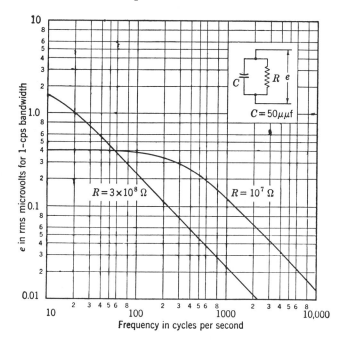

Fig. 5·31 Rms noise voltage produced by typical condenser microphone in bands 1 cycle wide as a function of frequency with two different load resistors.

between the condenser plates, or from noise in the input tube of the amplifier.

Environmental Influences. Condenser microphones are subject to all the environmental influences which affect high impedance electric devices. Humidity, which can cause leakage across insulating surfaces, is one. Special moisture-resistant coatings can be applied to the insulators. Electrostatic pickup of hum or noise is another. Careful shielding should easily eliminate this. High temperature, which reduces the resistivity of insulators, should also be avoided. Large variations in temperature can also change the relative dimensions of the structural parts and temporarily or permanently change the tension of the dia-

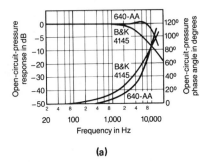

(a)

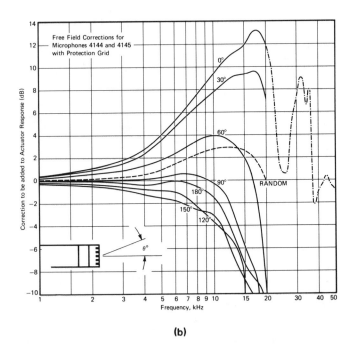

(b)

FIG. 5·32 (*a*) Phase shift in degrees and pressure response in decibels for two types of one-inch condenser microphones, 640 AA and B&K 4145. (*b*) Far-field directional characteristics of a one-inch condenser microphone—to be added to pressure response, e.g., electrostatic actuator response. (After Bruel & Kjaer).

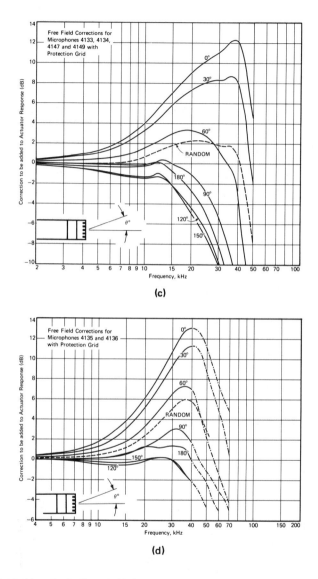

FIG. 5·32 (c) and (d). Free-field directional characteristics for (c) one-half-inch and (d) one-fourth-inch condenser microphones—to be added to pressure response.

phragm.   The insulated terminal must be small to reduce stray capacitance.   Despite the fact that the condenser microphone is a delicate instrument which can be damaged by rough handling, it is remarkably stable when treated properly.   It has been found that the 640-AA normally retains its calibration within 0.3 db over a period of several years if not maltreated.   Differences in air pressure or density between calibration and use, however, can upset the calibration by changing the characteristic frequencies of the corrective acoustic network behind the diaphragm.

D. Moving Coil Microphone

Structure.   Moving coil microphones are more complicated acoustically than either of the preceding two types.   Diagram-

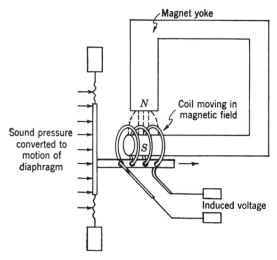

Fig. 5·33   Diagrammatic representation of the essential elements of a moving coil (dynamic) microphone.

matically, Fig. 5·33 shows that there is a diaphragm, driven by sound pressure, which carries a coil of wire.   Motion of this coil in a strong magnetic field results in an induced voltage.   The output of this coil is at very low impedance (about 20 ohms) until it passes through a transformer.   In moving coil microphones the biasing currents or potentials which carbon and condenser microphones require are replaced by a permanent magnet.

The combination of coil and diaphragm is always more massive

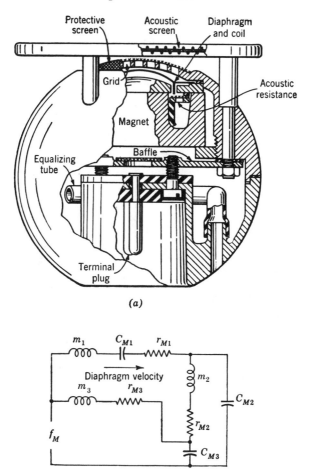

(a)

(b)

FIG. 5·34 Cross-sectional view of a W.E. 630-A dynamic microphone (a) and its equivalent circuit (b). The sound reaches the diaphragm through a protective screen and grid. The large acoustic screen on top counteracts the effects of diffraction at the higher frequencies. The diaphragm and coil have a mass m_1, a mechanical compliance C_{M1}, and a mechanical resistance r_{M1}. Immediately behind the diaphragm there is a compliance C_{M2} due to the air space. This air space communicates through an acoustic resistance r_{M2}, which also contains some mass m_2, to an acoustic chamber with compliance C_{M3}. The equalizing tube connects this acoustic chamber to the exterior space by acting as a mass m_3 and a resistance r_{M3}. The quantity f_M is equal to sound pressure times the area of the diaphragm.

[(a) After Marshall and Romanow[37] and (b) after Olson.[1]]

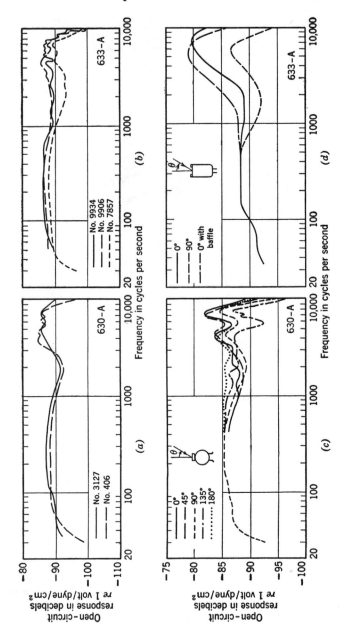

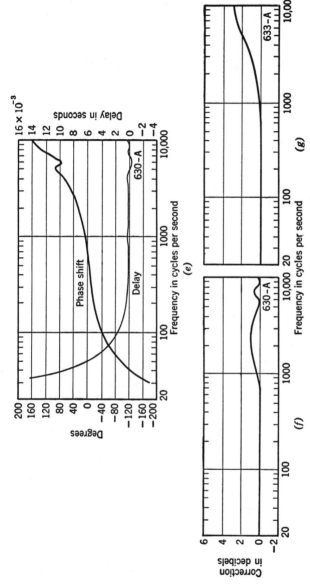

Fig. 5·35 Open-circuit voltage generated for a plane free-wave sound field incident on the face of the diaphragm ($\theta = 90°$) for (a) W.E. 630-A and (b) W.E. 633-A. The variation of response with angle of incidence is shown for (c) W.E. 630-A (approximate data) and (d) W.E. 633-A (average data for a number of microphones). The phase shift and envelope delay characteristics for the W.E. 630-A are shown in (e) (approximate data). Correction curves to be added algebraically to curves of the type shown in (a) and (b) to convert to response in a diffuse sound field are shown for (f) W.E. 630-A and (g) W.E. 633-A microphones. (Courtesy F. M. Wiener.)

than a diaphragm alone. Thus, in one type of dynamic microphone, the diaphragm assembly (when there is no damping)
resonates at 400 to 800 cps. This resonance is much more than
critically damped by an acoustic network, as Fig. 5·34[37] shows.
As a result of this damping the microphone responds as a mechanical resistive element, so that the velocity of the diaphragm is
proportional to the sound pressure and the factor of proportionality is nearly independent of frequency. Since the moving coil
converts velocity into electromotive force, the microphone as a
whole converts pressure into electromotive force.

Internal Properties. Distortion in the better dynamic microphones is very low, because it comes mainly from the iron of the
transformer and the non-linearity of the diaphragm compliance.
One would expect, however, that such a complex device would
have only an approximately uniform response as a function of
frequency. Figures 5·35a and 5·35b show how well two Western
Electric dynamic microphones have been corrected in the audio-
frequency range, through mutual cancelation of several unwanted
effects by others. These curves give the open-circuit output
voltage for a constant sound pressure field, so that they include
diffraction effects. The variations of response with angle of
incidence for these two types of microphones are shown in (c)
and (d). The phase shift curve is much more irregular than that
for the condenser microphone, as can be seen from (e), and the
time delay at both low and high frequencies becomes significant.
Curves (f) and (g) show, for the 630-A and 633-A microphones,
the ratios of responses for a diffuse sound field to the responses for
a plane sound wave incident parallel to the face of the diaphragm.

The self-noise generated by these microphones is essentially
that generated by a pure resistance because the mechanical circuit is resistance controlled and the voice coil inductance is not
important on open circuit. For the microphone of Fig. 5·34
the self-noise is −184 db *re* 1 volt for a band 1 cycle wide or −144
db *re* 1 volt for a band from 10 to 10,000 cps. These numbers
correspond roughly to equivalent sound pressure levels of −20
db and +20 db, respectively, *re* 0.0002 dyne/cm^2. The 630-A
microphone can operate in sound fields of 140 db *re* 0.0002
dyne/cm^2 at low frequencies and in much greater sound fields at
frequencies above 1000 cycles without undue distortion.

[37] R. N. Marshall and F. F. Romanow, "A non-directional microphone,"
Bell System Technical Jour., **15**, 405–423 (1936).

Environmental Influences. Moving coil microphones may be used with low resistance cables with no ill effects. Temperature and pressure variations change the performance of the acoustic circuits, although precise data on the magnitude of these variations are lacking. Alternating magnetic fields in the region of the microphone can induce relatively large voltages at power frequency in the voice coil. Although these microphones can be compact they usually contain a pound or more of metal. They are not too easily damaged by rough handling, being better than the condenser microphone in that respect. They maintain their calibration fairly well over a period of years when properly treated. Large changes in the density or viscosity of the gas in and around a dynamic microphone affect both its sensitivity and its frequency response.

E. Ribbon Microphone

Structure. The ribbon microphone is really a special case of the moving coil type in that the coil is reduced to a single length of ribbon. Figure 5·36 shows a sketch of a common type of ribbon microphone.[1] In this microphone the diaphragm is a corrugated ribbon of very thin metal, lightly stretched between the poles of a permanent magnet, and it serves also as the electrical conductor. This ribbon is exposed to the sound field on both sides. Sound waves incident on the front also act on the back, but the pressure on the back of the ribbon is delayed because the wave takes time to travel around the pole pieces.

Theoretical investigation of the sound pressure produced on the two sides of the ribbon by a plane free wave of constant sound pressure level shows that the net effective force acting to move the ribbon is proportional to frequency over a very wide frequency range. In other words, it is proportional to the gradient of the sound pressure in the free wave. It is known that the particle velocity in a plane free wave is directly proportional to the product of the pressure gradient and the reciprocal of the frequency. Also, in such a plane wave, the particle velocity is proportional to the sound pressure which, we have already said, is held constant. Therefore, if we want the velocity of the ribbon to be directly proportional to the particle velocity in the plane sound wave, we must make the ribbon behave like a mass. That is to say, its mechanical impedance should increase linearly with frequency. This effect is achieved by locating the fundamental resonance of the ribbon at very low frequencies, so that it will behave like a mass throughout the entire audio-frequency range.

If a ribbon (velocity) microphone has a flat frequency response when placed in a free plane wave sound field, its frequency response will not be flat in a free spherical wave sound field when it is brought near the source. The expression for the particle

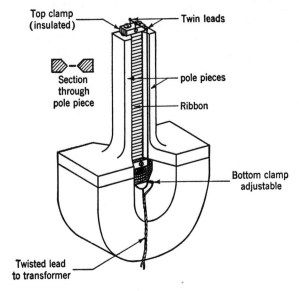

FIG. 5·36　Sketch of the ribbon and magnetic structure for a velocity microphone. (After Olson.[1])

velocity in a free spherical wave sound field is

$$u = \frac{p_0 r_0}{r \rho_0 c} \sqrt{1 + \left(\frac{c}{2\pi f r}\right)^2} \qquad (5 \cdot 10)$$

where u = particle velocity in the wave, in centimeters per second, at the distance r

$\quad\; p_0$ = sound pressure in the wave, in dynes per square centimeter, at a reference distance r_0 cm (It is assumed that p_0 is a constant independent of frequency.)

$\quad\; r_0$ = reference distance, in centimeters measured from the geometrical center of the source

$\quad\;\, r$ = distance from the origin of the spherical wave, in centimeters

ρ_0 = density of the air, in grams per cubic centimeter

c = speed of sound, in centimeters per second

f = frequency, in cycles.

It is obvious that, as one approaches the source, the particle velocity increases more rapidly at the low than at the high fre-

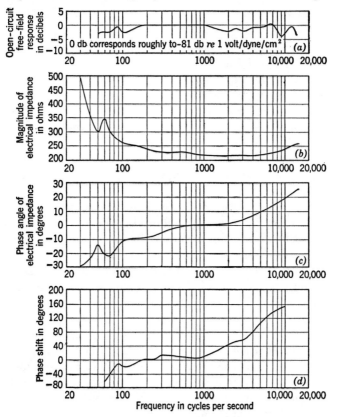

Fig. 5·37 (a) Relative response curve for an RCA velocity (ribbon) microphone. (b) Magnitude of electrical impedance, in ohms. (c) Phase angle of electrical impedance, in degrees. (d) Phase shift between open-circuit voltage generated in a plane free sound field and the pressure at the same point in the undisturbed field (this curve is approximate and is not for the microphone for which the response and impedance curves above are shown). (Courtesy L. J. Anderson.)

quencies. Hence, a flat response curve for a free plane wave field must change into one with a rise at low frequencies when the source of a spherical wave is approached.

Ribbon microphones are insensitive to waves which are incident parallel to the face of the ribbon. This insensitiveness can readily be understood by noting that the same sound pressure will be applied to both sides of the ribbon and that no net force will be developed to move it. The directivity pattern follows a cosine function, and for practical microphones it is remarkably independent of frequency, as can be seen in (a) of Fig. 5·57.

Internal Properties. It is difficult to overload a ribbon microphone, and its output has very low distortion. Its response to velocity is fairly uniform with frequency, but there are some peculiarities at extremely high and extremely low frequencies. As Fig. 5·37a shows,* transverse modes appear between 10,000 and 20,000 cycles per second. Between 1000 and 10,000 cycles per second the distance between faces becomes comparable with a wavelength, but the response is partially sustained by broad cavity resonances on both sides of the diaphragm. The phase characteristic of the microphone including the diaphragm is plotted in (d).

Environmental Influences. Being electromagnetic, ribbon microphones may have voltages induced in them by stray magnetic fields. Ribbon microphones are quite heavy and quite delicate. They can be damaged by moderate winds, and they are always housed in a case lined with a fine mesh cloth which passes sound but reduces the effects of puffs of air. For outdoor use, a supplementary cover is necessary; several are shown in Fig. 5·60.

F. Piezoelectric Microphones

Transducing Element. The last broad class of microphones which we shall discuss in this chapter employs piezoelectric crystals or dielectrics as the transducing elements. Piezoelectric microphones are more rugged than the condenser or ribbon types; they have less weight and a more uniform frequency response characteristic than the dynamic type; and they are lower in cost than any of the three other types. To offset these advantages, the most sensitive piezoelectric element, the X-cut Rochelle salt crystal, is not stable as a function of temperature, and it is permanently damaged if exposed to temperatures above 115°F, or if located for long periods of time in excessively low or high humidities. Other crystal substances and other crystal cuts, including new piezoelectric dielectric substances, which overcome some but

* This curve was supplied by L. J. Anderson of RCA-Victor Laboratories.

not all of these objections are now available, although at present they have either less sensitivity or higher internal electrical impedance or both. With modern vacuum tube circuits, these adverse factors are assuming less importance than they did previously, and it is expected that piezoelectric microphones will find even wider use in the future.

Three types of piezoelectric crystals are used in microphones today. These are the Rochelle salt, ammonium dihydrogen

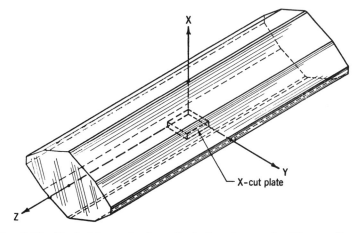

Fig. 5·38   Typical form of a large Rochelle salt crystal. The coordinate axes and the way in which an X-cut shear plate is cut from the crystal are indicated. (Courtesy Brush Development Co.)

phosphate (ADP),* and the lithium sulfate* crystals. Typical forms of the whole crystals of these three types are shown in Figs. 5·38 to 5·40.† Transducing elements are obtained by cutting slabs of material from these whole crystals. Usually these slabs are thin and either square or rectangular in shape. If the x axis of the crystal is perpendicular to the flat face of the slab, the crystal is said to be an X cut (see Fig. 5·38). Two other familiar slabs are the Y cut and the Z cut.

If two edges of a certain cut (X, Y, or Z) are parallel to the other two axes, and if Rochelle salt or ADP crystals are involved, a *shear plate* is obtained. That is to say, if a potential is applied

* The ADP crystals are sold under the trade name PN, and the lithium sulfate under the trade name LH.

† Nearly all the material for this section was supplied by the Brush Development Company, Cleveland, Ohio.

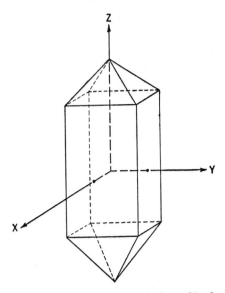

FIG. 5·39   Typical form of a large ammonium dihydrogen phosphate
(ADP or PN) crystal.   (Courtesy Brush Development Co.)

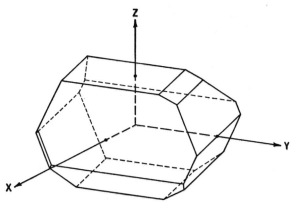

FIG. 5·40   Typical form of a large lithium sulfate (LH) crystal.   (Courtesy
Brush Development Co.)

between the two faces of the slab, shearing stresses are produced
in the plane of the plate.   For example, three possible states of
such a shear plate are shown in Fig. 5·41.   When a potential
E is applied across the two flat faces of the crystal (a), a deformation like that shown in (b) or (c) results depending on the polarity
of the applied potential.   Conversely, if one edge of a shear plate

is cemented to a surface and a force is applied *parallel* to the opposite edge, a potential will be developed between the two faces.
Microphones generally use either X and Y cuts of Rochelle salt
or Z cuts of ADP crystals.

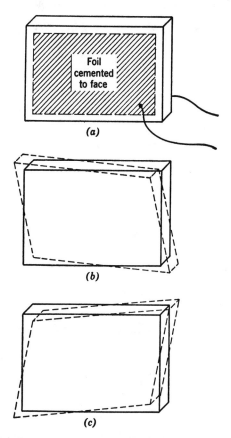

FIG. 5·41 The distortion of a shear plate when a potential is applied
between two foils cemented to its faces. (*a*) Placement of foils. (*b*) Distortion of shear plate with one polarity. (*c*) Distortion of shear plate with
opposite polarity. (Courtesy Brush Development Co.)

If a cut is taken from a shear plate in the manner shown in
Fig. 5·42*a*, a *45° expander plate* is obtained. Inspection of Fig.
5·41 shows that an observable effect for a shear plate when
voltage is applied is a lengthening or shortening of a diagonal
axis. Hence, if a cut is taken along that axis, potentials will

be generated by squeezing or extending the crystal along its length; see Fig. 5·42b.

Most piezoelectric crystals of commercial interest including Rochelle salt and ADP yield no significant output when subjected to hydrostatic pressure.   This is because the algebraic sum of the

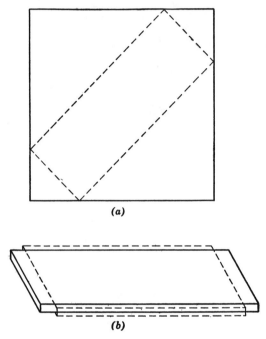

(a)

(b)

Fig. 5·42   (a) Method of cutting a 45° expander bar from a shear plate. (b) Sketch showing expansion of sides and compression of length of such a bar when a potential is applied between the two faces.   (Courtesy Brush Development Co.)

three piezoelectric constants excited by such a field is zero. The lithium sulfate (LH) crystal is an important exception, however.   The sum of its piezoelectric constants is not zero, and in fact it is sufficiently high to make the crystal useful as a microphone element when subjected directly to sound pressure.

Structure.   A type of microphone which uses expander bars as the active elements is sketched in Fig. 5·43.[38]   The sound

[38] A microphone using ADP expander bars and similar to this sketch is described by F. Massa, "A working standard for sound pressure measurements," *Jour. Acous. Soc. Amer.*, **17**, 29–34 (1945).

pressure acts on the end of the bars and alternately compresses and expands them about their undisturbed position. The air space around the sides allows for lateral expansion of the bars when they are undergoing longitudinal compression.

The principal disadvantage of such a microphone is its large mechanical impedance. For use in liquids, such an impedance is not objectionable, but in air, because of the large mechano-

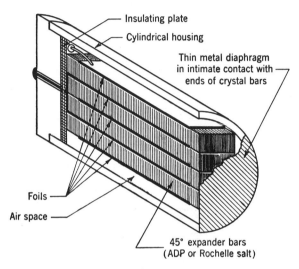

Insulating plate

Cylindrical housing

Thin metal diaphragm in intimate contact with ends of crystal bars

Foils

Air space

45° expander bars (ADP or Rochelle salt)

FIG. 5·43   Arrangement for mounting expander bars to form a pressure microphone. The foils are connected so that all capacitances are in parallel. The sound field acts on the thin metal diaphragm and causes expansion or compression of the bars along their length. (Prepared from rough sketch by Massa of Massa Laboratories.[38])

acoustic impedance mismatch, very small output voltages are obtained for normal sound pressures. To reduce this mechanical impedance appreciably without lowering the output voltage, two plates or bars may be combined to produce a Bimorph.* In a sense, a Bimorph is a mechanical transformer operating on a principle resembling that of a bimetallic strip. That is to say, the flat faces of two crystals are cemented together in such a way that when a potential is applied to them one expands and the other contracts. Or, from the mechanical point of view, a force acting perpendicular to the face of the "bimetallic strip" causes

* Bimorph is a registered trademark of the Brush Development Company.

a sizable compressive force in one plate and tensile force in the other.

Examples of a bender Bimorph and a torque Bimorph are shown in Figs. 5·44 and Fig. 5·45, respectively. The former makes use of two expander bars and the latter of two shear plates. Generally, the bender Bimorph is clamped at one end and the force applied at the other, whereas a torque Bimorph

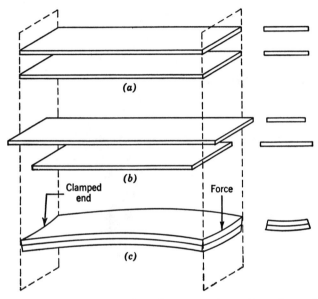

FIG. 5·44 (a) Two crystals ready to be cemented together to form a bender Bimorph. (b) Application of potentials of opposite polarity to the crystals causes the upper to lengthen and to contract in width and the other to shorten and to expand in width. (c) When these two crystals are cemented together and either a force f or electrical potentials are applied, the crystal assumes the shape shown. (Courtesy Brush Development Co.)

is held at three corners and the force applied at the fourth. A little thought will show that a force so applied to either type causes a greater force in the plane of the plate than would be obtained if the force were applied to the end of a single expander bar or along one edge of a single shear plate.

Electrodes may be applied in two ways to form either a series or a parallel arrangement of the two plates. For a series connection, the electrical terminals are the two outer foils. For a parallel connection, the foil between the crystals forms one terminal, and the two outside foils connected together from the other. A series Bimorph has one-quarter the capacitance and twice the voltage output of a parallel Bimorph.

Crystals in microphones using the Bimorph principle are generally mounted in one of the two forms shown in Fig. 5·46. In (a), a diaphragm-actuated construction is shown, and either ADP or Rochelle salt crystals are used. In (b) a directly actuated

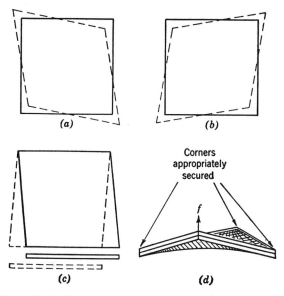

FIG. 5·45 (a)(b)(c) Distortion of shear plates when potentials of opposite polarity are applied across their faces. (d) Two shear plates are cemented together to form a torque Bimorph. When either a force f or electrical potentials are applied, the Bimorph assumes the shape shown. (Courtesy Brush Development Co.)

construction (sound cell) is illustrated. Here, two Bimorph bender units are held apart by two small blocks of rubber placed at the centers of two opposite edges. The sound pressure acting on the outer sides forces the centers of the plates and the unsupported edges together, thus producing the desired bending effect.

A sketch of one way in which a lithium sulfate (LH) crystal may be mounted to operate in a hydrostatic field is shown in Fig. 5·47.

Internal properties. The performance of a crystal transducer in converting force into voltage or charge can be represented by the equivalent circuit shown in Fig. 5·48. In this circuit, C_E is the electrical capacitance in farads, C_M is the mechanical compliance in meters per newton (1 newton equals 10^5 dynes), M is the effective mechanical mass in kilograms, and N is the electromechanical transformation ratio in volts per newton.

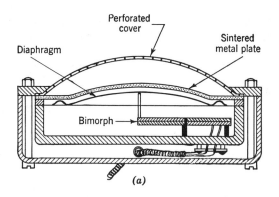

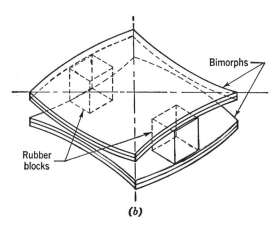

FIG. 5·46 (a) Diaphragm-type of crystal microphone using a torque Bimorph. The sintered metal plate is an acoustic damping element. (b) Sound-cell crystal microphone. The required compressive and tensile forces are produced in each of the four crystal plates when a force acts on the centers and the sides of the two bender Bimorphs.

For Rochelle salt, X-cut crystals, the electrical capacitance varies as a function of temperature. The factor of proportionality μ is shown in Fig. 5·49. For example, with the X-cut expander bar of Fig. 5·50, $N = 0.093/w$, $C_M = 31.4 \times 10^{-12}$

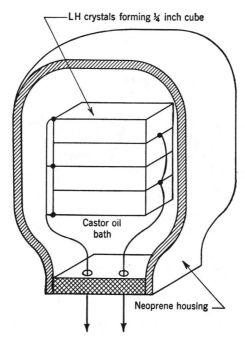

FIG. 5·47 Sketch of a hydrostatically actuated crystal microphone using lithium sulfate (LH) crystals as the active element. The castor oil bath is provided to convey the sound pressure uniformly to all surfaces of the crystal. Data taken on a cubical stack of six plates connected in parallel, $\frac{1}{4}$ in. on a side with each plate 0.04 in. thick, show that the capacitance is about 23×10^{-12} farad and the open-circuit output voltage is about -96 db *re* 1 volt per dyne/cm^2. (Courtesy Brush Development Co.)

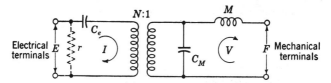

FIG. 5·48 Electromechanical equivalent circuit for a crystal microphone. C_e is the electrical capacitance in farads measured with the crystal unloaded (air loading is equivalent to no loading); N is the electromechanical transformation ratio in volts per newton (1 newton = 10^5 dynes); C_M is the mechanical compliance in meters per newton; M is the effective mass in kilograms; I is the electrical current in amperes; E is the voltage in volts; V is the velocity of motion of the crystal at its driving point in meters per second and F is the force at the driving point in newtons. The dotted resistor r is the bulk resistivity which is important only at the very low frequencies for all except ADP crystals. (Courtesy Brush Development Co.)

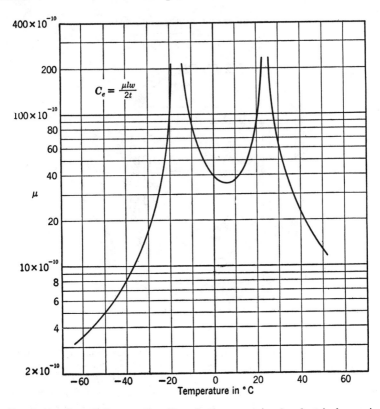

FIG. 5·49   Factor of proportionality μ in the expression for electrical capacitance C_e of an unmounted X-cut Rochelle salt expander bar as a function
of temperature. The discontinuities at $-18°C$ and $+22°C$ are known as
the Curie points.   (Courtesy Brush Development Co.)

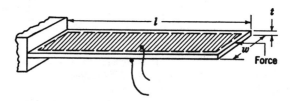

FIG. 5·50   Expander bar (45°-cut crystal) showing dimensions, method of
mounting, and point of application of force. (Courtesy Brush Development Co.)

l/wt, $M = 786\ lwt$, and $C_e = \mu lw/2t$. The dimensions l, w, and t are in meters.

The factors of proportionality for an ADP Z-cut expander bar are, respectively, 0.185, 47.4 × 10⁻¹², 737, and $\mu = 260 \times 10^{-12}$.

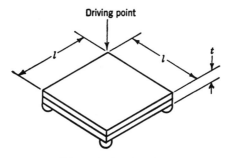

FIG. 5·51 Square torque Bimorph showing dimensions, method of mounting, and point of application of force. (Courtesy Brush Development Co.)

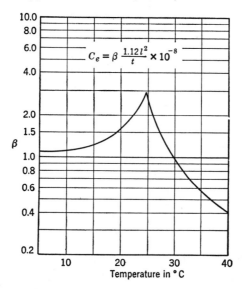

FIG. 5·52 Factor of proportionality β in the expression for electrical capacitance C_e of an X-cut Rochelle salt, square torque Bimorph mounted as shown in Fig. 5·51.

The element sizes for a Y-cut LH thickness expander bar (i.e., the electrical field is parallel to the mechanical deformation of the crystal) are, respectively, $N = 0.175\ t/lw$, $C_M = 16.3 \times 10^{-12}$ t/lw, $M = 832\ lwt$, and $C_e = 91 \times 10^{-12}\ lw/t$.

For square torque Bimorphs made from X-cut Rochelle salt shear plates as shown in Fig. 5·51, the element sizes are $N = 0.128/t$, $C_M = 2.40 \times 10^{-10} \, l^2/t^3$, $M = 246 \, l^2 t$, and C_e (parallel connection) $= \beta \times 1.12 \, l^2/t \times 10^{-8}$. The dimensions l and t

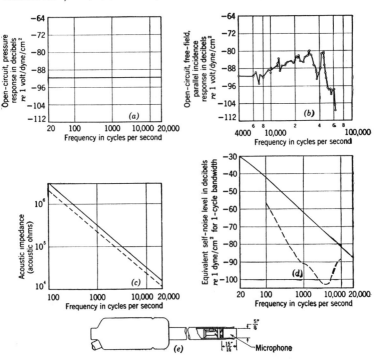

Fig. 5·53 Massa Laboratories type M-101 crystal microphone using ADP expander bars. (a) Pressure response. (b) Free-field response at grazing incidence to diaphragm. (c) Acoustic impedance looking into microphone ⅝ in. in diameter—solid line for microphone and dotted line for 0.001 cc of air. (d) Solid line—equivalent self-noise level for microphone when operating into 100-megohm grid resistor—100 μμf capacitance assumed; dotted line—threshold of hearing curve expressed in terms of sound pressure level per cycle bandwidth. (e) Configuration of the preamplifier housing and the support for the microphone.

are in meters. The factor β is given in Fig. 5·52. For ADP square torque Bimorphs, the factors of proportionality are, respectively (parallel connection), 0.233, 4.27×10^{-10}, 239, and $\beta = 0.0454$. When the plates are connected electrically in series, the value of N is doubled and that of C_e is reduced to one-fourth its parallel value.

Crystal microphones, like all others, are subject to diffraction effects related to their size. Typical response curves at audio and ultrasonic frequencies for a Massa Laboratories M-101 microphone are shown in Figs. 5·53a and 5·53b.[38] The configuration of the preamplifier housing and the support for the microphone used during these tests is shown in (e). The acoustic input impedance is shown in (c), and the self-noise in decibels re 1 dyne/cm^2 for a bandwidth of 1 cps is shown in (d). The data for (a), (c), (d), and (e) were given by Massa Laboratories.[38] Those for (b) were supplied by the Pennsylvania State College.[36] Frequency response curves for two types of crystal microphones are shown in Fig. 5·54. In that figure, (a) gives the response of a sound-cell type, with sound incident parallel to plane of diaphragm; (b) is for a diaphragm type; (c) gives the phase shift in degrees between open-circuit output voltage and pressure in free field before insertion of microphone of (a); (d) gives the phase shift for the microphone of (b) with $\phi = 90°$.

The non-linear distortion produced by the ADP or LH crystals is very small. Rochelle salt is an exception, however. In the temperature range from $-18°$ to $+24°$C, it exhibits hysteresis effects in the relation between the applied force and the voltage produced across a small load resistance. This hysteresis effect arises in the electrical capacitance C_e and is of negligible importance if the microphone operates in a near-open-circuit condition, such as into the input of a cathode follower stage. In microphones working at ordinary sound levels, the hysteresis effect in Rochelle salt is negligible even when the crystal is loaded.

The behavior of a crystal is affected by the mounting. Imperfect mounting pads restrain its motion in directions in which it should move freely and allow motion where it should be held rigid. The transducer ratio N is reduced by both effects. The compliance C_M and the effective mass M may be either increased or decreased, depending on the nature of the constraint.

All crystals have a bulk resistivity* which appears as a shunt resistance across the electrical terminals of the crystal. This factor is not of practical importance at ordinary temperatures except in ADP crystals. In Fig. 5·55, the frequency at which the resistivity and the capacitive reactance of ADP crystals (for a unit cube) are equal is plotted as a function of ambient tem-

---

* Bulk resistivity is the resistance in ohms measured between two faces of a unit cube.

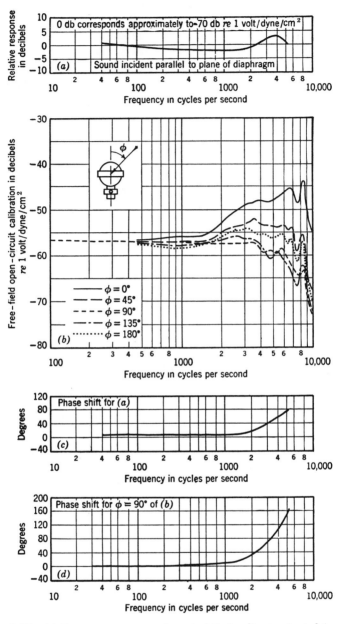

FIG. 5·54 (a) Frequency response characteristic for direct-actuated (sound cell), Bimorph-type, Rochelle salt crystal microphone; (b) same for diaphragm-actuated, Bimorph-type, Rochelle salt crystal microphone; (c) phase shift characteristic for (a); (d) phase shift characteristic for $\phi = 90°$ of (b). (All data are approximate.) (After Wiener.[34])

perature. Below this frequency the response of the crystal falls
off at 6 db per octave in frequency, which accounts for the designation "low frequency cutoff" in the legend. The notations
AAA and $AAA1$ designate the grade of crystal.

The random noise generated by thermal fluctuations of charge
in the insulating material of a crystal microphone is shunted by

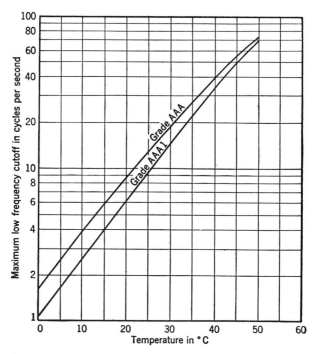

Fig. 5·55 Maximum expected low frequency cutoff in cycles for ADP
(PN) crystals as a function of ambient temperature in centigrade degrees.
The cutoff frequency is defined as that frequency where the capacitive
reactance and the resistivity (each measured between two faces of a unit
cube) become equal. (Courtesy Brush Development Co.)

the capacity of the crystal and the input resistance of the circuit
to which it is connected. This situation has been described in
Section 5·3. The spectrum level of the self-noise drops off at
6 db per octave as soon as the capacitive reactance becomes less
than the load resistance. A crystal which has been damaged by
heat or humidity is likely to have a high internal noise level.

We have already seen from Fig. 5·49 that the magnitude of the
electrical capacitance C_e for an X-cut Rochelle salt crystal is a

rapidly varying function of temperature, especially in the vicinity of normal room temperature (23°C). This anomalous behavior is usually described as a violent variation of the free dielectric constant with variations in temperature. The obvious way to avoid corresponding variations in the terminal voltage is to operate the microphone into an open circuit. This may be

TABLE 5·3

Property	Rochelle Salt	ADP	LH	Barium Titanate
Type of strain obtainable	Transverse shear; and expander	Transverse shear; expander; and longitudinal expander	Transverse and longitudinal shear, and hydrostatic	Transverse shear; expander; and hydrostatic
Common cuts	X; 45° X; Y; 45° Y	Z; 45° Z; L	Y	
Density, in kg/m³	1.77×10^3	1.795×10^3	2.06×10^3	5.6×10^3
Low frequency cutoff at 25°C	0.1 cps	AAA1, 9 cps AAA, 14 cps	<0.001 cps	Very low
Temperature for complete destruction	55°C (131°F)	*	*	Loses piezoelectric properties at 120°C
Maximum safe temperature	45°C (113°F)	125°C (257°F)	75°C (167°F)	90°C (194°F)
Temperature for appreciable leakage	50°C (122°F)	40°C (104°F)	*	
Maximum safe humidity (unprotected element)	84 %	94 %	95 %	Moisture absorption 0.1 %
Humidity above which surface leakage becomes appreciable (unprotected element)	50 %	50 %	50 %	95 %
Minimum safe humidity (unprotected element)	30 %	0 %	0 %	0 %
Maximum breaking stress (alternating compression-tension)	14.7×10^6 newton/m²	20.6×10^6 newton/m²	*	45×10^6 newton/m²

* No data available.

accomplished by using a cathode follower circuit and no microphone cable. In addition to causing variation in C_e, high temperatures decrease the resistivity and, if high enough, permanently damage the crystal. Data showing the approximate maximum safe temperatures, temperatures for appreciable leakage, and the temperatures for complete destruction are given in Table 5·3.

Humidity also affects crystals, especially those of the Rochelle-salt type. Rochelle salt chemically is sodium potassium tartrate with four molecules of water of crystallization. If the humidity is too low (less than about 30 per cent) the crystal gradually dehydrates and becomes a powder. If the humidity is too high (above about 84 percent) the crystal gradually dissolves. Neither result is reversible. Protective coatings are normally applied to all three types of crystals, but most of the coatings in use up to now do not afford permanent protection. Fortunately, in most instances, extremes of humidity are of relatively short duration and little, if any, harm results. Recently developed improvements offer promise of complete protection from the influence of humidity extremes.

To test a crystal for normality, measure its resistivity and electrical capacitance. If the resistivity is higher than normal and the capacitance is lower than normal, the crystal has dehydrated. If the resistivity is too low and the capacitance is too high, the crystal has partially or entirely dissolved. If the resistivity is low and the shunt capacitance has not changed, surface leakage is taking place.

Crystals are generally quite stable if operated within the temperature and humidity limits indicated in Table 5·3. Aging is due to the cements and protective coatings used and is usually completed in a few weeks.

A recent addition to piezoelectric substances is a ceramic material made from barium titanate. The material is rendered piezoelectric by permanently polarizing it with a high electrostatic potential of about 40,000 to 60,000 volts/cm for a period of several minutes to an hour. Pure barium titanate[39] has a Curie point like that of Rochelle salt, except that it occurs at a temperature of 120°C, well above the normal operating range for a microphone. Dielectric anomalies may also exist near 5°C and −70°C.

Accurate information on the physical constants of barium titanate microphones is not available. However, barium titanate and Rochelle salt plates cut to have the same electrical

---

[39] B. B. Bauer, "Piezoelectric ceramics," *Radio-Electronic Engineering*, pp. 3–6 (August, 1948). Also, B. Matthias, "The growth of barium titanate crystals," *Phys. Rev.*, **73**, 808–809 (1948) and B. Matthias and A von Hippel, "Structure, electrical and optical properties of barium titanate," *Phys. Rev.*, **73**, 268 (1948).

capacitance (3300 $\mu\mu$f) and mechanical compliance (1.57 $\times$ 10^{-7} m/newton) show that the barium titanate is the less sensitive of the two by about 18 db.   However, further refinement of the manufacturing process may lead to barium titanate plates which are nearly as sensitive as Rochelle salt plates.

G. Other Microphones

As stated at the outset, this chapter is not a catalog of microphones but a survey of the more common types with a few examples. Some other types should be mentioned. Armature microphones with moving iron can be made and used with either a permanent magnet bias or a high frequency carrier. Magnetostrictive bars and quartz crystal plates are useful for narrowband underwater sound work because at resonance their mechanical impedance closely matches the characteristic impedance of water. The author of a recent Swiss paper[40] describes an acoustic air-jet amplifier detector in which the sensitive boundary of the streaming air converts sound waves into vortices. The formation of the vortices measurably reduces the momentum of the jet and produces a pressure amplifiction as high as 1000.

5·5 Directional Microphones

Directional microphones are required in many kinds of sound measurements. They are useful in locating the direction of waves outdoors or in rooms. Furthermore, they are able to discriminate between sounds from a known origin and unwanted noise coming from other directions. Such microphones can be divided broadly into two types: (a) doublet and (b) dimensional.

A. Doublet Type

Suppose that we have a diaphragm, of area S, supported in free space. Let this diaphragm be connected to a transducer which responds only to displacements along the axis of the diaphragm (see Fig. 5·56). When a sound wave of any given frequency strikes this diaphragm at an angle θ, there is a pressure difference Δp between the two sides. When θ is 0° or 180° this pressure difference is large; but when θ is 90° both sides experience the same pressure, and the difference is zero. In fact it

[40] H. Zickendraht, "A new hydrodynamic principle of sound measurement," *Swiss Technics*, **22**, 8 (1943).

can be shown[41] that the difference pressure Δp is given approximately by

$$\Delta p = K\omega \cos \theta \qquad (5 \cdot 11)$$

$K\omega$, a constant times the angular frequency of the sound waves, is the pressure difference when $\theta = 0$. This system, characterized by a response proportional to $\cos \theta$, is a doublet microphone. Interesting and useful properties can be obtained when the motion of the diaphragm is controlled by its mass reactance ωm. The

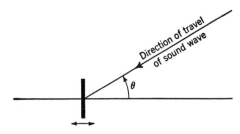

FIG. 5·56   A simple type of doublet is represented by the small disk shown here constrained to move axially.

velocity v (equaling force/impedance) of the disk, given in Eq. (5·12), is then independent of frequency.

$$v = \frac{\Delta p S}{\omega m} = K' \cos \theta \qquad (5 \cdot 12)$$

If the transducer is electromagnetic, generating a voltage e proportional to velocity, the electric output is independent of frequency but proportional to $\cos \theta$. The most familiar type of doublet microphone is the ribbon or "velocity" type[41] already described.   (See Fig. 5·57a.)

A doublet microphone by itself is bidirectional.   It is possible to reduce the sensitivity in one direction to zero by connecting a pressure-sensitive microphone in series electrically with a velocity microphone.   If the microphones have the same sensitivity to waves at $\theta = 0$ and if they are physically close together, a cardioid directivity pattern is obtained:

$$e = K(1 + \cos \theta) \qquad (5 \cdot 13)$$

where K is a constant as before and θ is the angle of incidence of

[41] H. F. Olson, *Elements of Acoustical Engineering*, 2nd edition, p. 239, D. Van Nostrand Company (1947).

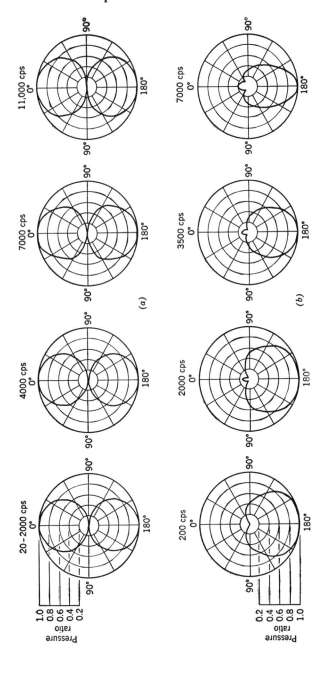

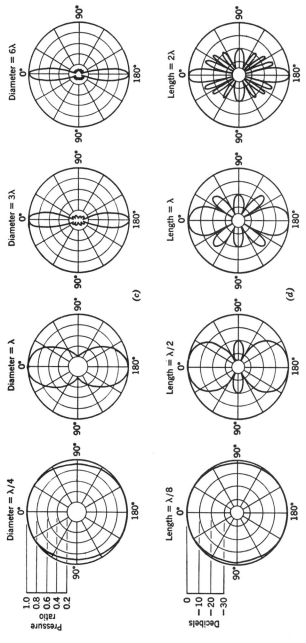

Fig. 5·57 Directivity patterns of six types of microphones. (a) Ribbon (velocity); (b) cardioid; (c) flat diaphragm in infinite baffle; (d) 10 microphones in row, equally spaced. (After Olson,[1] and Mason and Marshall.)

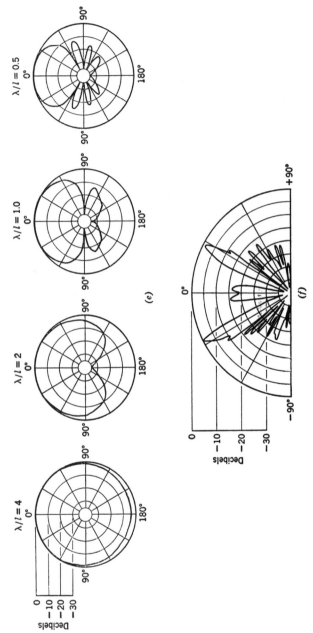

Fig. 5.57 Directivity patterns of six types of microphones. (e) Fifty tubes differing in length by equal increments; (f) thin bar. (After Mason and Marshall[42] and Beranek.)

the sound wave. At $\theta = 180°$, $e = 0$. The directivity characteristic will be greatly reduced in the region between $\theta = 125°$ and $\theta = 235°$ as compared to that for the velocity microphone. (see Fig. 5·57b.)

B. Dimensional Types

Directional microphones which depend on their shape and on the ratio of their average size to a wavelength for their directivity may be called dimensional types. These include reflectors, large

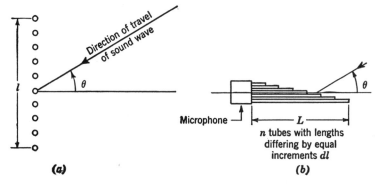

FIG. 5·58   (a) Directional array composed of 10 microphones whose electrical outputs are connected in series.   (b) Directional array composed of a group of hollow tubes differing in length by equal increments and connected to a pressure-actuated microphone.

diaphragms, horns, distributed arrays of sound-sensitive elements, and bars.

Reflectors, large diaphragms, and horns are about as directional as a rigid piston of the same diameter vibrating in a wall. Directional patterns for the rigid piston are given in (c) of Fig. 5·57.

Two types of distributed arrays are shown in Figs. 5·58a and 5·58b.   The array in (a) consists of a row of pressure-sensitive microphones of equal sensitivities and spacings.   If the microphones are connected in series, the net voltage produced is given by

$$E = \frac{K \sin \omega t}{n} \left[\frac{\sin \dfrac{n\beta}{n-1}}{\sin \dfrac{\beta}{n-1}} \right] \tag{5·14}$$

where K is a constant, n is the number of microphones, and

$$\beta = \frac{\pi l}{\lambda} \sin \theta \qquad (5 \cdot 15)$$

where l is the length of the array, λ is the wavelength, and θ is the angle of incidence of the sound wave. This equation says that, when θ equals zero, the wave arrives at all microphones in the same phase, and the maximum effect is produced. When θ is other than zero, the waves will arive more or less out of phase, and the voltage E will be smaller. The directional characteristic for ten microphones in a line is given in (d) of Fig. 5·57.

The tubular array in (b) of Fig. 5·58 has a similar directional characteristic.[42] A distinctive feature of this array is that only one pressure-sensitive element is necessary. A sound wave arriving along the $\theta = 0$ axis travels down the tubes, and the output of each tube is delivered to the microphone in phase. At other angles of incidence the wave takes longer to arrive at the microphone from the longer tubes, and a cancellation effect occurs.

When the length of the array is L,

$$E = \frac{K \sin \omega t}{n} \left[\frac{\sin \phi}{\sin \dfrac{\phi}{n}} \right] \qquad (5 \cdot 16)$$

where

$$\phi = \frac{\pi L}{\lambda} (\cos \theta - 1) \qquad (5 \cdot 17)$$

Directional characteristics for the tubular microphone of Fig. 5·58b are given in (e). The principal difference between the row and tubular microphones is that the microphone made of tubes has more discrimination in the second and third quadrants.

The final type of directional unit which we shall discuss here is sketched in Fig. 5·59.[43] It consists of a thin bar of length l, width w, and thickness t. When this bar is excited so that transverse waves form in it, nodal lines will occur evenly spaced (except near the ends) along its length. That spacing, $\lambda_t/2$, is

[42] W. P. Mason and R. N. Marshall, "A tubular directional microphone," *Jour. Acous. Soc. Amer.*, **10**, 206–215 (1939).
[43] G. W. Pierce, U.S. Patent No. 2063945.

$$\frac{\lambda_t}{2} = \frac{2l}{2n - 1} \qquad (5 \cdot 18)$$

where λ_t is the length of a transverse wave in the bar, l is the length of the bar, and n is an integer indicating the number of

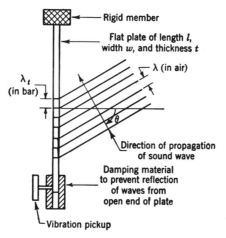

Rigid member

Flat plate of length l, width w, and thickness t

λ (in air)

λ_t (in bar)

θ

Direction of propagation of sound wave

Damping material to prevent reflection of waves from open end of plate

Vibration pickup

Fig. 5·59 Directional array formed by a bar clamped at one end and damped to eliminate transverse standing waves. A point of maximum motion of the end of the bar is achieved when θ is adjusted so that the separation between two points of equal phase in the air wave coincides with two points of equal phase in the bar wave. (After G. W. Pierce.)

nodal lines along the bar. The frequency of vibration f_t is related to the wavelength λ_t through the formula[44]

$$f_t = \frac{Kc_2\pi}{8l^2}(2n - 1)^2 = \frac{2\pi Kc_2}{\lambda_t^2} \qquad (5 \cdot 19)$$

where $c_2 = \sqrt{\text{Young's modulus/density}}$
$K = t/\sqrt{12}$ for rectangular bars
$l = $ length of bar,
$n = 0, 1, 2, 3, \cdots$.

Sound waves in air striking this bar will tend to excite it to resonance. Resonance will occur whenever the separation

---

[44] Lord Rayleigh, *Theory of Sound*, 2nd edition, Vol. 1, Macmillan and Company, Ltd., Chapter VIII (1937). This formula was given by Pierce in the form shown here.

between nodal lines in the air at the surface of the bar equals the wavelength in the bar (see Fig. 5·59). This occurs for

$$\sin \theta = \frac{\lambda}{\lambda_t} \qquad (5 \cdot 20)$$

where θ is the angle of incidence, λ is the wavelength of sound in the air, and λ_t is the length of a transverse wave in the bar. Hence, for any given ratio of wavelengths λ/λ_t less than unity and greater than zero there will be an angle θ at which the response of the bar will be a maximum. Obviously, unless one side of the bar is shielded, such a maximum will occur for sound incident from either of the two sides of the bar. A typical response curve measured for an aluminum strip at 18,510 cps with dimensions $12 \times 1.0 \times 0.125$ in. is shown in Fig. 5·57f.

5·6 Microphones in Winds

A. Medium Wind Velocities

Outdoor measurement of sound fields is often disturbed by wind. If the sound wave is intense enough and if the wind direction is not constant, spherical foam-rubber windscreens are commonly used. The material is an open-pored polyurethane foam, cut out to allow insertion of condenser or electret microphones of various diameters.

For a 9-cm (3.5-in.) diameter windscreen, the free-field response is affected less than ± 1 dB up to 15 kHz for angles of wave incidence between 0° and 120°. The self-noise levels generated for winds incident at 0° and at 90° and at velocities up to 160 km/h (100 mi./h) are shown in Figs. 5·60 and 5·61.[36] At frequencies below 100 Hz the wind-induced noise, measured in one-third octave bands, is about 103 dB at 160 km/h, dropping about 12 dB for each halving of wind velocity. The levels are about 20 dB lower at frequencies above 1000 Hz.

B. High wind velocity

For wind velocities that are high and steady in a well-defined direction, a nose cone may be used. One manufacturer's nose cone is shown in Fig. 5·62,[36] and the wind-induced noise levels for one-inch microphones equipped with this cone in place of the protective cover are shown in Fig. 5·63. The nose cone is solid and is designed to minimize the volume of air in front of

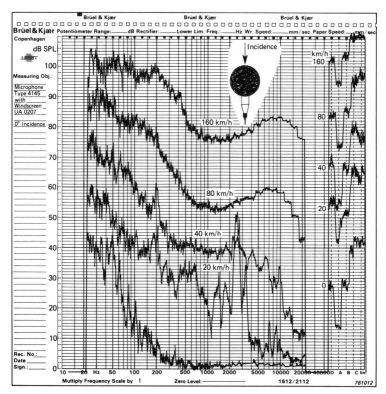

FIG. 5·60 Wind-induced noise levels in one-third-octave bands, for one-inch microphone inserted in 9 cm dia foam-rubber windscreen. Wind direction at 0° incidence. (Courtesy Bruel & Kjaer.)

the diaphragm. A circumferential slot near the base communicates directly with the diaphragm. This slot is covered with a fine wire mesh to preserve the exterior streamlining, and thus reduce turbulence.

Compared to the spherical foam rubber windscreens, the wind-induced noise levels below about 100 Hz are about 10 dB lower. At frequencies above 1000 Hz, the noise levels are roughly the same as for the foam-rubber windscreens.

R. L. Wallace, Jr.* studied various-shaped structures for housing microphones to be operated in a windstream with well-defined direction (unpublished data taken in the early 1940s). He concluded that the least wind noise is obtained when the

*Bell Telephone Laboratories, Murray Hill, NJ.

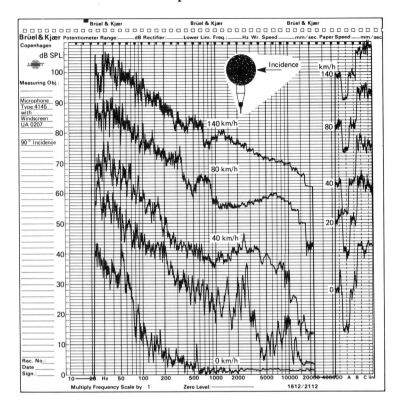

1612/2112

FIG. 5·61 Same as Fig. 5·60, except wind direction at 90° incidence. (Courtesy of Bruel & Kjaer.)

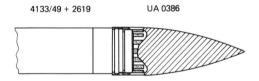

4133/49 + 2619   UA 0386

FIG. 5·62 Cross section of Nose Cone. The crosshatched area is solid. The sound reaches the diaphragm through slots around the circumference behind a fine-wire mesh.

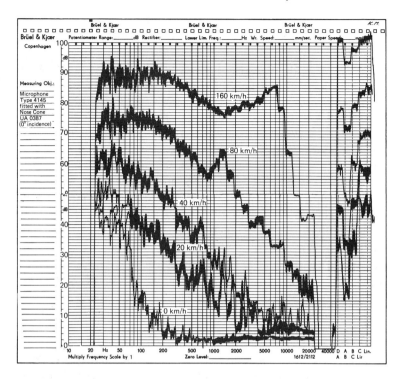

FIG. 5·63 Wind induced noise levels for one-inch microphone fitted with the Nose Cone of Fig. 5·62. (Courtesy of Bruel & Kjaer.)

microphone is mounted in the nose of a streamlined housing such as that shown in Fig. 5·64. The sound sensitive area that communicates with the microphone should be small. He used a narrow slot covered with sintered metal. No measured self-noise levels are available.

5·7 Measurement of Sound Intensity[45,46]

The human ear responds to sound pressure, and this quantity can be sensed by the various types of microphones described in this chapter. A source of sound will produce a sound pressure at a distance r from it that is related to the power radiated by the

[45]T. J. Schultz, P. W. Smith, Jr., and C. I. Malme, "Measurement of acoustic intensity in reactive sound field." J. Acoust. Soc. Am. **57**, 1263–1268 (1975).

[46]G. Rasmussen, *Itensity Measurements*, Bruel & Kajaer Report BA-7196-11 (1985). Bruel & Kjaer, DK-2850 Naerum, Denmark.

source in that direction. In sound control of machinery, we need to know the total power radiated by the source and the portions of it that are radiated in different directions—the directivity. In a plane wave, or a spherical wave at a sufficient distance from the source, the sound pressure at a point where the listener might be is directly proportional to the square root of the sound intensity, defined on p. 25. Expressed mathematically, $p_r = \sqrt{I_r \rho_0 c}$, where I_r is the intensity at that point in the near-plane wave and $\rho_0 c$ is the characteristic impedance of the medium.

If one were outdoors, finding the total power would simply be a matter of measuring the sound pressure at a number of points on the surface of a sphere surrounding the source, squaring the sound pressure at each point of measurement, multiplying each $p_r{}^2$ by the area S_r associated with that point of measurement, adding the values so obtained, and dividing by $\rho_0 c$. The directivity would be known from the $p_r{}^2 S_r$ in each direction.

In factory spaces, where the noise must be measured *in situ*, the far-field method of determining sound power from sound pressure measurements doesn't work. Sound pressure squared is not proportional to intensity when the measuring microphone is near the machine. Also, noise from surrounding machines will add to the measured noise and cause wrong results.

To find the total power radiated through a surface of area S_{total} enclosing the machine, the intensity I_n, associated with each sub-area S_n on the enclosing surface, must be measured directly, and all the $I_n S_n = P_n$ summed to get Total Power. From the sub-powers, P_n, the directivity, i.e., the radiation pattern, can also be determined.

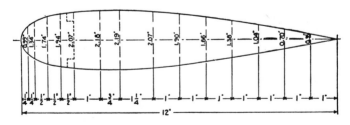

FIG. 5·64 Streamlined housing for a microphone to be used in a steady windstream. The sound reaches the microphone inside through a small acoustically-transparent opening in the nose.

The intensity at a point, or over a sub-area, defined on p. 26, is

$$I(\theta) = \frac{1}{T} \int_0^T p v_a \, dt = \overline{p v_a} \tag{5.21}$$

Note that v_a is the *component* of the instantaneous particle velocity in a specified direction θ. To illustrate, if the air particles are moving to-and-fro parallel to the floor, i.e., the wave is moving in a direction parallel to the floor, v_a is equal to the particle velocity v in the horizontal direction, i.e., $\theta = 0$. In the vertical direction, where $\theta = 90°$, v_a is zero. Also note that T must be a period of time that is long compared to the time it takes for one to-and-fro motion of an air particle in the lowest frequency component. Finally, if p is in newtons per square meter and v is in meters per second, I will be in watts per square meter.

According to the basic equation of acoustics, called Euler's equation, the particle velocity in a particular direction, v_a, can be closely approximated by integrating over time the *difference* in the sound pressure at two points, $(p_B - p_A)$, separated by an accurately known distance Δr. The equation is

$$v_a = -\frac{1}{\rho_0} \int_0^t \frac{(p_B - p_A)}{\Delta r} \, dt \tag{5.22}$$

where ρ_0 is the density of air in kilograms per cubic meter.

The sound pressure at a point can be found by averaging the pressures at Δr, i.e., $p = (p_B + p_A)/2$. So,

$$I(\theta) = \left(\frac{p_B + p_A}{2}\right) \int \frac{(p_B - p_A)}{\rho_0 \Delta r} \, dt \,. \tag{5.23}$$

In the associated electrical equipment, the signals from the two closely spaced microphones are converted to digital form and are brought through two separate one-third-octave digital filters to two circuits. In one circuit, the sum $(p_B + p_A)$ is taken. In the other the difference $(p_B - p_A)$ is taken and integrated over time. The time average of the outputs from the two circuits then yields $I(\theta)$.

The microphone setup for obtaining p_A and p_B at two points a distance Δr apart is shown in Fig. 5.65.[46] The microphones are either one-half inch in diameter, separated by 1.2 cm or 5 cm, or one-fourth inch, separated by 0.6 cm or 1.2 cm. The smallest separation is used for frequencies between 250 Hz and 12 kHz. The 5 cm separation is used for the range 31.5 Hz to 1.25 kHz. The 1.2 cm separation is used for the intermediate range, 125 Hz to 5 kHz.

When determining the total sound power radiated by a machine, a "surface" must be "drawn" around the machine. This might be a box, a sphere (or hemisphere) or a shape that approximates the shape of the machine. This enclosing "surface" is divided into sub-areas S_n and the area in meters of each is recorded. The sound intensity is then measured at the center of each sub-area and recorded beside its size, and the product taken to get $I_n S_n$. *During each measurement, the sound intensity probe must be held perpendicular to each sub-area.* We must remember that we are measuring v_a, not the maximum velocity, v.

The effect of the orientation of the intensity probe can be seen from the simple case shown in Fig. 5·66. In that case, the

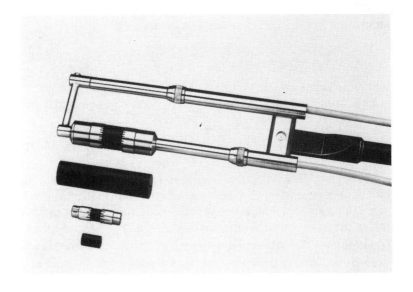

Fig. 5·65 One type of sound intensity probe showing two one-half inch diameter microphones separated by a 1.2-cm spacer. The lower one-fourth inch microphones are separated by the 0.6-cm spacer. The 5-cm spacer is also shown.

orientation shown on the left side gives I_{max}, because the wave is traveling directly toward the probe, yielding $v = v_a$. If the imaginary enclosure were a box, and the probe was near the top edge, obviously θ would not be zero, and v_a would be less than v.

The accuracy of measurement of $I(\theta)$ is dependent on several critical factors. First, the two microphones and the electrical circuitry must be identical in amplitude and phase characteristics at all orientations of the probe in a plane wave field or when calibrated in a highly reactive field (such as a closed coupler). Second, the separation must be known accurately, which is the reason for the precision spacers. Finally, the directional characteristic for the intensity probe must equal $\cos \theta$ exactly, or measurements of $I(\theta)$ will be incorrect, especially for values of θ near 90°.

Interestingly, noise from other sources (background noise) does not affect the total sound power measurement. Any sound entering one side of the enclosing "surface" leaves by the other sides. Also, there must not be any absorbing material within the surface, because all of the energy entering one side will not leave by another side.

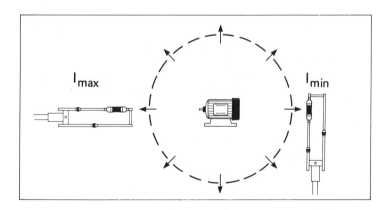

FIG. 5·66 The magnitude of v_a, and hence the measured intensity, $I(\theta)$ depends on the orientation of the probe. (Courtesy of Bruel & Kjaer)

6.

Signal Generators and the Measurement of Frequency

6·1 Scales of Human Responses vs Physical Stimuli

One of the three basic physical quantities which we must measure in order to define fully a sinusoidal sound wave of small amplitude at a point in space is frequency. The measurement of frequency received early scientific attention because, much more than amplitude, it determines pitch, the most obvious attribute of music. The other two basic quantities are pressure amplitude and either the complex acoustical impedance of the medium at that point or the phase and magnitude of the particle velocity.

In 1987, frequency standards are commercially available which exceed by orders of magnitude the accuracy and precision of such standards reported in this text 40 years ago. These accurate standards generally produce a single frequency, which is subdivided into other fixed frequencies that are more usable in laboratory or commercial applications. For example, one commercially available atomic frequency standard with a fundamental frequency of 9192 MHz, has outputs at 5 MHz, 1 MHz, and 100 kHz.[1]

In the first edition of this book, a somewhat philosophical discussion was given on how discrete frequencies should be spaced to conform to the "natural" way that people hear. It was stated there, that the property common to all psychoacoustic functions appeared to be explained by the Fechner Law. The Fechner Law says that the *sensation* (response of an individual)

---

[1]Hewlett–Packard Commercial Literature, "Frequency and time standards," Hewlett–Packard Corp., 1820 Embarcadero Road, Palo Alto, CA 94303.

caused by some *stimulus* (physical quantity that creates the sensation), changes in direct proportion to the logarithm of the magnitude of the stimulus. This is also known as the logarithmic law.

The Fechner Law came under close examination by Professor S. S. Stevens, of the Harvard Psycho-Physics Laboratory.[2] His exhaustive studies, involving some 20 different stimuli, showed that, for most types, sensations in human beings vary according to a power law, which states that equal stimulus ratios produce equal sensation ratios. We shall call this the *Stevens Law.* In Table 6·1, the measured exponents relating sensations to stimuli as Stevens determined them are listed.

Frequency is not listed in Table 6·1 as one of the stimuli that obeys Stevens Law. In the case of tones, the relation between the subjective reaction, which is measured in units called mels, and the physical stimulus of a tone, measured by its frequency in Hz, is determined neither by the Stevens nor by the Fechner Law, but rather by the position of mechanical resonance along the basilar membrane caused by the stimulus. (See Fig. 6·1.) Because this is such an odd scale, it is seldom used in acoustical instrumentation. Instead, there are two common ways of presenting data related to frequency. When measurements are made in which the identification of harmonics in a tone is needed, frequency is usually displayed on a linear scale. When measurements are made of sounds using an analyzer whose bandwidth is proportional to the frequency being measured, frequency is generally displayed on a logarithmic scale. Because sounds can be felt or heard over the frequency range of 1 Hz to 15 kHz, use of the logarithmic scale may require up to six decades of frequency in some cases.

In this chapter, we shall cover some of the modern and some of the older ways of producing frequencies of both high and lower accuracy and of comparing unknown with standard frequencies. We shall also discuss briefly signal generators for use in acoustic measurements.

6·2 Primary Frequency Standards

In the United States of America the primary standards of time and frequency are maintained at the U. S. Naval Observa-

[2]Reprinted with permission from S. S. Stevens, *Psychophysics* (John Wiley and Sons, New York, 1975).

TABLE 6·1 REPRESENTATIVE EXPONENTS OF THE POWER FUNCTIONS RELATING SUBJECTIVE MAGNITUDE TO STIMULUS MAGNITUDE. (Reprinted with permission from S. Stevens, *Psychophysics*, John Wiley and Sons, New York, 1975)

Continuum	exponent	Stimulus condition
Loudness	0.67	Sound pressure of 3000-hertz tone
Vibration	0.95	Amplitude of 60 hertz on finger
Vibration	0.6	Amplitude of 250 hertz on finger
Brightness	0.33	5° Target in dark
Brightness	0.5	Point source
Brightness	0.5	Brief flash
Brightness	1.0	Point source briefly flashed
Lightness	1.2	Reflectance of gray papers
Visual length	1.0	Projected line
Visual area	0.7	Projected square
Redness (saturation)	1.7	Red–gray mixture
Taste	1.3	Sucrose
Taste	1.4	Salt
Taste	0.8	Saccharine
Smell	0.6	Heptane
Cold	1.0	Metal contact on arm
Warmth	1.6	Metal contact on arm
Warmth	1.3	Irradiation of skin, small area
Warmth	0.7	Irradiation of skin, large area
Discomfort, cold	1.7	Whole body irradiation
Discomfort, warm	0.7	Whole body irradiation
Thermal pain	1.0	Radiant heat on skin
Tactual roughness	1.5	Rubbing emery cloths
Tactual hardness	0.8	Squeezing rubber
Finger span	1.3	Thickness of blocks
Pressure on palm	1.1	Static force on skin
Muscle force	1.7	Static contractions
Heaviness	1.45	Lifted weights
Viscosity	0.42	Stirring silicone fluids
Electric shock	3.5	Current through fingers
Vocal effort	1.1	Vocal sound pressure
Angular acceleration	1.4	5-Second rotation
Duration	1.1	White noise stimuli

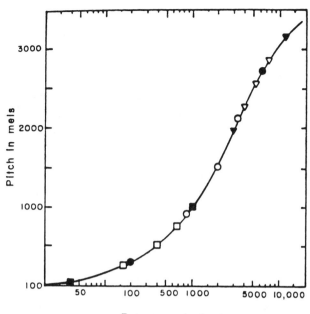

FIG. 6·1 The curve shows how pitch, scaled in subjective units (ordinate), varies with frequency. The circles, squares, and triangles represent data obtained in the experiment using equisection. The filled symbols mark the ends of three frequency ranges, and the empty symbols show the points arrived at when the observers divided the ranges into four equal intervals of pitch. (From Stevens.[2])

tory (USNO) and the National Bureau of Standards (NBS) in Washington, D.C. A primary standard does not require any reference for calibration.

The primary standard used by those institutions is based on periods of transition within the cesium atom. The cesium beam type of frequency standard thus provides access to one of nature's invariant frequencies in accordance with the principles of quantum mechanics. The basic unit of time, the second, is defined as the duration of 9,192,631,770 periods of transition within the cesium atom. An unknown frequency is determined by counting the number of cycles over a period of a second.

The best available of the cesium beam primary frequency standards has an accuracy of $\pm\,4\times10^{-12}$. Two, or in the case of the USNO, more than 12 such electronic standards are operated simultaneously and are intercompared to detect any drift in frequency. Adjustments can be made to bring any unit found drifting back into line.

A. U. S. Government Radio Time Signals

The time information derived from these primary standards is broadcast by the National Bureau of Standards over radio stations WWV and WWVB and by other stations throughout the world. The services of these stations include the broadcast of standard radio frequencies and standard time intervals accurately synchronized with the basic time periods. Instabilities in high-frequency propagation result because the paths that the radio waves take are affected by the height and ionic composition of the ionosphere, and more than one signal may arrive at a distant point over different paths. To average out these variations caused by propagation anomolies may require many days of data recordings in order to approach a precision that is better than 1 part in 10^8.

At this writing, the two NBS stations, WWV and WWVB, are located in Fort Collins, Colorado.[3] WWV broadcasts continuously on six carrier frequencies: 2.5, 5, 10, 15, 20, and 25 MHz. The time signals on the carriers are: Each second, a fast time-rise pulse of 5 cycles of 1000-Hz modulation is emitted. The 29th and the 59th second pulse during each minute is omitted. The hour is identified by an 0.8-sec-long, 1500-Hz tone. The beginning of each minute is identified by an 0.8-sec-long, 1000-Hz tone.

WWVB broadcasts continuously on a carrier of 60,000 Hz. Each second is indicated by a pulsed reduction of the amplitude of the carrier. This low-frequency carrier is far more stable than the WWV transmissions. It follows the Earth's curvature as though being guided by a duct having the ionosphere as a boundary rather than a reflector. Ionospheric variations have a much reduced influence on these very low-frequency carriers than on the higher frequency carriers. The resultant high phase-stability plus the long-range coverage makes WWVB valuable for standard frequency transmissions.

---

[3]NBS Special Publication 236, NBS Frequency and Time Broadcast Services, U. S. Government Printing Office, Washington, D. C. 20402.

6·3 Secondary Frequency Standards

A. Rubidium Frequency Standards

A secondary frequency standard requires calibrations both during manufacturing and at intervals during use depending on the accuracy desired. Rubidium frequency standards feature both quite high short-term and long-term frequency stability. The atomic resonant element prevents drift of a quartz frequency oscillator by the process of a frequency lockup. Because the rubidium gas cell is dependent upon gas mixture and gas pressure in the cell, some drift is expected and the unit must be calibrated against a primary standard according to the accuracy required. Unattended, the long-term stability is better than 1×10^{-11} over a period of a month.

One interesting application is to package the secondary standard to make it useable for transporting accurate time from one location to another by airplane. A battery power supply is used in transit. Secondary standard accuracy can be maintained over 6-hour flight times allowing for ambient temperatures within the range of -40 and $75\,°C$ and for ac and dc ambient magnetic field variations up to 1 Gauss peak.

6·4 Quartz Frequency Standards

A quartz frequency standard is adequate for many uses in the laboratory, particularly if it is calibrated against a primary standard radio signal as often as required. The state-of-the-art oscillators, using specially cut quartz crystals, have an aging factor in accuracy of frequency of less than 5 parts in 10^{10} per day. This degree of stability is accomplished by enclosing the crystal, the oscillator, and the automatic gain control circuitry in a closely thermostated oven. (See Sec. 6·6, below.)

6·5 Musicians' Frequency Comparison Standards

Musicians need a variable portable frequency standard for tuning of their instruments. In the United States, the tone (musicians speak of pitch) A_4, which has a frequency equal to 440 Hz, is the accepted standard used by symphony orchestras and pianists for tuning. In the first edition of this book, sophisticated tuning forks were still used by musicians for this purpose. In Fig. 6·2, an adjustable tuning fork is shown. The frequency is changed by means of weights that are caused to slide along the

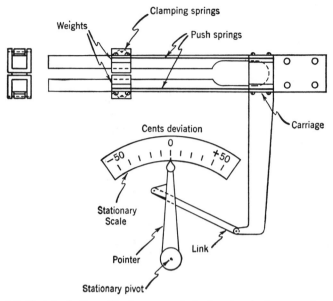

FIG. 6·2 Sketch of adjustable-frequency fork, showing the lever mechanism
for sliding the weights.

tuning fork blades by a lever mechanism. This mechanical link
between the pointer and the sliders serves to linearize the
scale, which would otherwise be compressed on the lower end.

The scale itself was calibrated in hundredths of an equally
tempered semitone, that is, in *cents* (1 cent corresponds to a
change of 0.057 779% in frequency). The fork was constructed
from an alloy steel containing 35% nickel and 12% chromium,
which has a temperature vs frequency coefficient of about -10
parts per million per centigrade degree. By controlling the fork
to 0.1 °C, the frequency could be held constant to at least 1 part
in 10^5.

Special methods were devised for increasing the accuracy of a
tuning fork as a frequency standard by surrounding each prong
with a tube at the outer end and carrying a heavy flange at its
inner end. Temperature variation lengthens the tube, thus dis-
placing the weight inward and increasing the frequency. An
alternative arrangement involved a crossbar between the
prongs which, when the temperature increased, would exert
pressure on the prongs.

The tuning fork of Fig. 6·2 was maintained in oscillation by means of a regenerative circuit, involving a pair of driving and a pair of sensing coils. Variation in frequency of less than one part in 10^6 was possible with a properly regulated power supply. Calibration was maintained by comparison with a standard frequency from NBS radio station WWV.

At this writing, musicians have available electronic devices for producing sufficiently accurate frequencies at ordinary room temperatures to properly tune their instruments (within 1 cent). The internal frequency of an electronic signal generator is compared to the instrumental frequency visually by a stroboscopic disk (Fig. 6·3).[4] Musicians find a stroboscopic disk easy to use and understand, especially, as explained later, simple frequency meters do not serve their purposes.

On the strobe instrument, control knobs enable the musician to choose the frequency desired, expressed in symbols like (C_4 to

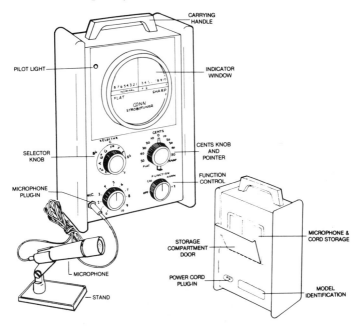

FIG. 6·3 Drawing of *Strobotuner* which uses a strobe-disk driven by a synchronous motor at 12 different speeds determined by a selector knob. (Courtesy C. G. Conn)

[4]Manual for Model ST-21 Strobotuner, 1982, C. G. Conn, 2520 Industrial Parkway, Elkhart, IN 46515.

B_4) for the octave starting with "middle C," and ($C_5 \cdots B_5$) for the next higher octave, and so forth. The strobe disk, rotated by a synchronous motor, changes speed for each of the 12 semitones within an octave (C,C#,D,D#,E,F,F#,G,G#,A,A#,B). Successive octaves, eight in number, are observed on different radial bands on the stroboscopic disk (see Fig. 6·4). Thus the tone C_5 through B_5 will be found on the fifth band out from the center of the strobe disk. The next (second) harmonics above these tones will be found on the sixth band; the fourth harmonics on the seventh band, and the eighth harmonics on the outermost band.

The tone sounded by the instrument is picked up by a microphone and, in turn, controls the on–off rate of a flashing light. When the rate of flashing of the light equals the rate at which the white openings in the proper ring on the strobe disk pass by, the ring stands motionless to the eye and the musician knows the frequencies are matched.

FIG. 6·4 Strobe-disk, showing eight bands, each with twice the number of segments of the nearest inner band. (Courtesy C. G. Conn)

The Strobe instrument has other features of convenience to the musician. Many wind instruments are of the transposing type. That is to say, they do not produce the same frequency as is read from the musical staff. There are three commonly used transposing keys: B♭, E♭, and F. To save translating the notes on the staff to the proper frequencies, a control dial on the strobe instrument can be set to do this for the musician (Fig. 6·5).

Piano tuning is more complicated. Unfortunately, the higher harmonics (the overtones) of a piano string are not exact multiples of the fundamental tone. In fact, each higher harmonic is *sharp* compared to an integral multiple of the fundamental. Usually, musicians use the ($C_4 \cdots B_4$) octave (sometimes called the temperament octave) to provide the 12 anchor fundamentals for the tuning procedure. For example, let us sound the string C_4 on the piano. You will hear not only the fundamental but each of the harmonics of the note sounded. *The frequencies of the appropriate harmonics of the C_4 string just struck become the frequencies which must be matched by the fundamentals of the strings at C_5, C_6, C_7 in the octaves above.*

Now, let us go to the strings whose fundamentals are in the octaves below the ($C_4 \cdots B_4$) octave. In tuning the lower strings, the appropriate harmonic of each lower note is tuned to have the same frequency as the fundamental of that note in the control octave.

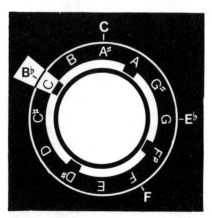

FIG. 6·5 Transposing dial that permits easy tuning of certain wind instruments. When the written note C is played on a B♭ instrument a B♭ tone is produced; or an E♭ tone on a E♭ instrument. The dial setting automatically makes the transposition. (Courtesy C. G. Conn)

If this procedure for both the higher and lower strings is not followed, a piano that is "perfectly" tuned (i.e., the fundamental tone of each string is made equal to an integral multiple or submultiple of its corresponding fundamental tone in the control octave) will sound lifeless and will produce aural "beats" when the octave is struck.

The piano tuner has other complications to take into account. The bass strings are "wound," that is to say, their mass is increased by winding a second wire tightly around the tension string. For these strings some of the overtones are stronger than the fundamental. Usually, the tuner will use the loudest harmonic of the wound string to make it equal in frequency to the fundamental of the anchor tone. Furthermore, the tones from a piano string are flatter shortly after being struck. The piano tuner must decide whether to use the initial part of a tone or the sustained part to match to the fundamentals in the control octave.

It is well known that a professional tuner must observe many other complexities in tuning a concert grand piano for a professional pianist—considerations that are well beyond the scope of this simple description.

6·6 Frequency Meters

Since the first edition of this book, clumsy vacuum tube circuits for the measurement of frequency have been replaced by digital frequency counters of high accuracy. Because of their importance in acoustical instrumentation, some detail is given here, by the courtesy of the Hewlett–Packard Co.[5]

A. Time Base

A frequency counter is a digital electronic device that measures the frequency or period of a periodic steady-state wave. Its accuracy depends on the accuracy of a built-in time base oscillator which is generally a quartz-crystal type with a frequency of between 1 and 10 MHz. The precision of the time base depends on whether the crystal oscillator is temperature controlled.

Without temperature control, the precision of the oscillator will vary about 2.5 parts per million for ambient temperatures between 0 and 50 °C. The precision may be improved by adding

---

[5]Anon., "Fundamentals of the electronic counters," Application Note 200, Hewlett–Packard, Santa Clara, CA 95051-7299.

an external capacitor to the oscillating circuit with an opposite temperature coefficient. Under the classification of "temperature controlled oscillators" the precision is about five times better than that quoted above.

Oven controlled crystal oscillators of various levels of sophistication can be added. Typically, the oven must be turned on a half-hour or so before use of the time base so that the temperature of the quartz crystal reaches equilibrium. In an oven that provides continuous heating proportional to the difference between the external temperature and the desired internal temperature, precision of the time base can be achieved to about 5 parts in 10^9 over an external temperature range of 0 to 50 °C.

In addition to temperature control of the quartz-crystal oscillating element, the line voltage must be controlled within, say, 10%. Aging of the crystal causes variations of 3 parts in 10^7 per month for the best oven controlled oscillators. Obviously, to maintain greater accuracy, comparison and resetting of the mechanism must be made against primary or secondary frequency standards.

B. Conventional Frequency Counter

A conventional frequency counter measures the frequency of an input signal. The frequency f of the signal is obviously the number of cycles n that occur in the time interval t. A block diagram is given in Fig. 6·6.

The input signal must have a strength that exceeds the specified value of the trigger level. This is usually accomplished with an automatic gain control.

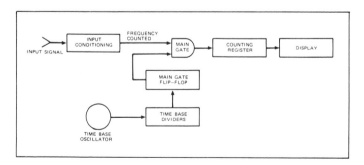

FIG. 6·6 Basic block diagram of the conventional counter in its frequency mode of measurement. (Courtesy Hewlett-Packard Corp.)

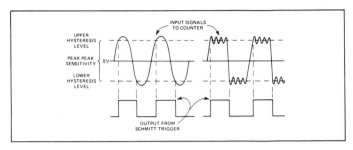

FIG. 6·7 Input characteristics. To effect a count the signal must cross through both the upper and lower hysteresis levels. Thus (right) the "ringing" on the input signal shown does not cause a count. (Courtesy of Hewlett–Packard Corp.)

In order to avoid false counts, "ringing" or superimposed noise on the input signal must be disregarded by the counter. To accomplish this, a count is not made until the input signal crosses both the upper and lower trigger (hysteresis) levels as shown in Fig. 6·7. To enable signals with a dc component to be counted, a capacitance is injected into the input circuit.

Pulsed input signals provide a special problem because they produce their own dc bias, which must not be eliminated. Thus a multilevel, say three-level, input control is usually provided to locate both the peak and the valley of the pulse outside the two hysteresis levels.

Finally, a slope control must be provided that determines whether the (Schmitt) circuit is triggered at the higher hysteresis level by a signal with a positive slope (going from one voltage level to a more positive value, regardless of polarity) or with a negative slope which causes an output pulse at the lower hysteresis level.

The total conditioning that must be applied to the input circuit of the counter is summarized in Fig. 6·8.

Returning now to Fig. 6·6, the conditioned input signal that is sent to the main gate is a pulse train, where each pulse corresponds to one cycle or event (pulse) of the input signal.

The second signal sent to the main gate is a conditioned signal from the time base oscillator (TB). First, the frequency of the TB is divided into decade steps, controlled selectively by an operating switch. The output of the TB divider goes to a flip–

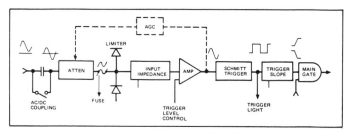

FIG. 6·8 This diagram summarizes the various conditionings of the input signal prior to its application to the main gate of the counter. (Courtesy of Hewlett–Packard Corp.)

flop circuit that produces a train of pulses. The period of this pulse train opens and closes the main gate.

A counting register, operating during the open period of the time base gate, yields the frequency of the input signal. For example, if the number of pulses from the input circuit of Fig. 6·8 is 5000, and the selected gate time is one second, the counting register and its display will show 5000 Hz.

C. Frequency Ratio of Two Input Signals

The block diagram of Fig. 6·6 showing the measurement of frequency against a standard time base clock can be adapted to the measurement of two input signals. In this case, the lower frequency source is substituted for the time base oscillator as shown in Fig. 6·9. Thus the lower frequency opens and closes the gate. The pulses delivered to the main gate by the higher frequency are counted. If, say, three pulses are counted while the gate is open, and if the gate is open for one period, the higher frequency is three times the lower frequency.

D. Time Interval Measurement

There are many cases when an accurate measurement of a time interval is wanted. The basic frequency measurement circuit is converted to this purpose in the block diagram of Fig. 6·10. Two input signals are needed, one is the "start" signal to open the gate and the other is the "stop" signal to close the gate. The pulses that are sent to the main gate by the time base oscillator are counted during the time the gate is open. Obviously, the accumulated number of pulses while the gate is open

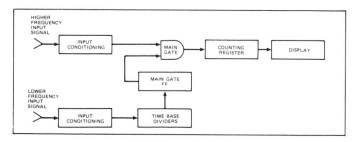

FIG. 6·9 Substitution of a second frequency for the time-base oscillator permits determination of the ratio of the two input frequencies. (Courtesy of Hewlett–Packard Corp.)

gives the time interval by simple multiplication of the period of one time base pulse by the number.

E. Pulse Count Measurement

The procedure for counting the total number of pulses in a sequence follows from Fig. 6·6. The pulses to be counted are the "input signal." The main gate must be held open until all the pulses are counted. This can be done by disconnecting the time base oscillator and using a manual or an electronic switch for gate control.

F. The One Hertz Error

The frequency counter shown in Fig. 6·6 has built into it an ambiguity of ± 1 count (see Fig. 6·11), because the first pulse from the conditioned input signal is not coordinated with the instant of opening of the gate. As Fig. 6·11 shows, the same

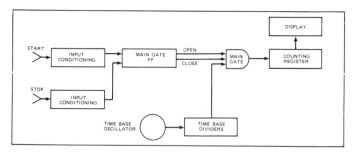

FIG. 6·10 Arrangement for accurate measurement of a time interval. (Courtesy of Hewlett–Packard Corp.)

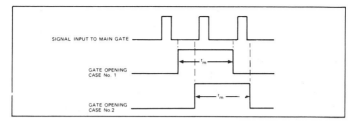

FIG. 6·11 The ± 1 count ambiguity. The main gate is open for the same time t_m in both cases. Incoherence between the clock and the input signal can cause two valid counts which for this example are 1 for case no. 1 and 2 for case no. 2. (Courtesy of Hewlett–Packard Corp.)

input with the two gate openings shown can yield either one or two valid counts. This error becomes important in the audio frequency range.

G. Reciprocal Frequency Counter

To avoid the ± 1 count error a second class of frequency counter is used which always measures the period of the repetitious input signal. The period P of the input signal is equal to the length of time that the main gate is open, divided by the number of input cycles (pulses) that occur in that time period. Obviously, this can be called "multiple period averaging."

One commercially available reciprocal frequency counter has the block diagram form shown in Fig. 6·12.[6] The main gate is opened and closed by the start and end of a chosen number of cycles determined by the two input signals. The number of

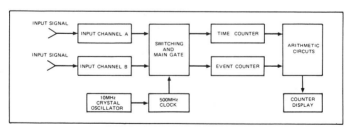

FIG. 6·12 Basic block diagram of a reciprocal counter (Courtesy of Hewlett–Packard Corp.)

[6]"Automatic frequency counter," Hewlett–Packard, 1820 Embarcadero Road, Palo Alto, CA 94303.

pulses received from the time-base oscillator in the open time of the gate is then counted by the event counter and used to determine the length of the open time. The product of the clock period and clock count divided by the event count is the average period of the input signal.

To obtain the average frequency, the arithmetic circuits take the reciprocal of this quotient. The great improvement in the accuracy of the reciprocal counter compared to the conventional frequency counter is shown in Fig. 6·13. The period measurement is more accurate up to the point where the input frequency equals the clock frequency. Above that point, frequency measurement is more accurate.

H. Interpolation Frequency Counter

Another, and still more accurate, method for determining the period and, hence, the frequency of a repetitious input signal is to use an interpolator to measure and reduce the one count ambiguity. The simplest way to discuss the concept is to describe an analog interpolator, a process that can also be handled digitally.

In Fig. 6·14, four time intervals, T, T_0, T_1, and T_2 are shown. The interval T is the result desired, namely, the period of the repetitious input signal. The time T_1 is the interval between the start pulse and the first clock pulse and T_2 the interval

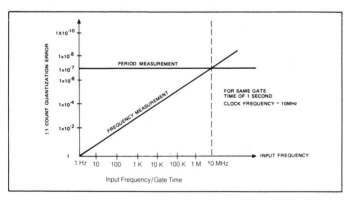

FIG. 6·13 The ± 1 count quantization error is less using the reciprocal technique vs the conventional frequency measurement method for all input frequencies less than the clock frequency. (Courtesy of Hewlett–Packard Corp.)

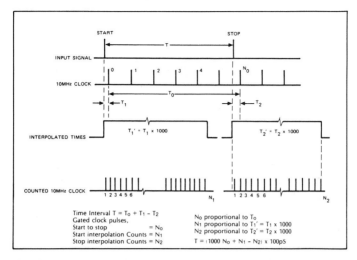

FIG. 6·14 Time intervals measured by analog interpolaters. Note that with a 10-MHz clock, 10 pS means 10^{-10} sec. (Courtesy of Hewlett–Packard Corp.)

between the stop pulse and the next clock pulse. Finally, T_0 is the time between the first clock pulse after the start pulse and the first clock pulse after the stop pulse. Obviously, $T = T_0 + T_1 - T_2$.

The interval T_0 is measured by accumulating the clock impulses N_0 during the interval. T_1 and T_2 are first multiplied by, say 1000, and then measured against the time-base clock, which yields N_1 and N_2. The significance of the ± 1 count uncertainty is reduced by a factor of 1000. So $N_1 = T_1 \times 1000$; $N_2 = T_2 \times 1000$ and $T = (1000N_0 + N_1 + N_2)$ times the reciprocal of 1000 times the clock pulse frequency.

I. Microprocesser Developments

As this is being written, programming for microprocessors is becoming available that promises to replace arithmetic circuits, time/event scalers, switching/main gate and related circuitry. One result is that the reciprocal technique will become the primary method of counting which will result in greater accuracy at reasonable cost. Also, phase measurement will become feasible at a reasonable cost.

6·7 Measurement of Frequency by Comparison

A. Drum

Another method of comparing the local with the standard frequency is shown schematically in Fig. 6·15. A sheet of facsimile paper is slowly drawn between a rotating cylinder and a conducting bar. Imbedded in the surface of the cylinder is a helix of wire. A pulsing circuit synchronized with the standard frequency is connected between the helix and the contact bar. A spot is produced on the facsimile paper each time the pulsing circuit operates. The speed of rotation of the cylinder is synchronized with the unknown frequency.

After the device has operated for a length of time, a record similar to that shown in Fig. 6·16 is obtained. If the cylinder is rotating at exactly a submultiple of the standard frequency, the rows of dots will trace straight lines on the paper along the direction of motion. If it rotates at a speed slightly greater than a submultiple of the standard frequency the rows of dots will slope downward, and vice versa. Two data are obtained from the experiment, namely, the displacement l_1 of the point B from a horizontal line drawn through A and C, and either the number of dots between A and B or the time t from which the number of dots can be calculated. In addition we must know the length l_2 (see Fig. 6·15), which is also the distance between A and A' in Fig. 6·16.

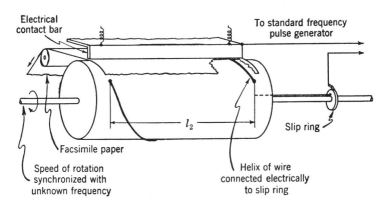

FIG. 6·15 Facsimile type of apparatus for measuring the variation of a frequency with respect to a standard frequency.

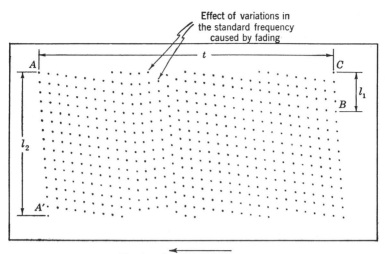

FIG. 6·16 Record obtained from the facsimile type of apparatus shown in Fig. 6·15.

The rotational frequency of the drum is given by the formula

$$f = \left(\frac{l_1}{nl_2} + 1\right)\frac{f_s}{\nu}, \tag{6·1}$$

where f is the rotational frequency of the cylinder in revolutions per second, f_s is the standard frequency in cycles per second, n is the number of points between A and B, l_1 is the distance between B and C measured in centimeters, l_2 is the distance between A and A' in centimeters, and ν is the nearest integral ratio of the standard frequency to the unknown frequency.

As an example, let us assume that we wish to determine the exact value of the rotational frequency of the cylinder whose approximate frequency is known to be 27.5 rps. Let the standard frequency be 440 cps. Immediately we see that $\nu = 16$. If the time for the record to progress from A to C is 1 hour, then n will equal $27.5 \times 3600 = 99,000$ points. If, further, $l_1 = 4$ cm and $l_2 = 10$ cm, then

$$f = \left(\frac{4}{10 \times 99,000} + 1\right)\frac{440}{16} = (1 + 4 \cdot 10^{-6})27.5 .$$

It is easy to see that in a period of 1 hour a comparison of f with the standard frequency can be made to less than 1 part in 10^7.

B. Wien Bridge

Largely because of the absence of vacuum tubes and sources of heat, a bridge circuit utilizing precison elements becomes an accurate method of measuring frequency. When the bridge is used, the controls are adjusted until the signal whose frequency is being measured can no longer be heard by ear. An important disadvantage of this type of measuring instrument is that it does not discriminate against the harmonics of a wave. This means that the frequency being measured may not *sound* balanced out, because the ear reconstructs subjectively the missing fundamental of a series of harmonics. A bridge circuit that is particularly adapted to frequency measurement is that of the Wien bridge. It makes use of simple resistive and capacitive elements, and range switching is easily possible.

Field describes a modification of the Wien bridge whose basic circuit is shown in Fig. 6·17(a). A three-terminal equivalent network eliminating the use of the transformer is shown in (b) of Fig. 6·17.

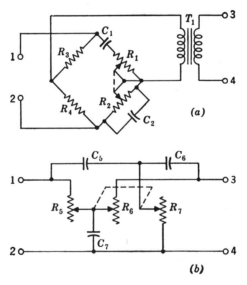

Fig. 6·17 Schematic diagram of two forms of Wien bridge.

The conditions of balance for circuit (a) are

$$f = \frac{1}{2\pi\sqrt{R_1 R_2 C_1 C_2}} \qquad (6\cdot2)$$

and

$$\frac{C_2}{C_1} = \frac{R_3}{R_4} - \frac{R_1}{R_2}. \qquad (6\cdot3)$$

In commercial forms of the bridge, it is common to make

$$\frac{C_2}{C_1} = \frac{R_1}{R_2} = 1 \quad \text{and} \quad \frac{R_3}{R_4} = 2. \qquad (6\cdot4)$$

Thus Eq. $(6\cdot3)$ is always fulfilled, and Eq. $(6\cdot2)$ becomes

$$f = \frac{1}{2\pi R_1 C_1}. \qquad (6\cdot5)$$

Continuous variation of the Wien bridge is obtained merely by turning a single dial which controls two variable resistances $(R_1$ and $R_2)$ mounted upon a common shaft. In order to extend the range of the instrument, the capacitances C_1 and C_2 are adjusted by a multipole switch, so that various frequency ranges are available.

Because changing the capacitances by a given factor always produces a corresponding but decreasing change in frequency, the various frequency ranges over which the instrument is used may be made to track with a single-dial calibration which need merely be multiplied or divided by constant factors for the additional frequency ranges. In commercial forms of the bridge, the multiplying factors are ten or multiples thereof, so that calibration of the bridge is simple.

For the three-terminal equivalent [Fig. $6\cdot17$(b)], a balance is obtained when

$$C_5 = C_6 = \frac{C_7}{2},$$

$$R_5 = R_6 = 2R_7. \qquad (6\cdot6)$$

Then

$$f = \frac{1}{2\pi R_5 C_5}. \qquad (6\cdot7)$$

In use, the unknown frequency is connected to terminals 3–4 and the amplifier and earphones to terminals 1–2. The circuit is adjusted until the desired tone reaches a minimum. As mentioned before, harmonics in the input wave reduce the accuracy of the bridge because they produce in the ear a subjective impression of the tone being measured.

C. Vibrating Reed

For the measurement of low frequencies, clamped steel bars excited directly by a vibrating machine or electromagnetically have been employed for many years. Hartmann–Kempf developed an electromagnetically excited series of bars, the frequency of each being separated from its neighbor by 1 cps. The amplitude of vibration of the bars was observed visually, and the device was quite useful in the approximate control of power frequencies. More recently, an American manufacturer has produced a single, mechanically excited metal reed, whose length is varied until the reed is brought into resonance as observed visually. Basically, this is a form of fork, but it is not constructed to the same precision as the fork described earlier in this chapter.

From the elementary theory of bars clamped at one end, we learn that for the fundamental frequency f we can write

$$f = \frac{\pi \kappa}{8 l^2} \sqrt{\frac{E}{\rho}} \text{ (approx.)}, \qquad (6 \cdot 8)$$

where $l =$ length of the bar, $E =$ Young's elastic modulus, $\rho =$ density, and $\kappa =$ the radius of gyration. (Note that $\kappa^2 = a^2/4$ for a bar of circular section and radius a, and $\kappa^2 = t^2/12$ if the bar is rectangular and of thickness t in the plane of vibration.)

The manufacturer of the variable length bar just described claims that it can be used to observe vibration frequencies between 9 and 300 cps.

D. Cathode Ray Oscilloscope

The cathode ray oscilloscope is often a very convenient means of comparing two frequencies which are integral ratios of each other. The simplest method of performing this comparison is to connect the unknown frequency to one pair of plates of a cathode ray tube and the standard frequency to the other pair. When the ratio approaches a value that can be expressed by simple integers, a pattern known as a Lissajous figure appears on the screen.

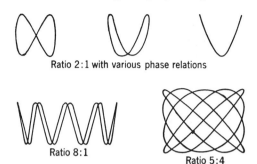

Ratio 2:1 with various phase relations

Ratio 8:1

Ratio 5:4

FIG. 6·18 Typical Lissajous figures with the ratios indicated.

When the ratio of frequencies is exactly integral, the pattern is stationary, and the frequency ratio is the number of times the side of the figure is tangent to a horizontal line divided by the number of times its end is tangent to a vertical line. (See Fig. 6·18.) If the ratio is not exactly integral, the pattern will move about on the screen because the relative phase of the two waves is continuously changing. When the ratio of the two frequencies is far from being integral, the pattern becomes a blurred rectangle.

A more satisfactory arrangement for determining higher order ratios of the two frequencies by means of an oscilloscope is shown in Fig. 6·19. To obtain the gear-wheel pattern (b) the high frequency is inserted in series with the anode at the point A of (a). The low frequency is caused to produce a circular or elliptical path on the screen by means of a resistance–capacitance phase splitter. If two frequencies bear an exact integral ratio to each other, the gear wheel will be stationary; otherwise it will rotate. More easily readable are the gear-wheel patterns of (c). These may be produced in either of two ways: by inserting the high frequency in the circuit at point B of (a) or by using a tube with center electrode and impressing the high frequency between this electrode and ground.

When the oscilloscope is used to compare the frequencies over a wide range, the size of the condenser in Fig. 6·19a must be adjusted for different frequencies to keep the gear wheel circular. A more complete circuit with suitable sizes of elements is given in Fig. 6·19d.

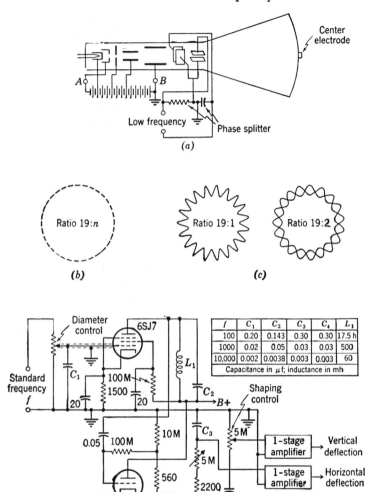

FIG. 6·19 (a) Circuit for producing spot-wheel or gear-wheel patterns; (b) spot-wheel pattern; (c) gear-wheel pattern (after Terman); (d) detailed design of phase-splitting circuit (courtesy General Radio Company).

6·8 Source Signal Generators for Acoustical Tests

Acoustical measurements are standardized both internationally and by nation. These include tests of:

Loudspeakers
Microphones
Audio Equipment
Filters
Hearing Aids
Audiometers
Sound Distribution in Rooms
Transmission Loss through Walls
Sound Isolation
Reverberation Time
Acoustic Impedance
Auto Correlation and Cross Correlation

Most of these tests require signal sources that not only provide the proper electrical signals, but interconnect with other equipment, such as microphones, loudspeakers, filters, and recorders so as to provide an efficient and accurate system for determining the acoustical parameters desired in the test.

A. Controlled Beat-frequency Oscillator

A sine-wave signal is used in many of the measurements above. A simplified block diagram of a sine-wave source is shown in Fig. 6·20. It is comprised of an accurate fixed-frequen-

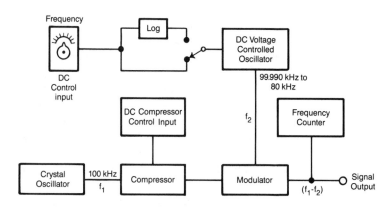

FIG. 6·20 Controlled beat-frequency oscillator.

cy crystal oscillator whose output is mixed in a modulator with the output of a variable frequency oscillator. A dc voltage source controls the frequency of the variable oscillator. The dc source either connects directly to the oscillator or through a logarithmic converter. Hence, the dial may have two frequency scales, one linear and one logarithmic.

The frequency of the output signal from the modulator is the difference between the frequencies of the two oscillators. A frequency counter and a display show the frequency of the wave at the output. The sine-wave source also has a dc compressor control input that can change the signal output level to meet some external need, such as a correction for irregularities in microphone and loudspeaker response.

B. Random Noise Generators

In performing many acoustical measurements, especially those on building structures, an electrical source of random noise is required. The amplitudes of a true random-noise signal should follow a normal distribution curve (so-called Gaussian amplitude distribution, shown in Fig. 10·2), out to four to five times the standard deviation σ.

Random noise is commonly specified in one of four ways: (a) "White Noise"—wide-band random noise with a flat spectrum level (defined on p. 27); (b) narrow-band random noise—random noise with bandwidth ranging from a few Hz to 1000 Hz; (c) one-octave and one-third-octave-wide bands of random noise; and (d) "Pink Noise"—wide-band random noise with a spectrum level that decreases 3 dB for each doubling of frequency.

White Noise. The internal generator of a random noise signal with a Gaussian distribution is either solid-state or gaseous discharge tube, one manufacturer using two zener diodes with a dc bias. Generally, high-pass filters between 2 Hz and a few tens of Hz are used to limit very-low-frequency fluctuations. Internal low-pass or band-pass filters are provided to limit the upper range of frequencies to those of interest and thus avoid unnecessary overloading of other inputs. Typical low-pass filters are some combination of 2, 5, 20, 50, and 200 kHz. The filters roll off at 12 to 18 dB per octave above and below the two cutoff frequencies.

Narrow-Band Random Noise. Narrow-band random noise is used where some averaging of fluctuations in a sound pressure field is desired, but at a fairly well-defined frequency. Typical narrow bandwidths of random noise range between a few Hz and a few hundred Hz.

One technique for obtaining a Gaussian distribution is to combine a very-high-frequency filtered random signal with a very-high-frequency tunable pure tone in a modulator and to select the difference signal with a low-pass filter. The meter reads the frequency of the tunable oscillator and the scale translates it down to the output frequency, with an accuracy of about 20 parts per million of the tuning frequency.

One-Octave and Third-Octave Bands of Random Noise. These bands are obtained by using digital filters at the output of the white noise generator. A digital output must be used to indicate to the frequency meter the midfrequency of the band to which the filter is set.

Pink Noise. Pink noise is simply generated by feeding the white noise signal through a filter that decreases the spectrum level by 3 dB for each doubling of frequency.

7.

Measurement of Acoustic Impedance

7·1 General Considerations

The introduction of the concept of impedance into acoustics by
A. G. Webster in 1919 followed its successful application in the
analysis of electrical circuit behavior. It is a very useful quantity, for, once it is known, the reaction of the air on a vibrating
system can be determined. For example, if the complex ratio
of force to particle velocity is known at the throat of an expo-

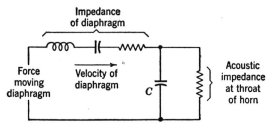

Fig. 7·1 Equivalent circuit of a driving unit for a horn loudspeaker. A
force produced by the electric circuit acts to drive a diaphragm. The diaphragm must move against the combination of the compliance C of a layer of
air between it and the horn throat and the impedance of the horn throat
itself.

nential horn, an electrical equivalent circuit can be drawn for a
horn loudspeaker system. Such a case is shown in Fig. 7·1,
where the elements include the mass, compliance, and resistance
of the diaphragm in the driving unit, the compliance of the layer
of air between the diaphragm and the throat of the horn, and,
finally, the impedance at the throat of the horn itself. From
this network the velocity of the driving diaphragm can be determined in terms of the force applied to the diaphragm. If the

driving force is a combination of several components of different frequencies, the diaphragm velocity is a similar combination of velocities of different frequencies, each with an amplitude equal to the ratio between the magnitude of the component force and the impedance for the corresponding frequency.

A. Types of Impedance

Reference to the terminology in Chapter 1 shows that three definitions for acoustic impedance are in use. The first of these is analogous to electric circuit impedance. In this text we call it the ASA impedance because it has been standardized by the American Standards Association. It is expressed as

$$Z_a = \frac{p}{Su} = \frac{p}{U} \quad \text{dyne-sec/cm}^5 \qquad (7 \cdot 1)$$

where p is the sound pressure, in dynes per square centimeter; u is the linear velocity in centimeters per second; S is the area for which the impedance is being defined, in square centimeters; $U = Su$ = volume velocity, in cubic centimeters per second.

The advantage of the ASA impedance is that changes in cross section in a conduit down which a sound wave is traveling do not change the impedance, because, for conduits whose lateral dimensions are small compared to a wavelength, the pressure remains the same at a change in cross-sectional area and the linear velocity change is inversely proportional to the ratio of the areas before and after the change. That is to say, there is continuity of volume velocity U at changes in cross section. As a further example of the use of this type of impedance, consider a pair of infinitely long tubes branching off from a main tube (see Fig. $7 \cdot 2a$). Assume that the cross-sectional area of the main tube is S and that of each of the smaller tubes is $S/2$. Then the impedance across the section aa, looking to the right, is

$$Z_{a1} = \frac{p}{u\frac{S}{2}} \doteq \frac{\rho c}{\frac{S}{2}} = \frac{2\rho c}{S} \qquad (7 \cdot 2)$$

where p is the pressure, u is the linear velocity and p/u for a long tube is equal approximately to ρc. Across bb looking to the right the impedance will be

$$Z_{a2} = \frac{p}{uS} \doteq \frac{\rho c}{S} \qquad (7\cdot3)$$

The analogous circuit diagram for this simple situation is drawn in Fig. $7\cdot2b$. For this case the pressure and the linear particle velocity are the same on both sides of the junction, but the area in either tube to the right is one-half that of the main tube.

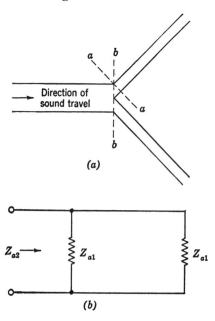

(a)

(b)

Fig. $7\cdot2$ (a) Sketch showing the impedance planes aa and bb at the junction of three conduits, two of which have one-half the cross-sectional area of the first. (b) Equivalent circuit diagram of sketch (a). The impedance looking to the right of aa is Z_{a1}, and that looking to the right of bb is Z_{a2}.

When the circuit is solved by familiar electrical theory, the impedance on looking into the parallel combination of the two tubes is the same as it would be if the larger tube were to extend indefinitely to the right. This is just what one would expect because the areas are continuous at the junction; the ASA impedance is again seen to be useful.

The second type of acoustic impedance, and the one most used throughout this book, is the specific (unit-area) acoustic impedance Z_s. It is defined as

$$Z_s = \frac{p}{u} \quad \text{dyne-sec/cm}^3 \qquad (7\cdot4)$$

The particular advantage of specific impedance is that it finds application in mathematical formulas of the boundary-value type, such as are common in the modern theory of room acoustics. There, the specific acoustic impedance at boundaries and sometimes in the wave is independent of the area being considered. For example, in a plane progressive wave, the value of Z_s is nearly the same at all points (equal approximately to ρc) regardless of the size of duct down which the wave is traveling. Another example is the mathematical prediction of the magnitude of standing waves along the length of a duct where we find that the result is independent of the lateral dimensions of the duct (if no

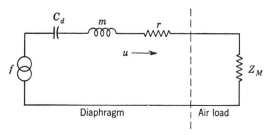

Fig. 7·3 Equivalent circuit showing the application of the concept of mechanical impedance to the air loading on an electroacoustic transducer. Z_M is defined as the ratio of the force exerted by a diaphragm on a given cross-sectional area of air to the resulting linear particle velocity.

dissipation at the side walls of the duct is assumed), so that an impedance not containing S should be used.

The third type of impedance, called the mechanical impedance, is equal to the ratio of the force exerted over a given area to the resulting linear velocity produced. Mathematically this is calculated as

$$Z_M = \frac{pS}{u} \quad \text{dyne-sec/cm} \qquad (7\cdot5)$$

The concept of mechanical impedance is useful in the analysis of mechano-acoustic transducers where the reaction to a driving force is to be determined. For instance, let us consider a diaphragm producing a sound wave in an infinitely long tube. Figure 7·3 shows the equivalent circuit for this condition. There f is a constant force generator (perhaps a voice coil in which a constant current is maintained), C_d, m, and r are the compliance, mass, and frictional resistance of the diaphragm, and Z_M is equal to $S\rho c$, where S is the area of the tube. Because Z_M is defined as the ratio of force to linear velocity, it may be drawn directly in the equivalent circuit.

B. Choice of Sign of Reactance ($-i$ vs. $+j$)

Unfortunately, because of different practices in physics and in electrical engineering, a conflict has arisen in the acoustical literature over the choice of sign for acoustic reactances. The situation can be best illustrated by writing the expressions for p, u, and Z_s in a plane progressive wave and using first the notation of physics,[1] which we shall call the $(-i)$ theory, and, second, the notation of electrical engineering, which we shall call the $(+j)$ theory. Setting $k = \omega/c$, and using physics notation, we write

$$p = P_+ e^{-ik(ct-x)} + P_- e^{-ik(ct+x)} \qquad (7\cdot6)$$

where P_+ and P_- are the amplitudes of the forward and backward traveling waves, respectively. We know from the basic equations of sound (see Chapter 2) that the particle velocity is

$$u = \frac{1}{i\omega\rho}\frac{\partial p}{\partial x} = \frac{P_+}{\rho c} e^{-ik(ct-x)} - \frac{P_-}{\rho c} e^{-ik(ct+x)} \qquad (7\cdot7)$$

and

$$Z_s = \frac{p}{u} = \rho c \coth [ikx + \psi], \qquad (7\cdot8)$$

where

$$\frac{P_-}{P_+} = e^{-2\psi} \quad \text{or} \quad \psi = -\frac{1}{2}\ln\frac{P_-}{P_+} \qquad (7\cdot9)$$

If we assume that at $x = 0$ there is a rigid wall, then, at that plane, u and $\psi = 0$. If the column of air has a depth $x = -d$ we get

$$Z_s = \rho c \coth [-ikd] = i\rho c \cot kd \qquad (7\cdot10)$$

For small values of kd, the cotangent can be approximated by

$$\cot kd \doteq \frac{1}{kd} - \frac{kd}{3} + \cdots$$

---

[1] P. M. Morse, *Vibration and Sound*, McGraw-Hill, 2nd edition (1948).

Therefore,

$$Z_s = i\rho c \left[\frac{1}{\omega \frac{d}{c}} - \omega \left(\frac{d}{3c} \right) \right] \qquad (7 \cdot 11)$$

Obviously the term d/c is analogous to a capacitance (called compliance in acoustics) and $d/3c$ to an inductance (called acoustic mass in acoustics). Because of the choice of $(-i)$ we have a negative sign for mass reactance and a positive sign for compliant reactance.

Using electrical engineering notation gives

$$p = P_+ e^{jk(ct-x)} + P_- e^{jk(ct+x)} \qquad (7 \cdot 12)$$

$$Z_s = -\rho c \coth [jkx - \psi] \qquad (7 \cdot 13)$$

where ψ is as defined in Eq. (7·9). Under the same assumptions as before, Z_s for a shallow column of air of depth $x = -d$ becomes

$$Z_s = -j\rho c \cot kd$$

or, approximately,

$$Z_s \doteq j\rho c \left[-\frac{1}{\omega \frac{d}{c}} + \omega \left(\frac{d}{3c} \right) \right] \qquad (7 \cdot 14)$$

Here the mass reactance is positive, and the compliant reactance is negative, as is usual in electric circuit theory. Hence, we see that if $\exp [-ik(ct - x)]$ is used in place of $\exp [jk(ct - x)]$ the signs of mass reactances will be negative and complaint reactances positive. Because most applied accousticians are familiar with electric circuit theory, the convention of $(+j)$ will be used throughout this book.

C. Choice of Hyperbolic Function

A further source of confusion which has originated in the literature is the choice of hyperbolic function for expressing the acoustic impedance in a medium. Referring back to Eq. (7·9), let us examine the consequences of reversing the sign of the ratio of P_- to P_+, that is,

$$\psi = -\frac{1}{2} \ln \left(-\frac{P_-}{P_+} \right) \qquad (7 \cdot 15)$$

Then Eq. (7·13) becomes

$$Z_s = -\rho c \tanh [jkx - \psi] \qquad (7 \cdot 16)$$

As before, let us assume that at $x = 0$, for a particular case, there is a rigid wall. Then Z_s (at $x = 0$) is infinite, so that $\psi = j(\pi/2)$. Hence, at $x = -d$,

$$Z_s = j\rho c \tan\left[kd + \frac{\pi}{2}\right] \qquad (7 \cdot 17)$$

The added $\pi/2$ term in the argument is an unnecessary complication. Hence, the hyperbolic cotangent (coth) form of the equation rather than the hyperbolic tangent (tanh) form will be used throughout this chapter.

7·2 Impedance-Measuring Methods

The several methods of measuring acoustic impedance can be divided roughly into three groups. In the first are those which utilize data taken at or very near the surface of the sample exposed to a plane wave sound field. (The term "sample" is used broadly here to indicate an acoustical material or element whose impedance is being determined.) The second group comprises those methods for which data are taken at various points somewhat removed from the surface of the sample. By analogy with electromagnetic wave theory, those methods are called "transmission line" methods. The third category is made up of those methods which require a known standard of acoustic impedance for comparison with the impedance to be determined. Acoustic and electroacoustic bridges, the method of Flanders, and the reaction on the source methods fall in this group.

A. Surface Methods

Table 7·1 lists these various methods for reference. All of them have certain advantages, although some are more conveniently carried out than others. They will be briefly summarized here before the more important ones are discussed in detail.

Method 1 is the most fundamental of those listed in the table, but it is almost never utilized. The measurement of pressure is not difficult and can be accomplished at a point by using small probe tubes. However, the measurement of particle velocity is not so simple. The chief difficulty in determining this quantity is the lack of any microphone of the pressure-gradient type sufficiently small to avoid disturbing the sound field by its insertion therein.

Method 2 [2,3] is a fundamental technique involving the measurement of magnitude and phase of sound pressure produced as a result of a known volume velocity of air through the surface of the sample.

B. Transmission Line Methods

Method 3 is the most widely used technique at this writing. First described by Taylor[4] for the determination of absorption coefficients, it was offered as a method for the measurement of impedance by Wente and Bedell.[5] The method requires the probing of the standing wave in front of the sample to determine the ratio of the sound pressures at a loop and a node and the position of a node relative to the surface of the sample. The measurement is usually made in a tube, with the source at one end and the unknown impedance at the other. The principal difficulty lies in the measurement of the pressures in the tube without disturbing the sound field. Three approaches to the solution of this difficulty have been described in the literature. One, by Hall,[6] employs a microphone which is imbedded in one side of the measuring tube. That side of the tube is then moved along relative to the other three sides. The second solution was first offered by Taylor[4] and has been perfected by Scott.[7] It makes use of a long, small-bore probe tube which is moved along the length of the main tube.[10] The third solution makes use of a miniature moving-coil or ceramic microphone.[8,9]

[2]R. K. Cook, "A short-tube method for measuring acoustic impedance," J. Acoust. Soc. Am. **19**, 922–923 (1947).

[3]O. K. Mawardi, "Measurement of acoustic impedance," J. Acoust. Soc. Am. **21**, 84–91 (1949).

[4]H. O. Taylor, "A direct method of finding the value of materials as sound absorbers," Phys. Rev. **2**, 270–287 (1913).

[5]E. C. Wente and E. H. Bedell, "Measurement of acoustic impedance and the absorption coefficient of porous materials," Bell Syst. Tech. J. **7**, 1–10 (1928).

[6]W. M. Hall, "An acoustic transmission line for impedance measurement," J. Acoust. Soc. Am. **11**, 140–146 (1939).

[7]R. A. Scott, "An apparatus for accurate measurement of the acoustic impedance of sound-absorbing materials," Proc. Phys. Soc. **58**, 253–264 (1946).

[8]H. J. Sabine, "Notes on acoustic impedance measurement," J. Acoust. Soc. Am. **14**, 143–150 (1942).

[9]L. L. Beranek, "Some notes on the measurement of acoustic impedance," J. Acoust. Soc. Am. **19**, 420–427 (1947).

TABLE 7·1

No.	Ref.	Method	Source	Frequency	Length	Pressure Detector	Measure
GROUP A. SURFACE METHODS							
1		Absolute measurement	Not important	Fixed			Pressure and particle velocity at a point
2	2,3	Pressure and phase change	Piston of known volume velocity	Fixed	Fixed	Fixed	Measure magnitude and phase change of sound pressure at the driving diaphragm or surface of sample
GROUP B. TRANSMISSION LINE METHODS							
3	4-10	Analysis of standing wave	Not important	Fixed	Fixed	Movable	Ratio of pressure maximum to pressure minimum and location of minimum with respect to point at which impedance is desired
4	5	Resonance and anti-resonance	High impedance	Fixed	Variable	Fixed at source	Ratio of pressure maximum to pressure minimum and length of conduit at pressure maximum
5	5,11	Analysis of standing wave	Not important	Fixed	Fixed	Two microphones	Pressures at two points whose separation is accurately known

6	12,13,14	Curve width	Point	Variable	Variable	Fixed	Pressure-frequency resonance curve (Determine curve width and resonant frequency.)
7	9,13	Curve width	Point	Fixed	Fixed	Fixed	Pressure-length resonance curve (Determine curve width and resonant length.)
8	15	Curve width or decay constant	Fixed—high impedance	Variable	Fixed	Fixed—high impedance	Same as for 6, or measure decay constant with level recorder (Sample is at center of chamber.)
				GROUP C. COMPARISON METHODS			
9	16-18	Acoustic impedance bridge	Not important	Fixed	Fixed	Two microphones	(Balance bridge until two microphone readings are alike in magnitude and phase.)
10	19	Electroacoustic impedance bridge	Not important	Fixed	Fixed	Two microphones	(Balance an electrical bridge whose arms contain the two microphones.)
11	20-24	Reaction on source	Electromagnetic transducer	Fixed	Fixed	None	Input electrical impedance at electromagnetic transducer
12	25	Comparator	Not important	Fixed	Fixed	Fixed	Two complex pressure ratios; one ratio for unknown to one standard, other for unknown to a second standard

Method 4 [5] requires a source of sound whose output is independent of acoustic loading. For low values of absorption by the unknown termination, this becomes a difficult assumption to satisfy.

Method 5 [5,11] has no advantage over method 3 when used in a tube. It does offer the possibility of measuring impedances in open air. At low frequencies a rather wide spacing between microphones becomes necessary because the pressures at two points near a pressure loop have nearly the same magnitude, and the phase changes slowly as a function of distance.

Method 6 was described by Hunt[12] for the measurement of the damping constant of discrete normal modes of vibration. It can also be used for determining acoustic impedance, as pointed out by Beranek[13] and utilized by Harris.[14]

Method 7 [9,13] meets the principal objection to method 3, namely, it eliminates the traveling probe microphone and its disturbing effects on the sound wave. Highly accurate data are possible over a wide frequency range if the absorption by the sample is not too high. The principal objection to the method is that either the source or the sample under test must be mounted on a moving piston.

Method 8 [15] is essentially the same as method 6. The principal difference is that the sample is located in the center of the chamber and not at the boundaries. This makes the method suitable for the investigation of the impedance of screens and gauzes.

C. Comparison Methods

Method 9, introduced first by Stewart,[16] is the simplest and most rapid to use. Later refinements of acoustic bridges have followed from

[10]Report No. TR1-55, "Standing wave analysis" (1955), Bruel & Kjaer Instruments Co., 185 Forest St., Marlborough, MA 01752.

[11]R. Bolt and A. Petrauskas, "An acoustic impedance meter for rapid field measurements," (abstract) J. Acoust. Soc. Am. **15**, 79 (1943).

[12]F. V. Hunt, "Investigation of room acoustics by steady-state transmission measurements," J. Acoust. Soc. Am. **10**, 216–227 (1939).

[13]L. L. Beranek, "Precision measurement of acoustic impedance," J. Acoust. Soc. Am. **12**, 3–13 (1940).

[14]C. M. Harris, "Application of the wave theory of room acoustics to the measurement of acoustic impedance," J. Acoust. Soc. Am. **17**, 35–45 (1945).

[15]C. M. Harris, "Acoustic impedance measurement of very porous screen," J. Acoust. Soc. Am. **20**, 440–447 (1948).

[16]G. W. Stewart, "Direct absolute measurement of acoustical impedance," Phys. Rev. **28**, 1038–1047 (1926).

the works of Schuster[17] and Robinson.[18] The principal difficulty is that suitable variable standards of acoustic resistance and reactance have not been developed.

Method 10 is a relatively new bridge technique.[19] The bridge has two acoustical arms and two electrical arms. One acoustical and one electrical arm are fixed. The variable electrical arm is adjusted to balance the unknown impedance in the remaining acoustical arm.

Method 11 received attention at an early date.[20–24] By it, the vibrating diaphragm of an electromechanical transducer is exposed to the acoustic environment whose impedance is desired. Measurements are made of electrical impedance as a function of either frequency or length of a tube on one end of which the sample is mounted. If the properties of the diaphragm are known, or are determined, the value of the unknown impedance reacting on the diaphragm can be found. The variable frequency method is inaccurate except for frequencies near resonance. The variable length method is inaccurate if the absorption of the sample is too high.

Method 12, reported by Flanders,[25] makes use of reasonably reliable standards of acoustic reactance, namely, a rigid wall and an eighth-wavelength tube. Mathematical calculations require a computer.

7·3 Surface Methods

One way of measuring the impedance directly at the surface of a sample is to force a known volume velocity of air through it

[17]K. Schuster, "Measurement of acoustic impedances by comparison," Electr. Nachr.-Tech., **13**, 164–176 (1936) (in German).

[18]N. W. Robinson, "An acoustic impedance bridge," Philos. Mag., [7] **23**, 665–680 (1937).

[19]A. P. G. Peterson and W. M. Ihde, communicated privately.

[20]A. E. Kennelly and K. Kurokawa, "Acoustic impedance and its measurement," Proc. Am. Acad. Arts and Sci., **56**, 1–42 (1921).

[21]A. E. Kennelly, "The measurement of acoustic impedance with the aid of the telephone receiver," J. Franklin Inst., **200**, 467–488 (1925).

[22]R. D. Fay and W. M. Hall, "The determination of the acoustical output of a telephone receiver from input measurements," J. Acoust. Soc. Am. **5**, 46–56 (1933).

[23]C. W. Kosten and Z. Zwikker, "The measurement of acoustic impedance and absorption coefficients by reaction on a telephone receiver," Akust. Zeits., **6**, 124–131 (1941) (in German).

[24]R. Fay and J. White, "Acoustic impedance of sample from motional impedance diagrams," J. Acoust. Soc. Am., **20**, 98–107 (1948).

[25]P. B. Flanders, "A method of measuring acoustic impedance," Bell Syst. Tech. J., **11**, 402–410 (1932).

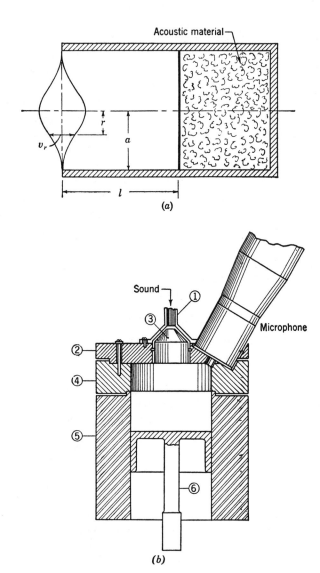

FIG. 7·4 (*a*) Measurement of acoustic impedance using a short tube to couple the source to the sample. (After Cook.[2]) (*b*) Same. (After Mawardi.[3])

and to measure the resulting change in pressure at the surface. To do this, Cook[2] utilized a short tube with an inside radius a and a length l (see Fig. 7·4). A clamped-edge diaphragm was used, and the volume velocity U was calculated from the formulas

$$U = 2\pi \int_0^{d/2} v_r r \, dr \qquad (7\cdot18a)$$

and

$$v_r = V_0\left[1 - \frac{J_0(k_1 r)}{J_0(k_1 a)}\right] \qquad (7\cdot18b)$$

where v_r is the velocity at any point on the diaphragm, V_0 is a constant, k_1 is the first-order normal wave number for the diaphragm, and J_0 is a Bessel function of zero order. The equation for the average sound pressure over the surface of the sample is given by

$$p_{\text{av.}} = \frac{-\rho c U}{\pi a^2 (Y \cos kl + j \sin kl)} \qquad (7\cdot19a)$$

Here, ρc is the characteristic impedance of air, $k = \omega/c$, and $Y = \rho c/z$, where z is the specific acoustic impedance of the sample.

Cook states that if the pressure is measured at the *center* of the sample, Eq. (7·19a) can be modified to read

$$\boxed{p_c = \frac{-\rho c V_0}{Y \cos kl + j \sin kl}} \qquad (7\cdot19b)$$

where V_0 is the velocity at the value of r for which $J_0(k_1 r) = 0$. When this approximation was used, the error was found experimentally to be less than 1 percent in a tube for which $l = 1$ cm, $a = 1.9$ cm, $f = 1000$ cps, and $Y = 0$ (rigid wall).

This method has several advantages. Frequency and temperature variations and losses at the side walls are less critical than for the transmission line methods. Gases other than air can easily be introduced into the tube. The most obvious advantage is that the apparatus is compact and inexpensive to build.

Mawardi[3] independently developed a surface method which differs from that of Cook in several respects. His cavity is so chosen that it can be assumed to be a lumped acoustical element. His source is designed to suppress the first symmetrical and all asymmetrical modes of vibration and is of sufficiently high impedance, acoustically, so that its volume velocity remains constant with changes in loading impedance. Hence, its strength can be calculated by measuring the pressure developed in a cavity of known impedance. Also, his probe microphone is chosen to have a very high acoustic impedance. With these assumptions, his theoretical treatment reduces to

$$\frac{E_2}{E_1} = \frac{Z_x}{Z_c + Z_x} \qquad (7 \cdot 20)$$

where E_2 is the complex voltage output of the microphone with the sample in place; E_1 is that with no sample in place; Z_c is the specific acoustic impedance of the air cavity coupling the source to the sample; and Z_x is the unknown specific acoustic impedance of the sample.

Mawardi's experimental apparatus is shown in Fig. 7·4b. Here the sound is delivered to the chamber with impedance Z_c through a wire-filled tube 1 and a circular slot between parts 2 and 3. The source of sound then appears as a narrow circular ring in one end of the chamber. This slot is packed with No. 18 copper wires to raise its impedance as high as possible.

The radius of the ring, as viewed from the chamber, is equal to 0.628 of the radius of the chamber itself. The width of the ring is not critical. The microphone with a very short probe tube attached samples the pressure in the chamber. It has high acoustic impedance.

The cavity in part 4 is the one for which Z_c is calculated. Because of its small size, $Z_c = -j(\rho c^2 / \omega l)$, where l is the length of the cylindrical cavity. Parts 5 and 6 constitute the sample holder.

The magnitude and phase of the voltages E_1 and E_2 were measured by Mawardi with an electronic voltmeter and phasemeter. At very low frequencies, corrections for the impedance of the source and for the heat losses at the boundaries of the cavity must be made. The impedance of the source may be determined when necessary by adding several cavities of known impedance in place of Z_x and then calculating the source impedance from the formula

$$\frac{E_2}{E_1} = \frac{(Z_c + Z_s)Z_x}{Z_c Z_x + Z_s(Z_c + Z_x)} \qquad (7 \cdot 21)$$

where Z_s is the specific acoustic impedance of the source. Corrections for heat losses at the boundaries are given in Fig. 4·14 (p. 145).

7·4 The Acoustic Transmission Line

A. Theory

The theory of the non-dissipative acoustic transmission line, that is, a smooth rigid-walled tube whose lateral dimensions are small compared to a wavelength, has been given in most texts.[26] In actual cases the dissipation at the side walls, and in

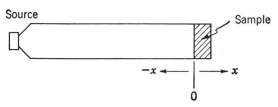

FIG. 7·5 Location of source and sample in an acoustic transmission line.

the gas, under certain conditions of temperature and humidity, is appreciable. Because the analysis of the dissipative case is sufficiently different from the non-dissipative treatment in those texts, it will be given here. The treatment is taken from Scott.[7]

Assume that the source of sound is at one end of the tube and that the sample under test is located at the opposite end, where $x = 0$ (see Fig. 7·5). If the lateral dimensions are sufficiently small, the sound field can be represented by two plane waves traveling in opposite directions in the tube. Then the expression for the excess pressure p_x at a point in the tube a distance x from the surface of the sample is (see Section 1 of this chapter)

$$p_x = P_0 e^{-\psi + j\omega t} \cosh \{ -(\alpha + jk)x + \psi_1 + j\psi_2 \} \quad (7\cdot22)$$

where $\psi = \psi_1 + j\psi_2$ is a complex quantity associated with the conditions of reflection at the sample; α is the attenuation constant for the wave due to energy losses at the side walls of the

[26]P. M. Morse, *Vibration and Sound*, 2nd edition, McGraw-Hill (1948).

tube and in the gas; and $k = \omega/c$, where ω is the angular frequency and c is the velocity of sound. It has already been shown in this chapter that $\psi_1 + j\psi_2 = \psi$ equals minus 0.5 of the natural logarithm of the ratio of the amplitudes of the direct and reflected waves in the tube; see Eq. (7·9).

The particle velocity u_x will be

$$u_x = \frac{P_0 e^{-\psi + j\omega t}}{\rho c}\left(1 - j\frac{\alpha}{k}\right)\sinh\{-(\alpha + jk)x + \psi_1 + j\psi_2\}$$

$$(7\cdot23)$$

The impedance ratio $p/(u_x\rho c)$ at any point $-x$ will be

$$\frac{Z}{\rho c} = \gamma/\phi = \left(\frac{k}{k - j\alpha}\right)\coth\{(\alpha + jk)x + \psi_1 + j\psi_2\} \quad (7\cdot24)$$

where γ is the magnitude, and ϕ is the phase angle of $Z/\rho c$. In order to write $\psi_1 + j\psi_2$ in terms of the impedance of the sample, let $x = 0$. Then,

$$\psi_1 + j\psi_2 = \coth^{-1}\left[\frac{Z}{\rho c}\left(1 - j\frac{\alpha}{k}\right)\right] \doteq \coth^{-1}[\gamma/\phi - (\alpha/k)]$$

$$(7\cdot25)$$

where γ is the magnitude, and ϕ is the phase angle of the impedance ratio. Conversely, when we wish to determine the impedance of the sample from measurements in the tube, we must first find values of ψ_1 and ψ_2. This, in effect, is equivalent to saying that we must determine the complex ratio of the reflection coefficient at the surface of the material.

Generally $(\alpha/k)^2 \ll 1$; therefore we can write, for the acoustic impedance at the surface of the sample under test,

$$\boxed{\frac{Z}{\rho c} \doteq \coth(\psi_1 + j\psi_2)} \quad (7\cdot26)$$

In Figs. 7·6 and 7·7 are shown two versions of a "transmission line calculator" described by Smith[27] for solving Eq. (7·26). The first chart gives the real and imaginary parts of $Z/\rho c$, and the

---

[27]P. H. Smith, "An improved transmission line calculator," Electronics **17**, 130 (January 1944). This calculator is manufactured by the Emeloid Company, Arlington, N.J.

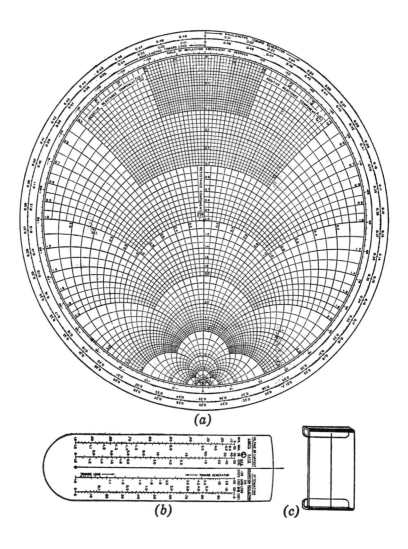

(a)

(b)   (c)

FIG. 7·6 (a) Smith chart for determining the real and imaginary parts of the value of a hyperbolic cotangent from the complex value of its argument. The rotatable transparent scale (b) pivots about the center of the chart. The transparent runner (c) rides on the rotatable scale. The column headed max./min. is $\coth \psi_1$, and the ring labeled "wavelengths toward load" is equal to $0.25 + \psi_2/2\pi$. The quantity L equals $20 \log_{10} [\coth \psi_1]$. (After Smith.[27]) Note: In 1988 these computations can be done by digital computer.

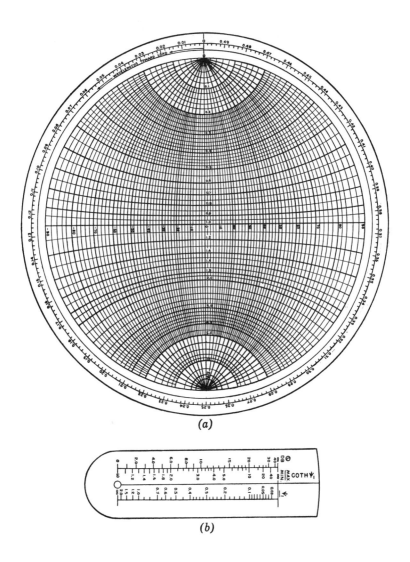

(a)

(b)

FIG. 7·7 Modified Smith chart for determining the magnitude and phase angle of the value of a hyperbolic cotangent from ψ_1 and the number of "wavelengths toward the load" (see text). (After Beranek.[9])

second gives the magnitude and phase angle. In order to use the chart, we must define a quantity

$$L = 20 \log_{10}[\coth \psi_1] \, db \tag{7·27}$$

The calculator is operated by moving a transparent runner (Fig. 7·6c) to the value of L on a transparent arm (Fig. 7·6b) which pivots about the center of the calculator, and at the same time aligning the hairline of the transparent arm with one of the numbers around the edge labeled "wavelengths toward the load." The impedance is read beneath the intersection of the hairlines of the runner and the rotatable arm. The "wavelengths toward the load," W, is related to ψ_2 by

$$W = 0.25 + \frac{\psi_2}{2\pi} \tag{7·28}$$

For more exact calculations the formulas for $Z = R + jX$ may be used:

$$\frac{R}{\rho c} = \frac{\tanh\psi_1(1 + \tan^2\psi_2)}{\tanh^2\psi_1 + \tan^2\psi_2} \tag{7·29}$$

$$\frac{X}{\rho c} = -\frac{\tan\psi_2(1 - \tanh^2\psi_1)}{\tanh^2\psi_1 + \tan^2\psi_2} \tag{7·30}$$

For high values of impedance, ψ_1 and ψ_2 less than 0.1, the following formulas may be used.

$$\frac{R}{\rho c} = \frac{\psi_1(1 + \psi_2^2)}{\psi_1^2 + \psi_2^2} \tag{7·31}$$

$$\frac{X}{\rho c} = -\frac{\psi_2(1 - \psi_1^2)}{\psi_1^2 + \psi_2^2} \tag{7·32}$$

B. Standing Wave Analysis

Movable Microphone. This technique, listed as Method 3 in Table 7·1, is the one most commonly used in tubes.[10] For it, a probe microphone is drawn along the length of the acoustic transmission line, and several of the maximum and minimum values of the sound pressure and the points at which they are located are measured. The ratios of these maximum to minimum values are usually expressed in decibels, so that our data amount to the quantities L' and L'' and the distances d_1 and d_2 of Fig. 7·8.

Our purpose in the next few paragraphs is to relate these quantities to ψ_1 and ψ_2 which are in turn needed to get $Z/\rho c$.

The magnitude of the pressure p_x in the measuring tube is obtained by rationalizing Eq. (7·22). This operation yields

$$|\, p_x \,| = B[\cosh 2(\alpha x + \psi_1) + \cos 2(kx + \psi_2)]^{\frac{1}{2}} \quad (7\cdot33)$$

This equation is valid if no changes in frequency, length, or temperature of the tube occur during the test. The maximum and

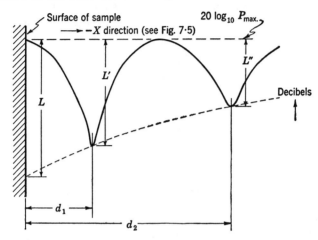

FIG. 7·8 Distribution of effective sound pressure in the impedance tube as a function of distance d measured from the surface of the sample. The source of sound is assumed to lie to the right of the page. The quantity L' equals $20 \log_{10} (P_{max.}/P_{min.})$ at $d = d_1$, with a similar definition for L'' at $d = d_2$. For the meaning of L, see the text.

minimum values of $|\, p_x \,|$ are found by differentiating (7·33) with respect to x and equating the result to zero. We then get

$$\alpha \sinh 2(\alpha x + \psi_1) - k \sin 2(kx + \psi_2) = 0 \quad (7\cdot34)$$

Now, if $\alpha^2 \ll k^2$, which is always the case for measuring tubes of practical diameters, we know that the first term will be small compared to the second and, hence, we can replace the sine term by its argument. Two solutions to Eq. (7·34) are possible:

$$2(kx + \psi_2) = 2M\pi + \frac{\alpha}{k} \sinh 2(\alpha x + \psi_1) \quad (7\cdot35)$$

$$2(kx + \psi_2) = (2N - 1)\pi - \frac{\alpha}{k} \sinh 2(\alpha x + \psi_1) \quad (7\cdot36)$$

where M and N are integers. For $|p_x|$ to be a maximum, the ratio of the distance D_M (measured from the place at which $|p_x|$ is a maximum to the surface of the sample) to the wavelength λ must be

$$\frac{D_M}{\lambda} = \frac{M}{2} - \frac{\psi_2}{2\pi} + \frac{\alpha}{2k^2\lambda} \sinh 2(\alpha x + \psi_1) \qquad (7 \cdot 37)$$

and for $|p_x|$ to be a minimum, the ratio of the sample distance d_N to the wavelength must be

$$\frac{d_N}{\lambda} = \frac{2N - 1}{4} - \frac{\psi_2}{2\pi} - \frac{\alpha}{2k^2\lambda} \sinh 2(\alpha x + \psi_1) \qquad (7 \cdot 38)$$

The effect of dissipation in the tube as represented by α, the attenuation constant, is to *decrease* the distance between a pressure minimum and the sample and to *increase* the distance between a pressure maximum and the sample by an amount

$$\frac{\alpha}{2k^2} \sinh 2(\alpha x + \psi_1) \qquad (7 \cdot 39)$$

The ratio of $|p_{\text{max.}}|$ to $|p_{\text{min.}}|$ is

$$\left| \frac{p_{\text{max.}}}{p_{\text{min.}}} \right| = \left[\frac{2 \cosh^2 (\alpha D_M + \psi_1) - \dfrac{\alpha^2}{2k^2} \sinh^2 2(\alpha D_M + \psi_1)}{2 \sinh^2 (\alpha d_N + \psi_1) + \dfrac{\alpha^2}{2k^2} \sinh^2 2(\alpha d_N + \psi_1)} \right]^{1/2}$$

$$(7 \cdot 40)$$

For low values of absorption at the termination to the tube, $\cosh^2$ will approximate unity, and $\sinh^2$ will be a small quantity. Hence, for ψ_1 *small* the second term in the numerator and denominator will be significant only at pressure minima. We also see that the ratio $|p_{\text{max.}}/p_{\text{min.}}|$ will become smaller as d_N increases because the argument of the second $\sinh^2$ in the denominator is twice that of the first.

A plot of Eq. $(7 \cdot 33)$ *vs.* distance from the sample is shown in Fig. $7 \cdot 8$. In that figure the quantities L' and L'' are equal to $20 \log_{10} [\text{Eq. } (7 \cdot 40)]$ at the first two values of the minimum spacing, d_1 and d_2, respectively; see Eq. $(7 \cdot 38)$.

For *small* values of ψ_1, that is to say, when there is no sample in the tube, Eq. (7·40) becomes

$$\left|\frac{p_{\text{max.}}}{p_{\text{min.}}}\right| \doteq \frac{1}{\alpha d_N + \psi_1} \qquad (7·41)$$

For *large* values of ψ_1 and for $\alpha^2 \ll 2k^2$, Eq. (7·40) becomes

$$\psi_1 = \coth^{-1}\left[\frac{p_{\text{max.}}}{p_{\text{min.}}}\right] \qquad (7·42)$$

Now if we define L as the ratio of $\left| p_{\text{max.}}/p_{\text{min.}} \right|$ in decibels for

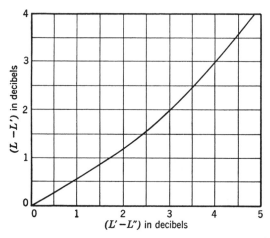

FIG. 7·9 Chart for determining the value of L, given the values of L' and L''. All quantities are in decibels. The quantity L will differ from L' and L'' only when the absorption in the tube is very small, but not zero.

$d_N = 0$, we have from Eq. (7·41) for ψ_1 *small*

$$L \doteq 20 \log_{10} \frac{1}{\psi_1} \qquad (7·43)$$

or for ψ_1 *large*, from Eq. 7·42

$$L \doteq 20 \log_{10}\left[\coth \psi_1\right] \qquad (7·27)$$

In order to use the Smith chart, which requires L and W, we need to convert our readings of L' and L'' to L. We do this by Fig. 7·9. This figure was obtained by subtracting $20 \log_{10}$ [Eq. (7·41)], for $d_N = d_1$, from Eq. (7·43) to get $L - L'$. Similarly $L' - L''$ is obtained by using $20 \log_{10}$ [Eq. (7·41)] for $d_N = d_1$

and d_2, respectively. These two difference quantities are expressed in terms of each other in Fig. 7·9. Hence, we can get L from measurements of L' and L''. It is important to recognize that L is the quantity that would have been obtained at d_1 and d_2 if α had equaled zero.

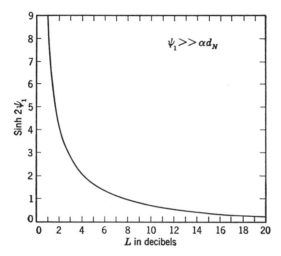

Fɪɢ. 7·10 Graph of sinh $2\psi_1$ vs. L. This graph is needed in the determination of ψ_2 as given in Eqs. (7·44) and (7·45). (After Scott.[7])

We still need to determine the value of ψ_2. It comes from Eq. (7·38) when $d_N = d_1$:

$$\psi_2 = k\left[\frac{\lambda}{4} - d_1 - \frac{\alpha}{2k^2}\sinh 2\psi_1\right] \qquad (7\cdot44)$$

The value of sinh $2\psi_1$ vs. L is plotted in Fig. 7·10. For circular tubes, α is given in Chapter 2, and $k = \omega/c$.

Variable Length. If the impedance is measured by method 4 of Table 7·1, the procedure is to vary the length of the tube and to measure the maximum and minimum pressures at the source end. The length is also observed at the point where the pressure is maximum. Let us call this length y_1. If the volume velocity of the source (the "strength of the source") remains constant during the length adjustment, ψ_1 will be given by Eq. (7·42) as before, and ψ_2 will be given by

$$\psi_2 = M\pi - k\left[y_1 - \frac{\alpha}{2k^2}\sinh 2\psi_1\right] \qquad (7\cdot45)$$

where M is the number of half-wavelengths standing in the tube. As before the $\sinh 2\psi_1$ is determinable from Fig. $7\cdot10$, α from Chapter 2, and $k = \omega/c$.

Pressure at Two Points. It is also obvious that, if the magnitude of the pressure is measured at two points y_1 and y_2 in front of the sample (method 5 of Table $7\cdot1$), ψ_1 and ψ_2 can be determined from Eq. $(7\cdot33)$. This solution can be accomplished

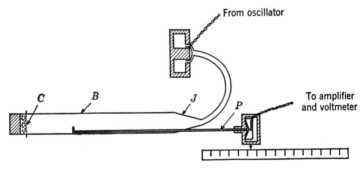

Fig. $7\cdot11$ Sketch of an impedance-measuring tube of the acoustic transmission line type. The sound pressure probe is a crystal microphone attached to a small diameter tube P which can be moved along the length of the main tube B. The surface of the sample under test is located at C.
(After Scott.[7])

without undue labor through the use of the commercial version of the Smith transmission line calculator (Figs. $7\cdot6$ and $7\cdot7$).

Requirements for Accuracy. For studies of the detailed mechanism by which sound is absorbed in a material, or for measurement of the mechanical properties of an electroacoustic transducer, an accuracy of 2 percent in both resistive and reactive components of the impedance is desirable in the required frequency range. To achieve such accuracy, we must satisfy the following requirements:[7]

(1) The bore of the tube must be uniform and the walls smooth and substantially rigid.

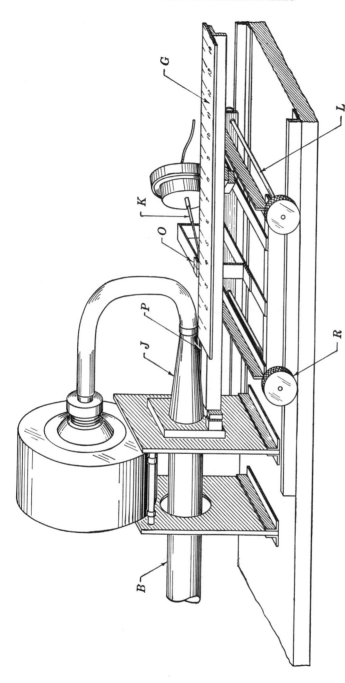

FIG. 7·12 Detailed sketch of the source end of an impedance-measuring tube of the acoustic transmission type. The trolley L rides on a pair of tracks, and the probe tube P is securely anchored to the trolley. Fine adjustments of its position can be made by the knurled nuts R. (After Scott.[7])

(2) The sound wave in the tube must consist of plane, uniform, axially directed waves.

(3) The face of the sample undergoing test must be substantially plane and mounted normal to the axis of the tube.

(4) The microphone used for exploration of the sound field must not itself appreciably affect the field and must be sensitive and stable.

(5) The measurement of the position of the microphone orifice must be accurate to about 0.1 mm.

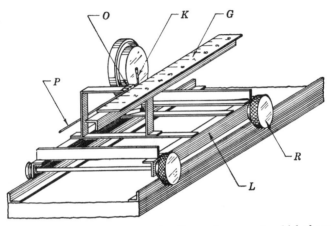

Fɪɢ. 7·13   Sketch showing details of trolley and manner in which the probe tube P is anchored.   (After Scott.[7])

(6) The sound pressure measured with the microphone must arise only from a single frequency.

(7) The frequency and ambient temperature must be stable.

An apparatus designed by Scott to meet these requirements is shown in Figs. 7·11 to 7·13.[7]   The main measuring tube B should be made of a length of precision seamless steel tubing with a wall thickness of ¼ in.   If possible, this tube should be buried in sand or coated with mastic to reduce mechanically borne waves. If the microphone orifice is located so that it travels along the central axis of the tube, experiment indicates that the inside diameter of the tube should not exceed the value given by

$$d = \frac{20,000}{f_h} \quad \text{cm} \tag{7·46}$$

where f_h is the highest frequency at which measurements are to be made.

The sample under test, C (Figs. 7·11 to 7·13), is mounted at one end of the tube, and the source of sound connects to the tube through a length of flexible tubing and a conical coupler J. The probe P is made of stainless steel tubing with internal and external diameters of 0.241 and 0.316 cm, respectively, and a length of 104 cm. One end of the tube is connected to a small cavity, of volume 2 cm^3, in front of a ceramic or piezoelectric crystal microphone. A massive case is used to enclose the microphone, and this in turn is mounted on a block of sponge rubber fastened to a four-wheeled trolley, L. A sleeve of rubber tubing K prevents the transmission of vibrational components from the wall of the probe tube to the crystal microphone.

A steel cursor O is mounted on the probe tube and arranged to run along a precision scale G divided in millimeters. Coarse adjustment of the position of the trolley is made by pushing it bodily along the track, and fine adjustment by movement of the knurled knobs R which form extensions to the wheels on one side.

The modification of the sound field caused by the introduction of the probe tube can be measured with a rigid piston in place at C. It is negligible for tubes whose diameter is greater than 4 cm because in those cases the area of cross section of the probe is less than 0.5 percent of that of the main tube.

The velocity of sound in the tube is given by the formula

$$c' = c \left(1 - \frac{0.76}{2r \sqrt{\pi}} \times \frac{1}{\sqrt{f}} \right) \qquad (7 \cdot 47)$$

where c is the velocity of sound in free space, in centimeters per second; r is the radius of the tube, in centimeters; and f is the frequency. Room temperatures and tubes in which isothermal conditions exist only in a region very near the side walls are assumed.

The frequency of the sound source must be held accurate to approximately one part in several thousand, if an accuracy of 2 percent is desired in the reactance term.

C. Resonance Analysis

This procedure includes methods 6 and 7 of Table 7·1. The essential construction of the apparatus is shown in Fig. 7·14. In

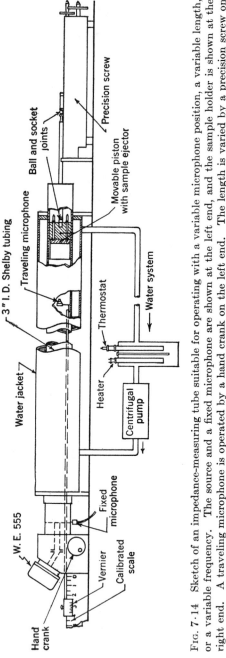

Fig. 7·14   Sketch of an impedance-measuring tube suitable for operating with a variable microphone position, a variable length, or a variable frequency. The source and a fixed microphone are shown at the left end, and the sample holder is shown at the right end. A traveling microphone is operated by a hand crank on the left end. The length is varied by a precision screw on the right end. The entire tube is held at constant temperature by a water jacket. (After Beranek.[9])

making measurements, either the length of the tube or the driving frequency is varied in such a way as to trace out a resonance curve. The probe microphone is located at the edge of the source end of the tube, and the source is approximately a point of very high impedance. The measuring tube is made of precision seamless steel tubing, and its length is chosen to be not less than one-half the wavelength of the lowest frequency at which measurements are to be made. The diameter is selected by Eq. (7·46). The sample under test is mounted on a movable piston at the end of the tube opposite the source of sound.

With this location of microphone, sample, and source, the equation for the square of the magnitude of the effective sound pressure at the fixed microphone when either the length or frequency is varied is[13]

$$|p|^2 = \frac{\dfrac{K'\omega^2}{l^2}}{4\omega_m{}^2 k_1{}^2 + [\omega^2 - (\omega_m{}^2 - k_1{}^2)]^2} \qquad (7\cdot48)$$

where K' is a constant of proportionality; ω is the driving frequency; l is the length of the tube (measured from the plane at which the impedance is desired to the plane of the source and the microphone); ω_m is a normal angular frequency of longitudinal vibration and is, along with k_m, determined by the impedance of the sample under test, the length of the tube, and the velocity of sound; k_1 is the total damping constant and is determined by the combined absorptions at the sample, the side walls of the tube, the source, and the microphone.

We have for the impedance ratio $(\gamma\underline{/\phi})$ of the sample under test

$$\boxed{\gamma\underline{/\phi} + \frac{k_m}{\omega_m} \doteq \coth\left[(k_m - j\omega_m)\frac{l}{c}\right]} \qquad (7\cdot49)$$

where $\gamma = |Z|/\rho c$, ϕ is the phase angle of $|Z|$, and Z is the impedance at the surface of the sample, which we are trying to determine.

When the length or the driving frequency is adjusted to give a *maximum* of the pressure p, the value of ω_m becomes

$$\boxed{\omega_m = \sqrt{(\omega^2 - k_1{}^2)}} \qquad (7\cdot50)$$

If the driving frequency is held constant, the length of the tube can be adjusted to a value l'', greater than the length l at which resonance occurs, or to a length l', less than l such that the square of the pressure at the microphone is decreased to $1/w$ of its resonant value (see Fig. 7·15a):

$$\left(\frac{p_{\text{max.}}}{p''}\right)^2 = \left(\frac{p_{\text{max.}}}{p'}\right)^2 = w \qquad (7\cdot51)$$

Then, because the impedance of the sample is constant, at least for the variable length case, it follows from Eq. (7·49) that

$$\omega_m' = \frac{l\omega_m}{l'} \qquad k_m' = \frac{lk_m}{l'}$$

$$\omega_m'' = \frac{l\omega_m}{l''} \qquad k_m'' = \frac{lk_m}{l''} \qquad (7\cdot52)$$

Because the dissipation k_1 is usually made up principally of k_m we can also say that $k_1' \doteq lk_1/l'$, and $k_1'' \doteq lk_m/l''$. Combining Eqs. (7·48) through (7·52), we obtain two simultaneous equations from which it is found that, if $l''^2 + l'^2 \doteq 2l^2$,

$$\boxed{k_1 \doteq \frac{\pi f(l'' - l')}{l\sqrt{w - 1}}} \qquad (7\cdot53a)$$

If the resonance curve is obtained by varying the frequency (see Fig. 7·15b),

$$\boxed{k_1 \doteq \frac{\pi(f'' - f')}{\sqrt{w - 1}}} \qquad (7\cdot53b)$$

where f'' and f' are the frequencies on either side of resonance at which the square of the sound pressure is reduced to $1/w$ of the value at resonance. With the aid of formulas (7·50), (7·51), and (7·53) the specific acoustic impedance of the termination may be determined by obtaining two resonance curves, one with the material in place and another without the material. If k_{na} is the damping constant and l_0 the resonant length with no absorbing material present,

$$k_m = k_1 - k_{na} \qquad (7\cdot54a)$$

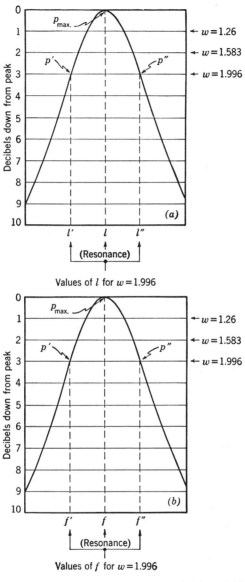

FIG. 7·15   Typical resonance curves for cases of (a) variable length and (b) variable frequency.   If there is no sample in the impedance tube the resonant length and frequency are called l_0 and ω_0, respectively.

and

$$mc = 2fl_0 \qquad (7\cdot54b)$$

where m is an integer equal to the number of one-half wavelengths standing in the tube. Then Eq. $(7\cdot49)$ may be written

$$\gamma \Big/ \phi + \frac{k_m}{\omega_m} = \coth\left[(k_1 - k_{na})\frac{l}{c} -j\frac{\omega}{c}\left\{\left(1 - \frac{k_1{}^2}{2\omega^2}\right)l - l_0\right\}\right] \equiv \coth[C - jD] \qquad (7\cdot55)$$

If the resonance curve is obtained by varying frequency, l_0 is determined from Eq. $(7\cdot54b)$, where f is replaced by f_0 (see Fig. $7\cdot15$).

Under the special condition that k_m/ω_m is small compared to ϕ, we can write $\psi_1 \doteq C$ and $\psi_2 \doteq -D$, and use Eq. $(7\cdot26)$ in calculating the impedance. Otherwise the more exact equation $(7\cdot55)$ must be used. The quantities C and D are

$$\psi_1 \doteq C \equiv \frac{k_m l}{c} \qquad (7\cdot56)$$

$$\psi_2 \doteq -D \equiv \frac{\omega}{c}\left\{l_0 - l\left(1 - \frac{k_1{}^2}{2\omega^2}\right)\right\} \qquad (7\cdot57)$$

From a practical standpoint, the required accuracy of 2 percent can be obtained only at the higher frequencies if the temperature of the gas is accurately known. This is best accomplished by providing a circulating water jacket which can be warmed by a thermostatically controlled heating element.

The driving unit of Fig. $7\cdot14$ connects to the tube through a high impedance coupling unit. This may consist of a tube 1 cm in diameter filled with approximately seventy No. 18 straight copper wires. The microphone connects to the interior edge of the main tube through a short length of tube with an inner bore of approximately 0.05 cm. Care must be taken in the construction to assure that the rod coupling the precision screw to the moving piston does not resonate at some frequency near the bottom end of the range in which data are desired. Also an air pressure release must be provided to allow for movements of the piston. This release is shown near the driving unit in Fig. 7·14.

The precision screw should be calibrated so that the incremental lengths can be read to an accuracy of at least 0.001 cm. Band-pass filters should be provided to eliminate harmonics generated by the loudspeaker. For convenience, the piston in which the sample is held is provided with an ejecting mechanism so that the sample can be retrieved undamaged.

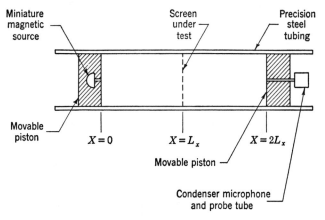

FIG. 7·16 Apparatus specially designed to measure the specific acoustic impedance of very porous sheets such as screens and gauzes. (After Harris.[15])

Harris[15] describes a form (Method 8) of the resonant method for the measurement of the impedance of very porous screen. The experimental arrangement is shown in Fig. 7·16. The screen under test is equidistant from two movable pistons. The length of the tube, $2L_x$, is adjusted to equal one-half wavelength at the frequency being investigated. Both the source and microphone have very high impedances. The real part R and the imaginary part Z of the specific acoustic impedance Z of the screen (defined here as the ratio of the pressure to the normal particle velocity at the surface of the screen with zero impedance backing) are given by

$$R = \rho k_m L_x \qquad (7\cdot58)$$

$$X = \frac{4\rho(f_0{}^2 - f_1{}^2)\pi L_x{}^2}{c} \qquad (7\cdot59)$$

where k_m is the damping constant for the sample under test and is found from Eqs. $(7 \cdot 53b)$ and $(7 \cdot 54)$; ρ is the density of air in grams per square centimeter; f_0 is the resonant frequency with the tube empty, and f_1 is the resonant frequency with the screen at $X = L_x$; and c is the velocity of sound in centimeters per second. Curves obtained with this device are shown in Fig. $7 \cdot 17$.

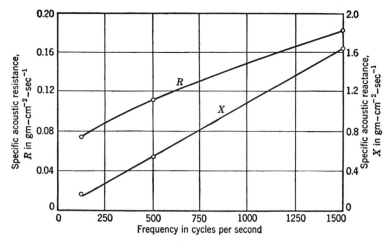

Fig. $7 \cdot 17$ Typical impedance curves obtained with the apparatus of Fig. $7 \cdot 16$ on a perforated sheet of brass, 0.021 in. thick with holes 0.054 in. in diameter and 33 percent open area. (After Harris.[15])

$7 \cdot 5$ Bridges

In electrical measurements, the impedance bridge has proved itself to be rapid and accurate for the determination of unknown reactances and resistances. The chief requirement for such a bridge is the availability of stable, accurately calibrated standards of inductance, capacitance, and resistance, at least one of which must be continuously variable. Unfortunately, although adequate standards have been developed for electrical measurements, suitable standards of acoustic resistance, mass, and compliance have not been available. However, the application of bridge techniques in acoustics, if perfected, would result in a considerable acceleration of the development of acoustic filters, horns, and electroacoustic transducers.

A. Acoustic Bridge

Schuster[17] and Robinson[18] describe the two acoustic bridge arrangements shown in Fig. $7 \cdot 18$. However, before going into

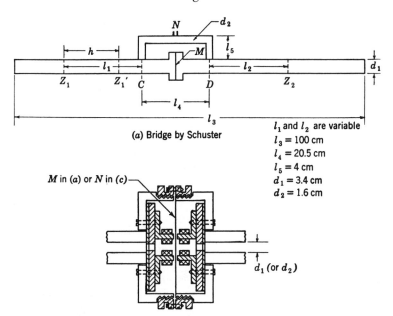

l_1 and l_2 are variable
$l_3 = 100$ cm
$l_4 = 20.5$ cm
$l_5 = 4$ cm
$d_1 = 3.4$ cm
$d_2 = 1.6$ cm

(a) Bridge by Schuster

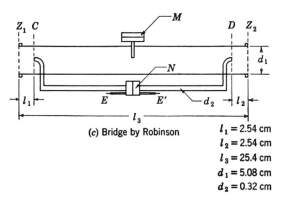

(b) Detail of Driving Unit M for Schuster Bridge
or Detector N for Robinson Bridge

(c) Bridge by Robinson

$l_1 = 2.54$ cm
$l_2 = 2.54$ cm
$l_3 = 25.4$ cm
$d_1 = 5.08$ cm
$d_2 = 0.32$ cm

FIG. 7·18 Sketches of acoustic impedance bridges by Schuster[17] and Robinson.[18] The unit in (b) is either a source or a microphone, depending on which type of bridge is used.

practical considerations, let us first review briefly the theory of
the acoustic bridge.

The specific acoustic impedance z_1', at the plane Z_1' [see (a)
of Fig. 7·18] in a tube, separated a distance h from the plane Z_1,
where an impedance z_1 is located, is given by the formula

$$\frac{z_1'}{\rho c}\left(1 - j\frac{\alpha}{k}\right)$$
$$= \coth\left[(\alpha + jk)h + \coth^{-1}\left\{\frac{z_1}{\rho c}\left(1 - j\frac{\alpha}{k}\right)\right\}\right] \quad (7\cdot 60)$$

where k equals ω/c as usual, and α is the attenuation constant in
the tube (see Eq. 2·35). This equation is the same as Eq.
(7·24). The impedances at the planes C and D will be given by
two formulas of the type of (7·60), where h is made to equal l_1
and l_2, and z_1 and z_2, respectively. M is a diaphragm driven at
a given frequency. Because the outgoing waves due to the
motion of the diaphragm M will arrive at points C and D with
equal magnitude and either 180 degrees out of phase in the case
of (a) of Fig. 7·18, or in phase in the case of (c) of Fig. 7·18, no
motion of a diaphragm placed at N will occur if the reflected
waves arriving at C and D from the terminations at Z_1 and Z_2
are also of equal magnitude and of the same phase. Our task,
then, is to adjust the standard impedance at Z_2 until its value
equals the unknown at Z_1. This condition will be realized when
there is no response at the detector N.

Changes in the length of one of the arms, l_1 or l_2, that is, the
value of h in (7·60), will result in a shift in phase of the reflected
wave. However, this shift is also accompanied by a small but
measurable change in the amplitude of the reflected wave
arriving back at point C (or D) because of the losses at the
boundaries of the tube shown by the constant α in Eq. (7·60).
It will be shown later that for the variable acoustic standards
presently available, a change in absorptivity is generally accompanied by a shift in phase. As a result, the balancing of an
acoustic bridge is usually tedious because of the interaction
between the two components, magnitude and phase of the comparison impedance.

As with the standing wave methods just described for determining acoustic impedance, the upper frequency limit at which
an acoustic bridge may be used depends on the diameter of the

main tube d_1. For axial driving and detecting, such as is shown in Fig. 7·18c, the diameter of the tube is determined by Eq. (7·46).

Temperature variations will not affect the accuracy of the bridge if both arms are kept at the same temperature. However, the calibration of the variable impedance standard usually depends on temperature. Suitable temperature control of the space surrounding the bridge and the standard must therefore be provided. The probe tubes inserted into the main tube at C and D in either (a) or (c) of Fig. 7·18 should have a cross-sectional area of less than 0.5 percent of that of the main tube if they are not to disturb the sound field.

The unit shown in Fig. 7·18b is used as the source in the Schuster bridge and as the detector in the Robinson bridge. When the bridge is calibrated initially, it will be found that, unless great care has been taken in the mechanical construction of that unit, the bridge will not be symmetrical. If asymmetry is found, the effect on the balance may be eliminated by adjusing small pistons E' and E of the type indicated in (c). These pistons slide in two small tubes communicating with the air spaces on the two sides of the diaphragm. Unfortunately, readjustment of the two pistons is often necessary for each frequency.

B. Variable Standards

Schuster and Stöhr[28] describe an acoustic impedance standard consisting of a disk of absorbing material P (see Fig. 7·19) of a certain thickness, behind which there is an air space of variable length s. The absorbing disk is mounted at the end of a tube W (called the resistance tube) which in turn is inserted into the main tube V of the bridge. Inside the resistance tube W there is another tube which is closed and serves as a rigid piston (piston tube). At any fixed plane Z_1 in the main tube, the acoustic impedance can be expressed through an energy reflection coefficient R and a phase shift θ. A variation in the position of the resistance tube W will essentially vary only the value of θ at the plane Z_1. If, however, the distance s is varied, both R and θ vary at the plane Z_1.

[28] K. Schuster and W. Stöhr, "Construction and properties of a variable acoustic impedance standard," *Akust. Zeits.*, **4**, 253–260 (1939) (in German); English translation: L. L. Beranek, *Jour. Acous. Soc. Amer.*, **11**, 492–494 (1940).

The variation of the absorption coefficient $A = 1 - R$ as a function of $s/(\lambda/4)$ is shown in Fig. 7·20 for a typical impedance standard. A maximum absorption A_m will be obtained at some particular value, say $s_m/(\lambda/4)$, and a minimum value A_0 will

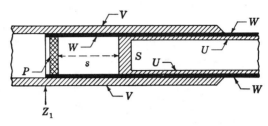

Fig. 7·19 Sketch of a variable impedance standard. A thin absorbing disk P is held in a tube W which in turn is free to slide in the main tube V of the impedance bridge. The phase angle of the reflection coefficient is changed by changing the position of W in V and the magnitude and phase angle together by varying s. (After Schuster and Stöhr.[28])

be obtained at $s = 0$. If the disk P is chosen with proper thickness and flow resistance, maximum absorptivity will approach 100 percent at s_m.

Schuster and Stöhr show that the optimum thickness H (cm) of the disk of absorbing material is related to the specific flow

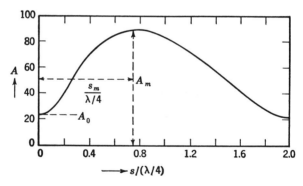

Fig. 7·20 Typical absorption curve for the variable impedance standard of Schuster and Stöhr.[28]

resistance per centimeter, r (rayls/cm), the porosity Y, the characteristic resistance of the air ρc, and the structure factor k' (a constant whose value is about 2) by the formula

$$Hr = \rho c Y \qquad (7·61)$$

The value of s_m (value of s in centimeters to yield A_m) is given by

$$\coth ks_m = \frac{\omega\rho}{r}\left(k' - \frac{1}{3}Y^2\right) \qquad (7\cdot62)$$

where $k = \omega/c = 2\pi/\lambda$ and ρ = density of air.

The value of the energy reflection coefficient at $s = \lambda/4$ is given by

$$R_{\lambda/4} = \frac{\omega^2\rho^2}{4r^2}\left(k'^2 - \frac{2}{3}Y^2k' + \frac{1}{9}Y^4\right) \qquad (7\cdot63)$$

Finally, the reflection coefficient for $s = 0$ is given approximately by

$$R_0 = 1 - \frac{4}{3}\frac{\omega^2\rho^2}{r^2}Y^4 \qquad (7\cdot64)$$

It is desirable that the reflection coefficient R_0 of the standard for $s = 0$ should be large. This will be true if the flow resistance r is large and if Y is small. However, such a condition leads to small values of H. If H becomes too small, the disk of absorbing material will vibrate, and its absorbing properties will be very irregular as a function of frequency. In general, the material chosen in the standard should be dense and stiff, and greater than 1 mm in thickness, so that the chance of its vibrating at low frequencies will be minimized.

The bridge arrangement itself may be used to calibrate the variable standard by comparing its impedance with the input impedance of a circular tube terminated rigidly at one end. The input energy reflection coefficient R_1 and phase angle θ_1 of a tube of length l terminated with an impedance having a reflection coefficient R_2 and a phase angle θ_2 are given by

$$R_1 = R_2 e^{-4\alpha l} \qquad (7\cdot65)$$

$$\theta_1 = \theta_2 - 2kl \pm 2n\pi \qquad (7\cdot66)$$

where α is the attenuation constant for the tube (see Eq. $(2\cdot35)$) and $k = \omega/c$. For a rigid termination, $R_2 = 1$ and $\theta_2 = 0$.

The variable impedance standard is placed in one arm of the bridge, and the rigidly terminated tube (calibrating tube) is placed in the other. If, after balance, the face of the standard impedance and the open end of the calibrating tube are located at distances l_1 and l_2, respectively, from the planes C and D of

Fig. 7·18, then, if bridge symmetry is assumed, it is possible to write

$$R = e^{-4\alpha(l_2 - l_1)} \qquad (7\cdot67)$$

$$\theta = -2k(l_2 - l_1) \pm 2n\pi \qquad (7\cdot68)$$

If a polar plot is made of R *vs.* θ with s as a parameter at each frequency, graphs of the type shown in Fig. 7·21 will be obtained. The impedance curve is roughly a circle which passes near the

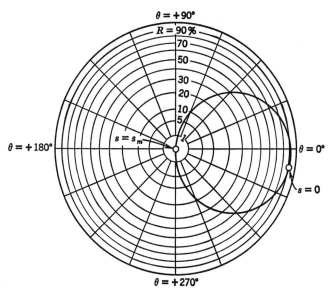

FIG. 7·21   Polar plot of R and θ, the magnitude and phase angle of the reflection coefficient, as a function of the distance s of Fig. 7·19. (After (Schuster and Stöhr.[28])

origin for $s = s_m$ and tends to be tangent to the outer circle of the polar plot when R approaches unity at $s = 0$.

If the impedance curve for the input of the calibration tube (the rigidly terminated tube in the other arm) were to be plotted on the same graph, with l as a parameter, a spiral about the origin would be obtained, starting at the outside edge ($R = 1$) and converging on the origin for $l \to \infty$. This means that balances of the bridge are possible only at points where the spiral and the small circle intersect, that is, for specific values s_n and l_n.

In order to avoid using excessively long values of the calibration tube in calibrating the variable standard for values of s approaching s_m, a method can be used whereby two variable standards are calibrated simultaneously. Call these standards I and II. First place I in one arm of the bridge and place a short (*ca.* 1-meter length) calibration tube with a rigidly terminated end in the other arm. A calibration point for I is obtained at a length $s = s_1$. Then the rigid end is removed from the calibrating tube, and I is attached instead. II is now put in the other arm of the bridge and the balance repeated. Note that in this case R_2 in Eq. (7·65) is no longer unity. By placing I and II alternately in place of the rigid termination, calibration of the standards can be carried out over the entire range of variation of s.

Inspection of Fig. 7·21 reveals that, in the vicinity of $s = 0$, variations in s do not essentially change the reflection coefficient, but cause only a variation in phase angle. Hence, when balances are made in this region, a number of near balances occur for values of s and l_1 such that $(s + l_1)$ is approximately constant. This follows because a change in l_1 just as for s causes chiefly a variation in phase angle. To avoid this ambiguity, the following procedure is adopted. First, the best balance is obtained by varying the position of the resistance tube and keeping the piston tube in a *fixed* position with respect to the main tube of the bridge. Then the balance is completed either by varying the piston tube alone, or by varying the entire assembly with respect to the main tube. In the first part of the balance, only the value of R is varied; in the second only the value of θ is varied.

Meeker and Slaymaker[29] describe a different form of variable acoustic impedance. Its characteristics can be calculated from its dimensions with a fair degree of accuracy, and, except for sensitivity to temperature changes, it is stable as a function of time. The construction is shown in Fig. 7·22. Sections 1 and 2 are metal; section 3 is an 18-ft length of plastic (Saran) tubing. Section 3 has an attached collar which slides within section 2 so that the length of the air column in section 2 may be varied, maintaining an acoustically tight connection. Section 2 has a similar collar which slides within section 1. The length of section 3 is sufficient to form a substantially infinite acoustic line,

[29] W. Meeker and F. Slaymaker, "A wide range adjustable acoustic impedance," *Jour. Acous. Soc. Amer.*, **16**, 178 (1945).

the input impedance of which affords a convenient calculable termination for section 2.

From Fig. 7·22, we see that the specific acoustic impedance Z_1 is given by

$$Z_1 = Z_{01} \coth \left[(\alpha_1 + j\beta_1) l_1 + \psi_1 + j\phi_1 \right] \qquad (7 \cdot 69)$$

where α_1 is the attenuation constant for the first section; $\beta_1 = k + \alpha_1$; $k = \omega/c$; Z_{01} is the input impedance for $l_1 \rightarrow \infty$; that is,

$$Z_{01} = \rho c^2 \frac{\alpha_1 + j\beta_1}{j\omega} \qquad (7 \cdot 70)$$

$$\psi_1 + j\phi_1 = \coth^{-1} \left(\frac{Z_2}{Z_{01}} \times \frac{S_1}{S_2} \right) \qquad (7 \cdot 71)$$

where S_1 and S_2 are the cross-sectional areas of section 1 and section 2, respectively.

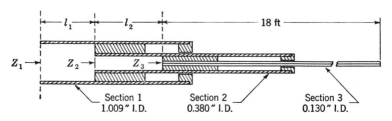

Fig. 7·22   Variable impedance standard consisting of three tubes of different diameters sliding inside each other.   (After Meeker and Slaymaker.[29])

The impedance Z_2 has the form given by Eq. (7·69) except that l_2 is substituted for l_1, and in Eq. (7·71) Z_3 is substituted for Z_2.   Because of the length of section 3, its input impedance may be written

$$Z_3 = \frac{\rho c^2 (\alpha_3 + j\beta_3)}{j\omega} \qquad (7 \cdot 72)$$

A plot of the input impedance Z_1 as a function of l_1 and l_2 can be drawn on the R *vs.* X plane as shown in Fig. 7·23.   When both l_1 and l_2 are zero, point $Z_3(S_1/S_3)$ is obtained.   Now if l_1 is kept zero and l_2 is varied from zero to its maximum length $\lambda/2$, the dashed spiral will be obtained.   If the spiral were continued by increasing l_2 beyond $\lambda/2$ it would wind around in ever tightening loops, eventually approaching $Z_{02}(S_1/S_2)$.   Mathematically, Z_{02} has the same form as does Z_{01} of Eq. (7·70).

If l_2 is held at zero and l_1 is varied, the largest solid spiral in Fig. 7·23 is obtained. Now if l_2 is held at $\lambda/2$ and l_1 is varied, a curve like that shown by the second largest solid spiral is obtained. In either of these two cases the spirals will wind about the point Z_{01} if l_1 goes beyond $\lambda/2$; otherwise the spirals stop as shown in Fig. 7·23 when $l_1 = \lambda/2$.

It is possible to obtain all the values of the input impedance Z_1 lying within the unshaded area of Fig. 7·23 by adjustment of l_1 and l_2 between zero and $\lambda/2$. When l_2 is set at some value

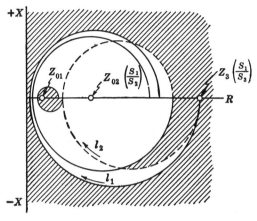

FIG. 7·23 Impedance circles for the variable impedance standard of Fig. 7·22.

such that $Z_2(S_1/S_2)$ lies at some point along the dashed curve, the spiral for Z_1 will start from that point and invariably wind about Z_{01}. If the dashed spiral is made to pass through point Z_{01}, the small area of unobtainable impedances about Z_{01} vanishes.

The accuracy with which the input impedance can be calculated depends on the following three factors:

(1) The ratio of the wavelength to the diameter of section 1 must be sufficiently large to assure continuity of volume velocity at the junction of sections 1 and 2.

(2) The humidity must be such that no significant molecular losses arise in the air.

(3) The temperature of the entire apparatus must be uniform and known.

A third type of impedance standard which is useful over a limited range of impedances and frequencies has been described by White.[30] The device consists of an electroacoustic transducer whose electrical terminals are connected to a variable electrical impedance. Electrical impedances are converted into acoustical impedances by this arrangement. The lower the mechanical impedance of the diaphragm of the transducer to begin with, the greater will be the range of acoustical impedances available.

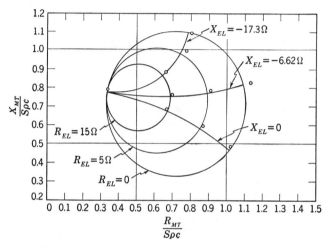

FIG. 7·24   Graph showing $X_{MT}/(S\rho c)$ and $R_{MT}/(S\rho c)$ as a function of R_{EL} and X_{EL} at 500 cps. S is the area of opening at which Z_{MT} is desired, and ρc is the characteristic impedance of air. The electroacoustic transducer was a W.E. 555, and $S = \tfrac{7}{8}$ in. $\times \tfrac{7}{8}$ in.

For this reason the transducer is generally of the moving-coil type.

The general theory of the transfer of acoustic to electrical impedances (the reciprocal case) is covered in detail in Section 6 of this chapter. The reader should first acquaint himself with that material if an understanding of this section is desired.

Briefly, the total mechanical impedance Z_{MT} looking to the left of terminals 3 and 4 of Fig. 7·28f, when an electrical load impedance Z_{EL} is connected across terminals 1 and 2, is

$$Z_{MT} = R_{MT} + jX_{MT} = Z_P + \frac{k^2}{Z_{EW} + Z_{EL}} \qquad (7\cdot73)$$

[30] J. E. White, "A continuously variable acoustic impedance," *Jour. Acous. Soc. Amer.*, **19**, 846–849 (1948).

where Z_P is the mechanical impedance of the diaphragm when it is unloaded, Z_{EW} is the electrical impedance of the coil winding when the diaphragm is blocked so that it cannot move, and $k = |k|e^{-j\alpha}$ is the complex electromechanical coupling coefficient. In Section 6 of this chapter a procedure for determining Z_P, k, and Z_{EW} is described by using measurements of electrical impedance for various known reactive air loads. These known air loads are obtained by means of a rigid-walled tube equipped with a variable piston.

Once these quantities have been determined it is only necessary to calculate values of Z_{MT} as a function of Z_{EL}. White has shown that such a set of calculations when plotted on the X_{MT} vs. R_{MT}

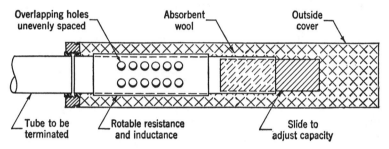

FIG. 7·25 Arrangement for producing a pure resistance termination. (After Jordan.[31])

plane will have the appearance of a displaced Smith chart (Fig. 7·6). A typical plot for the case of a particular W.E. 555 moving-coil unit at 500 cps is shown in Fig. 7·24. In that graph White has normalized the coordinates so that they yield $X_{MT}/\rho cS$ and $R_{MT}/\rho cS$, where S is the area of the throat opening of the W.E. 555 and its mechanical adapter, and ρc is the characteristic specific impedance of air. The area S in his case is equal to $\frac{7}{8}$ by $\frac{7}{8}$ in. The units of ρc and of R_{MT}/S are rayls, provided S is expressed in square centimeters.

Jordan[31] discusses qualitatively an arrangement shown in Fig. 7·25. He says that the principal design objective for this device is to obtain a pure resistance termination to a tube. Dissipation is obtained in the termination by allowing a tube to radiate the incident energy through small holes along its length whence it is absorbed. However, these holes also have the effect of adding

[31] E. C. Jordan, "A continuously variable acoustic impedance," *Jour. Acous. Soc. Amer.*, **13**, 8 (1941).

shunt acoustic mass to the circuit. This mass may be balanced out with an equal and opposite acoustic compliance obtained by terminating the section of tubing to the right of the holes (which is less than a quarter-wavelength long) by a sliding piston. The device can then be adjusted to act as a pure resistance at any given frequency. The magnitude of this resistance is varied by using two close-fitting concentric tubes, as shown, with an identical arrangement of holes. By sliding the outer tube around the inner one it is possible to change both the number and size of the holes through which radiation occurs. The change in number varies both the inertance and resistance, and the change in size varies the ratio of inertance to resistance. Hence, by rotating the tube and moving the piston the desired resistive termination is obtained. To prevent radiation into the surrounding room the entire terminating section can be covered with a closed-end tube filled with an absorbing material.

C. Electroacoustic Bridge

Bridge techniques in acoustics have not found widespread use because of the lack of suitable acoustic standards. Peterson and Ihde[19] have adapted electric bridge techniques to acoustics through the simple arrangement shown schematically in Fig. 7·26. Two arms of the bridge are acoustic, and two are electric. The acoustic admittance, Y_{c1} is a fixed arm and is equaled by Y_{c2}. All acoustic admittances are specific and have the units rayls^{-1}. The unknown admittance Y_x is in series with Y_{c2}. Two identical microphones with responses k_1 and k_2 detect sound pressure at the surface of the sample. The driving unit supplies sound to the two chambers through two identical sections of wire-filled tube. The voltages e_1 and e_2 are amplified and delivered to a bridge transformer. Shunting the primary of this transformer and forming two arms of the bridge are two electric admittances Y_{E1} and Y_{E2}.

The balance equations are derived as follows:

$$\frac{g_1 c_1}{Y_{E1}} = \frac{g_2 e_2}{Y_{E2}}$$

where

$$e_1 = \frac{k_1 u_1}{Y_{c1} + Y_{11} + Y_{M1}}$$

and

$$e_2 = \frac{k_2 u_2}{Y_{c2} + Y_x + Y_{22} + Y_{M2}}$$

are the voltages produced by the microphones; g_1 and g_2 are the transconductances of the amplifiers; u_1 and u_2 are acoustic velocities; Y_{M1} and Y_{M2} are the acoustic admittances of the

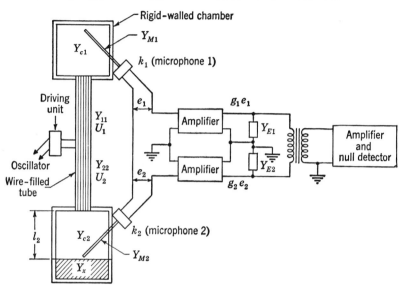

FIG. 7·26 Schematic diagram of an electroacoustic bridge. Y_{c1} and Y_{c2} are two equal acoustic elements, Y_x is the unknown acoustic admittance in series with Y_{c2}, and Y_{E1} and Y_{E2} are the two electrical arms. (After Peterson and Ihde.[19])

microphones; and Y_{11} and Y_{22} are the acoustic admittances of the source. Now, by proper choice of elements, Y_{M1}, Y_{M2}, Y_{11}, and Y_{22} may be made small compared to Y_{c1} and Y_{c2}, so that

$$e_1 = \frac{k_1 u_1}{Y_{c1}}$$

and

$$e_2 = \frac{k_2 u_2}{Y_{c2} + Y_x}$$

Therefore at balance,

$$Y_x + Y_{c2} = \frac{g_2 k_2 u_2}{g_1 k_1 u_1} \frac{Y_{E1}}{Y_{E2}} Y_{c1}$$

For initial balance, set $Y_x = 0$ by using a stiff plate; then

$$Y_{c2} = \frac{g_2 k_2 u_2}{g\, k_1 u_1} \frac{Y_{E1}'}{Y_{E2}'}\, Y_{c1}$$

Then mount the admittance to be measured. Solving for Y_x gives

$$Y_x = Y_{c2}\left[\frac{Y_{E1}}{Y_{E1}'}\frac{Y_{E2}'}{Y_{E2}} - 1\right] \qquad (7 \cdot 74)$$

On the initial balance set Y_{E2} equal to a convenient value, and balance the system with Y_{E1}; then, if the unknown balance is

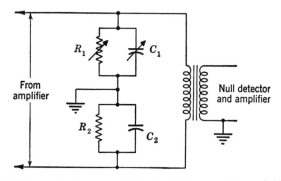

FIG. 7·27   Schematic diagram of the electrical arms Y_{E1} and Y_{E2} of the electroacoustic bridge and of the bridge transformer.   (After Peterson and Ihde.[19])

made with Y_{E1}, Y_{E2} equals Y_{E2}', and the formula simplifies to

$$Y_x = Y_{c2}\left[\frac{Y_{E1}}{Y_{E1}'} - 1\right]\text{rayls}^{-1} \qquad (7 \cdot 75)$$

The balancing network and bridge transformer are shown in Fig. 7·27. R_1 and R_2 are 10,000-ohm decade resistance boxes, and C_1 and C_2 are 1-μf decade condenser boxes. The specific acoustic admittance of the cavity is $j\omega l/\rho c^2$, where l is the length of the chamber, in centimeters; ρ is the density of air, in grams per square centimeter; and c is the velocity of sound, in centimeters per second. If Y_{M2} and Y_{22} are not negligible compared to Y_{c2}, their values should be determined as a function of frequency and added to Y_{c2}.

7·6   Reaction on the Source

A. Measurement of change of Electrical Impedance

Kennelly and Kurokawa[20] were the first to make use of the reaction of a column of air on the movement of the diaphragm of a telephone earphone (receiver). Fay and Hall[22] and Fay and White[24] developed the method further. In 1941, Kosten and Zwikker[23] reviewed the technique.

Two different variations of the technique arise in practice. One involves the variation of frequency, and the second the variation of a closed length of tube on the end of which the sample is mounted. Before selecting one of these alternatives, let us examine the general theory.

Refer to Fig. 7·28. The total electrical impedance measured at the terminals of the transducer is designated as Z_{ET} and the impedance of the coil winding as Z_{EW} when the diaphragm is held motionless. Let Z_M equal the mechanical impedance (units: dyne-seconds per centimeter) against which the electromagnetic force operates; let Z_A be the mechanical impedance of the air load; and let Z_P be the mechanical impedance of the diaphragm when unloaded. Then $Z_M = Z_P + Z_A$. By the principle of reciprocity, the ratio of the force F, developed by the transducer coil to the current i producing it, is equal to the ratio of the open-circuit voltage e generated in the coil winding to the velocity v of the coil.* We may therefore write

$$\frac{e}{i} = k^2 \frac{v}{F} \qquad (7·76)$$

where k is an electromechanical coupling coefficient. In this equation F is in dynes and v is in centimeters per second. The complete expression for determining the input electrical impedance of a *linear* transducer is equal to the right-hand term above plus the blocked electrical impedance of the coil winding:

$$Z_{ET} = Z_{EW} + \frac{k^2}{Z_P + Z_A} \qquad (7·77)$$

If the transducer is of the moving-coil type, k will be nearly

---

* Absolute volts and amperes must be used here. The number of absolute volts equals 10^8 times the number of practical volts, and the number of absolute amperes equals 10^{-1} times the number of practical amperes.

344 **Measurement of Acoustic Impedance**

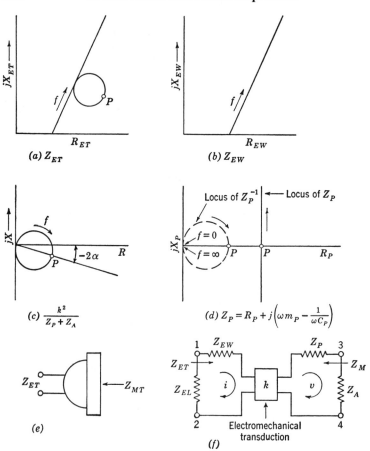

(a) Z_{ET}

(b) Z_{EW}

(c) $\dfrac{k^2}{Z_P + Z_A}$

(d) $Z_P = R_P + j\left(\omega m_P - \dfrac{1}{\omega C_P}\right)$

Locus of Z_P^{-1} ← Locus of Z_P

$f = 0$

$f = \infty$

(e)

(f)

1 Z_{EW} Z_P 3

Z_{ET} Z_M

Z_{EL} i k v Z_A

2 Electromechanical 4
transduction

Z_{ET} ←Z_{MT}

FIG. 7·28 This figure shows the steps involved in determining the constants of a transducer used for the measurement of acoustic impedance. (a) shows the locus of the total impedance $R_{ET} + jX_{ET}$ with frequency f as the variable; (b) shows the blocked electrical impedance $R_{EW} + jX_{EW}$; (c) shows the vector difference of (a) and (b) which is called the motional impedance; (d) shows the mechanical impedance of the diaphragm and its reciprocal for the case when Z_A is made zero. The value of k has been determined by measuring the value of the motional impedance both with $Z_A = 0$ and with $Z_A = -j\rho c$; (e) is a sketch of the transducer; and (f) is an equivalent circuit diagram of the transducer and its electrical and acoustical loads.

real; if the transducer is of the magnetic type, iron losses and phase shifts will occur and k will equal $\left| k \right| e^{-j\alpha}$. The second term in Eq. (7·77) is commonly called the motional impedance term.

Generally, the diaphragm itself is so located and shaped that it is impossible to describe an exact plane at which the impedance Z_A appears. Instead, a plane located some distance in front of the diaphragm is arbitrarily designated. To take account of this, the values of k and Z_P (both in phase and magnitude) are modified, and α is no longer associated strictly with iron losses, etc.

Equation (7·77) when plotted on an X *vs.* R coordinate system with frequency as the variable appears as (*a*) of Fig. 7·28. The arrow indicates the direction of increasing frequency, and the point P the frequency at which the reactive part of $(Z_P + Z_A)$ equals zero. If the diaphragm is rigidly blocked, the electrical impedance of the coil alone has the shape shown in (*b*). Vector subtraction of (*b*) from (*a*) will yield the motional impedance portion of Eq. (7·77) as shown in (*c*). If the mechanical impedance of the air Z_A, reacting on the diaphragm, is made zero, the mechanical impedance of the diaphragm Z_P will be as shown in (*d*). The dashed circle is the inverse of Z_P, whereas the solid line is Z_P directly.

It is seen that this set of diagrams can be constructed for any transducer when Z_{ET} has been measured for the air loads $Z_A = \infty$, and $Z_A = 0$. That is to say, if $Z_A = \infty$, one determines Z_{EW} from Eq. (7·77) by measuring Z_{ET}. Then, if Z_A is made zero, one gets Z_P in terms of k^2. To obtain the value of k one other measurement of Z_{ET} must be made when Z_A has any known value. Usually this is done by terminating the transducer in a rigid-walled tube whose length is adjusted to a value $\lambda/8$, whereupon $Z_A = -jS\rho c$. Here λ is the wavelength, ρc is the characteristic impedance of the air in rayls, and S is the cross-sectional area of the diaphragm and the terminating tube in square centimeters. Because all the constants in Eq. (7·77) are determinable by the above process, Z_A can be determined in terms of measurements of Z_{ET}.

The variable length of tubing and the impedance bridge during calibration of the transducer of (*c*) are shown in Fig. 7·29. To obtain $Z_A = \infty$, a one-half wavelength tube is used; for $Z_A = 0$, a one-fourth wavelength tube is used; and for $Z_A = -jS\rho c$ a one-eighth wavelength tube is used. The junction at which the

impedance Z_A joins onto the impedance Z_P can be arbitrarily
selected at any point along the tube without any loss of generality,
as we have already said.

When using the equipment of Fig. 7·29 to measure acoustic
impedance, it is desirable not to have to determine Z_P, k, and Z_{EW}
explicitly. When measuring a sample of acoustical material,

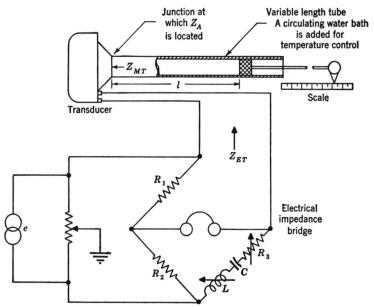

FIG. 7·29 Apparatus used for calibrating a transducer which is to act as
the source in determining acoustic impedance by the "reaction on source"
method. The electrical impedance bridge is a 1:1 bridge. (After Fay and
Hall.[22])

Fay and White[24] avoid the evaluation of these quantities by
mounting the sample on the face of the piston and then varying
the length of the tube. From their analysis one obtains the
equation

$$Z_{ET} = Z_{EW} + \frac{k^2 Z_P}{Z_P{}^2 - Z_0{}^2} - \frac{k^2 Z_0}{Z_P{}^2 - Z_0{}^2}$$
$$\times \tanh\left[(\psi_A + \psi_0) + j(\phi_A + \phi_0)\right] \quad (7\cdot78)$$

where the quantities in the argument of the hyperbolic tangent
are defined as

$$\psi_A + j\phi_A \equiv \coth^{-1}\left(\frac{Z_A}{Z_0}\right) \quad (7\cdot79)$$

and

$$\psi_0 + j\phi_0 \equiv \tanh^{-1}\left(\frac{Z_P}{Z_0}\right) \qquad (7\cdot80)$$

In these equations k, Z_P, Z_{EW}, Z_{ET}, and Z_A are the same as before. The quantity Z_0 is the characteristic mechanical impedance of the air column in the tube.

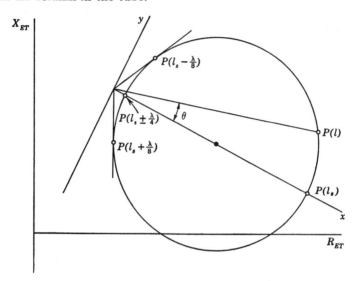

FIG. 7·30 Motional impedance circle obtained with the reaction-on-source method of Fay and White.[24]

In utilizing the relation of Eq. (7·78), the constants are lumped to give

$$Z_{ET} = R_{ET} + jX_{ET}$$
$$= A - B \tanh \ \ [(\psi_A + \psi_0) + j(\phi_A + \phi_0)] \qquad (7\cdot81)$$

where A and B are both complex numbers.

To measure the acoustic impedance of a sample mount the sample on the piston first. Then hold frequency, temperature, and loudspeaker conditions constant and make a plot of X_{ET} vs. R_{ET} with the length of the resonant tube l as a variable. The locus of the Z_{ET} vector on this plot is a circle for $\psi_A =$ constant (see Fig. 7·30). Now ψ_A is a measure of the power reflectivity of the sample under test plus the losses in the tube. That is to say, the ratio of the power in the incident wave starting down the tube to that in the wave arriving back after being reflected from the sample is $e^{4\psi_A}$.

After that test, two more circles must be obtained with the tube terminated by a totally reflecting piston and for lengths of tube which are one-half or a whole wavelength different. These three circles can be shown mathematically to have a common origin in a bipolar coordinate system.

When the length of the tube is varied over a range of $\pm\lambda/4$ (i.e., one-half wavelength in all), a plot such as that shown in Fig. 7·30 is obtained. From this circle, one needs to determine the radius, the coordinates of its center, and the origin for the bipolar family of which this circle is a member. (In Fig. 7·30, this origin lies at the crossing of the x, y axes). The center of the circle is accurately determined when a lot of points around its circumference are measured. The origin of the bipolar system may be found from the grouping of the points on the circle. Let us now see how this is done.

First define l_s as that length of tube for which the values of X_{ET} and R_{ET} fall farthest out on the x bipolar axis of Fig. 7·30. Then by increasing and decreasing the length of the tube from l_s by one-eighth wavelength, the points $P[l_s - (\lambda/8)]$ and $P[l_s + (\lambda/8)]$ will be obtained. The intersection of the tangents to the circle passing through these two points determines the origin of the bipolar coordinate system. Our problem, therefore, is to find the point $P(l_s)$ from our plot of Fig. 7·30.

Fay[32] has shown that if a chord is drawn through each pair of points on the circumference of the circle for which l is different by $\lambda/4$, the intersection of all such chords will be a common point lying on the x axis. Hence, the chord that passes through this common point and through the center of the circle gives us the x axis of the bipolar system. The value of l that gives a point directly on this axis and farthest out from the bipolar origin is l_s. The value of λ is calculated by dividing Eq. (7·47) by the frequency. The velocity of sound in free space, c, for various temperatures is given in Chapter 2.

The two circles obtained with the rigidly terminated tube of different lengths will not have the same diameter because of the dissipation at the side walls of the tube. The purpose of obtaining several circles under these conditions is to find the value of

[32] R. D. Fay, "An improved telephone receiver analysis," *Jour. Acous. Soc. Amer.*, **15**, 32 (1943).

the tube losses and thereby to subtract them out of the final answer.

Now referring back to Eq. (7·81) and to Fig. 7·30, we see that the impedance A lies at the intersection of the x, y axes, and that the motional impedance circle referred to that point on the X_{ET}, R_{ET} plane is given by the equation

$$-B \tanh \left[(\psi_A + \psi_0) + j(\phi_A + \phi_0) \right] \tag{7·82}$$

Now let r equal the radius of the circle of Fig. 7·30 in ohms and θ equal the inverse tangent of the ratio of the x to the y coordinate of any point $P(l)$. Analysis has shown that

$$|B| = -\frac{r \sin 2\phi}{\tan \theta} \tag{7·83}$$

$$\phi = -\frac{2\pi(l - l_s)}{\lambda} \tag{7·84}$$

where l_s is the length of the air column corresponding to $\theta = 0$; and

$$\sinh 2(\psi_A + \psi_0) = -\frac{\sin 2\phi}{\tan \theta} \tag{7·85a}$$

That is,

$$\boxed{\psi_A = \frac{1}{2} \sinh^{-1} \left(\frac{|B|}{r} \right) - \psi_0} \tag{7·85b}$$

As an example, let us analyze the typical set of data given in Table 7·2 and shown in Fig. 7·31. The value of $|B|$ is calculated from Eqs. (7·83) and (7·84); average of data obtained at many values of l are used. From Eq. (7·85b) the value of $\psi_A + \psi_0$ follows immediately. In the table, α is defined as the attenuation constant in the tube expressed in nepers per centimeter of length. Obviously, from the three sets of data we get $\psi_s = (\psi_A - \alpha \, \Delta l_s)$, a constant associated with the sample itself.

TABLE 7·2

Circle	r, ohms	l_s, cm	Δl_s, cm	$\psi_A + \psi_0$
1	9.12	69.85	0.00	$0.0477 = \psi_0$
2	7.12	139.33	69.48	$0.0612 = \psi_0 + \alpha\lambda$
3	2.90	67.39	−2.46	$0.1482 = \psi_0 + \psi_s + \alpha \, \Delta l_s$

The parameter ϕ_s is also needed. From Table 7·2 we obtain the quantity Δl_s which is equal to the shift in l_s after the sample was added from the value it had when the rigid piston terminated the tube. Because an l_s will be obtained for any length differing by $\lambda/2$ or a multiple thereof, $\lambda/2$ should be subtracted from the

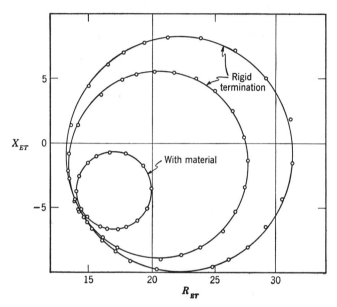

Fɪɢ. 7·31 Motional impedance circles for tubes of two different lengths. The points on the circles are for incremental variations in length. (After Fay and White.[24])

shift if a smaller number will be produced by doing so. The quantity ϕ_s is given by

$$\phi_s = \frac{2\pi}{\lambda}\,\Delta l_s \qquad (7\cdot86)$$

Once ϕ_s and ψ_s have been determined, we find the impedance of the sample from

$$\frac{Z_s}{\rho c}\left(1 - j\frac{\alpha}{k}\right) = \coth\left(\psi_s + j\phi_s\right) \qquad (7\cdot87)$$

while $k = \omega/c$, and ρc = characteristic impedance of air in free space. This equation is identical to Eq. (7·25), and the value of Z_s may be found by the methods described immediately following it.

Just as in impedance-measuring methods which use the transmission line technique, the temperature and frequency must be maintained accurately constant throughout the set of measurements.

When the method associated with Fig. 7·28 is used, that is, when frequency alone is varied, the diaphragm impedance Z_P must be low if $(Z_P + Z_A) - Z_P$ is to be determined accurately. Z_P is generally low only in the vicinity of resonance. Fay and Hall[22] designed a sound source which could be tuned to the frequencies at which measurements were to be made and for which R_P, the real part of Z_P, was small. It comprised a moving coil acting directly on an aluminum piston which was supported by radial wires whose effective length could be varied. The piston was mounted in a tube with a small clearance. No method could be found to seal the annular air space between the tube and the piston without introducing relatively great damping; hence the method of analysis was extended to take account of the sound which may leak by the piston. They state that the device was practical but somewhat difficult to use on account of extremely sharp tuning.

B. Measurement of Change of Sound Pressure

Acoustic impedance can be measured directly in terms of two other known impedances and three balance readings of an electrical potentiometer by a method due to Flanders.[25] A schematic diagram of that apparatus is given in Fig. 7·32.

A probe microphone is so located that it measures the pressure at the junction plane aa between the test apparatus and an acoustic impedance Z. The electric current through the resistance r and the primary arm of the mutual inductance m is proportional to the pressure measured by the probe microphone at aa provided no current flows in the earphones. The current I will produce a voltage E' across the secondary of m and the resistance r.

In performing measurements, an infinite impedance (rigid wall) is generally placed first at the plane aa. Then r and m are adjusted until balance is obtained. For this condition, I is proportional to the "open-circuit" pressure p_2 at the junction aa. That is to say, the sound pressure measured at the terminals aa is equal, by Thévenin's theorem, to the open-circuit pressure of the acoustic generator. Next, if two impedances z_1 and Z are successively placed at aa and if we call the internal acoustic

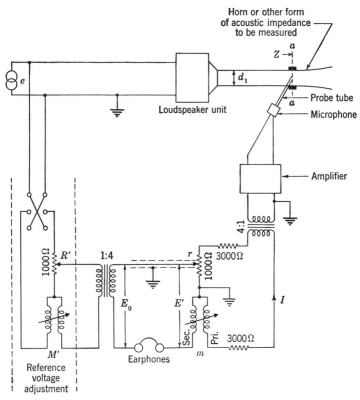

Fig. 7·32 Schematic diagram of an apparatus for measuring acoustic impedance by observing the complex pressure drop across the unknown impedance when supplied by a source of measured output acoustic impedance (After Flanders.[25])

impedance of the measuring equipment looking toward the loudspeaker z_s then two relations will hold:

$$p_1 = \frac{p_2 z_1}{z_1 + z_s} \qquad (7·88)$$

$$p_3 = \frac{p_2 Z}{Z + z_s} \qquad (7·89)$$

Elimination of the internal acoustic impedance z_s from these equations yields

$$\frac{Z}{z_1} = \frac{\left(\dfrac{p_2}{p_1} - 1\right)}{\left(\dfrac{p_2}{p_3} - 1\right)} \tag{7.90}$$

The reference voltage E_0 is constant for all three measurements and is equal to E' at balance. Hence, this must mean that $r + j\omega m$ is inversely proportional to I and hence to p. So Eq. (7.90) becomes

$$\frac{Z}{z_1} = \frac{(r_1 - r_2) + j\omega(m_1 - m_2)}{(r_3 - r_2) + j\omega(m_3 - m_2)} \tag{7.91}$$

In practice, the known termination z_1 is selected to be the input impedance of a closed rigid-walled tube whose length equals $\lambda/8$; that is, $z_1 = -j\rho c$ rayls. Also, calculation time is saved if m_2 for the infinite termination is made zero. To do this, m is set at zero and r at some mid-scale value when the infinite termination is in place, and M' and R' are adjusted until balance is achieved. The values of M' and R' are then kept unchanged while balances are obtained with the $\lambda/8$ tube or the unknown impedance in place. With $z_1 = -j\rho c$, and $m_2 = 0$, Eq. (7.91) becomes

$$\frac{Z}{\rho c} = \frac{\omega m_1 - j(r_1 - r_2)}{(r_3 - r_2) + j\omega m_3} \tag{7.92}$$

This formula is calculated with the aid of a vector slide rule.

The values of suitable circuit parameters are given in Fig. 7.32. For most cases it is found that the mutual impedance m should have two scales, zero to ± 50 and zero to ± 500.

The diameter of the measuring tube d_1 is designed from Eq. (7.46) as before. Particular care must be taken to see that there is no air leak at the junction point of the test apparatus with the unknown impedance.

8.

The Audiometer

8·1 Introduction

The audiometer is an apparatus for measuring the acuity of a person's hearing. Since audiometric procedures are used mainly for the detection and investigation of impaired hearing, the results of the measurement are usually expressed in terms of "hearing level" relative to the acuity of an average normal ear. In general, an audiometer comprises three basic devices: (1) a sound generator, which produces the signal to which the observer listens, (2) a means for controlling the sound level of the signal, and (3) a means for applying the sound to the listener's ear.

This general definition obviously includes a wide range of devices, and, although the present discussion will be confined to the modern audiometer, the history of its antecedents is interesting. Bunch has given an excellent review.[1] By means of standard procedures for acoustical and electrical measurements, all modern audiometers are adjusted and calibrated[2-7]

[1]C. C. Bunch, *Clinical Audiometry*, Chapters I and IX (Mosby, St. Louis, 1943).

[2]American National Standard, ANSI S3.6–1969 (reviewed 1973), "Specification for audiometers," Acoustical Society of America.

[3]American National Standard, ANSI S3.21–1978, "Methods for manual pure-tone threshold audiometry," Acoustical Society of America.

[4]American National Standard, ANSI S3.26–1981, "Reference-equivalent threshold force levels for audiometric bone vibrators," Acoustical Society of America.

[5]International Standard, IEC 651–1979, "Sound level meters," American National Standards Institute.

[6]International Standard, IEC 318–1970, "An IEC artificial ear for the calibration of earphones used in audiometry," American National Standard Institute.

[7]International Standard, ISO/DIS 8253, "Acoustics—Pure tone audiometric test methods," American National Standard Institute.

to give essentially identical results within practical tolerances. Thus, comparison of the results of audiometric tests made at various laboratories or clinics may be made within limits.*

Of the many types of sound signal which might be used for audiometric work, there are two which are employed currently, practically to the exclusion of all others; (1) pure tones, and (2) speech. Both types of audiometer are available in commercial form, although at present the pure-tone audiometer may be the more widely used. Because of the widespread usage of the commercial types of pure-tone audiometer, the term audiometer in the literature usually denotes one of the latter instruments unless otherwise specified.

With either type of instrument, the general procedure for determining a patient's hearing loss is usually the same. Starting with the sound signal at a level that is definitely audible to the patient, the operator gradually reduces its level by turning a calibrated dial until the patient signals that the tone is no longer audible. The reading of the dial, which is usually calibrated in decibels of hearing loss in steps of 5 dB each, is noted. The sound level is then brought up from a definitely inaudible level until the listener signals that the tone is again heard, and the dial reading noted. Several such pairs of readings may be taken, and the average is considered to represent the hearing level of the patient for the particular sound signal employed. When pure tones are used, and the hearing level is determined for sounds of a number of frequencies, the results may be plotted, for ease of visualization, on a graph of hearing level vs. frequency, as shown in Fig. 8·1. Such a graph is called an audiogram.

8·2 Pure-Tone Audiometers
A. Types

The pure-tone audiometer comprises three units: (1) an electronic oscillator for generating alternating electric currents of the desired frequencies, (2) an amplifier with an attenuator (volume control), and (3) an earphone for applying the sound to the listener's ear. Variations of this type of instrument may employ recordings to supply the sound signal or a loudspeaker to apply the sound to the listener's two ears simultaneously. The sound pressure level of the sound is adjusted by means of the attenuator dial, which is calibrated in units of hearing level

* CHABA Working Group, "Earphones in Audiometry," J. Acoust. Soc. Am. **83**, 1688–1689 (1988).

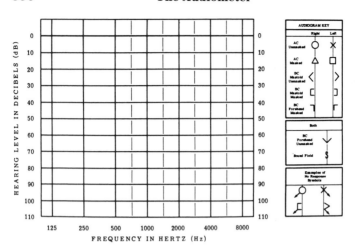

FIG. 8·1 Recommended form of audiogram and audiogram symbols for both air conduction (AC) and bone conduction (BC). (See Ref. 3.)

(decibels). The frequency of the sound is selected by means of another dial or other means which is marked in Hz (cycles per second). The two controls are thus similar to those on a radio set, one to tune to the desired frequency, and one to control the sound pressure level or volume of the sound. Commercial audiometers for pure tones are of the type shown in Fig. 8·2.

Either of two types of earphone may be employed: (1) an air-conduction type, similar to that on a telephone, from which the sound is conducted by air down the auditory canal to the ear-drum, or (2) a bone-conduction type, which is pressed against a bony portion of the head (usually the mastoid, back of the ear), from which the sound travels through the skull to the inner ear. Both types are used in diagnosis, and they may not yield the same results on a given ear. A marked differential between the results of an air-conduction test and those of a bone-conduction test on the same ear may assist in the diagnosis of the type of hearing impairment. For example, if the inner ear is normal but a mechanical obstruction exists in the middle or outer ear (e.g., otosclerotic fixation of the stapes in the oval window), the hearing loss for air-conducted sound may be much greater than for bone-conducted sound.

Two varieties of pure-tone audiometer are in common use: (1) the fixed-frequency or discrete-frequency type, and (2) the

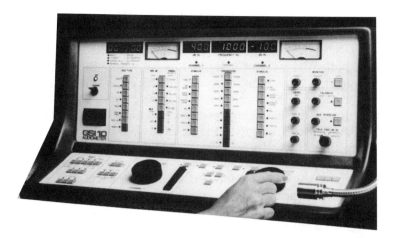

FIG. 8·2 Pure-tone and speech audiometer for air and bone conduction audiometric testing, meeting ANSI Standards.[2–7] (Courtesy Grason-Stadler, Inc.)

sweep-frequency type, as they are called. The discrete-frequency audiometer generates sounds of only a certain limited number of frequencies. The frequencies supplied are usually the octaves of 31.5 Hz. For example, a discrete-frequency audiometer may provide tones of 125, 250, 500, 1000, 2000, 4000, and 8000 Hz. These are the ones most frequently used for clinical audiometry. Some audiometers may provide, in addition, tones at the half-octave frequencies, in order to cover the frequency range in smaller steps and permit determination of the hearing-loss pattern in more detail.

B. Calibration of Air Conduction Types[*]

In order that all pure-tone audiometers may yield essentially identical test results, it is necessary that each be adjusted so that it produces the same level of sound in a listener's ear for a given setting of the frequency and hearing-loss controls. It is necessary also, of course, that the frequency of the sound produced be accurate, within reasonable tolerances, and that the steps on the hearing-level control be those indicated on the dial, within reasonable limits. For a hearing-level setting of zero (normal threshold) the level of the sound pressure produced in

[*] See Chap. 16, Sec. 16.4.C, "Equal Loudness Method."

a listener's ear must be that which represents the modal value of the threshold of hearing for a large number of normal ears.

The official calibration agency in the United States for pure-tone audiometers is the National Bureau of Standards in Washington, D.C. The values of sound pressure level in the ear for the "standard reference normal threshold" which are used by that agency are based on the data obtained by Beasley,[8] in the National Health Survey Hearing Study, made by the United States Public Health Service in 1935–1936. Sixteen Western Electric type 2A audiometers were used. From the known calibrations of these instruments, the reference normal threshold was set up in terms of the average voltage (at each of the various frequencies) across the earphone which would produce a threshold sound in the "average normal ear." The earphones themselves thus became the standard by which the reference normal threshold was defined. These were W.E. type 552 units.

At a later date, it was desired to use as standards three W.E. type 705A earphones which had been especially selected for stability of characteristics. It was necessary, therefore, to calibrate the 705A earphones, that is, to determine the voltage to be applied to them to produce sound at the level of the reference normal threshold in the ear of a listener. This was accomplished by a loudness-balancing procedure, in which an observer adjusted the voltage applied to one of the 705A units until the sound from it appeared as loud as that from the standard 552 earphone when the latter was operating at a known level. This procedure was followed at each of the standard frequencies, and at each of three sound levels: (1) at the observer's threshold, (2) at a level approximately 20 dB above threshold, and (3) at a level approximately 40 dB above threshold. A crew of six observers was used. From these measurements, the voltages which must be applied to the 705A earphones to produce the reference normal threshold were obtained, and the three 705A earphones now constitute the standards by means of which audiometers are calibrated at the National Bureau of Standards.

---

[8]W. C. Beasley, Bulletins 1–7, National Health Survey 1935–1936 (U.S. Public Health Service, Washington, D.C.).

TABLE 8·1*

Frequency Hz	Standard Reference Threshold Sound Pressure Levels Decibels Relative to 0.0002 Microbar
125	45.5
250	24.5
500	11
1000	6.5
1500	6.5
2000	8.5
3000	7.5
4000	9
6000	8
8000	9.5

NOTE 1: The reference threshold sound pressure level for intelligible speech from an earphone is 19 dB above 0.0002 microbar, measured in accordance with 8.3.B and based on 50 percent intelligibility of spondee words.
*See Ref. 2.

The calibration of an audiometer is conveniently done in three steps: (1) the calibration of the frequency dial, (2) the calibration of the attenuator (hearing-loss dial), and (3) the calibration of the earphone. The first two of these can be purely electrical measurements, made at the terminals of the earphone, by standard methods for measurement of voltage and of frequency, respectively. The third, the calibration of the earphone, is obtained at the seven standard frequencies by a loudness-balancing procedure similar to that described above.

C. Standard Reference Threshold Sound Pressure Levels

The standardized reference threshold is given in Table 8·1.[2]
Other earphones that are suitable for audiometric measurements may be calibrated to yield the same reference levels by use of the NBS 9-A coupler, Fig. 8·3. This is done by a "loudness balance" procedure. The respective signal voltages required by the standard earphone of Table 8·1 and the "other" earphone

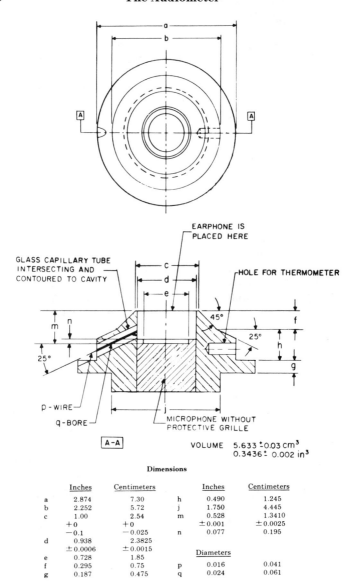

FIG. 8·3 National Bureau of Standards 9-A Coupler. (See Ref. 2.)

to produce equally loud tones are determined from judgments made by a group of not less than six subjects having otologically normal ears, by alternate listening or balancing. This loudness balance shall be done at a level of 20 to 40 dB above the zero reference threshold. If the signal voltages determined for the "other" earphone are then applied to it when mounted on the standard coupler, the pressure generated in the coupler by the "other" earphone corresponds to the standard reference pressure generated by the original earphone.

To obtain standard pressure values applicable to a type of coupler other than that on which Table 8·1 is based, but which is approved as an American National Standard, a direct comparison may be made of the pressures generated on the two couplers by the standard earphone of Table 8·1 with a given voltage applied to the earphone. For an earphone and a type of coupler both of which are different from those of Table 8·1, the two suggested procedures may be combined to obtain applicable standard pressure values. Separate determinations must be made for each frequency.

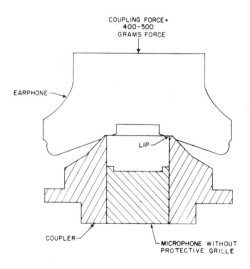

FIG. 8·4 Schematic drawing showing method of assembly in use of the NBS 9-A coupler. (See Ref. 2.)

D. General Requirements for Air Conduction Units

The American Standards, ANSI 3.6 and ANSI 3.21, cover a number of details that relate to the accuracy and calibration of audiometers. Part of those details relate to the vocabularity of the field, of which some of the more important terms are:

1. Sound pressure level (SPL) of an audiometer: The rms SPL referred to in the Standard is that developed in the coupler of Fig. 8·3. In other words, no attempt is made to state exactly what is developed at the eardrum of the person being tested. The reason is that the pressure developed there depends on the acoustic impedance looking back into the grille of the earphone and on the acoustic impedance of the cavity formed by the earphone and its cushion, the pinna, and the ear canal. Even with the best design of earphone, a moving coil type (dynamic type) earphone, the differences in pressure at the eardrums of a dozen people at each frequency between 100 and 10 000 Hz may cover a range of 10 to 20 dB. Thus, the "loudness balance" comparison is the true basis for calibration of an earphone.

2. Hearing level (of an ear), also called hearing loss: The hearing level at a given frequency for an ear of a particular person is defined as the amount in decibels by which the threshold of audibility for that ear exceeds the standard audiometric threshold (audiometric zero).

We have just stated that the audiometer threshold SPL, as indicated by "zero" on the dial, varies from one person to another. As a result, when a person's hearing level (loss) measures 10 or so decibels greater or less than audiometric zero, it doesn't necessarily mean that his hearing is different from that of the average young person. Thus partly for this reason, an otologist states that a person does not have a "hearing handicap" until the average of his hearing levels at 500, 1000 and 2000 Hz exceeds 25 dB.

3. Earphones: For tests by air conduction, a headphone is usually used, which consists of two earphones and a headband. Usually, each ear is tested separately, so that a method must be available to turn off the electrical signal to one earphone. The Standard specifies that the ear not being tested must remain covered by the "dummy" earphone. In addition, each earphone must be equipped with an earphone cushion for contact with the head and pinna of the subject. A recommended cushion is shown in Fig. 8·5.

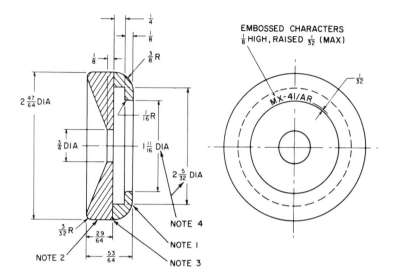

NOTES:

(1) Base material; Buna-S rubber.
(2) Cap material; sponge neoprene.
(3) Base (Note 1) and cap (Note 2) shall be securely bonded together by use of a suitable cement or other approved means.
(4) Durometer readings (Shore A): 20 ± 5 for the front cap; 40 ± 5 for the back base.
(5) Finished cushion shall withstand, without appreciable deterioration, an oxygen bomb test at a pressure of 300 psi and a temperature of 70°C for 48 hours.
(6) Dimension of the base may be modified to adapt to a chosen earphone.
(7) All dimensions are in inches.
(8) Tolerance, ±1/64 inch.

FIG. 8·5 Earphone cushion (MX-41/AR). NOTES: (1) Base material; Buna-S rubber. (2) Cap material; sponge neoprene. (3) Base (Note 1) and cap (Note 2) shall be securely bonded together by use of a suitable cement or other approved means. (4) Durometer readings (Shore A): 20 + 5 for the front cap; 40 + 5 for the back base. (5) Finished cushion shall withstand, without appreciable deterioration, an oxygen bomb test at a pressure of 300 psi and a temperature of 70 °C for 48 hours. (6) Dimensions of the base may be modified to adapt to a chosen earphone. (7) All dimensions are in inches. (8) Tolerance, + 1/64 inch. (See Ref. 2.)

4. Accuracy of frequencies and purity of tones: Each of the audiometer frequencies shall be within three percent of the indicated frequency. The SPL of any harmonic of the fundamental shall be at least 30 dB below the SPL of the fundamental. When the tone purity measurement is made, the hearing level shall be 100 dB from 500 to 4000 Hz, 90 dB at 250 and 6000 Hz, 80 dB at 8000 Hz, and 70 dB at 125 Hz.

5. Accuracy of Sound Pressure Levels (SPL): The dial that controls SPL should step in 5 dB intervals. The sound pressure produced by an earphone, as referred to the 705–A earphone and the 9–A coupler, i.e., Table 8·1, shall not differ from the indicated value of SPL on the audiometer dial by more than 3 dB at the indicated frequencies of 250 to 3000 Hz inclusive, by more than 4 dB at 4000 Hz, nor by more than 5 dB at frequencies above or below this range. A tone switch must be provided for manual switching that eliminates audible transients or extraneous frequencies.

E. Calibration of Bone Conduction Vibrator

By definition,[8a] a bone conduction vibrator is an electromechanical transducer intended to produce the sensation of hearing by vibrating the bones of the head. Tests of hearing are made by placing the vibrator in contact with the head of a person at one of two places: (1) the mastoid, which is the hard place behind the outer ear, or (2) the center of the forehead.

As in the case of air conduction tests of hearing, a standard reference threshold is defined,[8a] called, "Standard reference equivalent threshold force level."

The standard reference equivalent threshold force level is the threshold of bone-conduction hearing measured subjectively (on a large number of ears of otologically normal persons of both sexes, ages between 18 and 30 years) with a specified type of bone vibrator as transferred to a specified artificial mastoid. The artificial mastoid for bone conduction is equivalent to the artificial ear for air conduction.

The bone vibrator used in the subjective measurements of the threshold of bone-conduction hearing was called the B-71

[8a] American National Standard, ANSI S3.26–1981, "Reference equivalent threshold force levels for audiometric bone vibrators," Acoustical Society of America.

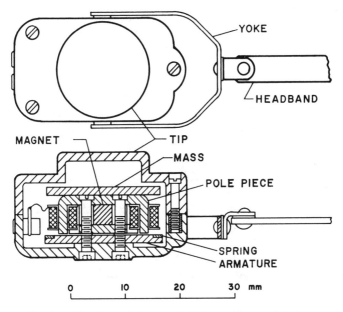

FIG. 8·6 Sectional drawing of the type B-71 bone vibrator.[8a,9] (See Ref. 4.)

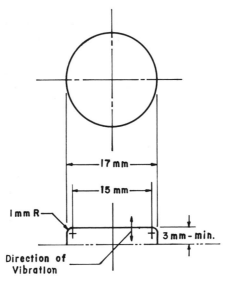

FIG. 8·7 The standard shape of the tip for a bone conduction vibrator.[8a] The effective plane circular must be within $\pm$ 10% of 175 millimeters squared. (See Ref. 4.)

and was used with a P-3333 headband. A sectional drawing of the B-71 bone vibrator is shown in Fig. 8·6.[9]

The tip shape of the vibrator must conform with the drawing of Fig. 8·7.[8a]

The result of the subjective tests was an average voltage measured at the output of a carefully preserved set of B-71 bone vibrators. In order to transfer these measurements to other bone vibrators that will be used with standard audiometers, an artificial mastoid that has a surface mechanical impedance similar to the mechanical impedance of the mastoid or center of the forehead is required. The "loudness balance" procedure is used.

Reference 8a gives a series of references that have led to a preferred mechanical impedance (in units Newton-second per meter) for the artificial mastoid. It, in turn, is approximated by an equivalent circuit comprised of three elements in series, a mass, a mechanical resistance and a mechanical compliance, having the sizes,

$$M = 0.77 \times 10^{-3} \text{ kilogram}$$

$$C_M = 2.25 \times 10^5 \text{ newtons per meter}$$

$$R_M = 19.3 \text{ newton-seconds per meter}$$

These values assume a contact tip area of 175 mm^2 and a static coupling force (headband force) on the human head of 5.4 newtons (550 grams mass).

Departures of $+ 120\%$ and $- 30\%$ in the impedance of the circuit are acceptable for any given design, but units of the same manufacture must not differ from each other by more than $\pm 25\%$ over the frequency range 250 to 4000 Hz.

A cross-sectional view of an artificial mastoid that is accepted in the American Standard[8a] is shown in Fig. 8·8.[10]

F. Reference Equivalent Threshold Force Level

The reference equivalent threshold force levels to which the bone conduction audiometer must conform are given in Table 8·2. These values are for type 4930 artificial mastoids and type

---

[9]"B-71, B-72 series bone vibrators," Engineering bulletin EB-34, Radioear Corporation, 375 Valley Brook Road, McMurray, PA 15317.

[10]"Types 4930 and 3505, artificial mastoid, artificial mastoid with calibrator," B&K Instruments, Inc., 185 Forest Street, Marlborough, MA 01752.

TABLE 8·2. Reference equivalent threshold force level calibration values.*

Frequency (Hz)	rms force level (dB re 1 μN)
250	61
500	59
1000	39
2000	32.5
3000	28
4000	31

NOTE 1: The reference thresholds at the frequencies above were obtained by transference of directly measured subjective data, employing the specified measurement devices. Interpolation suggests that an appropriate reference threshold level for 750 Hz would be 47 dB and for 1500 Hz would be 35 dB, both re 1 μN.

NOTE 2: To obtain force levels re 1 dyne, substrate 20 dB from values given above.

*See Ref. 4.

B-71 bone vibrators used with P-3333 headbands. Calibrations for "other" combinations of artificial mastoids and bone vibrators may be determined by loudness balancing, as described in Sec. C.

TABLE 8·3. Difference to be added to the levels of Table 8·2 to obtain forehead reference equivalent threshold force levels.*

Frequency (Hz)	Difference (dB)
250	13.5
500	15.0
750	12.5
1000	10.0
1500	9.0
2000	8.5
3000	7.5
4000	6.5

*See Ref. 4.

When bone conduction tests are made on the forehead, the amounts shown in Table 8·3 should be added to the values given in Table 8·2.

G. General Considerations for Bone-Conduction Audiometer Tests

It is expected that bone conduction thresholds will be determined with a bone vibrator that is connected to a standard audiometer as described earlier in this chapter. Results are recorded on the same chart as shown in Fig. 8·1, but normally limited to the frequency range of 250 to 4000 Hz.

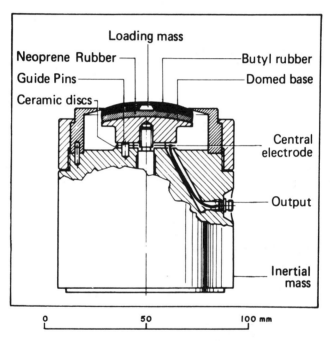

FIG. 8·8 Cross-sectional view of a Type 4930 artificial mastoid. (See Ref. 4.)

Before recording the bone conduction threshold, correction must be made for the air conduction hearing levels. This means that both the air and bone conduction tests must be made on a person, and that the amount by which the air conduction hearing level differs from the 0 dB threshold, must be subtracted from the observed bone conduction equivalent threshold force level. Also, the ear under test must not be occluded (closed off).

Sound reaching the test ear by air conduction from the bone vibrator is not a problem except, perhaps, at 3000 or 4000 Hz. At these frequencies, and these only, the validity of a bone conduction measurement can be checked by closing the ear canal with a small insert-type ear plug.

Finally, a masking noise of a suitable level must be produced in the nontest ear, because, otherwise, the bone conduction sound may be heard in that ear. A detailed formula is given in the Standard[8a] for determining the level of that noise which takes into account the air conduction hearing level of the nontest ear. An example is given for a particular person with a hearing level of 25 dB at 2000 Hz. In that case, the level of the masking noise in a one-third octave band centered on 2000 Hz was found to be 70 dB, as measured with the earphone on a 9A coupler. However, the Standard states, "The ultimate decision ...must be left to the judgement and skill of the qualified person making the audiometric test and may vary with the nature of the impairment of the person being tested."

8·3 Speech Audiometers

A. General Specifications for Speech Audiometers

American National Standard ANSI S3.6-1969 gives detailed specifications on audiometers that reproduce speech sounds from disks or tapes. It is also allowable to use the live voice. Speech levels must be monitored by a VU meter (see Chap. 11, Sec. 11.4.A) connected ahead of the attenuator on the audiometer.

B. Sound Pressure Level of Speech

The sound pressure level of a speech signal, as defined in the Standard, is determined as follows: The speech signal (spoken or from a recording) is connected to the input of the audiometer. The average peak deflection on the VU meter of the audiometer is observed. Then a 1000 Hz signal is connected to the input in place of the speech signal and its value is adjusted to produce the same VU meter reading on the audiometer. At the same time, the earphone of the audiometer is in place on the 9A coupler (Fig. 8·3). The rms sound pressure level of the

1000 Hz tone produced in the coupler is now observed. This observed quantity is the "sound pressure level of the speech signal".

C. Standard Reference Threshold Sound Pressure Level for Speech

The standard reference threshold SPL for speech from an audiometer earphone is 19 dB above 0.0002 microbar, measured in accordance with Sec. B above, and based on 50% intelligibility of spondee words. The different elements of the audiometer are related to each other as follows: The dial reading of the attenuator on the audiometer will read "zero" hearing threshold level for speech when the 1000 Hz calibrating tone brings the monitor VU meter to its standard reference deflection and simultaneously produces a SPL from the earphone in the 9A coupler of 19 dB. The overall frequency response, including the microphone, shall not deviate from the 1000 Hz response by more than ± 5 dB at the other test frequencies.

8·4 Miscellaneous Notes for Audiometry

The two ears of a patient are usually tested separately, particularly when a pure-tone audiometer is used. When the hearing loss for one ear is much greater than for the other, it may be necessary to make the sound signal in the poorer ear so very loud that it will be conducted through the head to the better ear*, giving rise to a false threshold response for the poorer ear. A similar situation occurs when endeavoring to obtain the bone-conduction threshold for an individual ear, because the stimulus from bone-conducted sound is nearly the same in both ears. As we said before, it is necessary to provide some means for preventing the response of the ear not being tested from interfering with the testing of the other ear. This is most easily and effectively done by applying a "masking" noise to the ear not being tested. Many separate devices, such as mechanical or electrical buzzers, have been used. Commercial audiometers frequently provide a built-in masking device which supplies the masking noise through an earphone.

---

* "Better ear" at *each* frequency means the ear (right or left) with the least hearing loss.

In some cases it is desirable or convenient to test both ears of a patient simultaneously to determine his least hearing loss. Some audiometers, therefore, are provided with two earphones, whose performance characteristics are as nearly alike as possible, so that the sound stimuli presented simultaneously to the two ears are the same. The threshold measured for a given signal will then always be that of the ear that has the least hearing loss for that signal, obviously.

By means of appropriate switching arrangements, it is possible to equip a pure-tone audiometer for use in determining the "equal-loudness contours" for an ear, at sound levels above the threshold of hearing. An "equal-loudness contour" is a graph showing the intensities of sounds of various frequencies which sound as loud to the listener as a 1000-cps tone of a specified intensity. To make the measurement, the listener is provided with a 1000-cps tone of a given intensity level in the earphone; the intensity of this tone remains constant during the test. By means of a switch, the standard 1000-cps tone is switched off and a tone of another frequency switched on; the observer adjusts the intensity of the latter tone until, after repeated switchings between the two tones, it sounds as loud as the standard tone. This process is repeated for tones of a number of frequencies. By following this procedure with various sound pressure levels of standard tone, a family of equal-loudness contours is obtained as shown in Fig. 5·14. Such contours are useful in showing the behavior of an ear for sounds above the threshold of hearing.

Most audiometers are equipped with a "tone interrupter," which is simply a switch to turn the signal off briefly. It is under the control of the operator, and it allows him to make sure that the patient is actually hearing the signal when he indicates that he is. It may also be used to interrupt the tone periodically to make it easier for the patient to fix his attention upon it, as in the pulse-tone procedure.

8·5 Rooms for Audiometry

The first requisite for a location in which audiometric measurements are to be made is that it be reasonably free from extraneous noise. If noise is present at a sufficiently high level, it may enter the ear under test along with the signal, masking

FIG. 8·9 Prefabricated audiological examination room. Approximately a six-foot cube, this room is ventilated and has a magnetically-sealed door and floating floor. (Courtesy Eckel Industries, Inc.)

the signal to a measurable extent and giving rise to falsely high readings of hearing loss. The more acute the hearing is, the greater will be the effect of ambient noise. It is difficult to set a practical maximum limit for the allowable level of ambient noise as measured with a sound level meter. However, the suitability of a given location for audiometric tests may be fairly well estimated by using the audiometer in that location to measure the hearing loss of a number of persons known to have approximately normal hearing. If the noise level is not high enough to shift their average threshold by more than 10 dB, it will usually not affect the audiometric measurements seriously. If the operator knows his own audiogram and knows it to be reasonably stable, he may use it alone to determine the influence of ambient noise.

Many clinics and research laboratories have built special rooms that are designed to keep out ambient noise. A number of suppliers manufacture prefabricated audiometric test rooms that will reduce reasonable ambient noise levels to satisfactory levels. One design, typical of those available, is shown in Fig. 8·9.

Special precautions must be taken if audiometry is conducted in factory spaces.

9.

Sound Sources for Test Purposes

Every acoustic measurement requires a source of sound. Unless the experiment being performed demands a prescribed radiator we are confronted with the problem of choosing among loudspeakers, earphones, or even the human voice to meet our needs. Our choice will depend, primarily, on five things: the frequency range, the output level, the acoustic impedance, the directivity pattern, and the nature of the sound wave to be radiated. The last category is added to the other four to take account of transient requirements or of unusual effects such as those peculiar to the human voice. Sometimes we just want to produce a sound of variable frequency and fairly constant level to get an idea of the cutoff frequencies and number of resonant peaks in a receiving system. In that case almost any medium-priced loudspeaker will suffice. Other times, however, three or four of the above-named five items will play an important part in our choice of sound source, and it must meet rigid specifications.

This chapter is divided into three sections dealing with (1) vocal sources, and with non-vocal sources of (2) low intensity and (3) high intensity. Naturally, we describe only those types of sound sources available today. As the science of electroacoustics progresses, more flexible instruments will become available. By comparison with the examples given here, the value of these new instruments can be more easily assessed and a choice made between the old and the new.

9·1 Vocal Sound Sources

A. The Human Voice

When a person talks, the air immediately in front of his lips is alternately compressed and rarefied, thus increasing or decreasing by a measurable amount the air pressure in this region relative to the normal atmospheric pressure. This "excess pressure" produces a traveling sound wave whose amplitude decreases by a factor of one-half (6 db) for every doubling of distance; it is assumed that there are no losses in the air or at the boundaries. The manner in which speech is produced is complicated, since it involves the coordinated use of lungs, vocal cords, and resonating passages in the throat, mouth, and nose. Many muscles cooperate in the act, including those involved in constantly

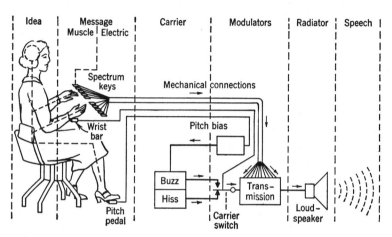

FIG. 9·1   Block diagram of the voder. This machine converts movements of the hands and a foot into speech. (After Dudley.[1])

changing the resonance characteristics of the system through positioning the tongue, palate, cheeks, lips, and teeth. The radiation properties of the mouth and nose when coupled to an aerial medium must also be considered. Various experimenters have studied the properties of the speech-producing mechanism. Among the researches which have given basic insight into the source and nature of the various sounds of speech are those of the Bell Telephone Laboratories as reported by Dudley.[1]

Dudley showed (see Fig. 9·1) that one can produce speech artificially by combining two basic types of sounds in the proper manner, namely, a "buzz" sound and a "hiss" sound. The

[1] H. Dudley, "Remaking speech," *Jour. Acous. Soc. Amer.*, **11**, 169–177 (1939); "Carrier nature of speech," *Bell System Technical Journ.*, **19**, 495–515 (1940).

buzz sound is analogous to the sound produced by the vocal cords and is composed essentially of a number of harmonically related tones with a "sawtooth" waveform. The vocal buzz tone has a pitch determined by the frequency of vibration of the vocal cords while the quality of the tone being sounded is determined by the shape of the resonant passages of the throat, mouth, and nose at that instant; that is, certain harmonics are amplified, and others are suppressed. To produce the same effect artificially, Dudley devised a means for continuously changing both the frequency of the buzz tone and the relative amplitudes of its harmonics by use of a pitch pedal and spectrum keys as shown in Fig. 9·1. An operator using this equipment to produce the appropriate syllables turns on the buzz tone with her wrist, modifies the shape of the spectrum with her fingers, and sets the frequency with her foot.

The hiss type of sound encountered in speech originates from the passage of the breath through the mouth, the lips, the teeth and over the tongue.   It is essentially a continuous band of noise, being composed of random frequency components having no true pitch.   However, it may be modified by the shape of the resonant cavities and by the way in which the air is passed through the teeth and lips.   With Dudley's speech-producing device, the hiss sound is turned on with the wrist bar, and its spectrum is modified by the spectrum keys.

Obviously, the relative intensity of hiss and buzz sounds when they are formed into speech is of importance in producing intelligibility.   Fortunately, however, English words seldom require that the two be produced simultaneously.   For example, to produce a word like *s-i-t*, the hiss type of sound is needed for the *s* and *t* with the spectrum modified in such a way that the familiar *ssss* or *tt* effect is achieved, whereas for the vowel *i* the buzz sound is used with its appropriate spectrum and fundamental frequency.

Demonstrations with this equipment indicate that the essential contribution to the intelligibility of either the voiced or unvoiced sounds comes from the variation of that part of the spectrum above 200 cps as a function of time, whereas the emotional content is due chiefly to the pitch—particularly to the inflection of the pitch.   In addition a large part of the intelligibility of speech is contained in the beginnings or endings of words, which are usually consonant or hiss types of sounds, although the vowels

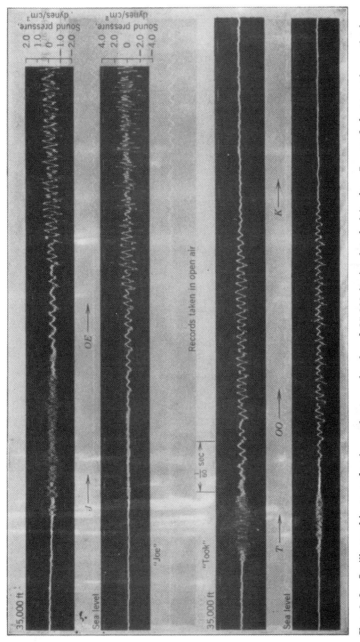

Fig. 9·2 Oscillographic records of speech at sea level and 35,000 ft simulated altitude. In rarefied atmosphere, the buzz type of sounds decrease by about 10 db in level and the hiss type of sounds remain nearly the same. The record at 35,000 ft was taken with 6 db more amplifier gain. It appears from the record at sea level that the peaks of the buzz sounds are greater in the negative direction than the positive, the ratio being about 3 to 2 or 3.5 db. (After Rudmose et al.[2])

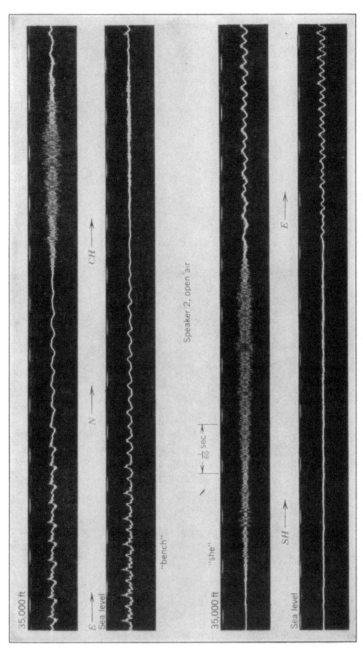

FIG. 9·3   Record illustrating the perseverance of CH and SH sounds at 35,000 ft simulated altitude.   See legend of Fig. 9·2 for further details.   (After Rudmose *et al.*[2])

or buzz types of sounds contain the greater part of the acoustic energy.

With this introduction to the question of speech production, let us investigate oscillographic records of typical samples of speech at both sea level and altitude. (See Figs. 9·2 and 9·3.) By altitude, we mean pressure altitude as determined from the pressure *vs.* altitude relation stated in Chapter 2 for the U.S. standard atmosphere. In these tests,[2] a suitable microphone was placed at a fixed point (18 in.) in front of a talker, and the electrical output was connected to the vertical plates of a cathode ray oscilloscope. By photographing the movement of the spot on the oscilloscope, an oscillogram was traced on a moving film to show the variation of sound pressure as a function of time for any given speech sound.

In the first of two experiments, each of a group of talkers, while seated in an anechoic chamber, was instructed to say the test sentence, "Joe took father's shoe bench out; she was waiting at my lawn." In the second experiment each of the talkers spoke the test sentence while seated in a large sound-deadened chamber from which the air was partially evacuated. In both experiments the voices were picked up by a standard microphone and were analyzed in the same manner.

The talkers (young men) were instructed to speak at a level 6 db lower than the level they could produce when speaking as loudly as possible without shouting. The "6 db down" condition of talking is called "one-half maximum effort," because the sound levels produced are approximately those which a talker produces when told to speak with one-half his maximum effort.

Records corresponding to sea level and 35,000 ft altitude are shown in Figs. 9·2 and 9·3 for the words *Joe, took, bench,* and *she.* The atmospheric pressure prevailing at the altitude designated on the left end of each record is indicated by a line down the center, and the variation in pressure above or below this value in dynes per square centimeter is shown on the right end of the upper two records of Fig. 9·2. At 35,000 ft the atmospheric pressure is slightly less than one-fourth of its value at sea level. One-sixtieth second time markers are superimposed on the top part of the film in the form of short white marks. In

[2] K. C. Clark, H. W. Rudmose, J. C. Eisenstein, F. D. Carlson, and R. A. Walker, "The effects of high altitude on speech," *Jour. Acous. Soc. Amer.*, **20,** 776–786 (1948).

Fig. 9·2, it can be seen that J, T and K are essentially hiss types of sounds, whereas OE and OO are buzz types of sounds. Similarly, in Fig. 9·3, CH and SH are hiss types, and E is a buzz type of sound.

At 35,000 ft of altitude, the vowel and semi-vowel sounds produced by the human voice decrease markedly in intensity especially at frequencies above 500 cps, and some of the consonant sounds—especially those formed principally by the rushing of air

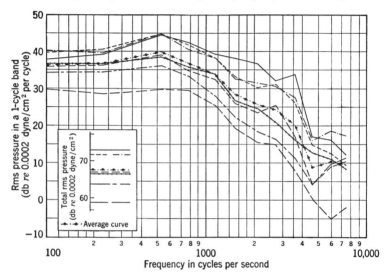

FIG. 9·4   Average spectral distribution of sound pressure produced by the voices of seven young men. A curve giving the average of all seven voices is drawn which agrees well with data taken earlier at the Bell Telephone Laboratories. The sentence, "Joe took father's shoe bench out; she was waiting at my lawn," was spoken. (After Rudmose *et al.*[2])

through the mouth—either remain unchanged or increase slightly in level.

In another set of experiments, the standard microphone was connected to a set of parallel filters and integrating circuits, and the average acoustic energy produced by the voice as a function of frequency was measured. The integrating device was so constructed and calibrated that it yielded a curve of rms sound pressure levels which approximate those that would be measured by using a filter with a bandwidth of 1 cps, thus yielding a curve of rms spectrum level *vs.* frequency. Data from seven different subjects are plotted in Fig. 9·4. The decibel average of the data at each frequency is also plotted. It is seen that the average total sound level is approximately 68 db *re* 0.0002 dyne/cm^2. An average of the differences in decibels between altitude and sea level data as a function of frequency for seven subjects is shown in Figs. 9·5 and 9·6. The data in Fig. 9·5 give the

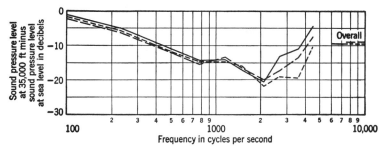

Fig. 9·5 Difference between the sound pressure level produced inside oxygen masks by talkers subjected to altitude of 35,000 ft and the sound pressure level produced by the same talkers inside masks at sea level. The test sentence of Fig. 9·4 was used. (After Clark *et al.*[2])

change in output of a standard microphone located within different oxygen masks. Those in Fig. 9·6 are for the subjects speaking directly into the rarefied air.

Time-interval measurements showed that about one-fourth of the total talking time was consumed by the space between the words. Hence, approximately 1 db needs to be added to the spectrum level as determined by the above if the measurements

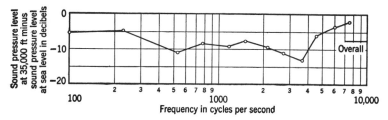

Fig. 9·6 Decrement in sound pressure produced in free space when the talkers were subjected to an altitude of 35,000 ft. The test sentence of Fig. 9·4 was used. (After Clark *et al.*[2])

of the average level of the speech *itself* are desired. The curves marked B_s in Fig. 9·7 have been so adjusted. The spectrum of speech produced by women is almost the same in shape, although it generally lies about 3 db lower on the graph and is shifted slightly in the direction of higher frequencies.

An understanding of the factors which govern the intelligibility of speech requires more data than given in Figs. 9·4 and 9·7. For example, we need to know the frequency of occurrence of individual syllable levels at each of a number of different levels. We want also the magnitude of variation of the frequency of occurrence in the different parts of the frequency spectrum.

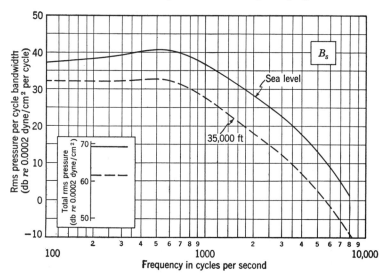

FIG. 9·7   Average speech level produced in an anechoic chamber by male voices at 1 meter distance at sea level and 35,000 ft in free space, considering only the intervals of actual phonation. One decibel has been added to the average curve of Fig. 9·4 to compensate for the pauses between words.

In 1939 the Bell Telephone Laboratories made measurements[3] of speech levels occurring in successive intervals one-eighth second long in various frequency bands.   To accomplish these measurements, an equipment was built which divided the speech spectrum into a number of frequency bands by use of electrical wave filters. The output of each of these filters was connected to an integrating device which measured the total energy of speech occurring during an interval one-eighth second long.   After measuring the energy in a particular one-eighth-second interval the device was reset to zero—a procedure which consumed one-eighth of a second's time

[3] H. K. Dunn and S. D. White, "Statistical measurements on conversational speech," *Jour. Acous. Soc. Amer.*, **11**, 278–288 (1940); N. R. French and J. C. Steinberg, "Factors governing the intelligibility of speech," *Jour. Acous. Soc. Amer.*, **19**, 90–119 (1947).

—and the process was repeated starting with the third one-eighth-second interval of time. A large quantity of data was taken by having a number of subjects read from English stories; the results are shown in Fig. 9·8. Each point of the curves should be interpreted as follows: Take, for example, the frequency band limited by the frequencies of 250 and 500 cps. The point on the upper curve in that band shows that 1 percent of the one-eighth-second time intervals had an rms sound pressure level greater than $+80.8$ db (re 0.0002 dyne/cm^2); the next point down shows that 4 percent had a level greater than $+77.8$ db and less than $+80.8$ db; similarly, 5 percent had a level greater than $+76.0$ db and less than $+77.8$ db, etc.

If we now consider the 1000–1400 cps band alone, as typical of all the bands, we can make a plot of the cumulative level distribution in the one-eighth-second intervals $vs.$ the rms sound pressure in decibels. Such a curve is shown in Fig. 9·9, except that the zero reference level used corresponds to the long-time average rms pressure in that band, namely, 62 db re 0.0002 dyne/cm^2. Inspection of this curve shows that speech energies in successive time intervals vary over a range of about 40 db. Generally, the weakest of these intervals contributes little to the intelligibility of speech because they are masked by ambient noise or by residual effects in the ear so that the total useful dynamic range of speech appears to be about 30 db. Of this number of decibels, the rms peaks lie about 12 db above the average level, and the weakest syllables lie about 18 db below the average level.

The above curves apply to cases in which the voice is talking into free space or those in which ordinary hand-held types of microphones are held near the lips. However, the spectrum of speech is considerably changed if the voice operates into an enclosure, such as an oxygen mask, gas mask, or noise shield. In those cases the lower tones of the voice are greatly amplified. Moreover, changes in the spectrum of speech may be encountered when the voice talks into fairly large enclosures such as gas or oxygen masks because of transverse and longitudinal resonances. Certain frequency regions above 1000 cps are often suppressed, whereas others are amplified. Unless the enclosure into which one talks is carefully shaped, and the proper microphone selected, speech may be rendered almost unintelligible.

A brief word should be interjected about the significance of

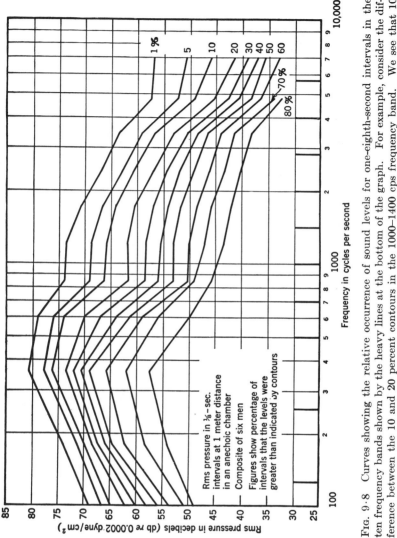

FIG. 9·8   Curves showing the relative occurrence of sound levels for one-eighth-second intervals in the ten frequency bands shown by the heavy lines at the bottom of the graph. For example, consider the difference between the 10 and 20 percent contours in the 1000–1400 cps frequency band. We see that 10 percent of the one-eighth-second intervals of speech fall between 62 and 66 db. (From Dunn and White.[3])

the nose in the production of speech. There is evidence to the effect that sounds passing through the nose contribute at least a small part to the intelligibility of speech. However, no well-defined experiments have been performed (to the best of the author's knowledge) to show the full extent to which the nose contributes to the intelligibility of speech, nor whether it con-

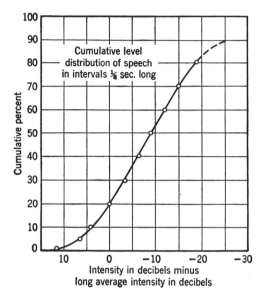

Fig. 9·9 Curve showing the cumulative level distribution of one-eighth-second intervals of speech plotted as a function of the difference between the level for the percentage of syllables indicated minus the long-time average level. The data were taken from Fig. 9·8, and the levels of the 1000–1400 cps band were chosen as illustrative of the others. The curve does not reach 100 percent because of pauses between words, which occupy about 10 to 15 percent of the time. (From French and Steinberg.[3])

tributes, as might be expected, to certain speech sounds more than to others.

Another factor of importance is the directionality of the voice at the higher frequencies. Dunn and Farnsworth[4] measured the sound pressure at over seventy positions about a talker's head in order to determine the magnitude of this characteristic. The position of the talker and the location of the angles θ and ϕ are

[4] H. K. Dunn and D. W. Farnsworth, "Exploration of pressure field around the human head during speech," *Jour. Acous. Soc. Amer.*, **10**, 184–199 (1939).

shown in Fig. 9·10. Their results have been averaged and plotted as shown in Fig. 9·11. These curves are for the sound pressure levels at angles θ and ϕ about the talker's mouth, relative to the pressure at the zero angles θ and ϕ.

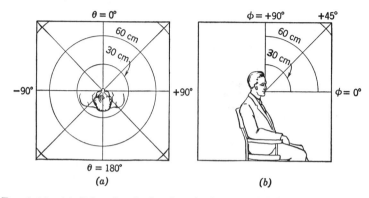

Fig. 9·10   (a) Polar sketch showing the locations of the angle θ relative to the position of the talker's head; (b) same for ϕ. (From Dunn and Farnsworth.[4])

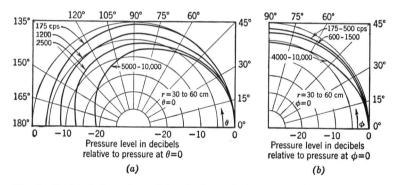

Fig. 9·11   Variation of speech levels about the human head.   (a) Variation in a horizontal plane.   (b) Variation in a vertical plane.   See Fig. 9·10 for exact locations.   (After Dunn and Farnsworth.[4])

An additional characteristic of the voice is the variation of its level and spectrum as a function of distance in front of the lips. Data of this type have been taken at the Psycho-Acoustic Laboratory at Harvard[5] and by Dunn and Farnsworth.[4]   Curves

[5] M. Abrams, S. Goffard, J. Miller, and F. Sanford, "The effect of microphone position on the intelligibility of speech in noise," Report No. IC-54, Psycho-Acoustic Laboratory, December 6, 1943.

showing the variation of the overall level, and the levels in the 8000–12,000 cps bands, as a function of distances ranging from 0.1 cm to 100 cm, are plotted in Fig. 9·12. The comparatively slow decrease of the sound levels as a function of distance at the higher frequencies is a consequence of the size of mouth opening compared to the wavelengths of the sounds being radiated and is a familiar occurrence in the region directly in front of a radi-

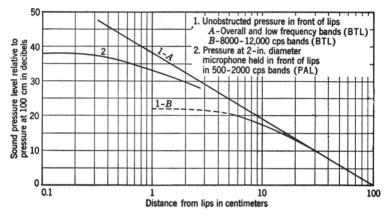

FIG. 9·12   Curves showing the variation of sound pressure level with position in front of the lips of a talker.   (1-A) Decrease of the total sound pressure level as a function of distance measured from the teeth.   This curve also holds for low frequency bands of speech.   (1-B) Decrease of sound pressure level in the 8000–12,000 cps bands as a function of distance measured from the outside of the lips.   (After Dunn and Farnsworth.[4])   (2) Decrease of sound pressure level in the 500–2000 cps bands at the face of a close-talking microphone as a function of distance from the outside of the lips.   (After Abrams *et al.*[5])

ating diaphragm whose diameter is not negligible compared to a wavelength.

B. Artificial Voices

In the laboratory an artificial voice is often more convenient to use as a research or test facility than the human voice.   Unfortunately, no entirely satisfactory artificial voice exists at this time although several have come into common use.   They will be described here to show their limitations, with the hope that this discussion may stimulate further research on this subject.

An early artificial voice is shown in Figs. 9·13 and 9·14.   It has been used as a means for testing the microphone end of telephone handsets and was described by Inglis, Gray, and Jenkins[6] in 1932. We shall designate it here as type I. It comprises a moving-coil loudspeaker unit (W.E. 555), an acoustic resistance at the throat of the unit, and a spacing ring. The opening from which the sound is radiated has about the same area as that of the open human mouth. The acoustic resistance at the opening has a value of approximately 41 rayls and, below 5000 cps, a reactance of less than 10 percent. The spacing ring serves as a reference plane for measurements of distance between the artificial voice and instruments under test. The height of the spacing ring is selected to be that at which the ordinary telephone transmitter is spaced from the lips in normal usage. It has been found that the pressure drops off with distance separation of the microphone from the spacing ring in the same manner as the pressure drops off with spacing from the lips of a person talking. The

FIG. 9·13 Photograph of type I artificial voice used for testing telephone microphones (transmitters). (Courtesy Bell Telephone Laboratories and Bell System Technical Journal.)

[6]A. H. Inglis, C. H. G. Gray, and R. T. Jenkins, "A voice and ear for telephone measurements," Bell Syst. Tech. J. 11, 293–317 (1932).

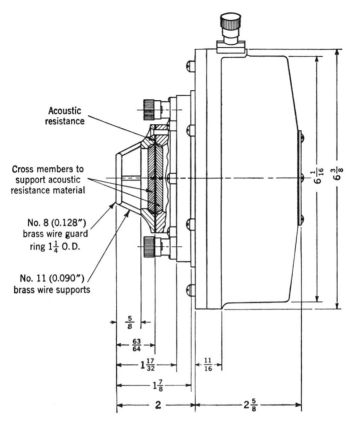

Acoustic resistance

Cross members to support acoustic resistance material

No. 8 (0.128″) brass wire guard ring $1\frac{1}{4}$ O.D.

No. 11 (0.090″) brass wire supports

$\frac{5}{8}$

$\frac{63}{64}$

$1\frac{17}{32}$

$\frac{11}{16}$

$1\frac{7}{8}$

2

$2\frac{5}{8}$

$6\frac{1}{16}$

$6\frac{3}{8}$

FIG. 9·14 Drawing of the type I artificial voice showing the important acoustic elements. (Courtesy Bell Telephone Laboratories and Bell System Technical Journal.)

sound pressure output is shown for the type I artificial voice in Fig. 9·15.

The second type of artificial voice[7] (type II) was developed for the express purpose of testing close-talking microphones where the user's voice level is high. It makes use of a moving-coil loudspeaker unit (B&K 4227) equipped with an especially designed mouth opening. This commercially available artificial voice (mouth simulator) is shown in the photographs of Figs. 9·16 and

[7]IEEE Standard No. 269, "Method for measuring transmission performance of telephone sets," (1983) IEEE, 345 E. 47th St., New York.

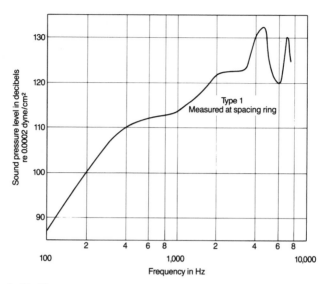

FIG. 9·15 Frequency-response curve of type I artificial voice using W.E.555 loudspeaker unit. The measurement of sound pressure was taken at the ring in a free field.

9·17. It consists of a high-fidelity loudspeaker mounted inside a housing having the appearance of a truncated cone. The "lip" ring in front of the sound opening provides a reference plane for measurements of distance. This mouth simulator has the frequency response shown in Fig. 9·18.

Three curves are given in that figure. The middle curve is for continuous operation at 10 W maximum average power with the microphone 2.5 cm in front of the "lip" ring. The upper curve is for 50 W power pulsed for 2 sec at 20-sec intervals. The bottom curve was drawn for a constant sound pressure level of 89 dB with a feed-back compressor between a monitoring microphone and the sound source output.

At 95 dB sound pressure level, measured 2.5 cm from the "lip" ring, the harmonic distortion is less than 2% between 315 Hz and 8 kHz.

A third type of artificial voice is shown in Figs. 9·19 and 9·20 (B&K 4128). This mouth simulator is contained in an artificial head which can be used separately or in combination with a torso. The head/torso simulator was developed for use in the

testing of telephones, headsets, microphones and hearing aids.[8]
It also contains two artificial ears, of the type described in Chap.
16 (B&K 0925).

The Type 5128 produces a sound pressure distribution around
the mouth of a median adult human being as shown in Fig. 9·21.
Plotted are curves of sound pressure level versus the radial distance r from the center of the mouth, and the parameter being
the axial distance a in front of the mouth—both measurements
being made on a horizontal plane at lip level. Thus $a = r \cos \theta$,
where θ is the angle on the horizontal plane between the axial

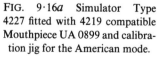

FIG. 9·16*a* Simulator Type
4227 fitted with 4219 compatible
Mouthpiece UA 0899 and calibration jig for the American mode.

FIG. 9·16*b* Mouth Simulator
Type 4227 fitted with 4219 compa-
tible Mouthpiece UA 0899 and
SFERT measuring jig.

[8]ANSI Standard S3.36-1985, "Specification for a manikin," Acoustical Society of America.

and radial lines. These data compare well with data taken by the International CCITT Study Group in 1984. The sound pressure levels are the average levels for the frequency region from 300 Hz to 3.3 kHz.

The frequency-response characteristic of any of these three artificial voices can be made nearly flat as a function of frequen-

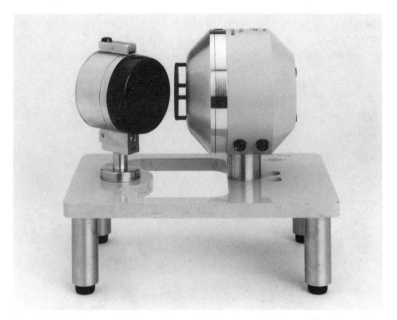

FIG. 9·17 Photograph of type II artificial voice used for testing close-talking microphones. The device shown immediately in front of the voice opening is holding a small, close-talking type of microphone in the approximate position which it would occupy in actual use. (Courtesy Bruel & Kjaer)

cy by suitable compensation networks.

Weber[9] has described a moving-coil type of artificial voice with an exceptionally flat frequency-response characteristic. Sketches of this unit, the frequency-response characteristic, and the harmonic distortion characteristic are shown in Figs. 9·22 and

[9]H. Weber, "Contribution to the production of orthotelephonic transmission systems," Technische Mitteilungen (published by the Schweiz Telegraphen- und Telephonverwaltung), Bern, Switzerland, Nos. 1 and 4 pp. 1–15 (1946) (in German).

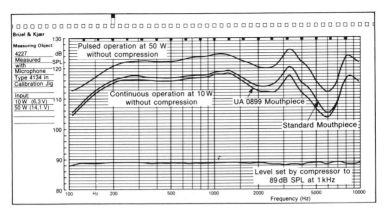

FIG. 9·18 Frequency response of the B&K 4227 at 2.5 cm distance at 10 W and 50 W without compensation and (below) with compensation. (Courtesy Bruel & Kjaer)

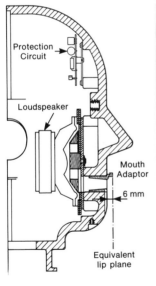

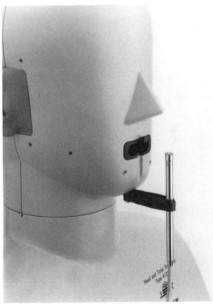

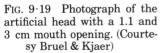

FIG. 9·19 Photograph of the artificial head with a 1.1 and 3 cm mouth opening. (Courtesy Bruel & Kjaer)

FIG. 9·20 Sketch showing B&K 4128 mouth simulator. (Courtesy Bruel & Kjaer)

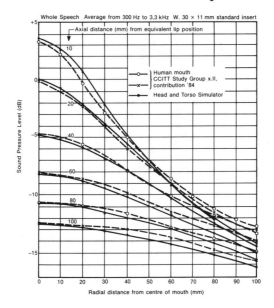

FIG. 9·21   Sound pressure level distribution in the near field in the horizontal plane around the Type 4128.(Courtesy Bruel & Kjaer)

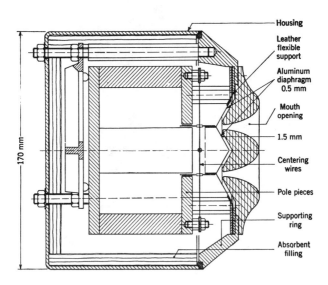

FIG. 9·22   Drawing of artificial voice with flat frequency response, high output, and low distortion. (After Weber.[9])

9·23. For the magnet, the permanent magnet structure from a well-designed 10-watt loudspeaker was chosen. The diaphragm was a combination of two aluminum cones with a wall thickness of 0.5 mm. The outer edges of the diaphragm were supported by a pliable sheet of leather. The voice coil end was centered and held in place by four fine wires of spring steel. In order to achieve the desired flat frequency response a special bakelite cover was provided for the unit. The back side of this cover was so shaped that a space of only 1.5 mm existed between it and the diaphragm. This small space produced damping and raised the limiting frequency to above 6500 cps. The opening to the outside had a diameter of 32 mm. The outside of this cover was in the shape of a short, rapidly flaring exponential horn. It brings about a fairly sharp beaming of the higher frequencies.

C. Artificial Throats

Little of the work done on apparatus for the calibration of throat microphones has been published. The essential difficulty with devices for testing throat microphones is in providing an exciter whose internal mechanical impedance as presented to the throat microphones under test is similar to the mechanical impedance of an actual throat. As a result of this difficulty, it has been common practice to drive the throat microphone under test with a known velocity constant throughout the frequency range. This corresponds to an infinite mechanical impedance. A possible mechanism for producing a known velocity amplitude as a function of frequency is shown in Fig. 9·24. The driving coil is actuated by an amplified audio-frequency signal and serves to vibrate the actuating piston. A second or search coil is provided to yield a voltage proportional to the velocity of the piston. Automatic velocity control can be achieved by connecting the output of the search coil to a rectifier and then using this d-c potential to control the gain of the audio-frequency amplifier supplying the driving coil.

To simulate the mechanical driving impedance of the human throat, an appropriate material would need to be inserted between the piston and the throat microphone capsule. One observer actually used pieces of fresh beefsteak to simulate the impedance of the human throat.* Other laboratories have used

---

* Information communicated privately to the author by the late Stuart Ballantine.

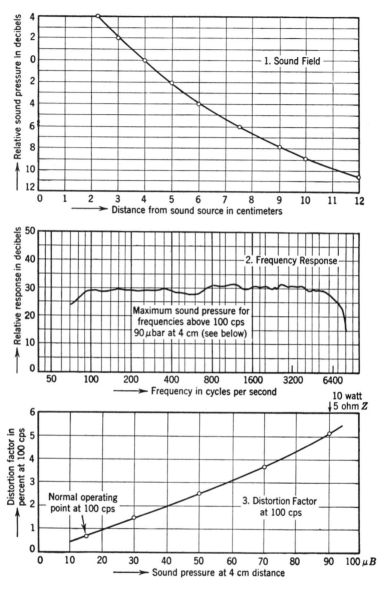

FIG. 9·23   Data on artificial voice of Fig. 9·22. (1) Decrease of sound pressure with distance, (2) frequency-response characteristic, and (3) distortion. (After Weber.[9])

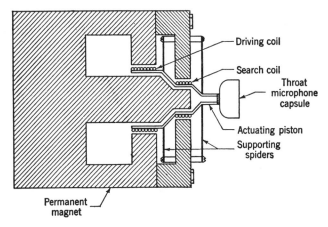

Fig. 9·24 Sketch of an artificial throat for testing throat microphones. The search coil is used to measure the velocity of the actuating piston, or it can lead to a feedback circuit which automatically controls the electrical current supplied to the main driving coil.

various types of synthetic rubbers and soft plastics with varying degrees of success. No experimental data have been published regarding their effectiveness.

9·2 Low Intensity Sound Sources

Under the general title of low intensity sound sources we shall group ordinary direct-radiator and horn-type loudspeakers and very small sources and earphones. We shall describe their properties over as wide a frequency range as they operate. Actually, one can draw no sharp distinction between low and high intensity sources except so far as common usage enables one to do so. Theatre sound systems, for example, employ loudspeakers which can be classified as high intensity sources, but we shall place them in the category of low-intensity sources. Another justification for placing ordinary direct-radiator and horn-type loudspeakers in this section instead of the next is that, in installations where high intensities are required, groups of individual low intensity units are often combined.

A. Loudspeakers

Direct-radiator and horn-type loudspeakers are convenient sources of sound for experimentation. The particular advantages of these types of loudspeaker are the efficiency of conversion of electric to acoustic energy and the fact that they respond more or less uniformly as a function of frequency for a given constant power available input (see Chap. 13). If they are operated within their rated limits of frequency and power input, they will produce sound fields which have less than a few percent of rms harmonic distortion. As standard sources of sound, they leave much to be desired, however, principally because of the lack of uniformity of the sound field which they produce. This nonuniformity arises from three sources: the breaking up of the diaphragm into higher orders of vibration, the radiation pattern of the moving diaphragm, and the combination of direct waves and waves refracted from the loudspeaker housing. These factors combine to produce a sound field which will vary over a range of many decibels both as a function of frequency and as a function of position of the observing point. This variation with position will be observed in an anechoic chamber even when moving radially away from the loudspeaker (see Chap. 3).

Most units falling in the category of direct-radiator and horn-type loudspeakers are designed to reproduce only something less than the full audible range of frequencies, although certain horn units will operate up to nearly 20 000 cps. For further information on the construction and properties of such loudspeakers, the reader is referred to Beranek[10] and Olson and Massa.[11]

B. Small Sources

Hearing-aid earphones operated in free space constitute useful "point" sources of sound at frequencies within a band from about 500 cps to about 4000 cps. The units are not designed basically to operate at higher frequencies, because the manufacturers have concentrated on getting high acoustic output in the important speech range. The band below 500 cps is attenuated owing to the low radiation impedance at low frequencies. The electroacoustic transducer element may be ceramic, magnetic or dynamic, although the first two types are more com-

[10]L. L. Beranek, *Acoustics*, 2nd ed. (Acoustical Society of America, 1986), Chaps. 7–9.

[11]H. Olson and F. Massa, *Applied Acoustics*, 2nd ed. (Blakiston's Sons and Co., 1938), Chaps. 7 and 8.

mon. Hearing-aid earphones are designed to produce a uniform pressure as a function of frequency in a small cavity. When such units are made to radiate directly into the air, their output at low frequencies becomes very small. The radiated pressure will increase as the square of the frequency (12 dB per octave) over most of the range, whereas at the higher frequencies (above 1 or 2 kc and below 4 kc) the rate of increase will halve (6 dB per octave). In the vicinity of 4 kc the unit will resonate. Above that frequency its output will diminish rapidly. If very irregular response curves are not objectionable, the units will radiate sound energy even in the ultrasonic part of the audio spectrum.

For a wide range of frequencies, extending up to 10^5 cps, miniature condenser microphones have proved useful when operated as loudspeakers. One type of instrument has been calibrated over the frequency range from 10^2 to 10^5 cps, and the results are shown in Fig. $9 \cdot 25a$.[12] This curve was obtained by the reciprocity technique in a sound-deadened room. The directivity pattern of this instrument at a frequency of 18.7 kc when mounted on a preamplifier is shown in Fig. $9 \cdot 25b$. Production tolerances on this particular instrument are sufficiently close that a deviation of not more than ± 2 dB from this curve should occur.

Results similar to those for the condenser microphone will be obtained by use of direct radiation from Rochelle salt or ammonium dihydrogen phosphate (ADP) crystals, although lower outputs will be obtained because of the less satisfactory impedance match between the diaphragm and the aerial medium. Transducers of this type have found common use in underwater sound measurement, and, if suitable scaling factors for the difference of characteristic impedance and wavelength in air are applied, the response in air may be calculated from data taken in water, or vice versa. Generally, however, the levels obtained with high impedance "loudspeakers" of this type are too small for general applicability.

Miniature dynamic loudspeakers also show some promise at high frequencies, although the response and directivity are quite erratic. One example is provided by the operation of a

[12]I. Rudnick, M. N. Stein, and F. Nicholas, "Calibration of transducers," Progress Reports 19 and 20, Acoustics Laboratory, Dept. of Physics, Pennsylvania State College (1947–1948).

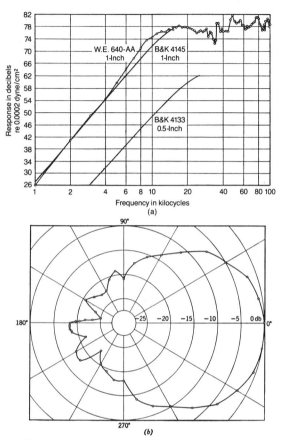

FIG. 9·25   (*a*) Frequency-response characteristics of 1 in. (W.E. 640AA and B&K 4145) and 0.5 in. (B&K 4133) condenser microphones used as loudspeakers. The sound pressure level was measured at a distance of 30 cm with a signal voltage of 30 volts and a polarizing voltage of 180 and 200 volts, respectively. (*b*) Directional pattern of the 1 in. unit at 18.7 cps.

dynamic microphone as a loudspeaker. The response curve of Fig. 9·26 was obtained when a constant voltage was held across the terminals.[12] This particular transducer could have been driven at a voltage level several decibels higher than that shown on the graph with a correspondingly higher acoustic output.

C. High Impedance Sources

In many types of laboratory tests a sound source of small dimensions and with high output acoustic impedance is required. Examples of such requirements are the injection of sound at points into model rooms, into impedance-measuring apparatus, or for studying the distribution of sound in broadcast studios, etc. The acoustic impedance of a single, small bore circular tube of sufficient length connected to a driving unit is more than adequately high for most purposes, but its power output is usually too small. Hunt[13] describes a sound source made from a number of parallel No. 18 bare copper wires packed into a tube which is connected to a source of sound. The spaces between the wires are equivalent to a number of capillary tubes operating in parallel. From Hunt's description one can infer that a sufficiently high impedance can be obtained by packing into the tube approximately 100 No. 18 wires per square centimeter of cross-sectional area.

D. Earphones

Earphones are commonly used in the laboratory for determining hearing acuity and the other psychological properties of hearing. At least five different types of earphones have found use in psychological studies: (1) moving-coil (dynamic); (2) diaphragm-type magnetic; (3) armature and reed-type magnetic; (4) piezoelectric (crystal); and (5) thermophone. As will be shown in Chap. 16; the sound pressure developed by a particular earphone at the eardrum of a listener is a highly variable

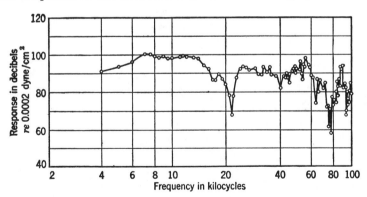

FIG. 9·26　Frequency-response characteristic of a moving-coil microphone (W.E. 633A) used as a loudspeaker. The sound pressure level was measured at a distance of 30 cm with a signal current of 0.1 amp.

[13]F. V. Hunt, "Investigation of room acoustics by steady-state transmission measurements," J. Acous. Soc. Am. **10**, 216 (1939).

quantity depending, in addition to the type of cushion and headband with which it is associated, on the shape and size of the
head, pinna, and ear canal.

Steady State Characteristics. Ideally, a high fidelity earphone
when drawn from a constant power source should produce the
same sound pressure at the entrance to the ear canal at all frequencies in the audible range regardless of the physiological characteristics of the wearer. The degree to which this will be true
is dependent on the type of earphone used.

Fundamentally, some designs of a given type of earphone are
less likely to meet the ideal requirements listed above than are
others. For example, undamped magnetic types exhibit a sharp
resonance in the middle of the frequency range, accompanied by
rapid phase shifts. Damped-diaphragm types of crystal and
magnetic earphones have been designed which exhibit a minimum
of amplitude distortion over a limited frequency range; but their
internal mechanical impedance is so high that changes in the
acoustic impedance of the medium to which they are coupled
cause proportional changes in the sound pressure produced at
the entrance to the ear canal.

The moving-coil type of earphone lends itself readily to the
production of uniform sound pressures over a wide frequency
range with a minimum difference in acoustic output for changes
in the acoustic impedance of the ear to which it is coupled. The
thermophone also has a low internal mechanical impedance, but,
unfortunately, the output sound pressure decreases in approximate inverse proportion to frequency.

In an effort to demonstrate the various factors which must be
considered in the selection of an earphone for test purposes, the
properties of four of the above types of earphones are portrayed
in Fig. 9·27.[14] A good design of each of the four types has been
selected to show the degree of perfection which had been attained
by 1948. It is seen that no design of earphone meets the idealized
requirements. The smoothness of the thermophone curve out
to high frequencies suggests that it might be compensated so as
to have a flat response as a function of frequency. Although this
is possible, the maximum undistorted output levels at the higher
frequencies are very low, so that it is not a suitable instrument
for most hearing tests above 5000 cps.

[14] Staff of the Electro-Acoustic Laboratory, *Response Characteristics of
Interphone Equipment,* O.S.R.D. Report No. 3105 (1944).

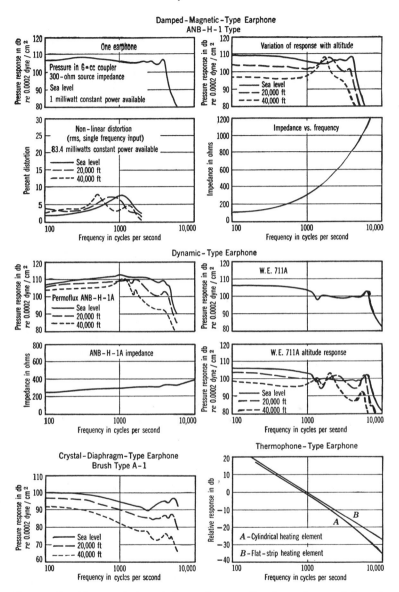

FIG. 9·27 Characteristics of damped magnetic, dynamic, crystal, and thermophone types of earphones.

The estimated drop in the overall level of the frequency response curves for an increase from 6 cc up to 24 cc in size of the cavity to which the earphone is coupled is as follows: magnetic, 11 db; dynamic, 7 db; crystal, 11 db; and thermophone, 6 db. For a diaphragm with infinite mechanical impedance the drop will be 12 db, and for a unit without a diaphragm, such as the thermophone, the drop is proportional to $20 \log_{10}$ of the combined volumes inside and external to the earphone before and after a change in the volume external to the earphone.

The rms non-linear harmonic distortion produced by the dynamic units for a constant power available of 83 mw is usually

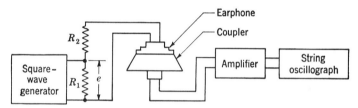

FIG. 9·28   Block diagram of apparatus used for testing the transient characteristics of earphones. The coupler (artificial ear) is described in Chapter 16. Since the resistance R_1 is small compared to R_2, e will remain constant regardless of the variations in impedance of the earphone. (After Mott.[15])

not greater than 1 percent over the frequency range above 50 cps exclusive of distortion in a coupling transformer which might be incorporated into the unit. For magnetic units this same type of distortion will usually be less than 8 percent at 83 mw power available. Data on crystal units have not been reported.

Transient Characteristics. The ear more often listens to transient sounds such as speech and music than it does to steady tones. In spite of this fact, experiments on the properties of hearing have emphasized the steady state. The casual observer might conclude that transient studies are of minor importance. This is certainly not true. Probably, the reason for so little experimentation on hearing under transient conditions may be attributed to a lack of knowledge of the way in which experimental earphones respond to transient excitation.

Mott[15] has investigated the response of some types of earphones when excited electrically by rectangular and square waves. His

[15] E. E. Mott, "Indicial response of telephone receivers," *Bell System Technical Jour.*, **23**, 135–150 (1944).

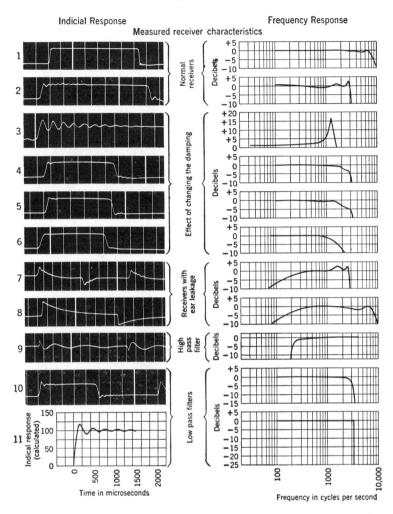

FIG. 9·29   Comparison of measured indicial response with measured steady-state frequency response of various types of earphones and electrical filters. The improvement in reproduction of the transient wave for a sloping cutoff compared with that for sharp cutoffs is apparent from curves 6, 10, and 11. (After Mott.[15])

experimental apparatus is shown schematically in Fig. 9·28. The square wave generator develops a voltage e across a resistor R_1 whose value is chosen small enough so that e remains constant as a function of frequency. The resistor R_2 is selected to have a resistance equal to the impedance of the source from which the earphone is designed to operate (see Chapter 13). The earphone is terminated in an artificial ear or coupler (see Chapter 16) having a shape and volume appropriate to the way in which the earphone is normally used. The miniature condenser microphone chosen by Mott has a substantially uniform pressure-response characteristic up to a frequency of 10,000 cps. A

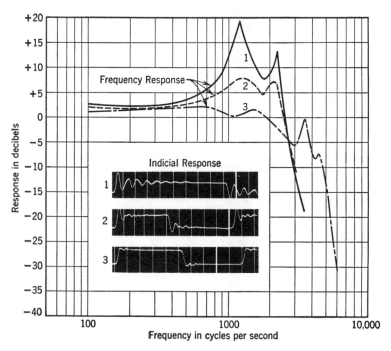

Fig. 9·30   Comparison of indicial response with the frequency response of three types of hearing-aid receivers.   (After Mott.[15])

rapid-recording string oscillograph[16] is used to take the records. His experimental results are shown in Figs. 9·29 to 9·32.

In the top graph of Fig. 9·29, the response of a high fidelity moving-coil earphone is shown. Each division of the oscillogram represents 0.001 sec. Except for a very tiny oscillation at the beginning and end of the transient, the reproduction of the electrical pulse is quite faithful.

Curve 2 shows the response of a magnetic bipolar type of earphone such as is found in a 1945 type telephone handset.

[16] A. Curtis, "An oscillograph for ten thousand cycles," *Bell System Technical Jour.*, **12**, 76 (1933).

The frequency response is fairly flat up to 3000 cps with a sharp cutoff above that point. The acoustic circuits of this earphone tend to damp the resonance of the diaphragm at 1600 cps and to extend the response up to 3000 cps. The oscillogram shows a small oscillation at the beginning and end of the transient.

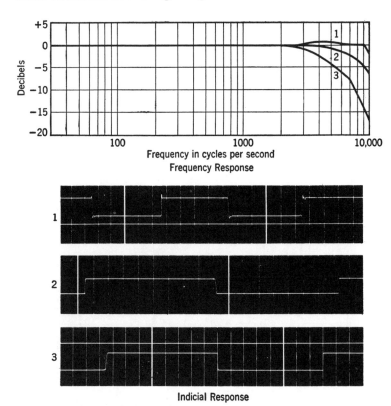

Frequency Response

Indicial Response

FIG. 9·31 Comparison of indicial and frequency responses for different amounts of damping in a string oscillograph. The improvement of the indicial response characteristic for a sloping upper cutoff is apparent. Even with excessive drooping, the response remains good. (After Mott.[15])

Curve 3, by contrast with curve 2, reveals the effect of removing the damping of the diaphragm. The transient response in this case is characterized by a slowly decaying oscillation whose frequency is equal to the natural frequency of the diaphragm.

The effects of various amounts of damping can be seen in curves 4 through 6. The earphone tested is the same as that for

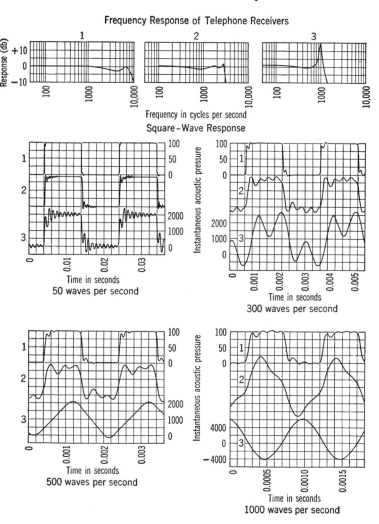

FIG. 9·32 Transient response of three types of earphones to square waves. The steady-state frequency response of each is given at the top of the graph. (After Mott.[15])

curves 2 and 3, and the changes in the shape of the frequency-response curve are brought about by relatively simple changes of the constants of the acoustic circuits. The results of the added damping appear in two ways: first, the small oscillations are damped out, and, secondly, the slope of the start of the transient is decreased. The optimum damping is, therefore, a compromise between permissible time delay and amplitude of oscillation.

Curve 7 was taken with the same earphone as that of curve 2, except that an air leak was provided to simulate the leakage around the cushion when the earphone is applied to the ear. The transient response has the appearance of a large pulse followed by several oscillations of the leak circuit.

Curves 7, 8, and 9 show that, when the low frequencies are absent, the transient response becomes difficult to interpret visually. Curves 10 and 11 are responses for low pass electrical filters.

The curves of Figs. 9·30 and 9·31 were taken to show the effect of added damping and of tapering off the frequency response curve gradually at the cutoff rather than abruptly. The curves of Fig. 9·32 show the response of three earphones to square waves of different frequencies.

Although this series of graphs does not show the response of earphones to all conceivable types of impulse sounds, they do illustrate three important facts: the frequency response must be flat; it must extend to as low and as high frequencies as possible; and it should taper off gradually rather than abruptly at a cutoff frequency.

9·3   High Intensity and Explosive Sources

A. Direct-Radiator and Horn Types

In this category are listed high power direct-radiator and horn sources which are not customarily used for the reproduction of music in theaters or homes. Included are modulated airflow loudspeakers and longitudinally vibrated rods.

Modulated Air-Flow Loudspeakers. Modulated air-flow loudspeakers have been known for many years. Their particular advantage lies in the fact that the transformation of mechanical and electrical energy into acoustic energy at high efficiencies is theoretically possible just as is the case for a siren. In contrast with a siren, however, the air horn is not a single frequency device.

The principle of operation can be judged from the sketch of Fig. 9·33. The air passes through a pair of slotted grids, one stationary and the other movable so that the air flow is interrupted when the two grids come together. An electromagnetic structure rotates the movable grid through a very small angle, varying the spacing between it and the fixed grid and producing changes in the rate of air flow through the grids.

Response curves on one particular design of air-flow loudspeaker are shown in Fig. 9·34.[17]   Two units mounted on two circular exponential horns with lengths of 4 ft and bell diameters of 18 in. were blown simultaneously.   The total power supplied to

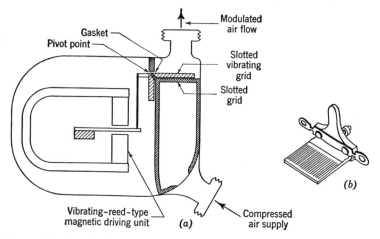

Fig. 9·33   Sketch showing principle of operation of a modulated air-flow loudspeaker unit.   (a) Assembly, (b) vibrating slotted grid.

the two units was 26⅔ watts in one case and 1⅔ in the other, and the air pressure was 25 lb/sq in.   The total amount of air consumed by the two units per minute would occupy 28 ft³ at atmospheric pressure.   The second and third harmonic distortions under these conditions of use are shown in Fig. 9·35.   These distortions are much higher than those of conventional low power loudspeakers.

In addition to the high distortions which arise, these units must be in careful adjustment if reasonable efficiencies are to be expected.

Longitudinally Vibrating Rods.   Rods may be set into intense vibration electrically if they are magnetostrictive in nature. Also, non-magnetostrictive bars may be driven mechanically or by an electromagnetic process.   Very little can be found in the literature on the use of magnetostrictive rods for high intensity

[17] T. E. Caywood and L. L. Beranek, "Performance of Eaves sound projector," O.S.R.D. Report 1528 (1943).

sources in air, although they have met with common use in water. One successful case of an electromagnetically driven bar has been reported by St. Clair.[18]

The St. Clair generator consists of a cylindrical bar of duraluminum supported at its mid-section and free to vibrate at either end (see Fig. 9·36). On the enclosed end, a single-turn coil having a cross-sectional area of about 0.3 cm^2 is milled concen-

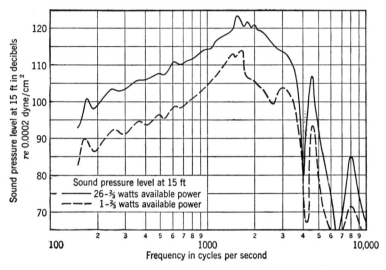

Fig. 9·34 Frequency-response characteristic of twin-unit modulated-airflow horn for constant power available. (After Caywood and Beranek.[17])

trically with the axis of the cylinder. This single-turn coil is placed in a polarizing magnetic field, and a varying current is induced in it by a multi-turn driving coil mounted inside it on the pole piece of the polarizing magnet. The single-turn coil then acts like the secondary winding of a step-down transformer.

The duralumin bar has an exceedingly sharp resonance peak, and at resonance its impedance becomes low enough that reasonably efficient coupling to the air results. To make this generator feasible for practical uses, it is necessary that its vibration control the frequency of the electrical source. This is accomplished by placing an insulated sheet of metal on the top of the central pole piece of the magnet. This sheet, along with the bot-

[18] H. W. St. Clair, "An electromagnetic sound generator for producing intense high frequency sound," *Rev. of Scientific Instruments,* **12,** 250–256 (1941).

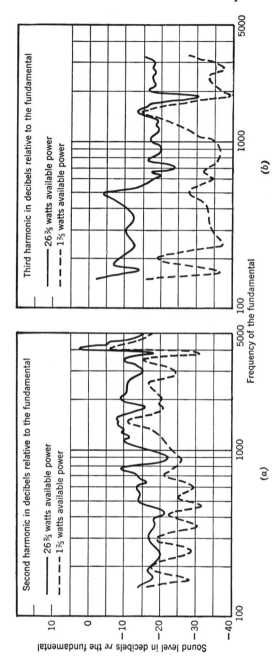

Fig. 9·35   Second and third harmonic distortion characteristics for twin modulated-air-flow horn expressed as number of decibels the harmonics are down from the fundamental component.   (After Caywood and Beranek.[17])

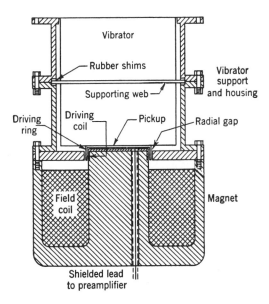

FIG. 9·36   Cross-sectional drawing of a St. Clair sound generator showing the vibrating duralumin cylinder, the supporting rubber shims, the driving ring, the capacitive pickup, and the magnetic field coil. (After St. Clair.[18])

tom end of the cylindrical bar, forms a capacitive pickup which can be fed back to the input of an amplifier in such phase as to form an oscillatory circuit.

By careful choice of the magnet, the material for the bar, the method of supporting the bar, and the air-gap widths, sound fields of 165 db *re* 0.0002 dyne/cm^2 between 10 and 20 kc are possible. Because the diameter of such a radiator may be made large (6 to 12 in.), the sound waves have nearly a plane front and are propagated with little divergence for a foot or more.

Delsasso[19] has made use of mechanically vibrated rods in laboratory experiments for the production of fairly high intensity

---

[19]L. P. Delsasso, University of California at Los Angeles. This information was communicated to the author privately.

sounds. The arrangement consists of a thin bar supported near the center. On the end of the bar from which the sound is radiated a cavity is formed by slipping over the end an adjustable ferrule. The depth of the cavity formed by this ferrule is adjusted experimentally to give maximum acoustic output when the bar is vibrating. Its depth will generally lie between one-eighth and one-fourth wavelength. The opposite end of the bar is excited by a rotating bakelite wheel which has been rosined in the manner of a violin bow. The axis of the rotating wheel is perpendicular to the length of the bar. The frequency of vibration is governed by the dimensions and properties of the bar, and the efficiency by the dimensions of the vibrating ferrule. When properly adjusted this simple apparatus will produce surprising outputs.

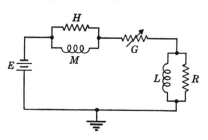

Fig. 9·37 Equivalent circuit of a siren. E represents the source of compressed air, L and R the acoustic impedance of the horn as viewed from the port being opened and closed, G the varying acoustic resistance of the port, and H and M the acoustic impedance of the opening supplying compressed air to the port. (After Jones.[20])

B. Sirens

Sirens find their greatest usefulness where intense sounds of variable frequency are desired and where low distortion is not an important consideration. Four types of sirens have been described recently. Two operate in the audio-frequency range and two in the audio-frequency and ultrasonic frequency range. Before discussing particular instruments, however, let us investigate the theory.

Jones[20] discusses an approximate theory which is helpful in the computation of the overall efficiency of a siren. He represents the performance of a siren by an equivalent electrical circuit (see Fig. 9·37). In that circuit the battery E represents the source of compressed air; the resistance H and the inductance M represent the acoustic impedance looking back into the pressure chamber through the port that the air traverses; the variable resistance G represents the varying size of opening through which the air passes when being "chopped"; the inductance L and the

[20] R. Clark Jones, "A fifty-horsepower siren," *Jour. Acous. Soc. Amer.*, **18**, 371–387 (1946).

resistance R represent the acoustic impedance of the horn as viewed from the port.   The impedances are acoustic impedances, defined as the ratio of pressure to volume velocity.   Values for these circuit elements are derived as follows.   Let us adopt the following notation:

ρ = density of air, in grams per cubic centimeter
c = speed of sound, in centimeters per second
S = area of horn throat, in square centimeters
a = radius of the orifice supplying the air to the port, in centimeters
Q, Q_1, and Q_2 are analogous to the Q of electrical circuit theory
ω_0 = angular cutoff frequency of the exponential horn
ω = angular frequency of the sound being produced
l = distance from the throat of the conical horn to the virtual apex of the cone, in centimeters
V = instantaneous volume velocity of the air through the port
A = instantaneous area of the opening

The usual formula for a circular piston gives the acoustic impedance as a series connection of an acoustic inductance L_A and an acoustic resistance R_A.   The values of L_A and R_A then depend markedly on frequency for $\omega a/c < 1$.   But if this impedance is expressed as the parallel combination of M and H, these values are independent of frequency and are given by Eqs. (9·1) and (9·2):

$$H = \frac{128\rho c}{9\pi^2 S} \quad \text{acoustic ohms} \tag{9·1}$$

$$M = \frac{8\rho a}{3\pi S} \quad \text{acoustic henries} \tag{9·2}$$

$$Q_2 = \frac{\omega M}{H} = \frac{3\pi}{16}\frac{\omega a}{c} \tag{9·3}$$

For a conical horn (no restriction on $\omega l/c$):

$$R = \frac{\rho c}{S} \quad \text{acoustic ohms} \tag{9·4}$$

$$L = \frac{\rho l}{S} \quad \text{acoustic henries} \tag{9·5}$$

$$Q_1 \equiv \frac{\omega L}{R} = \frac{\omega l}{c} \tag{9·6}$$

For an exponential horn (no restriction on ω/ω_0):

$$R = \frac{\rho c}{S} \sqrt{1 - \frac{\omega_0{}^2}{\omega^2}} \quad \text{acoustic ohms} \tag{9.7}$$

$$L = \frac{\rho c}{\omega_0 S} \quad \text{acoustic henries} \tag{9.8}$$

$$Q \equiv \frac{\omega L}{R} = \sqrt{\frac{\omega^2}{\omega_0{}^2} - 1} \tag{9.9}$$

Finally (approximately):

$$G = \frac{\rho}{2} \frac{|V|}{A^2} \tag{9.10}$$

Jones explored the designs of two types of sirens: those which have sine wave outputs and those which have essentially square

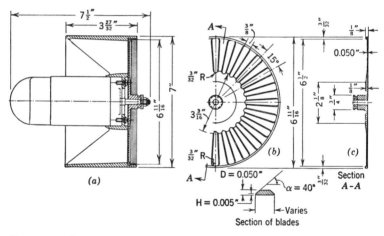

Fɪɢ. 9.38   Construction of siren by Ericson.   (*a*) Side view, (*b*) view looking into the siren from the output side, and (*c*) detail drawing of the siren interrupter disk.

wave outputs. The efficiency of a siren with sine wave output is always less than 50 percent, whereas that for a siren with square wave output will approach 100 percent if the total power output is considered or will approach 81 percent if the power in the fundamental only is considered.

From these considerations, the Bell Telephone Laboratories'

Victory Siren* was designed. In it the ports were rectangular and were fully open 38 percent and fully closed during an equal fraction of the period. The calculated efficiency lay between 70 and 90 percent, and the measurements tended to confirm these computations.

A small experimental type of siren was designed by H. L. Ericson at the Electro-Acoustic Laboratory, Harvard University,

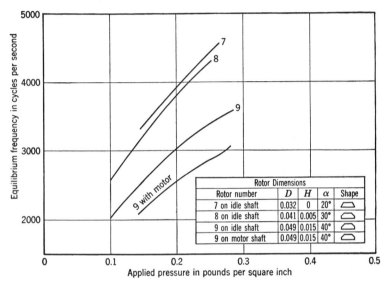

	Rotor Dimensions			
Rotor number	D	H	α	Shape
7 on idle shaft	0.032	0	20°	⬭
8 on idle shaft	0.041	0.005	30°	⬭
9 on idle shaft	0.049	0.015	40°	⬭
9 on motor shaft	0.049	0.015	40°	⬭

Fig. 9·39   Equilibrium frequencies of "free" rotation for the siren of Fig. 9·38 as a function of applied air pressure and rotor shape.   (After Ericson.)

in 1944. It was constructed as shown in Fig. 9·38. The rotor shown on the right in that figure had nearly the same construction as the stator and was designed to produce a tone between 1000 and 5000 cps.

Ericson observed that, when no electrical driving power was supplied to the siren, the air steam produced a "free" rotation of the rotor disk. This frequency depended on the shape of the rotor and the rate of air flow. Measured values of equilibrium frequencies as a function of applied pressure and rotor shape are shown in Fig. 9·39. Three other graphs for this particular siren are of interest. One, Fig. 9·40, gives the electrical power

* This siren was manufactured by the Chrysler Corporation during World War II.

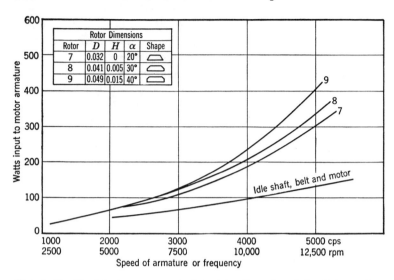

F<small>IG.</small> 9·40 Electrical power required to drive the rotor of the Ericson siren as a function of rpm (or frequency). No air was forced through the siren ports during these measurements.

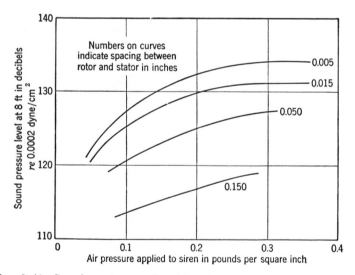

F<small>IG.</small> 9·41 Sound pressure produced by the Ericson siren at 8 ft in an anechoic chamber as a function of air pressure and spacing between the rotor and stator.

to drive the siren in still air as a function of rpm. A second, Fig. 9·41, gives the effective sound pressure produced at a distance of 8 ft in free space as a function of air pressure applied to the siren for different spacings between rotor and stator. Finally, in Fig. 9·42, the directional pattern at 4000 cps is shown.

In the ultrasonic range, sirens have proved to be efficient generators of intense sound. Allen and Rudnick[21] constructed a siren covering the range between 3 and 34 kc. The rotor consisted of a disk about 6 in. in diameter, with 100 equally spaced slots, and the stator contained 100 corresponding circular ports. A ⅔-hp motor was used to drive the rotor, and power inputs of 700 to 1200 watts were required depending on the speed of rotation. A cross-sectional drawing of the siren showing its general construction is given in Fig. 9·43. The 100 conically shaped holes in the stator have diameters of 0.094 in. and 0.188 in. at the throat and mouth, respectively. The throat diameter is half the distance between centers.

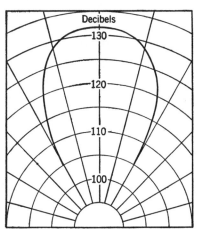

Fig. 9·42   Directional pattern of the siren shown in Fig. 9·38 at 4000 cps. (After Ericson.)

The air pressure used for lower power outputs was 0.2 atmosphere. Measured efficiencies between 17 percent and 34 percent were obtained in the frequency range 3 to 19 kc with an acoustic output between 84 and 176 watts. These figures correspond to levels of about 155 db re 0.0002 dyne/cm^2 at 3.25 kc (on the axis of the siren and 25 cm removed from it) and 158 db at 16.4 kc. With chamber pressures of about 2 atmospheres, acoustic power outputs of approximately 2 kw and an efficiency of about 20 percent were possible. The directional patterns were essentially those calculated for a narrow ring source.

The fourth type of siren which we shall discuss here was designed for the Army Air Forces to cover a very wide frequency

[21] C. H. Allen and I. Rudnick, "A powerful high-frequency siren," *Jour. Acous. Soc. Amer.*, **19**, 857 (1947).

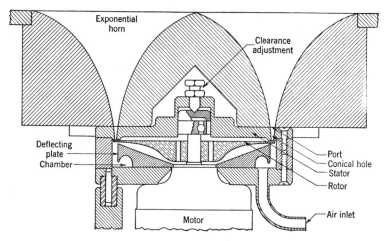

FIG. 9·43 Cross-sectional drawing of a siren designed for operation over a wide frequency range. (After Allen and Rudnick.[21])

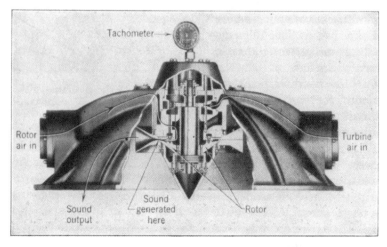

FIG. 9·44 Cross-sectional view of a centrifugal type of siren for producing large acoustic power outputs. The air is forced through radial slots in the rotor and matching slots in the stator. (Courtesy Ultrasonic Corporation.)

range extending from 10 cycles to 200 kc with the aid of three interchangeable rotors and stators.[22] A drawing showing a cross-sectional cut of the siren is given in Fig. 9·44. This siren differs from that of Rudnick in that the air is forced through the ports of the siren, both under pressure and centrifugally.

The three interchangeable rotor-stator combinations have the characteristics shown in Table 9·1. The estimated focal area at a distance of about 8 ft is 2000 to 3000 sq cm, and over this area sound pressure levels between 160 and 167 db *re* 0.0002 dyne/cm^2 were measured.

TABLE 9.1

Number of Slots	Max. Freq. Output, cps	Rotor Air Pressure, lb/ft^2	Rotor Flow, ft^3/min	Est. Power Output, acous. watts
80	13,300	1.0–16.0	300–1600	2000–9000
250	42,000			
800	200,000			

C. Explosive Reports

Pulses of acoustic energy have been shown to be valuable for certain types of measurements.[23] For example, they have been utilized for the determination of reverberation time as a function of frequency, the measurement of the radiation resistance of sound sources, and the random incidence calibration of microphones.

Weber assumes and then proves experimentally that a pistol report or electrical spark is approximately equivalent to the sudden heightening (at $t = 0$) of the temperature in a sphere of air. This action produces an excess pressure which decays according to the equation

$$p = P_0 e^{-\frac{3c}{r}\sqrt{1+\left(\frac{c}{\omega r}\right)^2}\,t} \tag{9·11}$$

where c is the velocity of sound, r is the radius of the sphere of air, P_0 is the initial excess pressure, and ω is the angular frequency $= 2\pi f$. Equation (9·11) can be expressed in terms of the Fourier integral:

[22] A. A. Smith, *Final Progress Report. Army Air Force Contract No. W33-038-ac-16045.* Ultrasonic Corporation, Cambridge, Massachusetts, February 27, 1948.

[23] W. Weber, "The acoustic spectrum of spark and pistol reports with examples of their possible applications in electro-acoustic measurements," *Akust. Zeits.*, **4**, 373–391 (1939) (in German); English translation, L. L. Beranek, *Jour. Acous. Soc. Amer.*, **12**, 210–213 (1940).

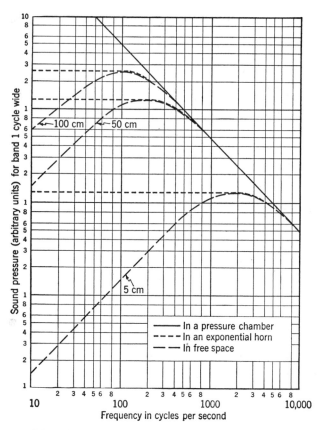

FIG. 9·45 Plots of the calculated sound pressure spectrum produced by a
spherically shaped volume in which the temperature is suddenly raised.
The sound pressure is expressed for a 1 cps bandwidth at the surface of the
spherically shaped volume at the instant of heating. The numbers on
the curves represent the radii of three possible spheres. The shapes of the
curves are different for the three different types of enclosures indicated.
(After Weber.[23])

$$p = P_0 \int_0^\infty A(\omega) \cos \left[\omega t + \tan^{-1}\left(\frac{\omega r}{3c \sqrt{1 + \left(\frac{c}{\omega r}\right)^2}} \right) \right] \quad (9\cdot12)$$

where

$$A(\omega) = \frac{1}{\pi} \frac{1}{\sqrt{\omega^2 + \left(\frac{3c}{r}\right)^2 \cdot \left(\frac{c}{\omega r}\right)^2 + \left(\frac{3c}{r}\right)^2}} \quad (9\cdot13)$$

Equation (9·13) is plotted in Fig. 9·45.   The phase angle is also important and may be determined from Eq. (9·12).   For small values of ω the rms pressure spectrum for a 1-cycle band rises in direct proportion to frequency.   It then flattens out and reaches a maximum for a frequency whose wavelength λ is equal to 3.5 times the radius of the sphere.   Finally, at still higher frequencies, the spectrum decreases inversely proportional to frequency.

The radius r of the initial sphere is a function of the total energy released by the report.   Weber shows that the initial pressure

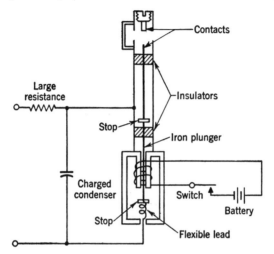

Fɪɢ. 9·46   Device for producing reports from the electrical discharge of a condenser.   (After Békésy.[24])

P_0 is about the same for all sizes of spheres and has a value of approximately 144,000 dynes/cm^2.

An experimental apparatus developed by Békésy[24] for producing reports by the discharge of a condenser is shown in Fig. 9·46. In operation, when the switch is closed the center armature is forced upward, and a discharge takes place between the two contacts.   The resistance of the conductors was chosen to be about 0.1 ohm, giving a time constant of $4 \cdot 10^{-2}$ sec when used with a condenser of 40 μf.   Pistol reports may be used to obtain higher intensities at the lower frequencies.

[24] G. von Békésy, "Mechanical frequency analysis of single oscillatory processes and the determination of the frequency characteristic of transmission systems and the average impedance of the equalization process," *Akust. Zeits.*, **2**, 217–224 (1937).

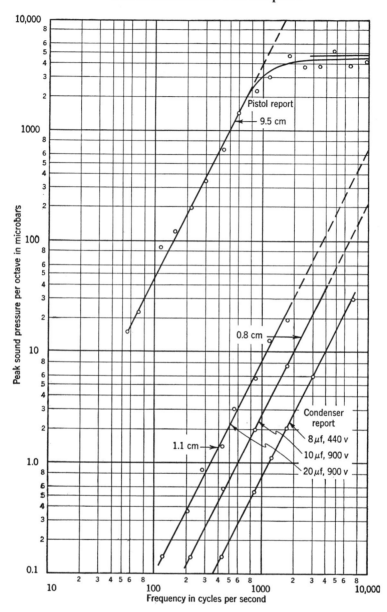

FIG. 9·47   Peak sound pressure for octave bandwidths measured with 30 cm separation between source and detector.   Four different source intensities are shown.   The numbers (in centimeters) on the curves give the approximate radii of the initial spheres.   (After Weber.[23])

The pistol or electrical report producer may be calibrated by mounting a standard microphone in an anechoic chamber a suitable distance away and connecting its output to two filter channels. One of the channels is a monitoring channel and contains a filter, say with a 600 to 1200 cps band. This channel is not changed throughout the measurements. The other channel contains an equalizing network, an amplifier, and a set of adjustable band-pass filters. The outputs of the two channels are connected to the two portions of a double-beam cathode ray tube. When the condenser is discharged, a camera is synchronized with the discharge so that a photographic record for each of the adjustable band-pass filters is obtained. These data then give the relative response of the different bands in the second channel with respect to the reference band of the first channel. The ratio of the peak voltage produced at the output of the filter bands to that produced at the input is determined by applying a square-top wave of electric voltage to the input. Weber found for his octave wide filter bands that the ratio of peak input to the peak output voltage was 6.2 for all the bands.

The fixed filter band gives data which may be used to correct for variations in the strength of successive reports. The peak pressure achieved in each of the bands is determined and the values are plotted to yield curves like those of Fig. 9·47. Weber found that a Flobert pistol produced a report with a spherical radius of 9.5 cm, a 20-μf condenser charged to a potential of 900 volts produced a report with a radius of 1.1 cm, and a 10-μf condenser charged to a potential of 900 volts produced a report whose radius was 0.8 cm.

The shapes of the electrical waves appearing on the face of the cathode ray tube for no filter and for 150–300 and 300–600 cps bands are shown in Fig. 9·48. The microphone was located 30 cm from a Flobert pistol in an anechoic chamber when these records were made.

D. Resonant Enclosures

It is occasionally necessary to produce for test purposes in a small enclosed volume sound pressures which lie in the range of 10^2 to 10^5 dynes/cm^2 (114 db to 174 db *re* 0.0002 dyne/cm^2) and which are reasonably free of harmonic components. Oberst[25]

[25] H. Oberst, "A method for producing extremely strong standing sound

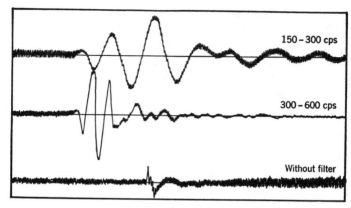

FIG. 9·48   Oscillograms of the sound pressure wave produced at a distance of 30 cm by a Flobert pistol. The three curves show the response in the 150–300 cps, 300–600 cps, and the overall bands. (After Weber.[23])

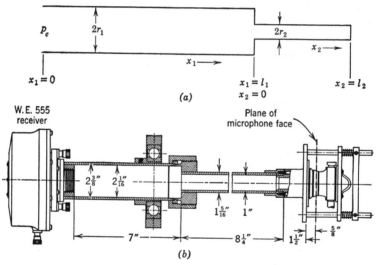

FIG. 9·49   (a) Diagram of a twin-tube arrangement for producing high level, low distortion sound pressures at a surface; (b) drawing of a tube arrangement of this type for use in testing microphones. (After Wiener *et al.*[26])

describes an apparatus which is capable of producing sound pressures of the order of 10^5 dynes/cm^2 with a distortion not in excess of 5 percent. At lower sound pressures, the distortion becomes progressively smaller.

waves in air," *Akust. Zeits.*, **5**, 27–38 (1940) (in German); English translation by L. L. Beranek, *Jour. Acous. Soc. Amer.*, **12**, 308–309 (1940).

Oberst found his apparatus useful in studying streaming phenomena in strong sound fields by the introduction of smoke and dust particles. The apparatus was used also for the testing of pressure-actuated microphones at high sound pressure levels.

The apparatus consists of two pieces of tubing of different lengths and diameters, which are joined together as shown in Fig. 9·49a. The smaller end is terminated by a high acoustic impedance. A source of sound terminates the opposite end.

The sound pressure at the closed end of the smaller tube, $p_2(l_2)$, a rigid termination being assumed, is

$$|\,p_2(l_2)\,|^2 = \frac{p_e{}^2}{A^2 + B^2 + \left[1 - \left(\dfrac{S_2}{S_1}\right)^2\right]C} \tag{9·14}$$

where $A = \cos kl_1 \cos kl_2 - \dfrac{S_2}{S_1}\sin kl_1 \sin kl_2$

$B = \sinh \beta_1 l_1 \cosh \beta_2 l_2 + \dfrac{S_2}{S_1}\cosh \beta_1 l_1 \sinh \beta_2 l_2$

$C = \sinh^2 \beta_2 l_2 \cos^2 kl_1 - \sinh^2 \beta_1 l_1 \sin^2 kl_2$

p_e = sound pressure at the source end of the tube

$k = \omega/c = 2\pi/\lambda$, in cm^{-1}

$l_1,\, l_2$ = length of tubes, in centimeters

$\beta_1,\, \beta_2$ = damping constants of the two tubes, respectively, i.e., the damping in a tube of radius r is $\beta = 3.18\ 10^{-5}\ \sqrt{f}/r$, in cm^{-1}

$S_1,\, S_2$ = cross-sectional areas of the two tubes, in square centimeters, respectively.

$r_1,\, r_2$ = radii of the two tubes, in centimeters, respectively.

Now, at resonance,

$$|\,p_2(l_2)\,|^2 = \frac{p_e{}^2}{B^2 + \left[1 + \left(\dfrac{S_2}{S_1}\right)^2\right]C} \tag{9·15}$$

and the conditions for resonance are

$$\cos kl_1 \cos kl_2 = \frac{S_2}{S_1}\sin kl_1 \sin kl_2 \tag{9·16}$$

Or substituting and rearranging,

$$\cot \frac{2\pi l_1}{\lambda} = \left(\frac{r_2}{r_1}\right)^2 \tan \frac{2\pi l_2}{\lambda} \tag{9·17}$$

For the special case where S_2/S_1 approaches zero, $l_1 = l_2 = \lambda/4$, and β_1 and β_2 are small, Eq. (9·15) becomes

$$\big|\, p_2(l_2) \,\big| \doteq \frac{p_e}{\beta_1 l_1 \beta_2 l_2} \tag{9·18}$$

A plot of Eq. (9·17) is given in Fig. 9·50. Resonances occur at the crossings of the lines for a constant ratio of l_1/l_2 (indicated

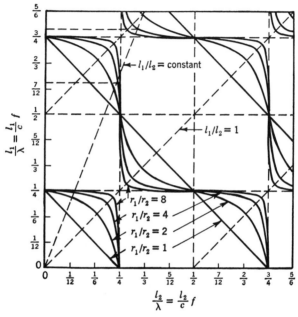

FIG. 9·50 Graphical solution to the equation $\cot (2\pi l_1/\lambda) = (r_2/r_1)^2$ $\tan (2\pi l_2/\lambda)$. The ordinates are l_1/λ and l_2/λ, respectively, and the parameter (solid lines) is r_1/r_2 equal to a constant. The dashed lines are for l_1/l_2 equal to a constant with λ (or f) varying along the axes. (After Oberst.[25])

by dashed straight lines intersecting the origin), with the lines for $r_1/r_2 =$ some constant. These resonant frequencies are not related by simple whole numbers. For example, let $r_1/r_2 = 2$ and $l_1/l_2 = 1$; then $(l_2/c)f = 0.176$; 0.324; 0.675; 0.824, etc. This means that the normal frequencies are not harmonically related, that is, the higher harmonics will not be at resonance at the same time as the fundamental. Hence, when the tubes are excited at one of the resonances, a nearly pure sinusoidal variation of pressure occurs at the closed end of the second tube.

Oberst used a wind-driven siren as a source of sound and produced a pressure of 9×10^4 microbars at a resonance frequency of 180 cps. His tube system was composed of two pipes whose dimensions were $l_1 = 107$ cm, $l_2 = 45$ cm, $r_1 = 6$ cm, and $r_2 = 1.25$ cm. Wiener,[26] for a tube system similar to that of Oberst, found the resonance frequencies to be

104	550	1030
178	630	1130
253	750	1250
362	860	1320
478	925	

For the higher frequency range, Wiener used two tubes whose dimensions were $l_1 = 17.8$ cm, $l_2 = 24.8$ cm, $r_1 = 5.23$ cm, and $r_2 = 3.33$ cm; see Fig. 9·49b. The resonance frequencies were

321	1610	3660
654	1930	4160
860	2690	4340
1050	2950	4850
1330	3360	

Wiener's sound source was a W.E. 555 moving-coil loudspeaker unit. With it he was able to produce sound levels of the order of 10^3 dynes/cm^2 with less than 1 percent harmonic distortion.

The sound pressure may be measured at the desired point inside the tube by a probe tube which is connected to a suitable condenser or crystal microphone (see Chapter 5). If the pressure is sufficiently large to overload the microphone, the probe tube can be lengthened and packed with absorbing material. To calibrate the probe microphone, the termination to the No. 2 tube is replaced by a standard microphone, and the outputs are compared at a sound level low enough that neither microphone is overloaded.

E. Whistles

If a source of compressed air at very high pressure is available, and if efficiency is of no particular concern, high intensity, sine wave sounds may be obtained from air whistles. Two principal types of whistles are suitable for producing such sounds: (1)

---

[26] F. M. Wiener et al., "Response characteristic of interphone equipment," O.S.R.D. Report 1095, Electro-Acoustic Laboratory, Harvard University, March 1, 1943.

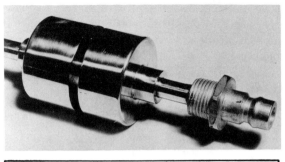

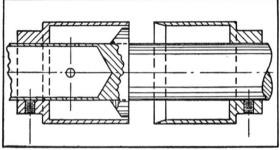

FIG. 9·51 Photograph and drawing of an annular-jet cylindrical air whistle. (Courtesy H. L. Ericson.)

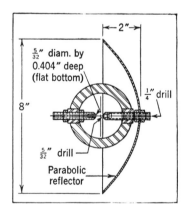

FIG. 9·52 Photograph and drawing of a Hartman air-jet whistle designed to operate at a frequency of 6800 cps. (Courtesy H. L. Ericson.)

the annular air-jet cylindrical whistle and (2) the Hartman air-jet whistle. The first type is discussed by Rice[27] and is shown in Fig. 9·51. The frequency of the whistle depends on its dimensions, the pressure at which the air stream is applied, and the temperature.

The second type of air whistle has been treated by Hartman[28] and is shown in Fig. 9·52. With this type of whistle, a jet of air is directed against a cylindrical cavity with a flat bottom drilled in a cylindrical block of metal. Because of the small size of the source, it is easy to place it at the focal point of a parabolic reflector and thereby obtain high intensities along an axis. Ericson[29] obtained levels of approximately 130 db at a distance of 10 ft along the axis of the parabolic reflector shown in Fig. 9·52.

[27] C. W. Rice, "Sonic altimeter for aircraft," *Aeronautical Engineering* (*Trans. A.S.M.E.*), **4**, 61–76 (1932).

[28] J. Hartman, *Acoustic Air-Jet Generator*, Det Hoffenbergske Establissement, Copenhagen, Denmark, 1939.

[29] H. L. Ericson, Grand Junction, Iowa (formerly at Cruft Laboratory, Harvard University). This information was communicated privately to the author.

10.

Characteristics of Random Noise:
The Response of Rectifiers
to Random Noise and Complex Waves

10·1 Introduction

Random noise of a truly wide-band character is seldom encountered except in such places as at the base of a waterfall, in a turbulent moving air stream, or at the unfiltered output of an amplifier which is passing thermal noise. Nevertheless, many types of noise, such as those produced by a crowd of people talking simultaneously, by an orchestra, by power looms, or by many other manufacturing processes approach randomness although their spectra of energy vs. frequency may not be "white" or wide-band.

In this chapter we shall restrict the use of the words "random noise" to that noise which has a distribution of instantaneous amplitudes that is "normal." Such a distribution is sometimes called a Laplacian or Gaussian distribution. Amplitude-limited or rectified noises no longer have a normal distribution of amplitudes and will be referred to as "amplitude limited noise," "rectified noise," etc. Any noise which has a uniform energy spectrum containing all frequencies in the audible range, as measured with a narrow-band analyzer, will be called "white" noise whether it is random or not. If it is random, it will be referred to as "random white noise."

To measure these types of noise, we use a sound level meter, usually in conjunction with suitable band-pass filters. The readings we get will depend on the nature of the noise, on the characteristics of the filters, and on the properties of the rectifying elements involved in the meter. It is the purpose of this chapter to outline the principal characteristics of random noise and to show how linear and quadratic (square law) rectifiers respond to pure, or complex, or inharmonically related waves, or to random noise. In subsequent chapters we shall discuss the available types of measuring instruments, and the degree to which they possess desired rectification characteristics. First, however, let us look at the more elementary results of the mathematical theory of statistics, because random noise must be represented by statistical concepts.

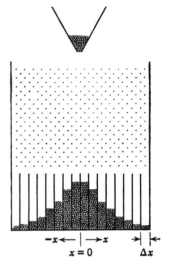

10·2   A Little Statistics

Any single property or quality of a group of things is characterized by an average and a *distribution* about the average. The distribution is specified by one or more parameters, called *statistics*. There are several distributions which are commonly encountered in physics, the "normal" (Gaussian or Laplacian), the Poisson, and various "skewed" distributions. Although the belief is widespread, it is not necessary to assume that a distribution is normal in order to apply statistical methods. Actually, statistics as a subject is not concerned with the prior assumption that any particular distribution of physical quantities will have any given form.[1] But, once the form of some primary or parent

Fig. 10·1   Galton's Quincunx. The Quincunx is one possible mechanical means for producing a distribution of items which approximates a normal distribution curve. A closer approximation to such a curve would be obtained if the vertical and lateral dimensions were increased and if the width Δx of the bins were decreased.

distribution is established, statistics does show how to deal with secondary or related distributions. Most physicists are aware that in many practical problems the distribution of the errors of their experiments is normal.[2] For this reason the normal distribution is often called the normal error "law." Now just what is normal distribution?

---

[1] R. H. Bacon, "Practical statistics for practical physicists," *Amer. Jour. Physics*, **14**, 84–98 (1946).

[2] W. E. Deming and R. T. Birge, "On the statistical theory of errors," *Rev. Mod. Physics*, **6**, 119–161 (1934).

Empirically we can obtain a normal distribution of small shot with the aid of a device called Galton's Quincunx (see Fig. 10·1). Here shot, falling from a small hole in the hopper at the top and passing through the symmetrical array of pegs, receive small sidewise impulses directed with equal probability to the right and to the left. They are finally collected in bins at the bottom. The upper boundary of the collected shot approximates a curve whose equation is,

$$P(x) = ke^{-x^2/(2\sigma^2)} \qquad (10\cdot1)$$

This equation represents the law of normal frequency distribution.* P is known as the probability density, and it is a function of the variable x. It has its maximum value k at $x = 0$. In the case of the Quincunx of Galton, if the bins are made Δx in width, the probable number of shot in a bin located at a position x from the center will be $\Delta x \cdot P(x)$.

Let us first explore the significance of the constant k. Equation (10·1) and Fig. 10·1 refer to a quantity of small shot which has been distributed in a number of bins of width Δx. The probability that a randomly chosen shot comes to rest a distance $x_1 = \Delta x$ from the mean, that is, has a deviation Δx, is $P_1\Delta x$; the probability that it has a deviation $x_2 = 2\,\Delta x$ is $P_2\,\Delta x$, etc. Furthermore, the probability that its deviation is either x_1 or x_2 is $(P_1 + P_2)\,\Delta x$. Thus the probability that its deviation lies between $-\infty$ and $+\infty$ is $2\sum_{j=1}^{\infty} P_j\,\Delta x$. This sum contains the P's corresponding to all possible x's between $-\infty$ and $+\infty$. Because it is certain that all deviations lie between $-\infty$ and $+\infty$, the limit of $\Sigma P\,\Delta x$ as $\Delta x \to 0$ becomes

$$\int_{-\infty}^{\infty} P\,dx = 1 \qquad (10\cdot2)$$

When we carry out this integration, we find the value of k to be

$$k = \frac{1}{\sigma\sqrt{2\pi}} \qquad (10\cdot3)$$

---

* In the general case this formula reads $P(x) = k\,\exp\,[-(x-\bar{x})^2/(2\sigma^2)]$, where $\bar{x}$ is the mean or average. For example, if $P(x)$ were the probability density for the heights of American people, $\bar{x}$ would be the average height of the entire population, and would, of course, not be zero, as the average of random noise is.

In other words, when k has the above value, the area under the curve in Fig. $10 \cdot 1$ is equal to unity. Note also that k equals the maximum value of P.

The mean value of the abscissa x occurs at zero because the distribution curve is symmetrical about $x = 0$.

In Eq. $(10 \cdot 1)$ σ is known as the standard deviation, and it determines the "sharpness" of the distribution curve. Analytically, it is the root-mean-square (rms) deviation of the items (shot) from the mean of the distribution curve. To show that this is true, let us form the series for the mean square deviation of the shot from $x = 0$:

$$\text{ms deviation} = \frac{2}{n} \sum_{j=1}^{n} x_j{}^2 P_j \, \Delta x \qquad (10 \cdot 4)$$

Now if, as before, we let $\Delta x \to 0$ and $n \to \infty$, we get,

$$\text{ms deviation} = \frac{\displaystyle\int_{-\infty}^{\infty} x^2 P \, dx}{\displaystyle\int_{-\infty}^{\infty} P \, dx} \qquad (10 \cdot 5)$$

When we substitute $(10 \cdot 1)$ to $(10 \cdot 3)$ in $(10 \cdot 5)$, we get

$$\text{ms deviation} = \frac{1}{\sigma \sqrt{2\pi}} \int_{-\infty}^{\infty} x^2 e^{-x^2/(2\sigma^2)} \, dx \qquad (10 \cdot 6)$$

On performing this integration we find that the mean-square deviation equals σ^2. Hence, σ equals the rms deviation.

There are three special values of x which have significance in practical problems, usually referred to as a group by the name precision indexes. They are: (1) a, the *average deviation;* (2) σ, the *standard deviation;* and (3) p, the *probable error.**

1. The average deviation a is defined as the mean deviation without regard to sign. That is to say, it is found, for distribution functions which are symmetrical, by the operation

$$a = \frac{2 \displaystyle\int_0^{\infty} x P \, dx}{2 \displaystyle\int_0^{\infty} P \, dx} = \sigma \sqrt{\frac{2}{\pi}} \doteq 0.798\sigma \qquad (10 \cdot 7)$$

2. The standard deviation σ, already derived.

3. The probable error p, defined as that value of the magnitude of x on either side of which there is an equal chance that an item

---

* The probable error should more correctly be called the *probable deviation.* However, we shall follow common usage here.

(shot) will lie.   It is found from the relation

$$\frac{1}{\sqrt{2\pi}} \int_{-p}^{p} e^{-x^2/(2\sigma^2)} \, dx = 0.5 \qquad (10\cdot 8)$$

The value of p is found to be an irrational fractional multiple of σ, namely, $p = 0.6745\sigma$.

10·3   Random Noise Handled by Statistical Methods

Random noise can be treated by the methods of statistical analysis, as can also the output of a rectifier connected to a source of random noise.   In such cases we are unable to predict precisely the amplitude of the input or output wave at any given instant.   Quantitatively, the most we can do is to determine the probability of occurrence of the noise peaks and zeros, to verify that they follow some law of distribution, to compute the values of their average, the mean-square deviation, and the higher statistical moments, and to calculate the correlation of an event at one instant with one at a slightly later instant.   Middleton[3] observes that a far-reaching consequence of the statistical character of the noise lies in the fact that there exists no relationship between the distribution of instantaneous amplitudes and the spectral distribution of the noise power (that is, the mean-square amplitude as a function of frequency) by which one may be obtained from the other.   For example, the rms spectra of normal and amplitude-limited random noise may be identical, but the distribution of the instantaneous amplitudes will be quite different, as we can readily observe on a cathode ray oscillograph. The reason for this is that information about the phases of the components is always lacking.   Thus for a given probability distribution of amplitudes, any number of differently shaped "power" spectra are possible, and vice versa.

Einstein and Hopf,[4] Schottky,[5] Nyquist,[6] and others have

[3] D. Middleton, "The response of biased, saturated linear and quadratic rectifiers to random noise," *Jour. Applied Physics*, **17**, 778–801 (1946); "Spurious signals due to noise in triggered circuits," Report 24, Cruft Laboratory, Harvard University (Dec. 1947).

[4] A. Einstein and L. Hopf, "A principle of the calculus of probabilities and its application to radiation theory," *Ann. d. Physik*, **33**, 1096–1115 (1910) (in German).

[5] W. Schottky, "On spontaneous varying currents in different electric conductors," *Ann. d. Physik*, **57**, 541–567 (1918) (in German).

[6] H. Nyquist, unpublished memorandum, "Fluctuations in vacuum tube noise and the like," March 17, 1943.

represented a random noise voltage by a Fourier series of the form

$$e(t) = \sqrt{R} \sum_{n=1}^{N} (a_n \cos \omega_n t + b_n \sin \omega_n t) \qquad (10 \cdot 9)$$

where $\omega_n = 2\pi f_n$, $f_n = n \, \Delta f$, n is an integer, and Δf is the width of the increments into which the frequency scale is divided. a_n and b_n are taken to be independent quantities, varying randomly as a function of time with magnitudes that are distributed normally about zero with a standard deviation equal to $\sqrt{w(f_n) \, \Delta f}$. There $w(f)$ is defined as the power spectrum of the noise, that is, $w(f)$ is the time average of the power which would be dissipated by those components of $e(t)$ in a resistor of R ohms, measured as a function of frequency by an analyzer with a bandwidth of 1 cps. Parenthetically, we note that *spectrum level* is defined as $10 \log_{10} [w(f)/w_0]$, where w_0 is a reference power.

One way to look at Eq. (10·9) is to imagine that we have an oscillogram of $e(t)$ extending from $t = 0$ to $t = \infty$. This oscillogram may be cut up into strips of length T. When a Fourier analysis is made of $e(t)$ for each strip, a set of independent coefficients a_n and b_n (multiplied by $\sqrt{R}$) will be obtained. These coefficients will obviously vary from strip to strip. We assume that this variation follows a normal distribution. In Eq. (10·9) we regard the a_n's and b_n's as random independent variables while t is kept fixed. This corresponds to assigning to the a's and b's values which they would have at a great many instants, because corresponding to each nth strip there is an instant, and this instant occurs at t [the t in (10·9)] seconds from the beginning of the strip. In a way, we are examining the noise voltage at a great number of instants located at random. Now when $N \to \infty$, $\Delta f \to 0$, the frequency range extends to cover all frequencies from 0 to ∞.

An alternative representation of the random noise voltage is

$$e(t) = \sqrt{R} \sum_{n=1}^{N} c_n \cos (\omega_n t - \phi_n) \qquad (10 \cdot 10)$$

where ϕ_1, ϕ_2, . . . , ϕ_n are angles distributed at random over the range $(0, 2\pi)$ and $c_n = \sqrt{2w(f_n) \, \Delta f}$. In this representation $e(t)$ is regarded as the sum of a number of sinusoidal components with random frequencies and random phase angles.

When a source of truly random noise, such as that given by Eq. (10·10), is connected to a resistor of R ohms, the probability that the electric current through the resistor lies in the range between I and $I + dI$ is $P(I)\, dI$, where $P(I)$, the *probability density*, is given by[7]

$$P(I) = \frac{1}{\sigma_0 \sqrt{2\pi}}\, e^{-I^2/2\sigma_0^2} \qquad (10\cdot11)$$

In other words, if we were to observe the current variation on a cathode ray tube for a long period of time, we would find that the percentage of the time that it lay between the two limits I and $I + dI$ was $P(I)\, dI$. The average current $\bar{I}$ for a random noise is zero. If a bias voltage producing a current $\bar{I}$ were to be placed in series with the source of random noise voltage, Eq. (10·11) would have to be modified by replacing I^2 with $(I - \bar{I})^2$.

In this equation, σ_0 is the standard deviation, and, as we said earlier, is the rms deviation. Let us see what this means physically. Assume that at a particular instant we have a current I_ν in a resistor. The energy which that current will dissipate in the resistor will equal $I_\nu{}^2 R\, \Delta t_\nu$, where Δt_ν is the length of time that I_ν will persist during each second on the average. Reference to Fig. 10·2, which is a plot of Eq. (10·11), shows that the value of I_ν will be achieved on the average $P(I_\nu)\, \Delta I_\nu$ times per second; that is, $\Delta t_\nu = P(I_\nu)\, \Delta I_\nu$. The total energy dissipated in one second, that is, the power dissipated, will be given by

$$\text{Power} = \frac{2}{n} \sum_{\nu=1}^{n} I_\nu{}^2 R P(I_\nu)\, \Delta I_\nu \qquad (10\cdot12)$$

Letting $\Delta I_\nu \to 0$ and $n \to \infty$, we get, on utilizing Eq. (10·11),

$$\text{Power} = \frac{R \int_{-\infty}^{\infty} I^2 P(I)\, dI}{\int_{-\infty}^{\infty} P(I)\, dI} = \sigma_0{}^2 R \qquad (10\cdot13)$$

In other words, $\sigma_0{}^2$ is the mean-square *current* in the resistor. That is to say,

$$\sigma_0{}^2 = \frac{1}{R} \int_0^{\infty} w(f)\, df \qquad (10\cdot14)$$

[7] S. O. Rice, "Mathematical analysis of random noise," *Bell System Technical Jour.*, **23**, 282–332 (1944); **24**, 46–156 (1945); S. Goldman, *Frequency Analysis, Modulation and Noise*, McGraw-Hill (1948), Sections 7·17–7·19.

where $w(f)$ is the time average of the power which would be dissipated by those components of $I(t)$ which lie in the frequency range between f and $f + 1$ cps if they were to flow through a resistance of R ohms. If a spectrum of the noise were available in terms of rms current $A(f)$ in frequency bands 1 cycle in width plotted as a function of the frequency f, then

$$w(f) = A^2(f)R \qquad (10 \cdot 15)$$

If $w(f)$ has a uniform value of w_0 (watts per cycle of bandwidth)

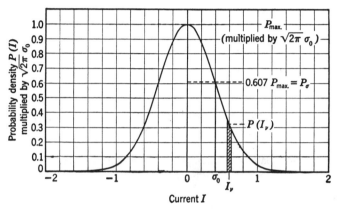

FIG. 10·2   Normal distribution curve. This curve is a plot of exp $(x^2/2\sigma_0{}^2)$, which is the probability density $P(I)$ multiplied by $\sqrt{2\pi}\sigma_0$. The value of the standard deviation σ_0 has been arbitrarily chosen to be 0.4.

in the frequency band between the limits f_a and f_b, then, upon substituting the limits f_a and f_b for 0 and ∞ in Eq. (10·14),

$$\sigma_0{}^2 = \frac{(f_b - f_a)w_0}{R} \qquad (10 \cdot 16)$$

As an example, let us determine the proportion of time that a random current with a distribution curve equal to that shown in Fig. 10·2 has a value within the range of 0.5 and 0.55 amp. To get this number, we must find the value of $P(I)\ dI$. This is equal to $0.05 \times 0.41 \times \sqrt{2\pi}\ \sigma_0 \doteq 0.02$, or 2 percent of the time. $P(I)$ is seen to be symmetrical about $\bar{I} = 0$ and approaches the I axis at both extremes. The probability is very small that the noise current will have a very large positive or a very large negative value at any given time. The standard deviation, $\sigma = 0.4$, falls at that value of I for which $P = 0.607$ of the maximum value of P. For a normal distribution curve [one which obeys a formula of the form of Eq. (10·11)], P_σ will always have a value equal to $(I_\sigma - \bar{I}) = 0.607 P_{max} = 0.607/(\sqrt{2\pi}\sigma)$.

Now that we have stated the probability that the current $I(t)$ will lie between I and $I + dI$, we shall list some other important properties of a random noise current. These results are taken entirely from Rice,[7] and the reader is referred to his excellent treatment for details of their derivation. No attempt is made here to clarify their derivation.

10·4 Some Statistical Properties of Random Noise[7]

A. Expected Number of Zeros per Second

The expected number of zeros of $I(t)$ which will occur per second is

$$\text{Zeros per second} = 2\sqrt{\frac{\int_0^\infty f^2 w(f)\,df}{\int_0^\infty w(f)\,df}} \qquad (10\cdot17)$$

For an ideal band-pass filter whose pass band extends from f_a to f_b the expected number of zeros per second for a white random noise is

$$\text{Zeros per second} = 2\sqrt{\frac{f_b{}^3 - f_a{}^3}{3(f_b - f_a)}} \qquad (10\cdot18)$$

If $f_a = 0$ (low pass filter) the number of zeros per second will equal $1.155 f_b$. If f_a approaches f_b, the number of zeros per second approaches $f_a + f_b$.

B. Expected Interval of Time between Two Successive Zeros

For an ideal *narrow* band-pass filter, the probability that the time between two successive zeros lies between τ and $\tau + d\tau$ is approximately

$$\frac{d\tau}{2}\frac{a}{[1 + a^2(\tau - \tau_1)^2]^{3/2}} \qquad (10\cdot19)$$

where

$$a = \sqrt{3}\,\frac{(f_b + f_a)^2}{f_b - f_a}$$

and

$$\tau_1 = (f_b + f_a)^{-1}$$

C. Expected Number of Maxima per Second

The expected number of maxima per second is

$$\text{Maxima per second} = \sqrt{\frac{\int_0^\infty f^4 \cdot w(f)\, df}{\int_0^\infty f^2 \cdot w(f)\, df}} \qquad (10\cdot 20)$$

For a band-pass filter the expected number of maxima per second is

$$\sqrt{\frac{3(f_b{}^5 - f_a{}^5)}{5(f_b{}^3 - f_a{}^3)}} \qquad (10\cdot 21)$$

For a low pass filter where $f_a = 0$, Eq. (10·21) becomes $0.775 f_b$.

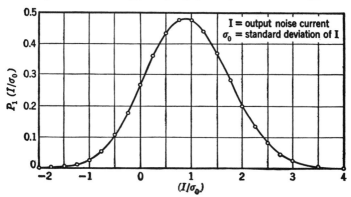

FIG. 10·3 This curve, when divided by σ_0 and multiplied by dI, yields the probability that a maximum of random current I chosen at random from the universe of maxima lies between I and $I + dI$. It applies to noise passed through an ideal low pass filter. (After Rice.[7])

The expected number of maxima per second lying above the line $I(t) = I_1$ is approximately, for I_1 *large*,

$$e^{-I_1{}^2/2\sigma_0{}^2} \times \tfrac{1}{2} \quad \text{[the expected number of zeros per second]} \qquad (10\cdot 22)$$

where σ_0 is the rms value of the current I.

For an ideal low pass filter the probability that a maximum chosen at random from the universe of maxima lies between I and $I + dI$ may be found with the aid of Fig. 10·3. $P(I/\sigma_0)$ is the probability density for I/σ_0 as before.

For large values of I/σ_0 the probability can be represented by an asymptotic formula:

$$\frac{P_1\,(I/\sigma_0)\, dI}{\sigma_0} = \frac{5}{3\sigma_0{}^2}\, e^{-I^2/2\sigma_0{}^2}\, I\, dI \qquad (10\cdot 23)$$

D. Expected Number of Maxima per Second in Excess of a Specified Value

The expected number of maxima per second N in excess of a specified value V_0 has been derived by Middleton[3] and is shown graphically in Fig. 10·4 for two types of filter characteristics—rectangular and Gaussian.

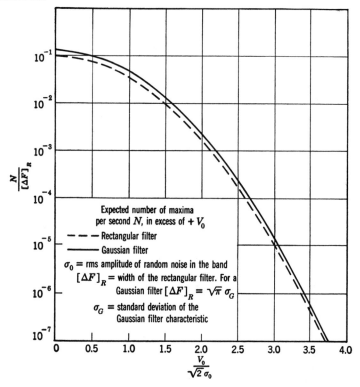

FIG. 10·4 These curves, one for a filter characteristic with a Gaussian shape and one for a filter characteristic with a rectangular shape, when multiplied by the bandwidth yield the expected number of maxima per second N in excess of a specified value V_0. The abscissa equals $V_0/\sqrt{2}$ divided by the rms value of the current in that band.

E. Properties of the Envelope of the Peaks

When we pass noise through a *relatively narrow band-pass filter*, one of the most noticeable features of an oscillogram of the output current is its fluctuating envelope. It has, roughly, the character of a sine wave of the mid-band frequency whose amplitude fluctuates irregularly, the rapidity of fluctuation being of the order of the bandwidth.

The envelope $\mathcal{R}$ is defined as follows: Let f_m be a representative mid-band frequency. Then if $\omega_m = 2\pi f_m$, the noise current may be represented by

$$I = \sum_{n=1}^{N} c_n \cos{(\omega_n t - \phi_n)}$$

$$= \sum_{n=1}^{N} c_n \cos{(\omega_n t - \omega_m t - \phi_n + \omega_m t)}$$

$$= I_c \cos{(\omega_m t)} - I_s \sin{(\omega_m t)} \qquad (10 \cdot 24)$$

where the components I_c and I_s are

$$I_c = \sum_{n=1}^{N} c_n \cos{(\omega_n t - \omega_m t - \phi_n)} \qquad (10 \cdot 25)$$

$$I_s = \sum_{n=1}^{N} c_n \sin{(\omega_n t - \omega_m t - \phi_n)} \qquad (10 \cdot 26)$$

The envelope $\mathcal{R}$ is a function of t defined as

$$\mathcal{R} = \sqrt{I_c^2 + I_s^2} \qquad (10 \cdot 27)$$

I_c and I_s are two normally distributed random variables, and they are independent since the product of their mean values is zero. They both have the same standard deviation, namely, σ_0.

The probability that the envelope lies between $\mathcal{R}$ and $\mathcal{R} + d\mathcal{R}$ is

$$\frac{\mathcal{R}}{\sigma_0^2} e^{-\mathcal{R}^2/2\sigma_0^2} \, d\mathcal{R} \qquad (10 \cdot 28)$$

For an ideal band-pass filter, the expected number of maxima of the envelope in 1 sec is $0.641(f_b - f_a)$.

When $\mathcal{R}$ is *large*, say $\mathcal{R}/\sigma_0 > 2.5$, the probability that a maximum of the envelope, selected at random from the universe of such maxima, lies between $\mathcal{R}$ and $\mathcal{R} + d\mathcal{R}$ is approximately

$$P_R\left(\frac{R}{\sigma_0}\right) d\left(\frac{\mathcal{R}}{\sigma_0}\right) = 1.13\left(\frac{\mathcal{R}^2}{\sigma_0^2} - 1\right) e^{-\mathcal{R}^2/2\sigma_0^2} \frac{d\mathcal{R}}{\sigma_0} \qquad (10 \cdot 29)$$

A curve for the probability density $P_R(\mathcal{R}/\sigma_0)$ for the range $0 \leq \mathcal{R}/\sigma_0 \leq 4$ is shown in Fig. $10 \cdot 5$.

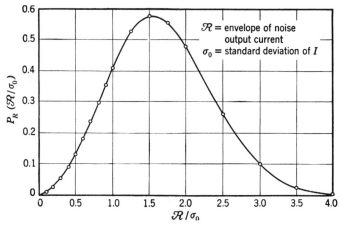

FIG. 10·5   This curve, when divided by σ_0 and multiplied by $d\mathcal{R}$, yields the probability that a maximum of the envelope $\mathcal{R}$ chosen at random from the universe of maxima lies between $\mathcal{R}$ and $\mathcal{R} + d\mathcal{R}$.   It applies to noise passed through an ideal low pass filter.   (After Rice.[7])

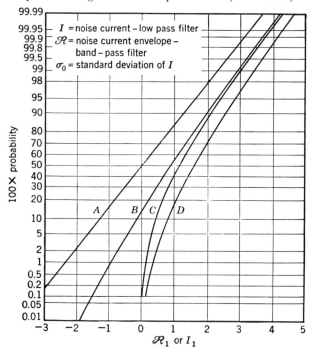

FIG. 10·6 A = probability that I is less than I_1; B = probability that I_{max} is less than I_1; C = probability that $\mathcal{R}$ is less than $\mathcal{R}_1$; D = probability that $\mathcal{R}_{\text{max}}$ is less than $\mathcal{R}_1$.   (After Rice.[7])

F. Probability that the Amplitude or Envelope Is Less than a Specified Value

In Fig. 10·6, four curves are shown which give the relation of values of I and $\Re$ to certain quantities as follows:

Curve A shows the probability, for a low pass filter, of the random current I being less than a specified value I_1.

Curve B shows the probability, for a low pass filter, that a maximum in I selected at random is less than a specified value I_1.

Curve C shows the probability, for an ideal band-pass filter, that the envelope $\Re$ is less than a specified value $\Re_1$.

Curve D shows the probability, for an ideal band-pass filter, that a maximum in $\Re$ selected at random is less than a specified value $\Re_1$.

10·5 Ratio of RMS to Rectified Average Current in Random Waves

The rms current for a random wave is σ_0, as we have already shown. The average current (measured with a linear rectifier in the circuit) is equal to the average deviation a, that is, $I_{av.} = \sqrt{2/\pi}\,\sigma_0 = 0.798\sigma_0$. In decibels, the ratio of the rms to the rectified average current is 1.96 db.

For a sine wave, the ratio of the rms to the average current is $0.707/0.636 = 1.111$, or 0.91 db. Hence, if two meters, one having a square-law and the other a linear characteristic, are calibrated to read alike on sine waves, then on random noise the rms meter will read 1.05 db higher than the linear meter.

10·6 Fluctuation of Energy of Filtered Random Noise as a Function of Interval Length and Bandwidth

We have presented formulas for some of the statistical properties of the random noise current $I(t)$ and its envelope $\Re(t)$. It was stated that the mean value of $I(t)$ was zero and that its standard deviation was proportional to the square root of the frequency integral of the power spectrum; see Eq. (10·14). In measurement, we are often not interested so much in the mean current (with the sign of the current taken into account) as in the energy dissipated by that current in a resistance. Rice[8] treats this problem for the cases of two types of band-pass filters; one with a flat top and vertical sides and the other with the shape of a normal distribution curve. Parts of his work are given here.

[8] S. O. Rice, "Filtered thermal noise—Fluctuation of energy as a function of interval length," *Jour. Acous. Soc. Amer.*, **14**, 216–227 (1943).

Suppose that the input of a filter is connected to a source of random noise and that the output current $I(t)$ flows through a resistance R. The energy J dissipated during the interval of time T extending from t_1 to $t_1 + T$ in the resistance is

$$J(t_1, T) = R \int_{t_1}^{t_1+T} I^2(t) \, dt \qquad (10 \cdot 30)$$

When the starting point t_1 of the interval is regarded as chosen at random, J is a random variable although its distribution is not normal. It will have an average value $\bar{J} = m_T$, which is not equal to zero, and an rms deviation μ_T—both of which depend on the value of the time interval T considered.

The average value m_T of the energy J is found to be

$$m_T = T \int_0^\infty w(f) \, df = T \sigma_0^2 R \qquad (10 \cdot 31)$$

where $w(f)$ is the time average of the power that would be dissipated by those components of $I(t)$ which lie in the frequency range between f and $f + 1$ cps if they were to flow through a resistance of R ohms, and σ_0 is the standard deviation of the random noise current; see Eq. (10·14). If the power spectrum passed by the filter has a uniform value w_0 (watts per unit of bandwidth) between the frequency limits f_a and f_b, the average energy $\bar{J}$ becomes

$$m_T = (f_a - f_b) T w_0 \qquad (10 \cdot 32)$$

The value of the rms deviation μ_T of J is complicated to write except for very small and very large values of T, or for $(f_b - f_a) \ll f_a$, or for $f_a \to 0$. The exact formula for all values of T and all bandwidths is

$$\mu_T^2 = 2w_0 T^2 \{ 4f_b F[4\pi T f_b] + 4f_a^2 F[4\pi T f_a]$$
$$-2(f_a + f_b)^2 F[2\pi T(f_a + f_b)] + 2(f_b - f_a)^2 F[2\pi T(f_b - f_a)] \}$$
$$(10 \cdot 33)$$

where

$$F[x] = \sum_{n=1}^\infty \frac{(-1)^{n-1} x^{2n-2}}{(2n)!(2n-1)(2n)} \qquad (10 \cdot 34)$$

A range of values of $F[x]$ is given in Table 10·1. An approximate formula for $x > 7$ is

$$F[x] = \frac{\pi}{2x} - \frac{\log_e x + 1.577}{x^2} \qquad (10 \cdot 35)$$

For very small values of T, Eqs. (10·32) and (10·33) yield

$$\mu_T \doteq \sqrt{2} \, m_T \qquad (10 \cdot 36)$$

and, for very large values of T,

$$\mu_T \doteq w_0 \sqrt{(f_b - f_a)T} = \sqrt{w_0 m_T} \qquad (10 \cdot 37)$$

TABLE 10·1

x	$F[x]$	x	$F[x]$
0	0.25	20	0.0671
1	0.2466	30	0.0468
3	0.2222	50	0.0292
5	0.1863	100	0.0151
7	0.1529	200	0.00768
10	0.118	400	0.00388
16	0.081	1000	0.00156

If $(f_b - f_a) \ll f_b$, Eq. (10·33) can be written

$$\mu_T \doteq 2m_T \sqrt{F[2\pi T(f_b - f_a)]} \qquad (10 \cdot 38)$$

This equation divided by m_T is plotted as y_A in Fig. 10·7. The shape of the y_A curve suggests that $\sigma_T/m_T = 1$ at $T = 0$. The true value is 2, but it drops to the value unity very quickly as T increases, the rapidity of the drop depending on the mid-band frequency.

For $f_a \to 0$, and no restriction on f_b, we get

$$\mu_T = 2.828 m_T \sqrt{F[4\pi T f_b]} \qquad (10 \cdot 39)$$

This equation divided by m_T is plotted as y_D in Fig. 10·7, where $(f_b - f_a)$ is now equal to f_b.

As an example of the use of this information, suppose that the total energy produced by a filtered random noise is to be measured by a thermocouple and Grasott fluxmeter over intervals of 10 sec. If the random noise has a constant power of 10^{-5} watt for a 1-cps band and the bandwidth is 1000 cycles, what is the average energy and the rms deviation to be expected from a series of such measurements? From Eqs. (10·32) and (10·37), the average reading obtained with the fluxmeter will be $m_T = 0.1$ watt-sec, and the standard deviation of the readings will be $\mu_T = 0.001$ watt-sec.

On occasion one is interested in the rms deviation $\mu_{S,T}$ of the difference between two J's whose starting points are separated by a time S. For example, we might record a random noise from a source and play it back delayed by S seconds for comparison with the output of the source itself. We want the standard deviation of the quantity

$$J(t_1,T) - J(t_1 + S,T)$$

$$= R \int_{t_1}^{t_1+T} I^2(t)\, dt - R \int_{t_1+S}^{t_1+S+T} I^2(t)\, dt \qquad (10 \cdot 40)$$

where t_1 is chosen at random as before. For the case, when $S = T$, Rice determines the value of $\mu_{T,T}$ as follows:

$$\mu_{TT} = 4m_T \sqrt{F[u] - F[2u]} \qquad (10\cdot41)$$

In this instance one interval of length T starts when the other one stops. $F[u]$ was given in Eqs. (10·34) and (10·35) and Table 10·1, and $u = 2\pi T(f_b - f_a)$. The ratio $\mu_{T,T}/m_T$ is plotted as y_C in Fig. 10·7.

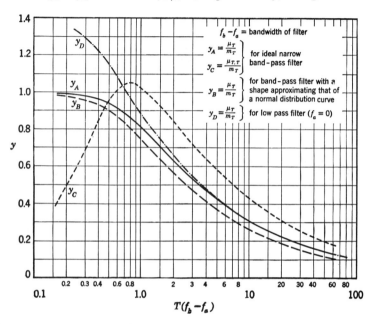

FIG. 10·7   Ratios of rms deviation of energy to mean energy developed by a random current in a resistor as a function of the product of bandwidth and time for various types of filters.   (After Rice.[7])

Narrow band-pass filters seldom can be approximated with an idealized flat-topped vertical-sided characteristic. Suppose instead that the pass band be assumed to have the same shape as that of a normal distribution curve (Fig. 10·2). It can be shown that an ideal band-pass filter which would pass the same average amount of energy would have a bandwidth of $f_b - f_a = \sigma \sqrt{\pi}$, where σ is the standard deviation of the filter characteristic. (Note the similarity between σ and $1/Q$ of electrical circuit theory as a means of designating the sharpness of a resonance curve.)   The equation for μ_T is somewhat involved and will not be presented here. However, the results are given in the form of the curve labeled y_B in Fig. 10·7.

10·7   Response of Simple Rectifiers to Pure Tones and Random Noise

We usually measure noise currents or voltages with the aid of a rectifier used in conjunction with a d-c meter. The indications of the meter depend on the characteristics of the rectifying element. For example, the rectifier can be so chosen that it will read either (a) the peak amplitude, (b) the rms amplitude, or (c) the average amplitude of the noise. Frequently, the noise is measured in conjunction with a discrete single-frequency component, and some knowledge is desired of the behavior of the indicating instrument as the amplitude of one or the other is varied. A detailed discussion of the construction of rectifying elements to produce a particular kind of rectification will appear in the next chapter. Let us consider here the rectifier as a more-or-less perfect instrument and determine that the relations must exist among the d-c readings of meters having different rectification characteristics when subjected to random noise and combinations of sine waves. First let us observe the response of an instrument which is designed to read values approaching the peak amplitude of a complex wave.

A. Peak-Indicating Instruments

Peak-indicating instruments are those which respond as closely as possible to the maximum value reached by a voltage in a stated interval of time. The peak value of a complex wave with harmonically related frequencies is determined by the relative amplitudes and phases of the various component waves. The relations among the peak, rms, and average amplitudes of several differently shaped, recurrent waves are listed in Table 10·2. For waves with a short duty cycle (one which is near zero in amplitude over most of the cycle), the ratio of the peak to the rms or average amplitude becomes high. This is particularly well illustrated by the cases involving random or narrow rectangular waves.

Non-recurrent waves are more difficult to handle analytically than recurrent waves, because any particular amplitude can only be predicted by statistical analysis. Let us consider the case of a number of inharmonically related waves,

$$E_s = E_1 \cos (\omega_1 t + \phi_1) + E_2 \cos (\omega_2 t + \phi_2)$$

$$+ E_3 \cos (\omega_3 t + \phi_3) + \cdots \quad (10\cdot42)$$

TABLE 10·2   VALUES OF I_{rms} AND I_{av} vs. E FOR UNIT RESISTANCE AND HALF-WAVE RECTIFICATION

Wave	Equation	I_{rms}	I_{av}	$20 \log I_{\text{rms}}/I_{\text{av}}$, db	Previous Column minus 3.93 db
	$e = E \sin \omega t$	$0.5E$	$0.318E$	3.93	0
	$e = \dfrac{-2E}{\pi}\left[\sin \omega t - \dfrac{1}{2}\sin 2\omega t + \dfrac{1}{3}\sin 3\omega t - \cdots\right]$	$0.408E$	$0.25E$	4.26	0.33
	$e = \dfrac{-2E}{\pi^2 p(1-p)} \displaystyle\sum_{n=1}^{n=\infty} \dfrac{1}{n^2}\cos(np\pi)\sin(np\pi)\sin(n\omega t)$ For $\beta = \pi$, i.e., $p = 0.5$, $e = \dfrac{8E}{\pi^2}\left[\sin \omega t - \dfrac{1}{9}\sin 3\omega t + \dfrac{1}{25}\sin 5\omega t - \cdots\right]$	$0.408E$	$0.25E$	4.26	0.33
		$E\sqrt{p}$	Ep	$-10 \log_{10} p$	$(-10 \log_{10} p - 3.93)$

Waveform	Equation				
	$e = \dfrac{4E}{\pi}\left[\sin\omega t + \dfrac13\sin 3\omega t + \dfrac15\sin 5\omega t + \cdots\right]$	$0.707E$	$0.5E$	3.01	-0.92
	$e = \displaystyle\sum_{n=1}^{N} C_n\cos(\omega_n t - \phi_n)$	$0.707\sigma_0$	$0.3985\sigma_0$	4.96	1.03
	$E(\cos\theta_1 + \cos\theta_2)$	$0.707E$	$0.394E$	5.08	1.15
	$\dfrac{2\sqrt3 E}{\pi}\left[\cos\omega t - \dfrac15\cos 5\omega t + \dfrac17\cos 7\omega t - \dfrac1{11}\cos 11\omega t + \cdots\right]$ $= \dfrac{3E}{\pi}\left[\sin 2\omega t + \dfrac13\sin 6\omega t + \dfrac15\sin 10\omega t + \cdots\right]$	$0.576E$	$0.333E$	4.76	0.83
	$\dfrac{2E}{\pi}\left[\sin\omega t - \sin 2\omega t + \dfrac13\sin 3\omega t + \dfrac15\sin 5\omega t - \dfrac13\sin 6\omega t + \cdots\right]$ $= \dfrac{2E}{\pi}\left[\dfrac{\pi}{4} - \left(\cos\omega t - \dfrac13\cos 3\omega t + \dfrac15\cos 5\omega t - \cdots\right)\right]$	$0.707E$	$0.5E$	3.01	-0.92

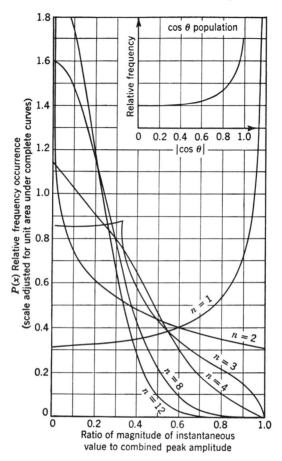

FIG. 10·8 Probability density for the instantaneous value obtained from the combination of n cosine functions. $E_s = E_1(\cos\theta_1 + \cos\theta_2 + \cdots + \cos\theta_n)$; E_s = instantaneous value of the combination; E_1 = peak value of each component; θ_ν = phase angle of each component; nE_1 = combined peak amplitude. The complete curves are symmetrical about zero. (After Slack.[9])

where $E_1, E_2, \ldots, \omega_1, \omega_2, \ldots$, and $\phi_1, \phi_2, \ldots$ are arbitrary amplitudes, angular frequencies, and phases. The true peak value of the summation E_s will equal

$$E_p = E_1 + E_2 + E_3 + \cdots \qquad (10\cdot43)$$

As the number of components increases, E_p will be achieved less and less often in any given interval of time, and soon it becomes impractical to design an instrument which will give readings approaching E_p within close tolerances.

Slack[9] has determined the probability of occurrence of any particular instantaneous amplitude for a series of the form

$$E_s = E_1(\cos\theta_1 + \cos\theta_2 + \cos\theta_3 + \cdots + \cos\theta_n) \quad (10 \cdot 44)$$

where E_1 is the peak value, θ_ν is the phase angle of any particular component, and n is the total number of terms. The θ's are selected at random. Her results are given in the form of three charts in Figs. $10 \cdot 8$ to $10 \cdot 10$. The first of these charts gives the probability distribution $P(E_s/nE_1)$. From this chart the percentage of time that any particular amplitude ratio E_s/nE_1 is expected to occur in the interval $\Delta(E_s/nE_1)$ is given by the product $P(E_s/nE_1) \cdot \Delta(E_s/nE_1)$. For example, the percentage of time that the ratio E_s/nE_1 is expected to fall between 0.6 and 0.7 for $n = 2$, is $0.38 \times 0.1 = 0.038 = 3.8$ percent. These curves are symmetrical about zero because there is equal probability of negative and positive values of E_s. Figures $10 \cdot 9$ and $10 \cdot 10$ show the percentage of time that E_s/nE_1 exceeds any particular value along the abscissa.

The application of these results to the design of a "peak" voltmeter is straightforward. Let us assume the ideal rectifying circuit shown in Fig. $10 \cdot 11$. Furthermore, let us assume that the time constant R_bC_b is very long. Under these circumstances an equation for continuity of charge can be formed such that the total charge passed by the rectifier is equal to the charge which leaks off the condenser through the resistor R_b.

During each second a total charge of E_b/R_b will leak off the condenser C_b. Whenever E_s exceeds E_b, a charge will be added to C_b. The charge passed per second by the rectifier whenever E_s lies in the interval between E_ν and $(E_\nu + \Delta E)$, for values of $E_\nu > E_b$, is

$$\Delta q_\nu = \frac{(E_\nu - E_b)}{R_r} P(E_\nu) \Delta E_\nu \quad (10 \cdot 45)$$

For all intervals where $E_s > E_b$,

$$q = \int_{E_b}^{\infty} \frac{(E_s - E_b)}{R_r} P(E_s) \, dE_s \quad (10 \cdot 46)$$

[9] M. Slack, "The probability distributions of sinusoidal oscillations combined in random phase," *Jour. Inst. Elec. Engrs.*, Part III, **93**, 76–86 (1946).

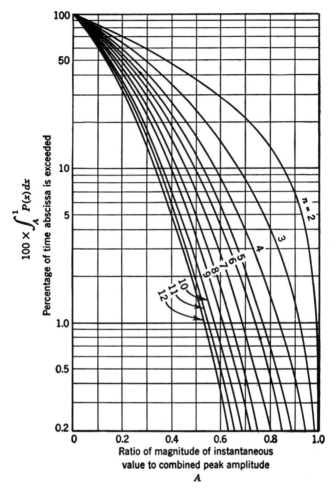

Fig. 10·9   Percentage of time the ratio of magnitude of instantaneous value of n inharmonic sine waves to the combined peak amplitude indicated on the abscissa is exceeded.   (After Slack.[9])

On equating E_b/R_b to q and rearranging, we get

$$\frac{1}{E_b} \int_{E_b}^{nE_1} E_s P(E_s)\, dE_s - \int_{E_b}^{nE_1} P(E_s)\, dE_s = \frac{R_r}{R_b} \quad (10\cdot47)$$

This equation says that, the nearer we desire the voltage E_b to be to the peak voltage nE_1, the smaller R_r/R_b must be.   This condition is not too difficult to satisfy for $n < 4$, but, for greater

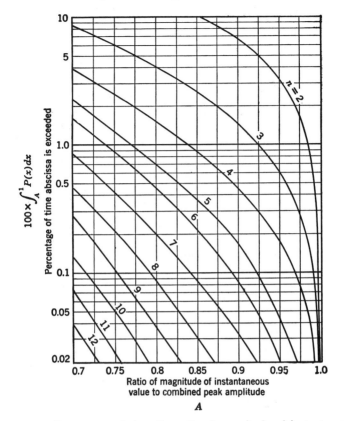

Fig. 10·10 Percentage of time the ratio of magnitude of instantaneous value of n inharmonic sine waves to the combined peak amplitude indicated on the abscissa is exceeded. (After Slack.[9])

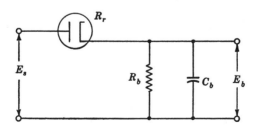

Fig. 10·11 Idealized circuit for a peak voltmeter. R_r is the average rectifier resistance when conduction takes place. R_b and C_b are chosen so that the time constant is very long. E_b is the meter reading of the instrument when a wave E_s is impressed on the input.

values, very small ratios of R_r/R_b are necessary, because $P(E_s)$ for E_s approaching nE_1 becomes very small (see Fig. 10·8). Equation (10·47) is plotted in Chapter 11, p. 470, in connection with the design of practical rectifiers.

Equation (10·47) is also valid for calculating the response of a "peak" voltmeter to random noise, provided the upper limits of integration are extended to infinity and the probability distribution for random noise is assumed. As can be found from the curves in the next chapter and from measurements made by Jansky,[10] peak meter readings are about four times (12 db) greater than rms meter readings when random noise is being measured. The observations by Jansky also indicate that the peak value of a white random noise increases as the square root of the width of the filter band through which it is passed. This result is also shown by the theory above which says that the ratio of "peak" to rms readings is independent of the rms value of the amplitude of input signal, and we already know that for a white random noise the rms value of the amplitude is proportional to the bandwidth.

B. Mean-Square (Square-Law) Indicating Instruments

The output of a rectifying element which delivers a direct current proportional to the square of the applied voltage is the simplest of all cases to calculate. Rice[7] treats this case assuming two sine wave components plus random noise, each with arbitrary amplitudes. As before, we set

$$e = E_1 \cos (\omega_1 t + \phi_1) + E_2 \cos (\omega_2 t + \phi_2) + \sigma_e \quad (10·48)$$

where E_1, ω_1, and ϕ_1 were defined for Eq. (10·44) and σ_e is the rms amplitude of the random noise voltage. Then the average direct current delivered by a square-law rectifier with the characteristic shown in Fig. 10·12 will equal

$$I_{dc} = a_1 \left(\frac{E_1{}^2}{2} + \frac{E_2{}^2}{2} + \sigma_e{}^2 \right) \quad (10·49)$$

where a_1 is a constant of proportionality depending on the characteristic curve of the rectifier. One sees that the direct current is proportional to the power which the voltage e would deliver to

[10] K. G. Jansky, "An experimental investigation of the characteristics of certain types of noise," *Proc. Inst. Radio Engrs.*, **27**, 763–768 (1939).

a load resistance.   The meter scale is usually calibrated, however, in terms of the rms amplitude.   For the case of white random noise alone, i.e., $w(f)$ = constant [see Eq. (10·14)], the rms amplitude σ_e will be proportional to the square root of the bandwidth, where the limits of 0 and ∞ are replaced by the limits

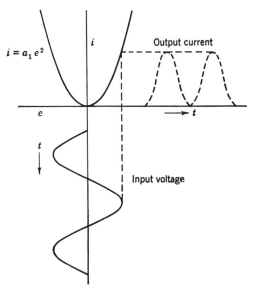

FIG. 10·12   Rectification characteristic of an ideal full-wave quadratic (square-law) rectifier. a_1 is the rectifier characteristic.

of the pass band.   Jansky has confirmed this relationship experimentally.

C. Average Indicating Instruments

We find it very difficult to calculate the average current delivered by a linear, half-wave rectifier to its load when the input wave is other than random or cannot be analyzed into a Fourier series.   Rice,[7] Bennett,[11] and Middleton[3] have published partial treatments, and Jansky[10] has added experimental data.

A relatively simple case of rectification by a linear half-wave rectifier (see Fig. 10·13) occurs when two inharmonic waves of arbitrary phase and angle are impressed on its input.   Starting

[11] W. R. Bennett, "Response of a linear rectifier to signal and noise," *Jour. Acous. Soc. Amer.*, **15**, 164–172 (1944); "New results in the calculation of modulation products," *Bell System Technical Jour.*, **12**, 228–243 (1933).

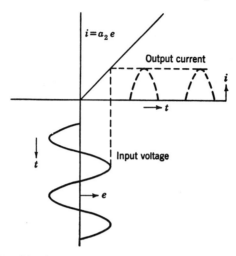

FIG. 10·13   Rectification characteristic of an ideal half-wave linear rectifier,
a_2 is the rectifier characteristic.

with

$$e = E_1 \cos (\omega_1 t + \phi_1) + E_2 \cos (\omega_2 t + \phi_2) \qquad (10 \cdot 50)$$

Bennett finds that the average direct current produced in the
output of such a rectifier will be

$$I_{dc} = a_2 \frac{2E_1}{\pi^2} [2A - (1 - k^2)K] \qquad (10 \cdot 51)$$

where

$$A = \int_0^1 \sqrt{\frac{1 - k^2 Z^2}{1 - Z^2}} \, dZ$$

$$K = \int_0^1 \frac{dZ}{\sqrt{(1 - Z^2)(1 - k^2 Z^2)}}$$

and a_2 = rectifier constant
  $k = E_2/E_1$
  Z = integration variable
  a_2 = rectifier characteristic.

A graph of Eq. (10·51) is shown in Fig. 10·14. Note that the
average current for a single wave ($E_2 = 0$) is 0.318 instead of
0.636 because half-wave rectification is assumed.

We see from Fig. 10·14 that the average direct current for
two sine waves of equal amplitude is 1.26 times that for a single

sine wave. We also know that the rms amplitude of two sine waves is 1.414 times that for a single wave. Hence, if the reading of a meter with a square-law rectifying characteristic is compared with one having a linear characteristic, the former reading will be 1.0 db greater than the latter provided they were calibrated to read alike on sine waves.

In his later paper,[11] Bennett deals with the linear rectification of a single sine wave, $E_s = E_1 \cos \omega t$, in combination with random noise. First, he assumes that the probability density function

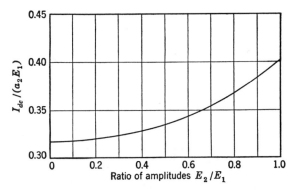

FIG. 10·14 Graph showing the direct current produced by a half-wave rectifier as a function of the ratio of the amplitudes of two impressed inharmonic sine wave components with amplitudes E_1 and E_2. The slope of the rectifier characteristic is a_2. (After Bennett.[11])

for the noise voltage is that given in Eq. (10·1). Then he writes the probability density function for a sine wave as follows:

$$P_s(E_s) = \begin{cases} 0 & ;\ |E_s| > E_1 \\ (E_1{}^2 - E_s{}^2)^{-\frac{1}{2}}/\pi; & |E_s| < E_1 \end{cases} \quad (10\cdot52)$$

where E_1 is the peak amplitude of the sine wave. This function is graphed in Fig. 10·8 as the curve for $n = 1$. He then determines the distribution curve for the resultant instantaneous amplitudes of the combined noise and pure tone voltages from Eqs. (10·11) and (10·52), using rules of manipulation common in statistical theory. When the rectifier is linear and half-wave with a constant of proportionality a_1, the following expression is obtained:

$$I_{dc} = a_1 \frac{\sigma_e{}^2}{2\pi} e^{-P} \{I_0(P) + 2P[I_0(P) + I_1(P)]\} \quad (10\cdot53)$$

where $P = (E_1{}^2/4\sigma_e{}^2)$, $I_0(\quad)$, and $I_1(\quad)$ are complex Bessel functions, σ_e is the rms amplitude of the random noise voltage, and E_1 is the peak amplitude of the sine wave.

The information contained in Eq. (10·53) is plotted in graphical form in Fig. 10·15. The result shown is that, if two voltmeters, one square-law and the other linear, are made to read alike on pure tones, the linear will read about 1 db lower than

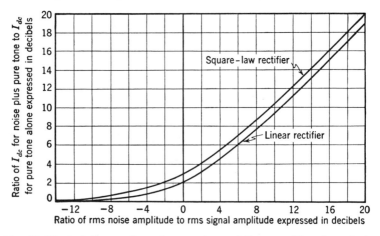

FIG. 10·15   Relative readings of square-law and linear rectifiers for a single sine wave plus random noise. (After Bennett.[11])

the square-law on random noise, as mentioned before. This result has been checked quantitatively by several observers, and one set of such comparisons is given in the next chapter.

10·8   Response of Biased and Saturated Linear and Square-Law Rectifiers to Random Noise

We have discussed the response of simple linear and quadratic (square-law) rectifiers to random noise, sine waves, and complex waves. Often we need to deal with rectifiers of a more complex nature; those which saturate at high signal levels, those which are biased so that they respond only when the input voltage exceeds some particular value, and those which are both biased and have a saturation level. In addition, the rectifier is often connected to random noise passed by a low pass, or by a wide band-pass, or by a narrow band-pass filter. A very comprehensive study of these cases has been published by Middleton.[3] He gives the spectral distribution of energies in the output of the rectifier connected to a source of random noise for each of the different filter bands just named. Although those results are very interesting, we shall confine our remarks here to the part of his analysis dealing with the d-c component in the output of rectifiers connected to sources of random noise.

The d-c component of the energy delivered at the output of the rectifier is independent of the spectral distribution of the noise at the input. That is to say, for a given voltage-current

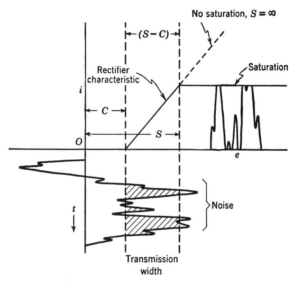

Fig. 10·16 Rectification characteristic for a linear half-wave rectifier with a cutoff level C and a saturation level S. The impressed noise is assumed to be random. (After Middleton.[3])

characteristic of the rectifier the d-c power output depends only on the mean-square voltage of the input noise. This is a very important result because for any given rectification characteristic we need only a graph of the output power *versus* the standard deviation of the input noise voltage to obtain the complete performance of a rectifier coupled to a d-c indicating meter.

The dynamic characteristics for biased and saturated, linear and quadratic rectifiers are shown in Figs. 10·16 and 10·17. The rectifiers operate at some bias such that the cutoff is C volts and saturation occurs at S volts, both measured from the operating point O as indicated in Fig. 10·16, where S always exceeds C. The transmission width is defined as $S - C$ for the linear rectifier (see Fig. 10·16) and $2(S - C)$ for the quadratic rectifier (see Fig. 10·17). We shall distinguish two quadratic characteristics, types A and B. Type B is made up of two parabolic curves joining at S as shown in Fig. 10·17. The type A quadratic rectifier (not shown) differs from type B only in that it

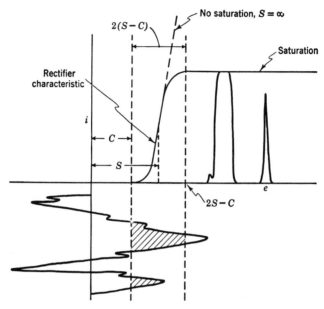

Fig. 10·17 Rectification characteristic for a type B quadratic half-wave rectifier with a cutoff level C and a saturation level $2S - C$. The type A rectifier differs from type B only in that the saturation level occurs at S, i.e., the curve levels off abruptly at S. (After Middleton.[3])

levels off abruptly at $e = S$. Mathematically, the instantaneous output currents i for the three types are:

For the linear rectifier,

$$
\begin{aligned}
i &= a_2(S - C); & S &\leq e \\
&= a_2(e - C); & C &\leq e \leq S \\
&= 0 & ; & e \leq C
\end{aligned}
\tag{10·54}
$$

For the type A quadratic rectifier,

$$
\begin{aligned}
i &= a_1(S - C)^2; & S &\leq e \\
&= a_1(e - C)^2; & C &\leq e \leq S \\
&= 0 & ; & e \leq C
\end{aligned}
\tag{10·55}
$$

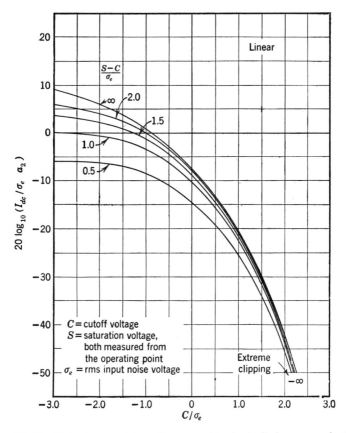

FIG. 10·18   Output current for a linear rectifier in decibels expressed relative to $a_2\sigma_e$ as a function of the ratio of C to σ_e. $(S-C)/\sigma_e$ is the parameter.   (After Middleton.[3])

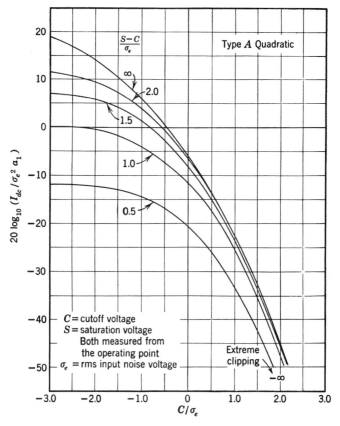

Fig. 10·19 Output current for a type A quadratic rectifier expressed relative to $a_1\sigma_e^2$ as a function of the ratio of C to σ_e. $(S - C)/\sigma_e$ is the parameter. (After Middleton.[3])

For the type B quadratic rectifier,

$$i = 2a_1(S - C)^2 \qquad\qquad ; \quad (2S - C) \leqq e$$
$$= a_1\{2(S - C)^2 - (e - 2S + C)^2\}; \quad S \leqq e \leqq (2S - C)$$
$$= a_1(e - C)^2 \qquad\qquad ; \quad C \leqq e \leqq S \qquad (10·56)$$
$$= \quad 0 \qquad\qquad\qquad ; \quad e \leqq C$$

As before, a_1 is the rectifier constant for a quadratic (square-law) rectifier characteristic, and a_2 is that for a linear rectifier characteristic.

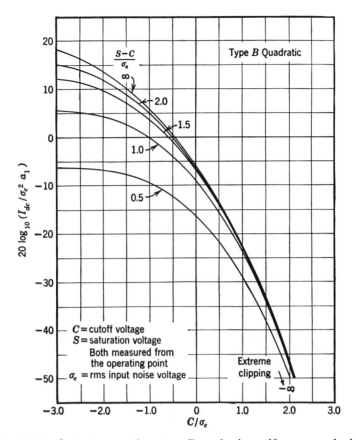

Fig. 10·20 Output current for a type B quadratic rectifier expressed relative to $a_1\sigma_e^2$ as a function of the ratio of C to σ_e. $(S - C)/\sigma_e$ is the parameter. (After Middleton.[3])

The average d-c outputs, I_{dc}, of the above three rectifier characteristics when connected to a source of random noise are portrayed in Figs. 10·18 to 10·20. Those figures are plots of $20 \log_{10} (I_{dc}/\sigma_e a_2)$ or $20 \log_{10} (I_{dc}/\sigma_e^2 a_1)$ vs. C/σ_e. The parameter is $(S - C)\sigma_e$. As before, σ_e = rms input random noise voltage, C is the cutoff voltage, and S is the saturation voltage.

11.

Indicating and Integrating Instruments for the Measurement of Complex Waves

11·1 Introduction

Most acoustical measurements involve the use of electrical indicating instruments. These instruments may take the form of voltmeters, ammeters, power meters, or graphic level recorders. They have certain static and dynamic characteristics, and associated with them are means for converting alternating waves into the deflection of a pointer or stylus or a digital register.

In selecting a meter or a recorder we usually concern ourselves with its internal impedance, its frequency limitations, the accuracy of its calibration, and its inherent stability. If we restrict ourselves to measuring sine waves, these factors are the principal ones. However, the story is different when we begin to measure complex waves such as random noise, speech, or pulses of short duration.

If we select a meter at random from a laboratory shelf its reading may differ from that of a perfect power meter because of the shape of the wave (if it is recurrent), the ratio of the peak to the rms value of the wave (whether the wave is recurrent or not), the impedance of the generator producing the wave, and the magnitude of the voltage which it supplies. For example, a common "peak" meter reads the root-mean-square (rms) value of a complex wave at low signal levels, and some value below the true peak value at higher signal levels. On bands of random noise it reads the rms value at low levels and a fixed number of decibels above rms at high levels, regardless of the bandwidth of the noise. Furthermore, its readings are strongly dependent on the impedance of the source.

This chapter discusses the principles of operation of and the factors which contribute to the performance of several types of meters. Charts are shown to relate the accuracy of the readings to the physical parameters of the instruments. The theoretical bases for these charts may be found, for the most part, in the previous chapter. There, formulas and graphs from which the output of square-law and linear devices could be determined for inputs of random noise or inharmonically related sine waves were developed.

Our first topic will be peak meters. Then we shall take up in succession average, rms, logarithmic, logarithmic ms. and *VU* meters and graphic level recorders. Finally, we shall discuss a method for measuring the integrating characteristics of any given meter.

11·2 Indicating Instruments

A. Peak Meters

Peak meters have found extensive use in electrical measurements, principally because their performance is largely independent of diode characteristics and because they are simple to construct and to duplicate. Moreover, peak meters can be made to operate reliably over a wide frequency range. For tests involving sinusoidal potentials, their readings are the same as those of either linear or quadratic types of meter if all are properly calibrated. However, for complex signals, considerable differences in readings among the three types will be found.

In its idealized form, the peak-reading voltmeter consists of two elements, a capacitance and a linear half-wave rectifier. If a sine wave is applied between the terminals 1 and 2 of the circuit of Fig. 11·1, the condenser C_b will acquire a charge during the rising part of the positive portions of the first few cycles. After that, the potential of the condenser in this idealized circuit should remain at the peak value of the driving voltage. When a high impedance voltmeter is connected across C_b, its deflection should read proportional to the peak voltage of the applied wave. In actual practice, however, these conditions are not realized. Leakage may exist between terminals 3 and 4 so that the potential across the condenser decays after a cycle has passed its positive peak. Additional current will flow through

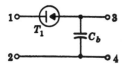

FIG. 11·1   Circuit of an idealized peak-reading voltmeter. The voltage to be measured is connected across terminals 1 and 2 and the near-peak voltage appears across terminals 3 and 4.

the rectifier into the condenser near the peak of the next positive portion of the wave. We expect, therefore, that the average potential across terminals 3 and 4 will be somewhat lower than the peak amplitude of the input wave. Let us see what leakage between terminals 3 and 4 means.

In the previous chapter we derived an expression relating the potential E_b (see Fig. 11·2) to the ratio of R_r (the effective rectifier resistance when conducting) to R_b as follows:

$$\frac{1}{E_b} \int_{E_b}^{\infty} EP(E)\,dE - \int_{E_b}^{\infty} P(E)\,dE = \frac{R_r}{R_b} \qquad (11\cdot1)$$

where R_b is the leakage resistance provided across C_b; E_b is the average voltage across the condenser C_b; E is the instantaneous value of the input voltage; $P(E)$ is the probability distribution of the instantaneous amplitudes of the input wave. The reactance of C_b is assumed to be small compared to R_b and R_r at all frequencies. It is also assumed that the impedance of the source supplying the wave is small compared to R_r. If this is not true, the source impedance must be added to R_r. The formula above will now be applied to the determination of the performance of a practical "peak" meter when measuring rectangular pulses, a number of inharmonic waves, and random noise.

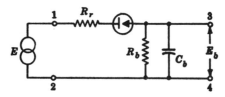

FIG. 11·2   Effective circuit of a peak-reading voltmeter. The generator E is assumed to have zero impedance. R_r is the effective resistance of the rectifier when it is conducting current. R_r also includes the resistance of the generator if it does not have zero impedance. R_b is the leakage resistance in the circuit tending to discharge the condenser C_b. The near-peak voltage E_b appears across terminals 3 and 4.

Rectangular Pulses. Let us describe a recurrent rectangular-pulse wave as one which has a period T and an amplitude E_{max}. The E_{max} value persists during a portion of the cycle equal to ΔT. As an example, a rectified *square* wave has an amplitude E_{max} which persists for a time $\Delta T = T/2$ during each period T. During the remainder of the cycle $(T - \Delta T) = T/2$ the amplitude of the wave is zero.

Now let us calculate the value of E_b from Eq. (11·1) for the rectangular wave. By definition (see Chap. 10), $P(E)dE$ is the percentage of time that the wave has a value lying between E and $E + dE$. Now $P(E)dE$ is zero at all times except when $E = E_{max}$. Hence, we can drop the integrals in Eq. (11·1) and get

$$\frac{1}{E_b}\left[E_{max}\,P(E_{max})dE\right] - P(E_{max})dE = \frac{R_r}{R_b} \qquad (11\cdot2)$$

But $P(E_{max})dE = \Delta T/T$, that is, the percentage of the time that the wave is at its peak. This quantity, $\Delta T/T$, is commonly called the duty cycle. Thus,

$$\left(\frac{E_{max}}{E_b} - 1\right)\frac{\Delta T}{T} = \frac{R_r}{R_b} \qquad (11\cdot3)$$

or

$$\frac{E_{max}}{E_b} = \frac{R_r}{R_b}\frac{T}{\Delta T} + 1 \qquad (11\cdot4)$$

This formula clearly shows that the voltage across terminals 3 and 4 of Fig. 11·2 approaches the peak value closely only if the average rectifier resistance is very small compared to the product of the duty cycle times the leakage resistance R_b. A curve of $20\log_{10}(E_b/E_{max})$ vs R_r/R_b for a rectified square wave ($\Delta T/T = 0.5$) is given in Fig. 11·3.

Inharmonic Waves. Some noise spectra are a combination of inharmonic sine waves. Hence, we are interested in knowing how a peak meter responds to such an input signal. Unfortunately, this is a very difficult problem to solve if the components have different amplitudes, as has been indicated by Bennett.[1] In order to gain an idea of the way such an input signal

[1] W. R. Bennett, "Distribution of the sum of randomly phased components," Q. Appl. Math. **5**, 385–393 (1948).

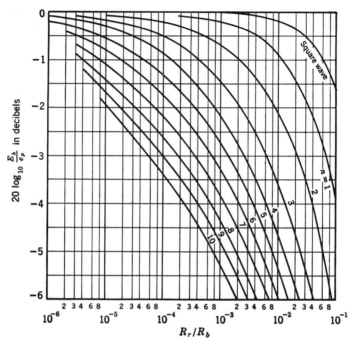

FIG. 11·3   Plot in decibels of the reading of a peak meter below the peak voltage of the sum of n inharmonically related sine waves. E_b is the voltage appearing across terminals 3 and 4 of Fig. 11·2. R_r is the effective rectifier resistance when it is conducting plus the generator resistance. R_b is the effective leakage resistance across the condenser of Fig. 11·2. E_1 is the amplitude of each of n components. e_p equals n times E_1. Because some peak meters are calibrated to read the same as rms meters when measuring sine waves, the curve for $n = 1$ should be subtracted from the other curves to obtain the true error in meter reading as a function of R_r/R_b. For purposes of this subtraction R_r must include only the generator resistance. A curve of $20 \log E_b/E_{\max}$ for square waves is included at the top for comparison.

affects the reading of the peak meter of Fig. 11·2, let us select for analysis the more simple case of n components of equal amplitude. Such a complex wave is expressed mathematically as

$$E = E_1(\cos \omega_1 t + \cos \omega_2 t + \cdots + \cos \omega_n t) \qquad (11·5)$$

where, ω_1, ω_2, ω_3, ..., ω_n are the angular frequencies of the various components, all of which have the same amplitude, E_1.

In the previous chapter we gave probability distributions, $P(E)$, for different numbers of waves ranging from $n = 1$ to $n = 12$. From these values, the ratio of the voltage E_b (see Fig. 11·2) to the peak value of the combination of n waves e_p, can be computed, where

$$e_p = nE_1 \qquad (11\cdot6)$$

The results are shown in Fig. 11·3. The coordinates of that graph are $20 \log(E_b/e_p)$ in decibels vs the ratio of R_r to R_b. As before, R_r is the effective rectifier resistance while it is conducting plus the generator resistance, and R_b is the total leakage resistance across C_b.

The reader should remember that the value of the effective rectifier resistance R_r is a function of the amplitude and of the shape of the wave. The sharper the peaks, the lower is the value of R_r, as one can convince himself by looking at a current vs voltage curve for a small signal rectifier. He also must remember that the impedance of the source adds in with the effective value of the rectifier resistance R_r. If R_r plus the source impedance approach $0.01R_b$, startling inaccuracies will result, as can be seen from Fig. 11·3. Therefore, in the use of peak meters, high impedance sources and range multipliers preceding the meter must be avoided.

Factors other than the magnitude of R_r plus the source impedance enter into the accuracy of "peak" meter readings. At very low signal levels rectifier characteristics may be quadratic. This means that the meter will read the rms value of the applied wave rather than the peak. At very low frequencies the reactance of the condenser C_b will not be small compared to R_b. As a result the readings will be lowered. For an understanding of the performance at low frequencies with sine waves, the reader is referred to an article by Schade.[2] For most complex waves, the requirements on the $R_b C_b$ product are severe.

Tuttle[3] utilized the arrangement of Fig. 11·4 in a voltmeter

[2]O. H. Schade, "Analysis of rectifier operation," Proc. Inst. Radio Engrs. **31**, 341–361 (1943).

[3]W. Tuttle, "Type 726-A vacuum tube voltmeter," General Radio Experimenter **11**, 12 (May, 1937).

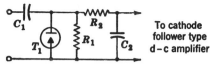

Fig. 11·4 Schematic circuit diagram of a practical peak-reading voltmeter. (After Tuttle.[3])

which has found wide use. In essence this is the same circuit as that of Fig. 11·2, provided the reverse resistance of the rectifier is large compared to R_1 and the effective forward resistance R_r is small compared to R_1. The principal difference between the two circuits is that a dc leakage path must be provided through the generator in the case of Fig. 11·2, whereas such is not necessary in the case of Fig. 11·4. The condenser C_1 is analogous to C_b of Fig. 11·2, and R_1 is analogous to R_b. In Tuttle's instrument, the resistances R_1 and R_2 have values of the order of 50 and 10 megohms, respectively.

R_1 is provided to permit the discharge of the condensers C_1 and C_2 when the input voltage is changed. The combination of R_2 and C_2 acts to filter the ac component of the voltage from the input to the dc amplifier. The condenser C_1 will build up a charge until its potential is nearly equal to the peak value of the positive part of the cycle of the applied alternating voltage. When equilibrium is reached, the rectifier will conduct current only during a very short period of time near the crest of the applied voltage. Hence, the voltage which appears across R_1 (and the diode) is the applied alternating source in series with a negative steady potential. Once a steady state is reached, no direct current will flow through C_2, and, hence, R_2 becomes a shunt across the input to alternating current. The power absorbed by the rectifier can be calculated as follows: The applied alternating voltage appears across the parallel combination of R_1 and R_2 and the power lost in that form can readily be calculated from the equation

$$\frac{e_g^2 R_1 R_2 (R_1 + R_2)}{[R_g(R_1 + R_2) + R_1 R_2]^2}.$$

In addition, the dc potential on C_1 appears across R_1. This loss is taken from the applied voltage in the form of a pulse of current near the peak of each positive half-cycle. Because of the shortness and the magnitude of these pulses of current through the rectifier, resistance in the source reduces seriously the flow of rectified current and lowers correspondingly the meter reading. For example, if R_1 equals 50 megohms and the source resistance R_g equals 4 megohms, the ratio of the effective resistance of the rectifier R_r plus R_g to R_1 plus R_g will be about 0.07. Reference to Fig. 11·3 shows that for a sine wave and a ratio of R_r/R_b of 0.07, the developed voltage will be down 3.0 dB from the peak. In addition there is another 3.0-dB loss from the resistance loading to alternating current so that the meter reading will be halved. That such a reduction in meter reading actually occurs is confirmed by Tuttle. For two sine waves and R_g equal to 4 megohms, the reduction would be about 8 dB, whereas for random noise the meter would indicate 2 dB above the rms instead of about 11 db—a reduction of 9 dB. As in all nonlinear circuits, the impedance of the source cannot be neglected in the analysis of the circuit performance.

Random Noise on Peak Meters. The root-mean-square magnitude of a sine wave can be determined by a peak meter simply by multiplying the reading by 0.707 or subtracting 3 dB. Also, it was stated in Chap. 10 (Ref. 10 there) that if a normal peak meter (R_b/R_r between 10^3 and 10^4) is used to measure a random noise, the reading will be about 12 dB above the rms value of the noise. Less well understood, however, is that if the constants of the circuit of Fig. 11·2 are properly chosen, the instrument will read the root-mean-square value of a number of other signals correctly. These are combinations of inharmonic sine waves, random noise and square waves. No data are available on impulse noise, but it is expected that the modified circuit will not read correctly, although the error may not be too large for recorded loop playbacks of impulsive sounds if the crest factor (ratio of the peak to rms values) is not too high.

From Eq. (11·1) we can determine the interrelations among R_r/R_b, E_b, E, and $P(E)$. This equation assumes that the reactance of the capacitor C is small compared to R_r and R_b at all frequencies of the input wave of interest. When Eq. (11·1) is valued for random noise, we get the lower curve of Fig. 11·5. In the lower curve, for each point, the value of E_b was plotted as if the meter were calibrated to read the rms voltage of a sine wave (even though it would actually be responding to something approaching the peak value of the sine wave at that point). The ordinate of the plot is the ratio of the reading on a modified peak

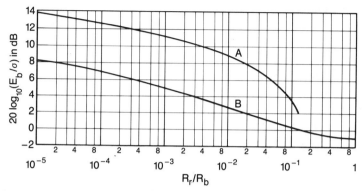

FIG. 11·5 Plot in decibels of the reading of a peak meter above the rms amplitude σ of random noise as a function of R_r/R_b. See the legend of Fig. 11·2 for definition of terms. The upper curve applies to the true ratio of E_b/σ. The lower curve applies to meters as ordinarily calibrated, that is to say, when the calibration is such that the indication is equal to that of an rms meter when measuring sine waves.

meter to the true rms voltage of the random noise, in dB. We see that if the value of the ratio R_b/R_r equals about 8, the true rms value of a random noise will be read. The readings will be equally valid for inharmonically related sine waves, because their response falls in the same family of curves, of which random noise is the limit (see Fig. 11·3).

Peterson[4] took a peak meter of 1956 and placed resistors first in series with R_r (10k to 100k ohms) and then in parallel with the 125 megohm resistor R_b to obtain the various values of R_b/R_r shown on Fig. 11·5. The data fell on the calculated curve. He concludes that popular types of peak meters of that day, could easily be adapted to easily read rms values of random noise simply by connecting the proper value of a large resistance in series with the input terminal.

B. Average Meters

Many audio-frequency electronic meters read something akin to the average amplitude of the impressed wave after it has been linearly rectified. In the preceding chapter it was stated that when a linear half-wave rectifier is connected to a ran-

[4]A. P. G. Peterson, "Response of peak meters to random noise," General Radio Experimenter **7** (December 1956).

dom noise voltage its reading will be 1 dB *lower* than that of a square-law meter. This difference in meter reading is about the same for combinations of inharmonic waves, although the exact value can be computed from the equation

$$E_{\mathrm{av}} = \int_0^\infty EP(E)\,dE. \qquad (11\cdot7)$$

Here E_{av} is the average amplitude of the wave; E is the instantaneous amplitude; and $P(E)$ is the probability distribution of the instantaneous amplitudes for the rectified wave. Values of $P(E)$ for combinations of n inharmonic sine waves and for random noise were given in the previous chapter. Because accuracies greater than 1 dB are frequently not desired, except when measuring pure tones, no great effort has been made on the part of experimenters to distinguish between rms and average indicating instruments when reporting data. Parenthetically it should be noted that the calibrations of the two types of meters are always made so that they read alike on pure tones.

The simplest type of average indicating instrument consists of a half-wave rectifier connected in series with a resistor and a milliammeter (see Fig. 11·6). This arrangement will not be truly linear because of the curvature of the characteristic near the origin (see Fig. 11·6a). The use of a very large resistance R or of large signal voltages or both will make the readings approach their theoretical average value. The usual method of design is to plot the diode characteristic (i vs e) from the published characteristics or from measurements. Then, with arbitrary values of added resistance, new functions are plotted by adding the voltage drop in the external resistance to that of the rectifier for a range of values of the input voltage. This done, one can

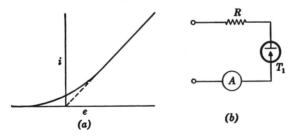

FIG. 11·6 (a) Output current vs input voltage characteristic of a diode rectifier. (b) Schema of an average-reading voltmeter.

choose the resistance according to the degree of linearity desired. Such a procedure has been outlined by Laport.[5]

Ballantine[6] developed a meter using electrical feedback which removes to a large degree the curvature of the rectification characteristic near the origin. This is accomplished by means of the circuit shown in Fig. 11·7. The linearization of the rectifier characteristic is accomplished as follows: The rectifier current I_2 is a function of the grid-cathode voltage of T_1; that is,

$$I_2 = f_1(E_1) . \tag{11·8}$$

The function of $f_1(E_1)$ is the characteristic of the amplifier and the rectifier. If R_1 is small compared to the reciprocal of the transconductance of the tube,

$$E_1 = E_0 - R_1 I_2 \tag{11·9}$$

so that

$$I_2 = \frac{E_0 - E_1}{R_1} . \tag{11·10}$$

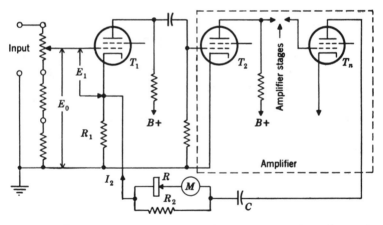

FIG. 11·7 Schematic circuit diagram of an average-reading electronic voltmeter in which inverse feedback is employed to linearize the rectification characteristic and to produce stability of operation. (After Ballantine.[6])

[5]E. A. Laport, "Linear rectifier design calculations," RCA Review **3**, 121–124 (1938).

[6]S. Ballantine, "Electronic voltmeter using feedback," Electronics **11**, 33–35 (September 1938).

The desired linear relationship between I_2 and E_0 is shown graphically in Fig. 11·8. Equations (11·8) and (11·10) are shown graphically in Fig. 11·8a; R_1 is assumed to be equal to unity. From the intersection of the curves for these two formulas at a given current I_2, the corresponding value of E_0 is determined, and the points of Fig. 11·8b are obtained. If the constants of Eqs. (11·8) and (11·10) are properly adjusted, the value of I_2 vs E_0 just determined will be the linear function desired. The feedback arrangement of Fig. 11·7 also tends to stabilize the amplifying circuit so that aging of tubes and fluctuations in supply voltage have only a minor effect on the calibration.

Stevens[7] describes still another compensating arrangement for achieving linear rectification. His circuit makes use of diode rectifier disks arranged in the form of a bridge as shown in Fig. 11·9a. The element sizes shown are his. During each half-cycle, a pair of the rectifying elements will be conducting, and the junction between the 500- and 20 000-ohm resistors will always be positive. This condition can be represented by the equivalent circuit of (b), the input voltage being a series of positive half-sine waves e_1. If $R_2 \gg R_1$, the voltage e_2 will be

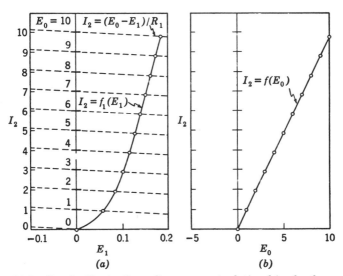

FIG. 11·8 Graphs illustrating voltage-current relationships for the meter of Fig. 11·7.

[7] S. S. Stevens, "Rectilinear rectification applied to voltage integration," Electronics **15**, 40–41 (January 1942).

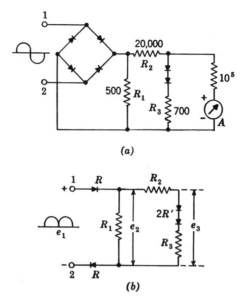

(a)

(b)

FIG. 11·9 Schematic circuit diagram of an average-reading voltmeter employing diode disks. The circuit is designed to linearize the rectification characteristic and to produce stability of operation. (After Stevens.[9])

$$e_2 = \frac{R_1 e_1}{R_1 + 2R}. \tag{11·11}$$

The current through R_2 will equal

$$i_2 = \frac{e_2}{R_2 + R_3 + 2R'}, \tag{11·12}$$

and

$$e_3 = i_2(R_3 + 2R'). \tag{11·13}$$

Combining (11·11), (11·12), and (11·13) yields

$$e_3 = \frac{(R_3 + 2R')R_1 e_1}{(R_1 + 2R)(R_2 + R_3 + 2R')}. \tag{11·14}$$

If $R_1 \doteq R_3$, $R \doteq R'$, and if $R_1 \langle\langle R_2 \rangle\rangle 2R'$, then

$$e_3 \doteq e_1 \frac{R_1}{R_2}. \tag{11·15}$$

The desired linear relationship is evident from this equation.
The linear relationship between e_3 and e_1 of Eq. (11·15) will

hold only if the source impedance is zero. If an impedance R_s is inserted between the generator e_1 and the input terminal 1, the value of R_3 must be increased to $R_3 \doteq (R_1 + R_s)$, as can be seen from Eq. (11·14). This fact probably explains why Stevens chose R_3 to be greater than R_1. It is emphasized again that one important consequence of nonlinear circuits is that the source impedance enters into their performance in a way that precludes the use of "simulated" zero-impedance sources* in analyzing or measuring their characteristics.

It should also be noted that the circuit of Fig. 11·9 removes the effects of frequency and temperature, in addition to waveform distortion, because variations in R which are accompanied by similar variations in R' will not affect the ratio of e_3 to e_1. This is an important improvement because the resistance of some rectifying elements is a function of frequency and temperature. A person might think that no nonlinear element remains to provide rectification in the circuit. Actually, the rectifying bridge acts as a reversing switch, with the reversal taking place in nearly zero time if R_2 is large enough.

C. Root-Mean-Square Meters

Mean-square voltage and sound pressure measurements are of fundamental importance in acoustics, because electric power and acoustic intensity are directly proportional to them in many measurement situations. Because the mean-square power or intensity of a continuous-spectrum random noise is directly proportional to the bandwidth, a spectrum determined by using a filter having a certain bandwidth can easily be converted to yield spectra of other bandwidths. A very common conversion of this type is from octave-band or third-octave-band levels to spectrum levels.

In the original (1949) text, rms measuring instruments were restricted to vacuum thermocouples, which are very delicate and easily damaged by overload, and copper-oxide disks. Today, there are modern analog instruments, which will be discussed in this chapter, and digital microprocessors which can measure accurately the rms level of complex signals, including those with relatively high crest factors.

*A "simulated" zero impedance source is, for linear circuits, a source whose open-circuit voltage is continuously adjusted as a function of frequency, so that the voltage it produces across a load of varying impedance is constant.

Analog RMS Detectors

Peak-Meter Modification. In the section on "Random noise on peak meters" above we learned that the circuit constant can be selected, as Fig. 11·5 shows, to convert a peak meter in an rms meter. When the instrument is calibrated to read the rms value of a sine wave correctly, it will also read correctly all combinations of inharmonically related sine waves, random noise and repetitive pulsed and square waves. Although no analysis is available, rms value of isolated impulses read on such an instrument may not be accurate unless a repetitive recorded playback of the transient is made. A logarithmic transfer circuit will be necessary if a meter that reads in decibels is desired.

Mean-Square Detector (MS Detector)

One type of mean-square detector that has found large usage is presented here because it leads logically to the next type to be described. It is diagramed in Fig. 11·10. The resistor R_1 includes the resistance of the meter. Using a squaring device with the characteristic shown, a current i will be produced which is proportional to V^2. Mathematically, this relation is described by the equation for a parabula,

$$i = pV^2. \qquad (11·16)$$

The value of p, a constant, can be chosen to yield one of a family of parabolas. In Fig. 11·11 such a family is shown with $p = 1, p = 1/2, p = 1/5$ and $p = 1/10$. The choice of p will depend on the peak amplitude in volts of the impressed signal. A large crest (ratio of peak to rms) factor on a portion of the waves

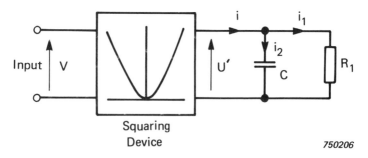

Squaring
Device   750206

FIG. 11·10   Sketch illustrating how the differential equation for a "direct"-type squaring device can be derived. (Courtesy of Bruel and Kjaer.)

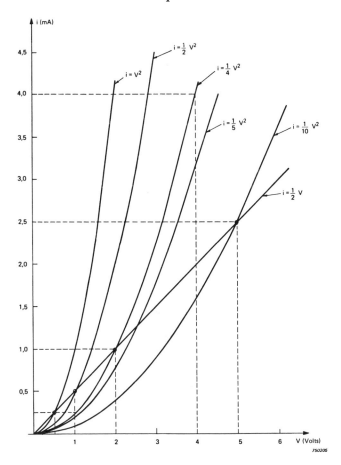

FIG. 11·11   Parabolas with different parameters, p. (Courtesy of Bruel and Kjaer.)

measured requires a squaring function that is truly parabolic over a very wide range of impressed voltages.

In practice, the parabolic function is generally comprised of a series of straight-line segments produced electronically in some manner like that of Fig. 11·12(a). Here, a series of five diodes are shown, each permanently biased by means of a fixed dc voltage. Whenever the input voltage exceeds the bias voltage for a particular diode, it conducts. Thus, the parabola shown in Fig. 11·12(b) is constructed of a number of linear segments. To

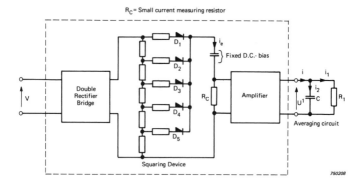

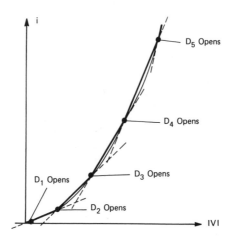

FIG. 11·12   Method for approximating the parabolic characteristic of the squaring device. (*a*) electronic circuitry, (*b*) output current, *i*, which is proportional to the mean-square of the input voltage, *V*. (Courtesy of Bruel & Kjaer.)

obtain full wave rectification, a quadruple-diode bridge circuit of the type shown in Fig. 11·9 is used.

From Fig. 11·12, we see that

$$i = i_1 + i_2 , \qquad\qquad (11\cdot17a)$$

$$i_1 = U'/R_1 , \qquad\qquad (11\cdot17b)$$

and

$$i_2 = C(dU'/dt) \, . \qquad (11\cdot17c)$$

Then,

$$pV^2 = \frac{U'}{R_1} + C\frac{dU'}{dt} \qquad (11\cdot18)$$

Let, $k = pR_1$ (a constant)

$$kV^2 = U' + R_1C\frac{dU'}{dt} \qquad (11\cdot19)$$

Inspection shows that when V is steady, i.e., $dU'/dt = 0$, U' will equal the mean square of the input voltage, i.e., V^2. When V is a fluctuating continuous signal (periodic or random), U' is also proportional to the mean-square voltage V^2, but averaged over a time period set by the product R_1C, which is the time constant of the circuit.

Because most measurements require the *root*-mean-square (rms) value of V, a square rooting operation must be performed. This can be done by marking the scale of the indicating meter accordingly, but the rms markings then become very nonlinear, especially if a logarithmic marking is also desired in combination. However, a simple solution exists to this problem of achieving both the rms value of V and a linear scale.[8]

Root-Mean-Square Detector (RMS Detector)

Let us return to Fig. $11\cdot12(a)$. Let us take a part of the voltage across C and feed it back into the squaring device. Simply stated, this operation would work as follows,

$$MS/RMS = RMS \, , \qquad (11\cdot20)$$

where RMS, here, is the rms output voltage which, when fed back, acts as the divisor for what would otherwise be the MS output voltage. This apparent bootstrap operation is accomplished by the revised circuit of Fig. $11\cdot13$.

In the feedback circuit, the former constant, p, for a single parabola, now is a sequence of values for a family of "sliding" parabolas,

---

[8]C. G. Wahrmann and J. T. Broch, "On the Averaging Time of RMS Measurements," Bruel and Kjaer, No. 2, 1975, and "Averaging Time of RMS Instruments," No. 3, 1975, Bruel and Kjaer Instruments, Inc., 185 Forest Street, Marlborough, MA 01752.

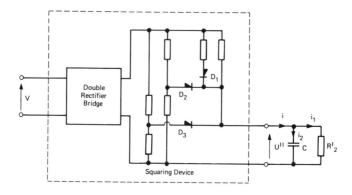

FIG. 11·13   Electronic circuit used to produce a "gliding parabola" characteristic and an output current, i, which is proportional to the root-mean-square of the input voltage, V. (Courtesy of Bruel & Kjaer.)

$$p = \frac{K}{U''} \tag{11·21}$$

where K is a constant.

As before, Eqs. (11·16) and (11·17) hold. So,

$$\frac{KV^2}{U''} = \frac{U''}{R_2} + C\frac{dU''}{dt} \tag{11·22}$$

or,

$$KV^2 = \frac{(U'')^2}{R_2} + \frac{C}{2}\frac{d(U'')^2}{dt}. \tag{11·23}$$

If we let $k_2 = KR_2$, Eq. (11·23) becomes,

$$k_2 V^2 = (U'')^2 + \frac{CR_2}{2}\frac{d(U'')^2}{dt} \tag{11·24}$$

Equations (11·24) and (11·19) are of the same form, except that U' is proportional to the mean-square voltage, while U'' is proportional to the root-mean-square voltage. Also, a linear scale results, because U'' (rms) is directly proportional to V when $dU''/dt = 0$. As before, U'' is also proportional to the rms values of a continuum fluctuating signal, but averaged over a time period set by the product $R_2C/2$.

Averaging of RMS and MS Signals

In both types of detector shown in Figs. 11·12 and 11·13, averaging of a continuous fluctuating signal was accomplished with an RC circuit. We note, however, that

$$R_2C \text{ [feedback circuit]} = 2R_1C \text{ [direct circuit]} (11 \cdot 25)$$

This means that when we discuss the characteristics of an RC averaging circuit, as shown in Fig. 11·2, we must let C in it equal $C/2$ in (Fig. 11·13).

An RC averaging circuit behaves like a low-pass filter, whose upper cut-off frequency $(3 = dB$ down$)$ is

$$f_0 = 1/(2\pi RC) (11 \cdot 26a)$$

and

$$T = 1/(\pi f_0) = 2RC. (11 \cdot 26b)$$

Wahrmann and Brock have gone into great detail to explain how an RC averaging network behaves on transient signals. On relatively slowly varying signals, the bandwidth shown by Eq. (11·26) above, is adequate to yield an average output that is near the true integrated output over some reasonable time period. However, when a very short impulse is applied to the circuit, the bandwidth should be about twice that indicated above.

For example, there is no difference between (a) true integration/averaging and (b) RC-weighted averaging of a rectangular pulse, with a circuit bandwidth, f_0, as given by Eq. (11·26) above, provided that the time constant T is at least 10 times the effective width of the pulse t_x. If $T/t_x = 2$ or less, the bandwidth, f_0, should be twice as large. For $2 > (T/t_x) < 10$ the averaging error for f_0 given in Eq. (11·26) is 1 dB at most.

Logarithmic-mean-square detector (LMS Detector)

Sound levels are measured in decibels. In order to provide a linear scale for an indicating meter reading in decibels, the logarithm of the root-mean-square output of the detector is needed, which we shall call E_{out}, or simply, E_0.

Wahrmann[9] derives a new linear differential equation of the same form as Eqs. (11·19) and (11·24), by substituting in Eq. (11·18),

$$E_0 = x \log_e U'; \quad U' = e^{E_0/x}. (11 \cdot 27)$$

With rearrangement, this yields

---

[9] C. G. Wahrmann, "The correctness of RMS and LMS circuits," 1976 (communicated privately to the author in 1987).

$$\frac{xpV^2}{e^{E_0/x}} = i_2 = \frac{x}{R_1} + C\frac{dE_0}{dt}. \tag{11·28}$$

Again, the left side is made dependent on the output voltage E_0 [see Eq. (11·22) for comparison]. The right side of Eq. (11·28) is a first order linear differential equation, but the first term is a constant. This equation can also be expressed as

$$xp\exp\left(\frac{2x\log_e e - E_0}{x}\right) = i_2 = \frac{x}{R_1} + C\frac{dE_0}{dt}. \tag{11·29}$$

The circuit of Fig. 11·14 is derived from this equation.

In Fig. 11·14, the resistor R_1 has been replaced by a constant current source I. The time constant is determined by the ratio $(Cx/I) = (RC) = (T_{av}/2)$, and $E_0 = x\log U'$.

The value of E_0 will be correct, except when V is a suddenly-applied large signal, which would call for a very large increase in i_2. This demand requires that the circuit of Fig. 11·14 have a higher crest factor capability than the circuit of Fig. 11·12.

As we shall discuss in Chap. 20, the Sound Level Meter, we often want to determine the logarithm of the long-time average mean-square of a varying input signal, V. This is designated in the international and USA standards as L_{eq}, in dB.

In today's instruments, the LMS or RMS output, E_0 or U'', is followed by a periodic sampler. A reconversion circuit is required to convert E_0 back into mean-square-amplitudes. The sampled MS amplitudes are added and divided by the total number of samples. Finally, a log converter is needed to obtain L_{eq}. The sampler can also be placed after the reconversion circuit.

If the input signal consists of a single or a few short pulses, errors will occur if the sampling rate is too low compared to the reciprocal averaging time of the MS or LMS circuit. The solution, of course, is to use a higher sampling rate or to reduce the averaging time, or both.

11·3 Graphic Level Recorder

The widespread use of computers has resulted in the availability of dozens of different types of recorders, printers and plotters. These divide themselves into a number of writing categories: ink-pen (direct contact); ink-jet; laser; daisy-wheel (impact); stylus on waxed paper; heated stylus on thermal or

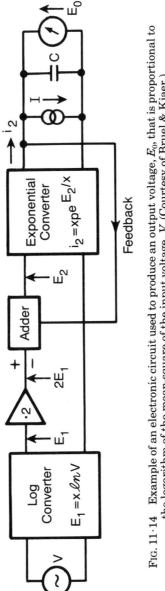

FIG. 11·14 Example of an electronic circuit used to produce an output voltage, E_0, that is proportional to the logarithm of the mean-square of the input voltage, V. (Courtesy of Bruel & Kjaer.)

waxed paper; multi-pen, multi-color, and so forth. There are several paper-handling categories, continuous feed; step-wise feed; strip chart; fixed X-Y; and others. Some recorders are lightweight battery operated; others are made for fixed laboratory use. No attempt is made here to review all the varieties.

One common level recorder, which is of the continuous-feed strip-chart type, is shown in block diagram form in Fig. 11·15. When measuring sound levels, it is usually preceded by a sound level meter, the output of which is usually a fully-processed dc signal proportional to the sound pressure wave at the microphone.

The input signal to the level recorder passes through a logarithmic attenuator whose maximum acceptable input voltage is usually under 50V rms or dc. If the signal is ac, it next passes through a logarithmic rms detector with a variable averaging time. The time constant of the averaging circuit may range from 0.01 sec to several seconds. This range covers recording of reverberation times (relatively small averaging time), through the recording of continuous random noise (longer averaging time) and up to recording of vibration signals (very-long averaging time.)

The heart of the recorder is an "error" amplifier whose input is governed by two input dc signals. One input signal is the dc output of the ac detector or the dc amplifier. The other output is from a servo-potentiometer, whose position is determined by the position of the recording pen on the strip chart.

As shown in the figure, the output of the error amplifier goes to a free-moving coil on a magnetic drive system. The coil moves in a uniform magnetic field and its direction of movement is determined by the direction of flow of the current through it.

The speed of movement of the pen depends on the rate of response of the output amplifier to a sudden change in voltage from the error amplifier. Writing speeds commonly vary from one to several thousand mm/sec, with maximum acceleration of about 100 m/sec^2.

The drive coil is connected mechanically to the pen or stylus and either directly or by servo to the servo-potentiometer. When a change in dc voltage is sensed by the error amplifier, it will become unbalanced and will send direct current to the drive coil. The resulting movement causes the voltage from the

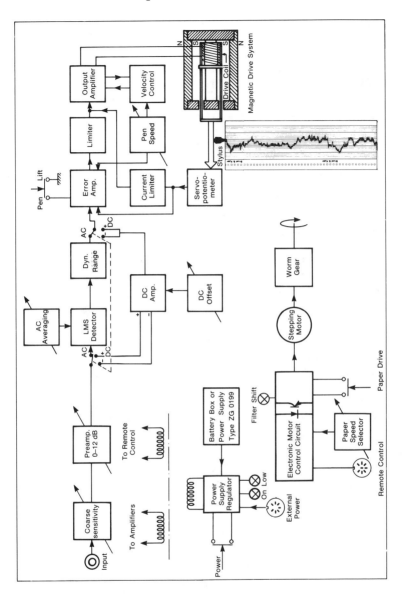

FIG. 11·15   Block diagram of a typical commercially available strip-chart
level recorder. (Courtesy of Bruel & Kjaer.)

servo-potentiometer to increase (or decrease) in the same direction as the change of input voltage. When the voltages from the two inputs are equal, the output of the error amplifier is zero and the movement of the pen stops.

The paper speed can be controlled precisely by a crystal oscillator and a variety of speeds are usually possible. Ranges of paper speed might be from 0.01 mm/sec up to 100 mm/sec.

11·4 Miscellaneous Instruments

A. *VU* Meter

The *VU* meter[10] is an instrument especially designed for use at telephone and radio terminals by engineers who monitor the transmission of speech and musical programs. It is calibrated in decibels with respect to a power of 1 mw in R ohms for a frequency of 1000 Hz. The preferred value of R for calibration is 600 or 150 ohms. A special type of meter scale is specified as well as a preferred rectification characteristic and dynamic response of the indicating needle. Readings from the meter are expressed in *vu* (volume units) to avoid confusion with other types of meters calibrated in decibels with respect to arbitrary reference powers.

The principal uses which a *VU* meter is expected to serve are:

(*a*) Indication of a suitable level which will avoid distortion of the wave in transmission through amplifiers or the like.

(*b*) Checking of the transmission losses or gains in an extended program network by simultaneous measurements at a number of points on particular peaks or impulses of the program wave which is being transmitted.

(*c*) Indication of the comparative loudness with which programs will be heard when finally converted to sound.

(*d*) Indication of a satisfactory level to avoid tripping of protective overload devices in the system.

(*e*) Sine wave transmission measurements.

Human judgment tests show that the readings taken on an rms or average type of meter are almost as satisfactory in indicating the onset of waveform distortion in a speech or music

---

[10]American National Standard, "Practice for volume measurements of electrical speech and program waves," ANSI C16.5-1954 (R-1961), American National Standards Institute.

transmission system as are readings taken on a peak-indicating instrument. This fact is also indicated on a theoretical basis by the graphs shown earlier in this chapter. That is, if by some independent test the level at which distortion takes place has been determined, the rms or average meter will show that overload point on transient sounds as well as will a "peak"-indicating meter. Of more importance, however, is the fact that rms or average instruments give more accurate indications of the power gain of a transmission system [see (*b*) above] than does a peak-indicating instrument. No advantage of one type of meter over another is found in connection with item (*c*) above. Item (*d*) is probably not of as great importance as item (*b*). Item (*e*) will be served equally well by any one of the three types. Hence, an essentially average indicating type of rectifier has been specified for incorporation in the *VU* meter. This selection makes it possible to use a copper oxide type of rectifier with the attendant advantages of low cost, ruggedness, and elimination of power supply.

Other points of importance in the design of the *VU* meter have to do with visual comfort and the selection of a suitable reference level. All factors taken together have resulted in the following specifications:

Rectifier. The volume indicator must employ a full-wave rectifier, and it must read average ($i = e_{in}$) or something near, ($i = e_{in}^{1.2}$ maximum).

Scales. The face of the instrument shall have the two scales shown in Fig. 11·16, one of which shall be displayed prominently. (A special coloring of the scale and numerals and the method

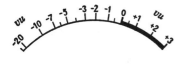

FIG. 11·16 Scales for *VU* meters. Both scales may be printed on the dial of a single meter with either in the upper (preferred) position. The colors of the letters and the background are also prescribed.

for combining the scales are also specified, but those details are beyond the interest of this text.)

Dynamic Characteristics. If a 1000-cps voltage of such amplitude as to give a steady reading of 100 on the voltage scale is suddenly applied, the pointer should reach 99 in 0.3 sec and should overswing the 100 point by at least 1.0 and not more than 1.5 percent. This corresponds to near-critical damping.

Response vs Frequency. The sensitivity of the volume-indicator instrument shall not depart from that at 1000 cps by more than 0.2 dB between 35 and 10,000 cps or more than 0.5 dB between 25 and 16,000 cps.

Calibration. The reading of the *VU* meter shall be zero *vu* when it is connected across an *R*-ohm resistance in which there is dissipated 1 mw of sine wave power at 1000 cps, or *n vu* when the calibrating power is *n* dB above 1 mw.

Impedance. For bridging across an *R*-ohm line, the impedance shall be at least $12.5R$ when measured with a sinusoidal voltage sufficient to deflect the pointer to the 0-*vu* or the 100 mark on the scale. Of this impedance, not over half can be in the rectifier plus the indicating instrument, which means that half must be in the form of a pure resistor.

B. Grassot Fluxmeter

The Grassot fluxmeter is useful in the integration of voltages and currents over relatively long intervals of time (5 to 30 sec).[11] It employs a coil moving in a magnetic field, as do other types of galvanometer. Its peculiar characteristics are that the torque tending to return the coil to its rest position is as small as possible. It is always highly damped in use by means of low circuit resistance, and the suspension is of necessity not of the pivot type, in order to keep the frictional resistance down. Generally a silk fiber is used as the suspension for the moving coil.

Dunn has shown that the average value of a voltage applied to the terminals of a Grassot fluxmeter during the time between $t = 0$ and $t = T$ is given by

$$\int_0^T e\,dt = A\theta_{t'} + \frac{DR}{A} \int_0^{t'} \theta\,dt \qquad (11\cdot30)$$

[11]H. K. Dunn, "The Grassot fluxmeter as a quantity meter," Rev. Sci. Instr. **10**, 368–370 (1939).

where A is a constant equal to the product of the field strength, coil area, and number of turns; D is the restoring torque; R is the resistance of the circuit; $\theta_{t'}$ is the total angular displacement at the time t'; and t' is a period of time longer than T. The time t' is that at which the moving coil finally comes to rest after the removal of the voltage e. Thus, Eq. (11·30) shows that the deflection is proportional to the integral of the generated voltage, except for the drift error represented by the last term associated with the restoring torque.

In use, the fluxmeter must be at rest both at the beginning and at the end of the interval of measurement and must remain in a circuit of constant resistance during the interval. The drift error is made as small as possible by keeping D and R small and A large. In one instrument tested by Dunn, the maximum drift error was found to be 4 percent in an interval of 30 sec, the meter resistance being 50 ohms and the total circuit resistance 20 ohms.

If it is known that e is somewhat evenly distributed over the entire interval, although it may vary widely over shorter portions of it, the error will then be not greatly different from that obtained with constant voltage in the same interval. If e is so distributed, a point-by-point calibration with constant voltages reduces the error to a minimum.

C. Vacuum Thermocouple

As described in 1949, the vacuum thermocouple has been developed and is available commercially in a wide range of sizes. Its chief advantage is that the dc output is proportional to the square of the instantaneous current in the heater over a wide range of input currents. Its chief disadvantages are that it is fragile and that it burns out with a very slight overload. Generally, the vacuum thermocouple is employed as a transducer in precision voltmeters used for measuring the rms amplitude of steady-state voltages. Occasionally, it is used in a ballistic manner; that is, short pulses of current give maximum deflections of a galvanometer which are nearly proportional to the total energy of the pulse.

Dunn[12] has shown that if irregular currents, such as those

---

[12]H. K. Dunn, "Use of thermocouple and fluxmeter for measurement of average power of irregular waves," Rev. Sci. Instr. **10**, 362–367 (1939).

produced in a telephone by speech, are passed through the heater of a vacuum thermocouple, the integral of the direct voltage or current in the output over a sufficiently long period of time is proportional to the total energy dissipated in the heater. To show this, Dunn makes the following assumptions: (a) The time rate of heat production in the thermocouple is proportional to the square of the instantaneous current in the heater. (b) The rate of loss of heat follows Newton's law, that is, is proportional to the difference of first powers of heater temperature and ambient temperature. (c) The rate of temperature rise is proportional to the net rate of heat gain. (d) The couple voltage is proportional to the temperature difference between hot and cold junctions.

Assumption (b) will fail beyond some limiting temperature, where loss by radiation begins to bring the difference of fourth powers into prominence.

The first three assumptions combined give the differential equation

$$\frac{d\theta}{dt} = c_1 i^2 - c_2 \theta \qquad (11 \cdot 31)$$

where θ is the temperature difference, i is the instantaneous heater current, t is the time, and c_1 and c_2 are constants. The solution for the temperature at the time t_1 is

$$\theta = c_1 e^{-c_2 t_1} \int_0^{t_1} e^{c_2 t} i^2 dt . \qquad (11 \cdot 32)$$

When assumption (d) is added,

$$e_c = c_3 \theta = c_1 c_3 e^{-c_2 t_1} \int_0^{t_1} e^{c_2 t} i^2 dt , \qquad (11 \cdot 33)$$

where e_c is the open-circuit voltage developed in the couple, and c_3 is a constant.

First, let us consider the case of a steady-state current i in the heater, where i equals I_{dc} if there is no alternating component, or it equals $I/\sqrt{2}$ if the current is cosinusoidal with a peak amplitude I. From Eq. (11·33), with t_1 large,

$$e_c = \frac{c_1 c_3}{c_2} i^2 , \qquad (11 \cdot 34)$$

or, if the output circuit resistance is R,

$$i_c = \frac{c_1 c_3}{c_2 R} i^2 \equiv k i^2 . \qquad (11 \cdot 35)$$

Dunn tested experimentally the relationship in Eq. (11·35) for a vacuum thermocouple using a carbon heater with a resistance of 1000 ohms and a couple resistance of 12 ohms. The nature of the results is shown in Fig. 11·17. The response is nearly linear until the input power reaches a value of about 2.5 mw. Beyond this value the deviations from linearity are large. The limiting factor here is the corresponding large temperature of the heater θ. If instantaneous high values of the input current to a thermocouple occur, Eq. (11·35) will remain valid provided they are of sufficiently short duration not to raise the relative temperature of the thermocouple beyond the limiting value indicated by the break in the static characteristic from linearity. To prove this, Dunn determined the linear range of the same thermocouple by using pulses of known duration and repetition rate. He obtained linearity as long as the average input power did not exceed the limiting power of 2.5×10^{-3} watt shown in Fig. 11·17.

These results can also be extended to include the measurement of random noise. In this case the time average of Eq. (11·33) is desired.

$$\int_0^{t_2} e_c \, dt = c_1 c_3 \int_0^{t_2} \left[e^{-c_2 t_1} \int_0^{t_1} e^{c_2 t} i^2 dt \right] dt_1 . \qquad (11 \cdot 36)$$

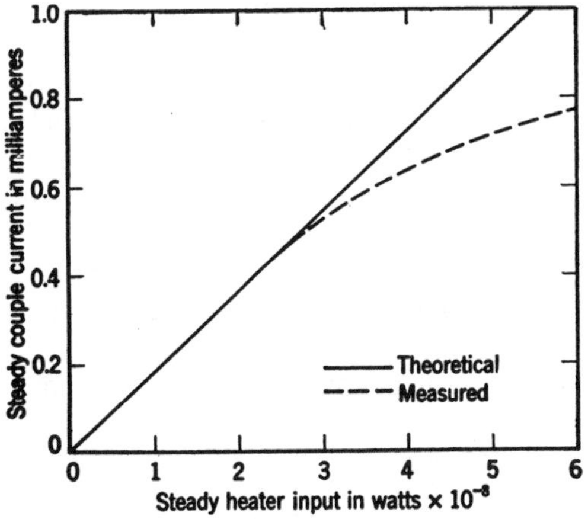

FIG. 11·17   Plot of direct current produced by a vacuum thermocouple as a function of ac heater input in milliwatts.

Integrating by parts and observing that $i(t) \equiv i(t_1)$ reduces this equation to

$$\int_0^{t_2} e_c \, dt = \frac{c_3 c_1}{c_2} \int_0^{t_2} i^2 \, dt - \frac{c_3 \theta(t_2)}{c_2}. \qquad (11 \cdot 37)$$

This expression clearly shows that the irregular heater current must be made zero at some finite time T and that t_2 must become infinite. Then $\theta(t_2)$, the temperature difference, will be reduced to zero. In practice, however, t_2 need be only a few seconds longer than T.

Equation (11·37) does not specify what type of instrument should be used to integrate the couple voltage. For time intervals of the order of 10 to 30 sec, the fluxmeter, to be described later, is extremely convenient. For intervals of this length, friction of the moving coil must be kept at an absolute minimum. Also the restoring torque must be as small as possible to prevent large errors due to backward drift of the needle.

Dunn gives a circuit (Fig. 11·18) for monitoring the temperature limit and disconnecting the thermocouple to prevent damage on overload. The device is set by first finding the temperature limit for linear response of thermocouple through the use of steady inputs, then adjusting the two potentiometers so that the thyratron just strikes at this point.

11·5 Measurement of Integrating Characteristics

Tests of the time-averaging characteristics of acoustical measuring instruments, such as the sound level meter, are described in an American Standard.[13] For the tests that are designed to determine the exponential time constants for the exponential-time-averaging characteristics of the detection circuit, the source signals are single sinusoidal tone bursts at a frequency in the range from 1000 to 2000 Hz, 2000 Hz being preferred. The reading of the indicating meter (analog, digital, chart) is compared in level (decibels) with the reading obtained with the same signal turned on continuously. An "infinite" frequency response of the electrical circuitry preceding the detector is assumed.

For the sound level meter, a "fast" averaging characteristic

[13]American National Standard, "Specification for sound level meters," ANSI S1.4-1983, Acoust. Soc. Am.

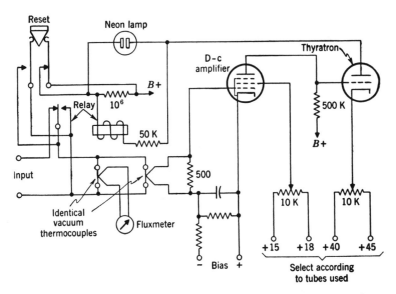

FIG. 11·18 Schematic circuit diagram of an arrangement for preventing overload operation of a vacuum thermocouple. (After Dunn.[11])

is defined as an exponential time weighting of 125 ms, and "slow" as 1000 ms. The theoretical deviation, ΔL, for a single tone burst relative to that of a continuous signal, is given by

$$\Delta L = 10 \log [1 - e^{-t_1/T}] . \qquad (11·38)$$

For a continuous sequence of bursts,

$$\Delta L = 10 \log \{ [1 - e^{-t_1/\tau}] \div [1 - e^{-T/\tau}] \} \qquad (11·39)$$

where, t_1 is the tone burst duration in sec, τ is the exponential time constant in sec, and $T = (1/f_p)$ in sec, where f_p is the repetition frequency of the bursts in Hz.

The Standard tests are made with the values of t_1 shown in the second column of Table 11·1. The amplitude of one of the tone bursts (whose duration is near that of the exponential time constant) is chosen to give an indication that is 4 dB below the upper limit of the primary indicator range on the instrument when the signal is continuous. Then the tests are made for other durations. The maximum response to the test tone burst referred to the response to a continuous signal, as calculated from Eq. (11·38), is given in column 3. For the sound level

TABLE 11·1 TONE-BURST RESPONSE AND TOLERANCE LIMITS FOR FAST AND SLOW EXPONENTIAL-TIME-AVERAGING CHARACTERISTICS.

Exponential time weighting	Duration of test tone burst ms Continuous	Maximum response to test tone burst referred to response to a continuous signal[a] dB 0	Tolerance limits on max. response for each instrument type dB		
			0	1	2
	200	− 1.0	± 0.5	± 1	+ 1, − 2
Fast	50	− 4.8	± 2	· · ·	
(τ = 125 ms)	20	− 8.3	± 2	· · ·	· · ·
	5	− 14.1	± 2	· · ·	· · ·
	2000	− 0.6	± 0.5	· · ·	· · ·
Slow	500	− 4.1	± 0.5	± 1	± 2
(τ = 1000 ms)	200	− 7.4	± 2	· · ·	· · ·
	50	− 13.1	± 2	· · ·	· · ·

[a] See Eq. 11·36.
Source: ANSI S1.4-1983

meter, the tolerance limits given in the last three columns are for Type 0 (Laboratory grade), Type 1 (Precision grade) and Type 2 (General Purpose grade). The tests must be carried out for all level ranges of the instrument. The exponential time constant should also be tested for an indication of the steady level 5 dB above the lower limit of the indicator range at 200 ms for "fast" and 500 ms for "slow".

When a signal is suddenly applied, or a step occurs in the signal level, the maximum overshoot allowed for the sound level meter is specified in Table 11·2 for "fast" and "slow". When

TABLE 11·2 MAXIMUM OVERSHOOT FOR FAST AND SLOW EXPONENTIAL TIME WEIGHTING.

Exponential time weighting	Maximum overshoot for instrument type dB		
	0	1	2
Fast	0.5	1.1	1.1
Slow	1.0	1.6	1.6

Source: ANSI S1.4-1983

the suddenly applied signal is turned off, the meter indication must decay by 10 dB in 0.5 sec or less, for fast and 3.0 sec or less, for slow.

The rms accuracy of the exponential-time-averaging characteristic is determined by comparing the indications for two test signals, (1) a continuous sequence of rectangular pulses and (2) a sequence of tone bursts, to the indication for a reference sinusoidal signal. The test is made by applying the 2000 Hz sinusoidal reference signal to the instrument under test and simultaneously to a reference system having a true rms response, within 0.1 dB tolerance. The indication of the reference meter is noted. Next apply the rectangular pulse sequence and adjust its amplitude to give an indication of the reference true rms meter identical to that for the reference sinusoidal signal. Then, the instrument under test must give an indication that differs from its indication with the reference sinusoidal signal by no more than the tolerance allowed for the type of instrument (see Ref. 13).

The tone burst test is made using a tone burst generator and the procedure just described is repeated using the required crest factor. For the sound level meter, the crest factor capability must be sufficient to meet the requirements of the grade (greater than 10 for Laboratory and Precision grade meters and greater than 3 for General Purpose grade meters). The relation between crest factor and tone burst duty factor for this case is given by

$$(u'/u) = \sqrt{(2T/t_1)}, \tag{11·40}$$

where u' is the peak value of the signal measured with reference to the arithmetic mean, u is the mean-square value of the signal (the instantaneous value being measured with reference to the arithmetic mean) T is the fundamental period of the signal, and t_1 is the time during which the signal is at its peak value.

In the early edition of this book, the author described a method for determining the peak and rms characteristics of a detector-meter combination that made use of a multitone oscillator having ten inharmonically related signals, which could be turned on in any combination.

The reading of the meter under investigation is observed as the signal is made more and more complex, starting with one and ending with all ten components. Theoretically, the reading of an rms meter should increase in proportion to the square root of the number of components acting, if their amplitudes are equal. A peak meter should give readings which increase linearly with the number of components up to a certain point, as shown earlier in this chapter, depending on the sum of the effective rectifier resistance and the generator impedance. Above that point, the reading of the peak meter increases as the square root of the number of components. The readings of an average meter should lie about 1 dB below those for a square-law meter when more than two inharmonic components are present. Obviously, overloading should be avoided by attenuating the input voltage by known amounts as the number of components is increased. It should also be observed that, for sufficiently low input signals, the rectification characteristics are such that linear, peak, and rms meters may read alike.

The ten oscillators used to produce these tones can be of the resistance-capacitance type. One set of inharmonic frequencies which was used is: 159, 394, 670, 1000, 1420, 1900, 2450, 3120, 4300, 5100 cps. Care should be taken to combine the outputs in such a manner that there is no interaction among them.

If a reliable thermocouple type of meter is available, its reading can be compared directly to that of the meter under test. Otherwise, the expected rms readings can be calculated. The measurements can be made with random noise in frequency bands of arbitrary width in place of inharmonic tones provided comparison is made with the reading of a meter of known rectifying characteristic. It must be remembered that, for those instruments whose input impedance is nonlinear (e.g., peak meters), the impedance of the test generator influences the meter indication to a large degree.

The results of the application of these types of test to the calibration of several older commercial meters is shown by the data in Table 11·3.

As an example of the interpretation of the data in these tables, let us select an old GenRad No. 2 voltmeter for detailed analysis. The circuit of that instrument is given in Fig. 11·4. Let us first plot the data of Table 11·3 on semi-logarithmic graph paper (see Fig. 11·19). If the meter were to read peak voltages accurately, the points would fall on a straight line with a slope of 3 dB for each doubling of the number of compo-

TABLE 11·3 THE FOLLOWING VALUES ARE THE AMOUNTS IN DECIBELS BY WHICH THE INDICATIONS OF VARIOUS METERS DEVIATE FROM THE THEORETICAL RMS VALUES WHEN DIFFERENT NUMBERS OF PURE TONES (INHARMONICALLY RELATED) ARE MEASURED. THE AMPLITUDES OF THE TONES WERE SET TO EQUALITY BY MEANS OF A NARROW-BAND WAVE ANALYZER. PLUS VALUE MEANS THAT THE METER READS ABOVE RMS. THE RMS AMPLITUDE OF EACH TONE WAS 0.7 VOLT, AND THE THÉVENIN IMPEDANCE OF THE MULTI-TONED SOURCE WAS 200 OHMS.

Meter	*Number of Pure Tones (Inharmonic)*								
	2	3	4	5	6	7	8	9	10
	Peak-Indicating Instruments								
No. 1	+ 2.9	+ 4.8	+ 5.9	+ 6.1	+ 6.2	+ 6.5	+ 6.4	+ 6.8	+ 7.1
No. 2	+ 2.2	+ 4.0	+ 5.4	+ 6.2	+ 6.9	+ 7.3	+ 7.4	+ 7.6	+ 7.6
No. 3	+ 1.8	+ 3.5	+ 4.9	+ 5.7	+ 5.9	+ 6.4	+ 6.6	+ 6.8	+ 7.1
No. 4	+ 2.7	+ 4.2	+ 5.8	+ 6.5	+ 7.3	+ 7.4	+ 7.7	+ 8.0	+ 8.1
	Other Instruments								
Thermocouple	− 0.1	0.0	0.1	+ 0.2	+ 0.1	+ 0.1	+ 0.1	+ 0.1	+ 0.1
No. 5	− 0.2	− 0.3	− 0.2	− 0.3	− 0.3	− 0.3	− 0.3	− 0.2	− 0.3
No. 6	+ 0.3	+ 0.7	+ 0.5	+ 0.4	− 0.4	0.0	0.0	− 0.1	− 0.2
No. 7	− 0.9	− 0.7	− 0.5	0.0	− 0.2	− 0.4	− 0.3	− 0.4	− 0.5
No. 8	− 0.7	− 0.7	− 0.5	− 0.6	− 0.7	− 0.7	− 0.7	− 0.6	− 0.5
Bal 300	− 1.0	− 0.7	− 0.6	− 0.8	− 0.8	− 0.8	− 0.9	− 0.9	− 1.0
No. 9	− 1.0	− 1.0	− 0.9	− 1.1	− 1.0	− 1.1	− 1.2	− 1.2	− 1.3
No. 10	− 1.1	− 1.0	− 1.0	− 1.0	− 1.1	− 1.1	− 1.1	− 1.1	− 1.1
No. 11	− 0.8	− 0.8	− 1.3	− 1.3	− 1.4	− 1.4	− 1.5	− 1.5	− 1.5
No. 12	− 1.3	− 1.2	− 1.1	− 1.1	− 1.1	− 1.2	− 1.2	− 1.3	− 1.4
No. 13	− 1.5	− 1.8	− 1.8	− 2.0	− 1.9	− 2.1	− 2.1	− 2.0	− 2.0

nents. Such a condition is seen to exist for this meter in the range between two and six components. Below and above this range, however, the readings appear to vary more nearly as the mean square of the amplitudes than as the sum of the amplitudes.

The deviation for two components is caused by insufficient voltage from the generator. This is revealed clearly by the plot of Fig. 11·20 which gives 20 log $(E_M/2E)$ as a function of E, where E_M is the meter reading and E is the amplitude of each of two equal sine waves with inharmonic frequencies. This plot reveals that the amplitude of each component used in obtaining Table 11·3 was 0.7 volt.

For more components than six, the data of Fig. 11·19 start

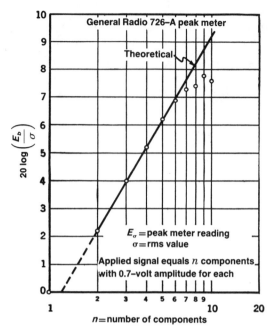

Fig. 11·19 Plot of the readings of an old peak voltmeter in decibels referred to the rms amplitude of n inharmonic components as a function of n. A horizontal line on this graph indicates square-law rectification in the voltmeter. A line, sloping at the rate of 3 dB per doubling of n, indicates that the meter reads the peak value of the waves.

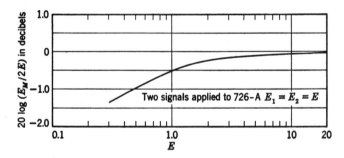

Fig. 11·20 Plot of the meter reading of an old peak voltmeter as a function of the amplitude of two equal sine waves with inharmonic frequencies.

leveling off at about 7 dB. Inspection of Fig. 11·3 reveals that this corresponds roughly to a ratio of effective rectifier plus source resistance R_r to leakage resistance R_b of the order of 4×10^{-6}. Because R_b for this voltmeter is about 5×10^7 ohms, the sum of the effective rectifier resistance and the source resistance was about 200 ohms.

12.

Analysis of Sound Waves

12·1 Introduction

We seldom find pure tones in nature. Speech, music, noise, and explosive sounds are complex phenomena, varying in time, frequency composition, and intensity. No single number can adequately describe these variables, and their complete specification is unduly laborious. At one extreme we may measure their overall magnitude with a square-law or average indicating instrument, at the other we may measure the magnitude in successive short intervals of time in a large number of narrow contiguous frequency bands. In practice, some sort of compromise is often necessary. Sometimes we select an instrument which measures a single quantity more or less closely correlated to the quantity we really desire. For example, the conventional sound level meter is designed to give a single reading related to the loudness of the sound which it measures. For the specification of sound levels in aircraft, the average sound level in four contiguous octave bands between 500 and 4000 cps is found to be a useful designation of the interfering effect on the spoken word.[1] Different data would be required to determine the masking effect of intense low frequency tones on higher frequency sounds.

Even when we have decided to analyze a complex noise into a spectral distribution we must choose the value of several parameters. The "fineness" of the analysis, that is, the width of the frequency bands into which the noise is divided, the amount of time allotted to observing the fluctuation of the noise in each

---

[1]American National Standard, ANSI S3.14-1977, "Rating noise with respect to speech interference," Acoustical Society of America.

band, and the rectification characteristic of the integrating meter must all be decided upon. Even the form in which the data are plotted represents a compromise between utility and accuracy. In this chapter, we shall present a number of methods for analyzing sound, calibrating analyzers, and presenting data representing judicious compromises employed by various laboratories and individuals.

12·2 Analysis of Steady-State Sounds

In this section we shall use the words "steady-state sound" to mean any sound which can be analyzed leisurely. Such sounds include, besides steady tones, random noise and many types of machinery and vehicle noise which, although fluctuating in amplitude and frequency during short intervals of time, have the same average spectrum at one time as another when integrated over sufficiently long intervals of time. Most portable analyzers are suitable for the measurement of these kinds of sounds. Data obtained from such analyzers tell us little about the statistical properties of the noise except its average amplitude as a function of frequency. They also give us information about the slow recurrent fluctuations such as the beat frequency produced by two airplane propellers rotating at nearly the same rate.

At least six different varieties of analyzers are used to measure steady-state sounds, as we shall see shortly. These include (a) heterodyne type, (b) constant-percentage bandwidth type, (c) contiguous band type, (d) mechanical resonance type, (e) Henrici type, and (f) optical type.

A. Heterodyne-Type Analyzer

The heterodyne type of analyzer has a constant-width band-pass filter whose mid-frequency can be continuously varied along the frequency scale. This type of analysis is accomplished by adding the output of a variable frequency oscillator to the incoming signal in a non-linear circuit and then passing the summation frequency though a band-pass filter. The principle of operation is shown more completely in the block diagram of Fig. 12·1. For simplicity let us assume that the microphone is placed in a sound field consisting of a single frequency component of 1000 cps (1 kc). After amplification the 1-kc signal is combined in a non-linear element with a 49-kc signal generated

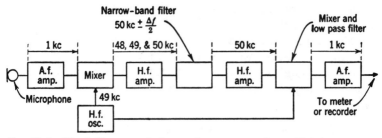

FIG. 12·1 Block diagram of a heterodyne-type analyzer. This instrument yields a continuous analysis of a complex sound in the frequency range between 30 and 20 000 cps for a bandwidth of Δf cps. As designed, the high frequency oscillator varies over a range of 30 to 50 kc.

by the local (H.F.) oscillator. Sum and difference frequencies are produced. These are amplified, and the summation frequency is selected by a narrow-band filter with a mean frequency of 50 kc. After the wave has passed through the filter, it is again combined in a non-linear element along with the 49-kc output of the local oscillator to produce a difference frequency of 1 kc. This difference frequency is amplified and passed on to the indicating meter or recorder. Obviously, if the local oscillator is made to vary over a frequency range extending downward from 50 kc, the indicating meter will respond only when the sum of the oscillator frequency and the incoming signal is 50 kc plus or minus one-half the bandwidth of the 50-kc filter. One manufacturer supplies a range of filters having bandwidths of 3.2, 10, 32, 100, 320, and 1000 Hz.

For rapid analysis a motor can be employed to sweep the frequency of the H.F. oscillator over its range. At the same time, a graphic level recorder may be connected to the output, and the recording medium is advanced in synchronism with the motor driving the oscillator. In this manner a record of the form shown in Fig. 12·2a is obtained. From 15 seconds to 2 minutes are usually required for obtaining a record of this type. (See p. 526 for sweep frequency errors.)

If the noise being analyzed is made up of components whose amplitudes do not fluctuate with time, such an analysis can be accurately reproduced when it is repeated. However, if the components slowly fluctuate in amplitude or in frequency or in both, as indicated by the octave band analysis in Fig. 12·2b, the record will have to be rerun a great many times.

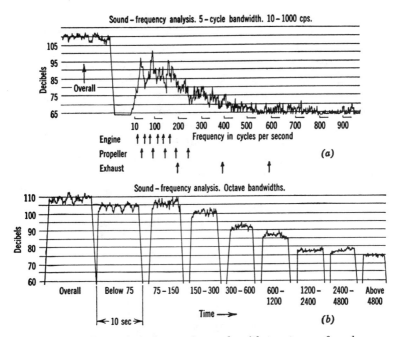

FIG. 12·2   Analyses of airplane noise made with two types of analyzers. (a) Plot of sound pressure level *vs.* frequency as obtained with a heterodyne-etype analyzer and graphic level recorder. The overall level is recorded at the left edge as a function of time for a period of about 10 sec. (b) Plot of sound pressure level measured in octave frequency bands for periods of time of about 10 sec. The data were recorded with a graphic level recorder.

The filter should have as steep low frequency and high frequency cutoffs as possible because an effective increase in bandwidth occurs whenever the sides are not nearly vertical. This increase in bandwidth can be determined for most practical filters by methods outlined near the end of this chapter.

A very important consideration for any type of analyzer and especially for the heterodyne type of analyzer is the need for adequate attenuation in the non-pass bands of the filter (or filters). We shall discuss the necessary non-pass-band attenuation in Section 12·4.

B. Constant-Percentage Bandwidth Analyzer

We have seen that for the heterodyne type of analyzer the bandwidth in cycles per second is constant regardless of the frequency to which the analyzer is tuned. For sounds which are steady in frequency that type of analyzer is quite satisfactory. For sounds whose components fluctate in frequency, the extreme selectivity of the heterodyne type of analyzer in the high frequency range makes accurate data unobtainable. Inaccuracies result because a component lies within the band only part of the time. To get around this, several bandwidths are often provided in the analyzer, and wider ones are used for measuring the higher harmonics. Although this arrangement is acceptable for manual operation, constant switching of filters is not feasible for automatic operation.

An analyzer in which the bandwidth is proportional to the frequency to which the device is tuned has several advantages over the constant bandwidth type. In the first place it provides minimum error when measuring noises of the type just described, since any attenuation caused by frequency modulation

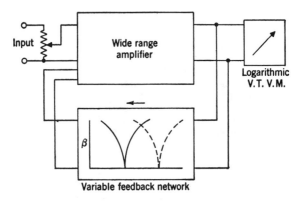

Fig. 12·3   Block diagram of a sound analyzer utilizing a variable feedback network. The network is of the Wien-bridge type and has a bandwidth that is proportional to the mean frequency. (After Scott.[3])

of the sound will be equal for all components, which will then remain in their true relative proportions. Also, for continuous spectrum types of noise, whose power spectrum slopes downward with increasing frequency, a gradually widening bandwidth reduces the requirement on the maximum attenuation outside the pass band.

A constant-percentage bandwidth analyzer using an inverse-feedback principle was developed by Scott.[2,3] This type of instrument is commercially available with bandwidths that are commonly 1%, 3%, 1/10 octave (7%), 10%, and 1/3 octave (23%) in width. The filter design can be two single-pole butterworth filters in series or a two-pole butterworth filter, the latter being used for the wider bandwidths. In analog form, the filters are continuously tunable, because they require only resistors and capacitors, but over a range of about one-half decade, such as 25–75 Hz, 75–150 Hz, 250–750 Hz, or, alternatively, 20–63 Hz, 63–200 Hz, 200–630 Hz. By using ganged variable resistors wound on tapered cards, a logarithmic frequency characteristic can be achieved. Digital filters are best adapted to logarithmic frequency scales and constant bandwidth. [By contrast, a fast-Fourier-transform filter (FFT) intrinsically gives constant bandwidth on a linear frequency scale.]

An analyzer operating on these principles is more stable than the heterodyne type. In the latter the tuning depends on the high frequency oscillator, and a relatively small percentage shift in its frequency will result in a large percentage shift in the analyzer tuning. In the degenerative circuit, the selectivity is determined by the constants of the feedback network, and since these can be high quality mica condensers and wire-wound resistors, the analyzer can be made to be inherently stable. Most heterodyne instruments must have their frequency reset each time measurements are made, so that the frequency stability of a constant-percentage frequency type appears to be an important advantage.

In Fig. 12·4 the selectivity curves of a degenerative analyzer of the type described by Scott are compared to those of a modern heterodyne analyzer. At 25 cps a heterodyne analyzer with a 5-cps bandwidth is noticeably broader in tuning than the degenerative type. At higher frequencies the heterodyne analyzer becomes increasingly more selective in terms of percentage of frequency to which it is tuned, so that, by the time 400 cps is reached, it is difficult to determine the amplitude of discrete components unless the frequency is very stable. In general, it is

[2]H. H. Scott, "The degenerative sound analyzer," J. Acoust. Soc. Am. **11**, 225–232 (1939).

[3]H. H. Scott, "A new type of selective circuit and some applications," Proc. Inst. Radio Engrs. **26**, 226–235 (1938).

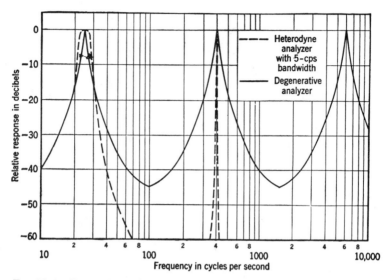

FIG. 12·4 Comparison of the selectivity curves of a heterodyne analyzer (having a constant bandwidth of 5 cps) with a degenerative analyzer (having a constant-percentage bandwidth of 2 percent). The comparison is made in each of three decades of the audible frequency range. Small percentage changes in the frequency of a component at a high frequency will shift it outside the filter of the heterodyne-type analyzer. (Courtesy General Radio Co.)

more important to know the relative amplitude of the components of a noise than it is their exact frequency, so that a constant-percentage bandwidth analyzer has an important advantage in this respect.

C. Contiguous-Band Analyzer

The most widely used type of analyzer for steady sounds is the contiguous-band type. Here, a spectrum of the noise or other complex sound is determined by switching a series of filters into the electrical circuit of an amplifier and noting the corresponding meter readings. Because of the advantages already cited for the constant-percentage bandwidth analyzer, it has been common to use filters with widths of one-third or one octave. The upper cutoff frequency of a one-third octave filter is 1.23 times the lower cutoff frequency, and, for the octave filter, the upper is twice the lower.

A typical set of data taken with an octave-band analyzer is shown in Fig. 12·2b. An advantage of stepwise operation over continuous operation is that time is available to observe the fluctuations of the noise and to decide on an average reading. In the record of Fig. 12·2b, the presence of beats between propellers of the airplane is clearly observable in the lower two frequency bands. Another advantage, already cited, of the wider bands at higher frequency is that the attenuation in the non-pass region below the pass band need not be as high as for constant bandwidth filters.

In the example of Fig. 12·2, the constant bandwidth analysis yields detailed information about the relative levels of the engine, propeller, and exhaust noises. It shows whether in some

TABLE 12·1 (RELATION BETWEEN PITCH IN MELS AND FREQUENCY IN CYCLES PER SECOND)

250-Mel Steps		300-Mel Steps	
Pitch, mels	Frequency cps	Pitch, mels	Frequency cps
0	20	0	20
250	160	300	200
500	394	600	500
750	670	900	860
1000	1 000	1200	1 330
1250	1 420	1500	1 900
1500	1 900	1800	2 550
1750	2 450	2100	3 450
2000	3 120	2400	4 600
2250	4 000	2700	6 200
2500	5 100	3000	9 000
2750	6 600	3300	16 000
3000	9 000		
3250	14 000		

parts of the spectrum a few single frequency components are dominant or whether, as at the higher frequencies, a great many components of approximately equal amplitude are present. On the other hand, this detail is not always needed, and fewer points may be adequate to specify the spectrum. For those purposes, the use of only eight or nine data points yielded by the octave-band analyzer is an advantage.

From the point of view of the ear, however, this division of the spectrum can be improved upon. A more satisfactory division yields bands which the ear considers to be equally wide in pitch. In papers by Stevens and Volkmann and by Galt[4] it is

[4] S. S. Stevens and J. Volkmann, "The relation of pitch to frequency: a revised scale," Am. J. Psychol. **53**, 329 (1940). This paper presents a revision of the mel scale published in *Hearing* by S. S. Stevens and H. Davis. R. H. Galt, "The importance of different frequency regions for speech intelligibility," presented at the thirty-fifth meeting of The Acoustical Society of America, Washington, D. C. (April, 1948).

shown that there is remarkable agreement among three basic functions pertinent to the ear's interpretation of equal pass bands. These are (1) the relation of subjective pitch to frequency (the unit of pitch is the mel); (2) integration of the relation of differential sensitivity to frequency (distribution of just noticeable differences in frequency along the frequency scale); (3) the position along the basilar membrane stimulated by sine waves of different frequency (the frequency "map" of the cochlea); and (4) bands of equal importance to speech intelligibility.

Stevens, Egan, and Miller[5] conclude that the agreement is such that, if we divide the frequency scale into equal-appearing pitch intervals (say intervals of 250 or 300 mels), we may be reasonably sure that our divisions will include equal numbers of just noticeable differences and equal linear extents along the basilar membrane. Galt[4] concludes that such a division would be nearly into equal bands of importance to speech intelligibility.

The frequencies corresponding to successive 250-mel or 300-mel steps are shown in Table 12·1.

Zero pitch occurs at about 20 cps. Other pitch intervals besides 250 or 300 mels can be selected if desired, by using Table 12·1.

The American Standard for calculating the loudness in sones or the loudness level in phons of a noise with a continuous random spectrum uses the charts of Figs. 12·5 and 12·6 and the formula[6]:

$$S_{\text{total}} = I_m + F(\Sigma I - I_m). \tag{12.1a}$$

Using measured noise in dB in either one-octave or one-third-octave bands, determine the loudness index I for each band from Fig. 12·5. The abscissa is the band mid-frequency in Hz. Then add together all the loudness indexes to get ΣI. The greatest of the loudness indexes is called I_m. The factor F equals 0.15 for one-third octave bands and 0.3 for one octave bands. Enter these values in Eq. 12·1a to get the total loudness index. Using S_{total}, enter Fig. 12·6 for the loudness level in phons (see Chap. 5, Sec. 5.4.A).

[5]S. S. Stevens, J. P. Egan, and G. A. Miller, "Methods of measuring speech spectra," J. Acoust. Soc. Am. **19**, 771–780 (1947).

[6]American National Standard, ANSI S3.4-1980, "Procedure for the computation of loudness of noise," Acoustical Society of America.

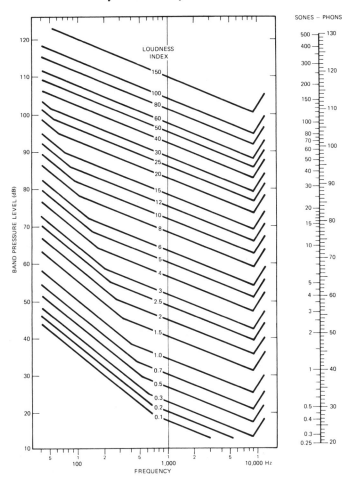

FIG. 12·5   Contours of equal loudness index. (see Ref. 6).

The stepwise nature of contiguous filter bands does not preclude automatic operation. Rudmose, Ericson, and Dienel[7] describe an arrangement which uses a graphic level recorder and an octave-band filter set which is switched automatically by an electromagnetic stepping device. An abbreviated schematic drawing showing the method of operation is given in Fig. 12·7.

[7]H. W. Rudmose, H. L. Ericson, and H. L. Dienel, "Design of an automatic octave sound analyzer and recorder," OSRD Report 969, November 21, 1942. This report may be obtained from the Office of Technical Services, Department of Commerce, Washington, D. C., PB No. 5858.

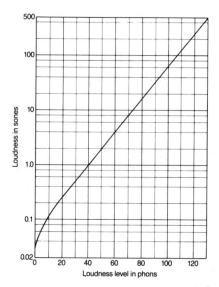

FIG. 12·6   Plot of loudness in sones as a function of loudness level in phons. The loudness level of a particular sound is equal to the sound pressure level of a 1000-cps tone which sounds equally loud. Here the sounds are assumed to be presented to an uncovered ear. (After Stevens[5]; also see Ref. 6).

Such an apparatus can be made for battery operation and is useful in the measurement of noise in vehicles.

D. Mechanical Resonance Analyzer

The use of mechanically vibrated reeds to indicate frequency is old. Less general, however, has been their application to the measurement of both amplitude and frequency. If we carefully select, drive, and adjust a group of reeds so as to cover a given frequency and amplitude range, we will have an analyzer which will portray simultaneously the entire spectrum of a complex sound. This sort of arrangement has particular value for lecture-room demonstrations and for the analysis of musical sounds.

A modern version of such an analyzer, described by Hickman,[8] is shown in Fig. 12·8. Light from a filament lamp (1) passes through a slit (2) and falls on small concave mirrors (3) which are mounted on tuned reeds. An image of the slit is brought to focus on a screen (4) by the mirror of each reed. The

[8]C. N. Hickman, "An acoustic spectrometer," J. Acous. Soc. Am. **6**, 108–111 (1934).

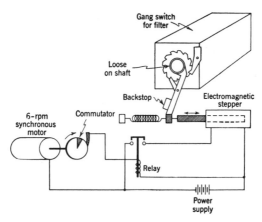

FIG. 12·7   Schematic diagram of an arrangement for automatic operation of an octave-band analyzer. The output of the analyzer is connected to a graphic level recorder. (After Rudmose *et al.*[7])

reeds are so tuned that the fractional increase in resonant frequency from reed to reed is constant. That is,

$$f_n = f_1 C^{n-1} \qquad (12 \cdot 1b)$$

where f_n is the frequency of the nth reed, f_1 is the frequency of the first reed, and C is a constant.

The low frequency reeds are shaped and driven so that they vibrate only in their fundamental modes. The reeds are so mounted that they may be moved with respect to the driving coil for the purpose of adjusting the amplitude of response. The amplitudes of the slit images at resonance are made equal for equal input voltages to the driving amplifier.

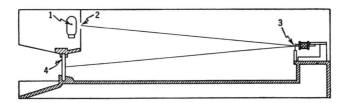

FIG. 12·8   Cross-sectional sketch of a vibrating-reed analyzer which gives both the amplitude and frequency of the components of a complex sound. The vibrating reed is mounted at 3 and is excited by the electromagnetic coil behind it. The amplitude of vibration of the reed is indicated on a ground glass 4. (After Hickman.[8])

The damping factor Δ depends for the most part on the material from which the reeds are made and the heat treatment to which they are subjected. In the Hickman device, the damping was made proportional to the frequency ($\Delta = -14.4f/1000$). That is, the rate of decay was about $f/8$ db/sec.

Typical resonance curves for a reed are shown in Fig. 12·9. The ratio of the amplitude of a given reed at resonance to its amplitude at a very low frequency is about 46 db. To cover the

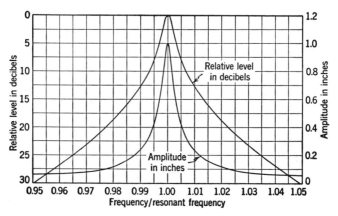

FIG. 12·9   Selectivity curves for any given reed in the mechanical analyzer. The upper graph (use the left-hand ordinate) shows the selectivity curve of a vibrating reed expressed in decibels *re* the maximum level. The lower graph (use the right-hand ordinate) shows the linear amplitude of the light trace on the ground glass. (After Hickman.[8])

frequency range of 50 to 3109 cps, Hickman used 144 reeds. For many purposes more reeds are necessary, although he states that this number was quite useful in studying vibrato and other musical effects.

E. Henrici Analyzer

The analysis of complex recurrent waves received considerable attention before the days of the electronic analyzer. Even today there are many instances in which it is easier for us to obtain an oscillogram of a complex wave and to analyze it at leisure than it is to attempt to do the analysis electronically by one of the methods described earlier in this chapter. For this purpose we find a mechanical analyzer particularly successful. Professor

Henrici[9] devised a precise and convenient analyzer based on the rolling sphere integrator (Fig. 12·10), which is still in use today. An excellent description of it including additional illustrations is given in Professor Miller's book[10] and will not be repeated here.

In using the instrument the curve of the wave to be analyzed must be redrawn to the standard scale required by the analyzer, which is 40 cm for Professor Miller's machine. Then a large carriage, free to move perpendicularly to the time axis of the

FIG. 12·10   Henrici analyzer. To analyze, the stylus s is moved along the curve b. The necessary movement of the carriage rotates the shaft r_2. This shaft and the wire belts on top of the carriage, which move when the stylus moves to the right or left, operate the five integrating elements shown. (After Miller.[10])

wave, is brought over the drawing. A stylus, mounted on the carriage in such a way that it is free to move in a direction parallel to the time axis, is grasped by the hands and made to move along the contour of the wave. As this is done the combined movements of the carriage and stylus cause a series of spheres, pulleys, and cylinders to revolve. The integration of these movements cause the coefficients of sine and cosine components to appear on dials. Obviously, the analysis that one

[9] O. Henrici, "On a new harmonic analyzer," *Phil. Mag.*, **38**, 110–125 (1894).

[10] D. C. Miller, *The Science of Musical Sounds*, 2nd edition, Macmillan (1926).

obtains is dependent on the fundamental wavelength that is assumed. More will be said on this in the following section on the analysis of transient sounds.

When the Henrici analyzer is properly set up, Professor Miller estimated that 5 minutes are required to redraw the curve to scale using a lantern projector; 5 to 10 minutes are required for the tracing of the curve; and 5 more minutes are required to reduce five sine and cosine combinations at a given frequency to five equivalent amplitudes and phase shifts of a sum of sinusoidal terms. The last operation is performed by a simple machine which he called an amplitude-and-phase calculator. This operation must be repeated for each additional five components.

F. Optical Analyzer

A rapid and compact piece of apparatus for the analysis of complex wave forms recorded on a variable area sound track

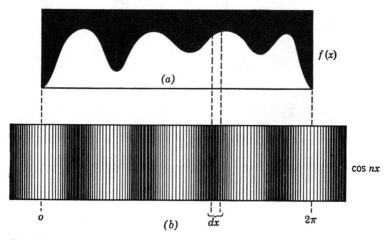

Fig. 12·11 (a) Appearance of a sound wave with an amplitude f when recorded on a variable area sound track (film). (b) The function $\cos nx$ when recorded on variable density film. (After Montgomery.[11])

(film) makes use of an optical arrangement.[11] With this device the function $f(x)$ is recorded on a variable area film (see Fig. 12·11). If light is transmitted through a narrow slit of width dx the total amount of light transmitted will equal $f(x)\,dx$. Now if we interpose a second film on which is recorded by the variable

[11] H. Montgomery, "An optical harmonic analyzer," *Bell System Technical Jour.*, **17**, 406–415 (1938).

density method the function cos nx, the total amount of light transmitted will equal the product $f(x) \cos nx \, dx$.

We know, of course, that any function $f(x)$ can be analyzed into a Fourier series of the form

$$f(x) = c_0 + \sum_1^n c_n \cos (nx - \phi_n) \qquad (12 \cdot 2)$$

where

$$c_n = \frac{1}{\pi} \int_0^{2\pi} f(x) \cos (nx - \phi_n) \, dx \qquad (12 \cdot 3)$$

and ϕ_n is determined from the relation

$$\int_0^{2\pi} f(x) \sin (nx - \phi_n) \, dx = 0 \qquad (12 \cdot 4)$$

The apparatus is designed to measure the total amount of light transmitted through the two records just described between the limits zero and 2π. To get c_n and ϕ_n, first slide the variable density film (cosine function) along the axis until the reading is first a maximum and then a minimum. The difference between the maximum and minimum values of light transmitted is proportional to c_n, that is, by Eq. (12·2), c_0 is subtracted out. The position of the cosine curve at which the maximum occurs is ϕ_n, by Eq. (12·4).

A photograph of Montgomery's optical analyzer appears in Fig. 12·12. The analyzer superimposes the function to be analyzed (on variable area film) on to a cosine screen (on variable density film) and measures the variation in the transmitted light as the cosine screen is moved along the x axis. This operation is repeated with a different cosine screen for each harmonic to be measured. The film containing $f(x)$ is placed in a holder A and strongly illuminated by an incandescent lamp and condensing lens B. Its enlarged image is projected onto a window behind which the cosine screens C slide. The transmitted light is collected by another lens and brought to a photocell D. A series of cams and levers is arranged to bring the cosine screens out of a drum-shaped magazine E (when needed) into the optical path, give them the small motion required for analysis, and return them to the magazine. The magazine is then rotated to bring the next screen into positon. The variations in the photocell output take place at the rate of about 2 cps. These variations are recorded linearly on a moving chart by a graphical recorder.

Montgomery's instrument was designed for records of $f(x)$ which are from one-sixteenth to five-sixteenths of an inch long and no higher than their length.   The cosine screens were made on photographic plates by printing negatives from variable density motion picture sound tracks of pure tones.   The important requirements for the cosine screens are good waveform, uniformity in modulation and average transmission, and accuracy

Fig. 12·12   Optical wave analyzer.   The cylinder on the right holds the variable density cosine screens.   The record to be analyzed is held in the carriage just above the small pointer on the scale.   Its image is projected onto the cosine screen.   The light cell is contained in the trapezoidal housing on the extreme right.   (Courtesy *Bell System Technical Journal*.)

in wavelength.   Montgomery found it possible to keep the harmonic content of the screens down to 5 percent.   The modulation varied from 79 to 44 percent in different screens and the average transmission from 20 to 24 percent.   Variations in the wavelength of the screens amounted to about 1 percent.

12·3   Analysis of Transient Sounds

A transient sound is one which occurs only once and, hence, cannot be analyzed at leisure.   Some sounds, which we shall call transient here, exist for as long as several seconds in a quasi-steady state. Others are of very short duration. Some of the methods of analysis described in this section look at an interval of the sound wave and analyze it as though the components present in that interval persisted with the same amplitude over a much greater length of time. Others respond continuously with greater or less accuracy to changes in spectral amplitudes. Apparatus is also described for determining the average energy produced by transient sounds, such as speech, over intervals of time ranging from a fraction of a second to many seconds.

A. Oscillogram Analysis

We are often interested in analyzing a single pulse of sound into its amplitude and phase spectrum as a function of frequency. For those pulses whose values are zero previous to zero time, and zero after a time T, analysis is readily accomplished with a mechanical analyzer of the Henrici type.[12]

A transient pulse, meeting these requirements, can be represented by a pair of Fourier integrals:

$$f(t) = \frac{1}{2\pi} \int_0^\infty A(\omega) \cos \theta(\omega) \sin \omega t \, d\omega$$
$$+ \frac{1}{2\pi} \int_0^\infty A(\omega) \sin \theta(\omega) \cos \omega t \, d\omega \quad (12 \cdot 5)$$

where $f(t)$ is the shape of the pulse, as obtained directly from an oscillogram, $A(\omega)$ is the amplitude of each component of frequency f, $\theta(\omega)$ is the relative phase of each component, and $\omega = 2\pi f$. A single pulse will be made up of an infinite number of components, uniformly distributed along the frequency scale, with the relative amplitudes and phases, $A(\omega)$ and $\theta(\omega)$.

It is known that[13]

$$A(\omega) \cos \theta(\omega) = \int_{-\infty}^\infty f(t) \sin \omega t \, dt$$
$$A(\omega) \sin \theta(\omega) = \int_{-\infty}^\infty f(t) \cos \omega t \, dt \qquad (12 \cdot 6)$$

[12] R. S. Shankland, "The analysis of pulses by means of the harmonic analyzer," *Jour. Acous. Soc. Amer.*, **12**, 383–386 (1941).

[13] W. E. Byerly, *Fourier Series and Spherical Harmonics*, Section **32**, Ginn and Co. (1893).

If the pulse had been recurrent we could have analyzed it into a Fourier series of the form

$$F(t) = \sum_0^\infty [a_n \sin (n\omega_1 t) + b_n \cos (n\omega_1 t)] \qquad (12\cdot7)$$

where $\omega_1 = 2\pi f_1$, and f_1 is equal to the repetition frequency of the pulse. Let us set $l = (1/f_1)$ equal to the length of the pulse.

With the aid of the Henrici analyzer we can analyze such a wave into its components a_n and b_n directly, where

$$a_n = \frac{2}{l} \int_0^l F(x) \sin (n\omega_1 x) \, dx \qquad (12\cdot8a)$$

provided that $F(x) = 0$ at both $t = 0$ and $t = l$. Here, $\omega_1 = (2\pi/l)$. Similarly,

$$b_n = \frac{2}{l} \int_0^l F(x) \cos (n\omega_1 x) \, dx \qquad (12\cdot8b)$$

For the special case that $f(t) = 0$ for $t < 0$ and $t > T$, the integrals of Eq. $(12\cdot6)$ can be rewritten with new limits of integration:

$$A(\omega) \cos \theta(\omega) = \int_0^T f(t) \sin \omega t \, dt \qquad (12\cdot9a)$$

$$A(\omega) \sin \theta(\omega) = \int_0^T f(t) \cos \omega t \, dt \qquad (12\cdot9b)$$

The similarity of $(12\cdot8)$ and $(12\cdot9)$ suggests that the pulse function $f(t)$ may be analyzed into its component amplitudes and phases with the aid of the Henrici analyzer. Restricting ourselves to these discrete frequencies, we may equate $(12\cdot8a)$ to $(12\cdot9a)$ and get

$$a_n = \frac{2}{l} \int_0^l F(x) \sin (n\omega_1 x) \, dx$$
$$= \int_0^T f(t) \sin \omega t \, dt = A(\omega) \cos \theta(\omega) \qquad (12\cdot10)$$

Now, a_n has values only at discrete points along the frequency scale corresponding to the product nf_1, whereas $A(\omega) \cos \theta(\omega)$ has a value at every frequency. However, a_n is equal to $A(\omega)$ $\cos \theta(\omega)$ at *these particular frequencies*. By making f_1, the repetition frequency of the pulse, very low, the number of components in a given frequency interval can be made as large as desired. To bring this about, let us set x in the first integral of Eq. (12·10) equal to t/k, where k is greater than unity. This division has the effect of diminishing the value of ω_1. We have

$$a_n = \frac{2}{lk} \int_0^{lk} F\left(\frac{t}{k}\right) \sin\left(\frac{2\pi n}{lk} t\right) dt$$

$$= \int_0^T f(t) \sin \omega t \, dt \tag{12·11}$$

We see that

$$\omega \equiv \frac{2\pi n}{lk}$$

$$T \equiv lk$$

$$f(t) = \frac{2F(x)}{lk} \tag{12·12}$$

$$x = \frac{t}{k}$$

To analyze this pulse with the Henrici analyzer, we should draw a number of waveforms of the shape of $f(t)$, for various values of k as follows: The extent of each wave l along the abscissa must equal l/k times the width of the Henrici analyzer, and its amplitude must equal $lk/2$ times the amplitude of $f(t)$.

In practice it is much simpler to obtain a series of waves by tracing them on cards with the aid of a photographic enlarger. In that case, instead of the amplitude being increased by the factor $lk/2$ as its length is decreased by $1/k$, it is also decreased by the factor $1/k$. Hence, the values of a_n and b_n obtained from the analysis must be corrected in order to give the true spectrum of $f(t)$. That is,

$$A(\omega) \cos \theta(\omega) \equiv \frac{lk^2}{2} a_n$$

$$A(\omega) \sin \theta(\omega) = \frac{lk^2}{2} b_n \tag{12·13}$$

As an example of this method of analysis, the pulse in the upper right-hand corner of Fig. 12·13 was studied by Shankland.

This pulse was charted first to a length of 40 cm, corresponding to
a k value of unity, that is, $l = 40$ cm. An harmonic analysis was
made with the Henrici analyzer, and values of $A(\omega)$ and $\theta(\omega)$
were calculated from the relations

$$\theta(\omega) = \tan^{-1} \frac{b_n}{a_n}$$

$$(12 \cdot 14)$$

$$A(\omega) = 20k^2 \sqrt{a_n{}^2 + b_n{}^2}$$

These quantities are plotted in Fig. 12·13 at values of n/k which
are integers. The pulse was next charted to a length of $l = 31.3$

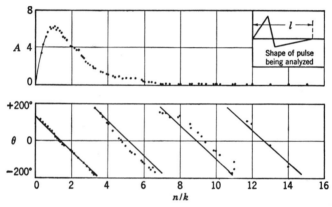

Fig. 12·13 Fourier analysis of a transient pulse. The upper right-hand
graph shows a pulse of length l which is analyzed in the two lower graphs.
The ordinates A and θ are the amplitudes and phases of the spectral components of the wave. The abscissa n/k equals the duration of the pulse l
in seconds times the frequency of each component in cycles. That is to
say, the frequency equals n/k divided by l in seconds. The quantity lk
is the width of the Henrici analyzer. (After Shankland.[12])

cm corresponding to $k = 1.28$. This curve was analyzed and
another set of A and θ values obtained. These quantities are
plotted at values of the abscissa n/k that are not integers and so
give new points in the continuous frequency spectrum. The
analysis of Fig. 12·13 was obtained with values of k equal to
1, 1.28, 1.52, 1.88, 2.51, and 3.54. The frequency at which each
component is plotted is given by $f = n/lk$, where lk is the width
of the Henrici analyzer.

B. Heterodyne Analyzer

By appropriate design, the heterodyne analyzer can be speeded up to permit the analysis of waves which are sustained for several seconds. In many cases, this rate of analysis is still much too slow, and one might inquire about the possibilities of designing such an analyzer so that it will cover the audio range of frequencies in, say, less than one-half second. Schuck[14] and Barber[15] have attacked this problem. Schuck reports a heterodyne analyzer

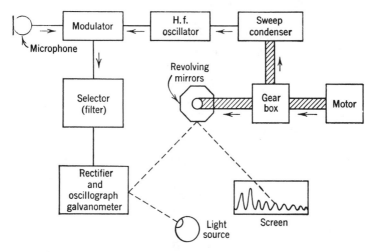

Fig. 12·14   Block diagram of a sweep frequency heterodyne-type analyzer. The output of a sweep frequency oscillator is combined with the microphone output in a modulator, and the combination frequency is selected and rectified to produce a vertical displacement of the oscillograph indicator. The element of time is introduced by the revolving mirror. (After Schuck.[14])

which completes an analysis within one-tenth second for the audible range of frequencies, and presents this analysis in visual form. Successive analyses are carried out once every tenth of a second, which is about as rapidly as the eye can follow changes in the pattern.

Schuck's device is shown in block diagram form in Fig. 12·14. The method of operation is similar to that of the heterodyne

[14] O. H. Schuck, "The sound prism," *Proc. Inst. Radio Engrs.*, **22**, 1295–1310 (1934).

[15] N. F. Barber, "Continuous frequency analysis by a variable frequency filter," Report ARL/R5/103.30/W, Admiralty Research Laboratory, Teddington, Middlesex, England (June 1947).

analyzer described earlier in this chapter. The construction differs in two respects, however. First, the carrier frequency is swept over the audio range a number of times per second. This means that a special design of filter (labeled "selector" in Fig. 12·14) is required. Secondly, the graph of amplitude *vs.* frequency is portrayed visually on a screen by a rotating mirror mechanism and an oscillographic galvanometer. The amplitude can be presented in decibels rather than in linear units if a logarithmic amplifier precedes the rectifier. The principal unusual feature of the analyzer is the selector, and it seems appropriate to discuss its design in some detail here.

The frequency response of the usual band-pass filter is determined by measuring the voltage at its output for various steady-state input signals of different frequency. The response of the filter to a sweep frequency input will be nearly identical to its steady-state response provided the sweep rate is very low. At high sweep rates, however, response curves of the type shown in Fig. 12·15 will be obtained.

These curves were derived by Barber[15] for a simple *LRC* circuit. Curve (*a*) is the normal static response of the filter. The other curves apply to various values of the parameter (f'/δ^2), where f' equals the time rate of change of the frequency; $\delta = f_0/Q$ is equal to the frequency range in which the transmitted power is more than one-half the peak power; f_0 is the resonant frequency of the filter; Q is the customary figure of merit of the resonant circuit; and f is the signal frequency equal to $f_0 + \Delta f$. It is seen that, as the speed increases, the frequency at which the peak amplitude occurs becomes greater, and the amplitude at resonance decreases. At fairly high sweep rates secondary maxima appear on the "following" side of the curve.

Barber has prepared the series of four curves shown in Fig. 12·16 as correction factors and a guide to the design of filters with one degree of freedom. In (*a*) he shows the decrease of peak amplitude as a function of sweep rate. The frequency lag in peak transmission is shown in (*b*) as a fraction of the nominal bandwidth (steady-state condition) and the effective bandwidth (sweeping condition). In (*c*), the ratios of the effective to the true bandwidth for various values of sweep rate f' are given. Finally, in (*d*) it is seen that there is an optimum design of filter for any given sweep rate, at which the ratio of effective to nominal bandwidth has a minimum value. It must be remembered that,

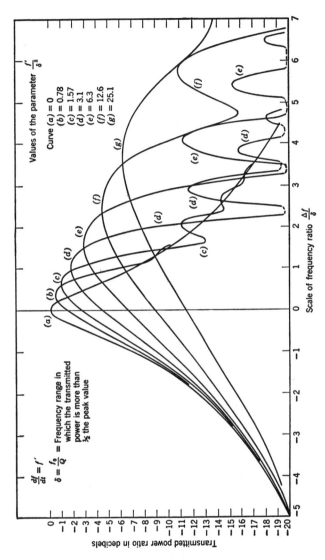

FIG. 12·15 Relative power transmission by a simple *LRC* filter as a function of sweep rate. The time rate of change of frequency equals f', the width of the filter equals δ, where δ is defined as the mean frequency divided by the Q of the filter. The ordinate equals the power passed in decibels relative to that passed by the filter at its maximum with $f' = 0$. The abscissa equals the deviation in frequency Δf from the mean frequency f_0 divided by the width of the filter δ. (After Barber.[15])

although the shift in frequency and the decrease in amplitude can be allowed for in calibration, the presence of secondary maxima will completely mask the detection of weak components in the vicinity of a strong component.

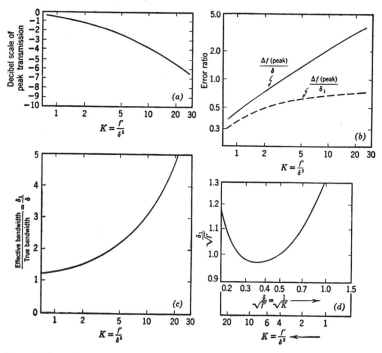

FIG. 12·16   Curves for a simple LRC filter with a sweep frequency input. (a) The relative power transmitted by the filter at the peak in continuous analysis.   (b) The frequency lag in peak transmission in continuous analysis as a fraction of the nominal bandwidth δ (full line), and as a fraction of the effective bandwidth δ_1 (dashed line).   (c) Increase in effective bandwidth with increase in speed in continuous analysis, the nominal bandwidth being prescribed.   (d) The relation between effective bandwidth δ_1 and nominal bandwidth δ in continuous analysis when the rate of change of frequency f' is prescribed.   (After Barber.[15])

Schuck concludes that, because of secondary peaks, it is not feasible to use an oscillating circuit with a single degree of freedom as the selector in a high speed analyzer.   As a solution to this difficulty, he proposes a filter design of the type indicated by the schematic diagram in Fig. 12·17.   The coupling between circuits is loose.   The width of the pass band depends on the resistance in each circuit and on the amount of coupling.   This system of filtering allows a sweep rate of roughly eight times that of a system of 1 degree of freedom before secondary maxima are encountered. A shift in resonant frequency and a broadening of the resonance curve also occur at high sweep rates with this design just as they do for the simple filter.

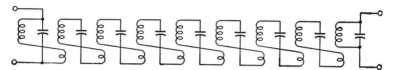

FIG. 12·17   Circuit diagram of a band-pass filter with improved transient characteristics. The coupling between stages is maintained loose. (After Schuck.[14])

Musical instruments such as the wind instruments and the bowed stringed instruments produce tones that can be held reasonably steady from 4 to 10 sec. A recording analyzer designed for use at sweep rates of the order of 2500 cps/sec was described by Hall.[16] He modified existing electronic equipment and combined it in such a way as to obtain an analyzer which yields a record of sound pressure level in decibels *vs.* linear frequency on

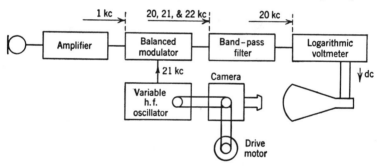

FIG. 12·18   Block diagram of a semi-automatic, medium-speed recording analyzer using a heterodyne circuit. The motion of the spot on the face of the cathode ray tube is photographed by a moving film. (After Hall.[16])

photographic paper. The schema of his instrument is shown in Fig. 12·18.

The band of frequencies to be analyzed passes from the microphone to a linear amplifier and through the heterodyning circuit. The output of the modulator connects to a filter which then

[16] H. H. Hall, "A recording analyzer for the audible frequency range," *Jour. Acous. Soc. Amer.*, **7**, 102–110 (1935).

delivers a voltage at 20,000 cps to the logarithmic voltmeter. From there it passes to one pair of plates of a cathode ray tube. The movement of the spot back and forth on the face of the tube is recorded photographically on a moving strip of photosensitive paper.

Hall's filter was a magnetostrictive type, although crystal or balanced-T types could also be used. It consisted of a rod of magnetostrictive material (nickel) whose length was equal to a

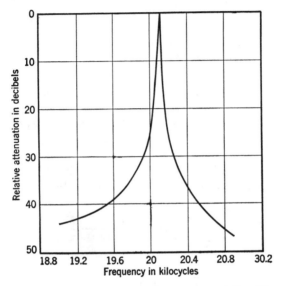

Fig. 12·19   Frequency-response curve of a magnetostriction filter expressed in power transmitted in decibels *re* that transmitted at resonance. (After Hall.[16])

half-wave of compressional motion in the material at 20,000 cps. The rod was supported at its mid-point, and two coils were mounted coaxially, one over each end of the rod. These coils were shielded from each other by a brass plate. At 20,000 cps a current in one coil set the rod into vibration and that vibration in turn induced a voltage in the second coil. The attenuation of such an arrangement is shown in Fig. 12·19. To obtain attenuations of over 60 db outside the pass band, two filters may be connected in tandem through a vacuum tube buffer. At low frequencies the attenuation is low, and in that region a conventional high pass filter is needed to supplement the characteristic of the magnetostrictive filter.

The trace is recorded on 35-mm photosensitive paper, a complete analysis from near 0 to 10,000 cps covering about 50 cm length. A frequency scale is photographed at the same time. This is produced by projecting the image of a slit, which is interrupted by a shutter geared to drive motor, upon the front of the oscilloscope screen. A typical recorded trace is shown in Fig. 12·20.

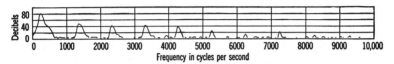

Fig. 12·20 Typical record obtained with the Hall analyzer. The trace is recorded on 35-mm photosensitive paper.

C. Freystedt-DTMB Analyzer

Another arrangement for measuring sounds which persist less than a second or so has been described in the literature.[17, 18] This equipment was first developed by Freystedt, and later an improved model was developed at the David Taylor Model Basin. The improved version sweeps the audio spectrum 60 times per second in a stepwise manner. By stepwise, we mean that the resolution is accomplished by switching successively a sequence of filters, each having a bandwidth of one-third octave, into the circuit.

A block diagram of the device is shown in Fig. 12·21. The signal is applied simultaneously to a parallel arrangement of 28 channels. Each of 27 of these 28 channels contains a filter whose width is one-third octave, an amplifier, and a signal rectifier. The twenty-eighth channel passes the total noise spectrum.

By means of an electronic switch the rectified output of each of the 28 channels is successively applied 60 times per second to a common line. (See Fig. 12·21a. The Freystedt version used a mechanical commutator and was one-sixth as fast.) There are 30 steps in the switch, so that each channel is connected for an interval of $\frac{1}{1800}$ sec. The two extra steps are required for

[17] V. E. Freystedt, "An audio frequency spectrometer," *Zeits. f. technische Physik*, **16**, 533–539 (1935) (in German).

[18] R. Roop and G. Cook, "An acoustic analyzer," The David Taylor Model Basin and the Bureau of Ships, Navy Department, May 1942. This report is obtainable from the Office of Technical Services, U.S. Department of Commerce, Washington, D.C., No. PB 38054.

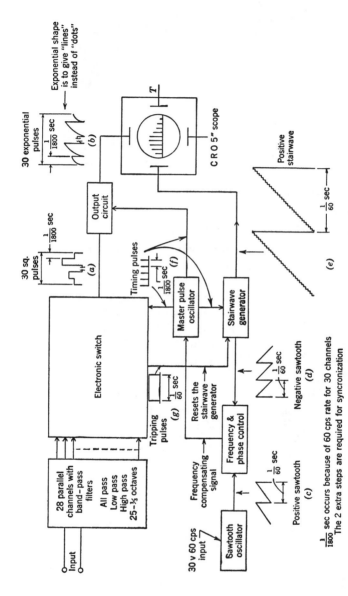

FIG. 12·21 Schematic diagram of David Taylor Model Basin automatic analyzer having 25 one-third octave bands plus low pass, high pass, and all pass bands. The analysis appears as a series of vertical lines on the cathode ray tube T. The output of each filter band is sampled 60 times a second. (After Roop and Cook.[18])

synchronization. The common output line leads through another network, called the output circuit, to the vertical plates of a cathode ray tube T. The electronic switch is also used to count the steps of a stairwave generator and to reset this circuit after 30 steps have been completed; see (g). The timing of the switch is controlled by a master pulse oscillator.

The x-axis deflection signal applied to the horizontal plates of the oscilloscope consists of 30 successive increases of voltage separated by intervals of constant voltage; see (e). This sweep

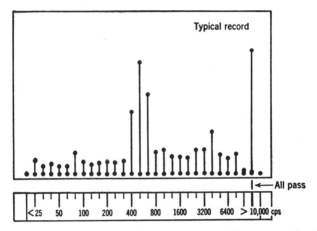

FIG. 12·22 Typical record obtained by photographing screen of cathode ray tube on DTMB analyzer. The vertical bars have heights proportional to the rms amplitude of the signals in the bands.

signal is obtained from a stairwave generator, which is controlled by the master oscillator and by the electronic switch. Another signal (d) from the stairwave generator is combined with a saw-tooth signal (c) synchronized to the power line frequency, and this combination is used to control the frequency of the master pulse oscillator so that it is exactly 30 times the line frequency. A signal from the master pulse oscillator also controls the output circuit and synchronizes it with the switching circuits.

The output circuit transforms the 30-step histogram (a) from the electronic switch into 30 logarithmically shaped pulses as shown in (b). The height of each logarithmically shaped pulse is proportional to the signal amplitude of the corresponding channel in the switch output. The pattern on the oscilloscope screen then assumes the appearance of a set of 30 vertical lines or "thermometers" which rise and fall as the output voltages of the corresponding channels change (see Fig. 12·22).

An improvement needed in this apparatus is the addition of a logarithmic amplifier as part of the output circuit so that the spectrum as displayed on the cathode ray tube will read in decibels *vs.* frequency.

D. Contiguous-Band Integrative Analyzers

We often are interested in determining the long time average amplitude or power as a function of frequency of a transient wave such as music or speech. One way of obtaining such spectral distributions is to divide the audio spectrum into a number of contiguous frequency bands and to attach electronic integrators to their outputs. Such integrating arrangements may employ a linear or square-law rectifying element, depending on whether the average amplitude or average power is desired. At least three procedures have been presented in the literature for accomplishing these two types of integration, and we shall describe them briefly here.

One method of integration makes use of the circuit shown in Fig. 12·23.[19] A vacuum tube T_1 is used to control the flow of current to a condenser C. In order to reduce the current to zero without recourse to a large negative bias on T_1, a second tube T_2 provides a path for a bucking current to flow through the condenser circuit. When the circuit is balanced by the proper adjustment of the bias resistor R, no current flows in the condenser C. But, when a positive voltage is impressed on the grid of T_1, the circuit is unbalanced, and a charge Q accumulates on C. The total charge Q and, hence, the potential V will be proportional to the average rectified voltage at the input times the period of time T that the circuit was in operation. The voltage V on the condenser may be read directly by connecting a vacuum tube voltmeter across it at the end of the known period T.

Stevens reports that the current to the condenser C cannot quite be made directly proportional to the applied alternating voltage on the grid of T_1. He suggests that a network of resistors and non-linear elements, such as copper oxide rectifiers, be connected ahead of the input to straighten out the characteristic. Such an arrangement is described in Chapter 11, Section 11·2, B.

[19] S. S. Stevens, "Rectilinear rectification applied to voltage integration," *Electronics*, **15**, 40–41 (January, 1942).

An extension of the single channel arrangement of Stevens was developed at the Electro-Acoustic Laboratory of Harvard by Rudmose *et al.*[20] The signal to be analyzed is fed into a set of thirteen band-pass filters connected in parallel through isolating resistance pads. Each of the filters has a bandwidth of 250 mels. See p. 511. The outputs of the thirteen filters and an overall channel are passed into an equal number of integrating circuits.

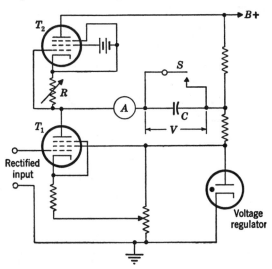

Fig. 12·23 Schematic diagram of an arrangement for charging a condenser C to a potential V which, in turn, is some desired function of the rectified voltage applied to the input of T_1. If T_1 is operated on a linear portion of its characteristic curve, V will be proportional to the time integral over the period T of the input voltage on T_1. (After Stevens.[19])

These circuits are essentially as in Fig. 12·23 except that T_1 is operated on the parabolic portion of its plate-current grid-voltage characteristic. This means that the plate current which flows is proportional to the mean-square voltage appearing at the input. In the Rudmose *et al.* apparatus, when the voltage on the condenser C reaches a certain value, a thyratron connected across it becomes conducting, the condenser discharges rapidly through it, and the current trips a relay. The relay is connected to the pallet lever of an Ingersoll pocket watch having a sweep second

[20] H. W. Rudmose, K. C. Clark, F. C. Carlson, J. C. Eisenstein, and R. A. Walker, "Voice measurements with an audio spectrometer," *Jour. Acous. Soc. Amer.*, **20**, 503–512 (1948).

hand, and the total number of counts is equal to the cumulative mean-square voltage for that interval.

A typical calibration curve for one of the channels appears in Fig. 12·24. This graph indicates that a square-law characteristic is achieved over a range of more than 20 db.

A third integrating analyzer was used by Sivian[21] to determine the average and rms pressure of speech in 15-sec intervals. His integrating device was the Grassot fluxmeter which is discussed

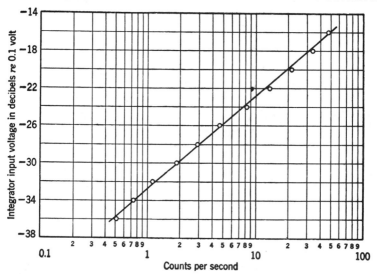

FIG. 12·24   Calibration curve on the square-law integrating device of Rudmose *et al.*[26] The number of counts indicated on the dial should be proportional to the square of the input voltage, as indicated by the solid line. The points are measured. This integrator yields the mean-square charge supplied to the grid over a range of at least 20 db.

in some detail in Chapter 10.   In addition he used an automatic timing arrangement developed by Dunn[22] which performed the timing operation and reset the fluxmeter.

E. Loop Recording Analyzer

Recording apparatus has become so common that it is not surprising to find uses for it other than the preservation of music

[21] L. J. Sivian, "Speech power and its measurement," *Bell System Technical Jour.*, **8**, 646–661 (1929).

[22] H. K. Dunn, "Use of thermocouple and fluxmeter for measurement of average power of irregular waves," *Rev. of Scientific Instruments*, **10**, 362–367 (1939).

or speech. It is particularly suited to the recording of sounds of temporary duration, thereby permitting their analysis at a later date. As an example, during World War II, recording techniques were employed to preserve the noise of passing vehicles. Subsequently, sections of the record, covering a few seconds each, were played over and over and analyzed by steady-state techniques. Wiener and Marquis[23] have described such a series of tests. Their experiment determined the noise spectrum of an airplane at the ground as it passed overhead in level flight.

The sound picked up by the microphone as the airplane flew overhead was recorded as a function of time for various altitudes and flight conditions. They used a Miller film recorder[24] which had a fairly flat response over a wide frequency range. The recording medium is a narrow film tape consisting of a celluloid base and a layer of transparent gelatin covered with a thin opaque coating. The recording head consists of a wedge-shaped stylus which is electromagnetically driven. When a signal is applied, the stylus moves in a direction perpendicular to the plane of the film and cuts a sound track of varying width corresponding to the waveform of the signal. Reproduction is by conventional optical means.

The recordings obtained in the field were reproduced in the laboratory, and two types of analysis were possible: (a) The reproduced signal was analyzed by means of a set of band-pass filters whose output voltage was recorded as a function of time by a high speed level recorder. Repeated playbacks with a different band-pass filter in place each time made it possible to obtain an analysis over the desired frequency range; and (b) the film was cut and pasted together to form a loop. This loop was 1 to 2 sec in length, and the noise to be analyzed was almost constant in that interval. The loop was then run continuously through the reproducer, and the output was analyzed with a heterodyne-type analyzer having a 20-cps bandwidth. It is quite possible that, if the tape were speeded up, successful spectrum analyses could be obtained of intervals a fraction of a second in length. A further advantage of this technique is that the records can be saved for subsequent study.

[23] F. M. Wiener and R. J. Marquis, "Noise levels due to an airplane passing overhead," *Jour. Acous. Soc. Amer.*, **18**, 450–452 (1946).

[24] R. Vermeulen, "The Philips-Miller system of sound recording," *Philips Tech. Rev.*, **1**, 107–114 (1936).

Magnetic tape or conventional optical sound-on-film types of recording[25] can also be used. Response curves, typical of modern sound-on-film recording apparatus, are shown in Fig. 12·25.[26] No special precautions are necessary in the joining of the two ends of a loop of 35-mm film because the transient developed is

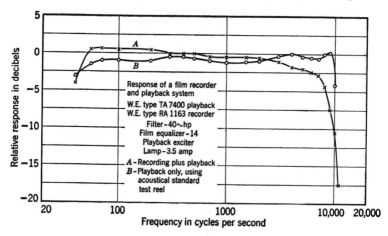

FIG. 12·25   Response curves on Western Electric film recorders. (Courtesy R. S. Gales, Naval Electronics Laboratory, San Diego.)

of insufficient length to affect analysis, provided the playback time for the loop is greater than a second or so.

F. Acoustic Diffraction Grating

As a substitute for a bank of parallel filters, Meyer and Thienhaus[27] propose the use of an acoustic diffraction grating. The grating consists of a series of evenly spaced parallel rods forming a section of a circular cylinder. The sound source is placed in front of the grating. As in the case of optical gratings, the

[25] C. F. Sacia, "Photomechanical wave analyzer applied to inharmonic analysis," *Jour. Optical Soc. Amer.*, **9**, 487–494 (1924).

[26] These data were taken at the Naval Electronics Laboratory, San Diego, California, and were supplied through the courtesy of Mr. R. S. Gales.

[27] E. Meyer and E. Thienhaus, "Sound spectroscopy, a new method of sound analysis," *Zeits. f. technische Physik*, **15**, 630–637 (1934) (in German); E. Thienhaus, *The acoustic diffraction grating and its application to sound spectroscopy*, Johann Ambrosius Barth, Leipzig (1935) (in German); E. Meyer, "A method for very rapid analysis of sounds," *Jour. Acous. Soc. Amer.*, **7**, 88–93 (1935).

intensity of a wave reflected from the grating is concentrated in a narrow beam by the interference of sound from each contributing grating element.   With such an arrangement, the spectrum of the sound can be formed along a circular arc whose length is of the order of 75 cm for the frequency range of 0 to 10,000 cps. If a series of sound-sensitive elements (piezoelectric crystals, for example) are placed along this arc, an electronic switch with as many positions as there are elements can be used to sample their

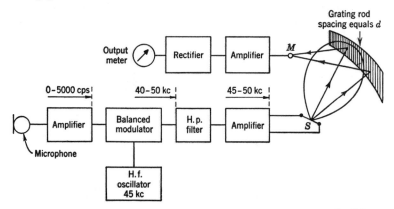

FIG. 12·26   Block diagram of an analyzer employing an acoustic diffraction grating.   The source S is an electromagnetically driven ribbon with its directivity pattern facing the far end of the grating.   The refracted waves for any given frequency culminate at a point, and the position of the microphone demarks that frequency.   The relative acoustic energy at that frequency is indicated on the output meter M.   (After Meyer and Thienhaus.[27])

outputs.   The same sort of circuit and display as shown in Figs. 12·21 and 12·22 would be feasible.

A block diagram of the Meyer and Thienhaus apparatus is shown in Fig. 12·26.   The input signal is combined in a balanced modulator along with a signal of 45 kc from a local H.F. oscillator. A high pass filter rejects all components below 45 kc, and the amplified output is sent through a ribbon loudspeaker S.   (See Fig. 12·27.)   A ribbon is used whose width is comparable to a wavelength and whose length is somewhat greater than a wavelength, so that cylindrical waves are radiated.   The ribbon is placed behind an opening in a circular baffle covered with sound-absorbing material to prevent secondary reflections.   This baffle lies on the circumference of the circle of Fig. 12·27.

The source S is located off the axis of the grating (see Fig.

12·27) so that the sound which strikes the far end has to travel
a greater distance and therefore be attenuated more than that
which strikes the near end.   Because the length of the ribbon
is not small compared to a wavelength, it has a directional pattern.   The maximum of this pattern is faced toward the distant
end of the grating so as to produce a uniform sound field over its
length.   This means that the long dimension of the ribbon is
parallel to the long dimension of the grating.
   A very high frequency band of 45 to 50 kc is chosen to keep the
length of the grating small.   For these wavelengths in air (0.8

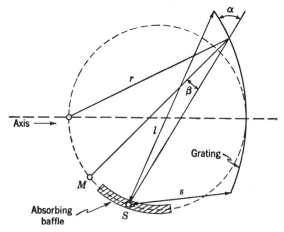

Fig. 12·27 Geometry of the relative locations of the acoustic grating,
microphone M, and the source S.

cm) the diffracting rods must be separated by about 1 cm, and a
total length of 3 meters is indicated.   Either a plane or a Row-
land circular grating can be used.
   If the radius of the grating is r and if the source and microphone lie on a circle of radius $r/2$, the absolute frequency discrimination Δf (the difference between the two closest components which can be distinguished from each other) is equal to

$$\Delta f = \frac{c}{(l - s)2} \qquad (12·15)$$

where l is the distance between the source and the more remote
end of the grating, s is the distance between the source and the
near end of the grating, and c is the velocity of sound.   The more
obliquely the grating is irradiated, the sharper the absolute fre-

quency discrimination. On the other hand, greater aberration is to be expected the farther the source is removed from the axis of the grating. Meyer and Thienhaus compromise on a location of the source which makes an average angle α of about 65° with the face of the grating (see Fig. 12·27).

For a given grating constant d (separation of diffracting rods) the angle β of the microphone position with respect to the source position for maximum intensity at a given wavelength λ is given by

$$\frac{\lambda}{d} = \cos \alpha + \cos (\alpha + \beta) \qquad (12 \cdot 16)$$

At any given angle α and for a particular lattice constant d there will be some frequency f_0 at which the source will radiate back at itself:

$$f_0 = \frac{c}{2d \cos \alpha} \qquad (12 \cdot 17)$$

It is seen from Fig. 12·27 and Eq. (12·17) that for a grating of any appreciable extent the angle α varies along the grating. This difficulty can be removed in large part by modifying the shape of the grating near the edges. This is done by trial and error with the aid of Eqs. (12·16) and (12·17).

Meyer and Thienhaus' grating was made from steel needles 3.4 mm in diameter fastened in two iron plates lying 12 cm apart. The construction is difficult because the grating constant must be held correct to within 0.02 mm. The grating has a theoretical resolving power of 125 cps and a dispersion of 8 cm/1000 cps, that is, the microphone position must be moved 8 cm for a frequency shift of 1000 cps.

The advantage of sound grating spectroscopy is the potential shortness of analyzing time. This time is limited by the difference in travel time between a ray of sound traveling from the source to the microphone via the farthest grating element and that via the nearest grating element. This time τ is given by the formula

$$\tau = \frac{2(l - s)}{c} \qquad (12 \cdot 18)$$

But according to Eq. (12·15) this is the reciprocal of the frequency discrimination. This relation is similar to one known in electrical communications, namely, $\tau = 1/\Delta f$, where Δf is the width of a filter band and τ is the time constant. Hence, by analogy, we see that it is possible to establish an acoustical spectrum within 0.01 sec with a resolution of 100 cps.

Full advantage of this short analyzing time can be achieved only if a number of microphone elements are distributed along the path where the acoustic "image" forms. Crystal elements sensitive to sounds in the 50-kc region and having a width of 1 cm are entirely feasible. These could then feed into an electronic switch to produce an analyzer with many bands. For a grating built like Meyer's, as many as 80 bands are possible.

G. Visible Speech Analyzers

The development of instrumentation for rapid and continuous analysis of complex sound waves received particular attention at the Bell Telephone Laboratories in the post-war years. An object of their researches has been equipment to permit the deaf to understand speech by viewing it in the form of visible patterns. An important by-product of their work, however, is the possibility of adapting their instrumentation to a multitude of other purposes.

The BTL apparatus is of three kinds[28] shown successively in Figs. 12·28, 12·30, and 12·31. The first device is designed to analyze a portion of speech 2.4 sec in length. As shown in Fig. 12·28, the signal is first amplified and then recorded on a loop of magnetic tape. This tape is made from Vicalloy metal, one-fourth inch wide and between 0.002 and 0.003 in. thick. In some of the later models a plated disk is used.

The recording is analyzed as a function of frequency with the aid of a heterodyne-type analyzer with a suitable bandwidth (say 200 cps). Each time the magnetic recording is played, the analyzer pass band is moved up 200 cps, while at the same time the stylus which records the output is moved to the right along the drum to trace another record.

[28] W. Koenig, H. K. Dunn, and L. Y. Lacy, "The sound spectograph," *Jour. Acous. Soc. Amer.*, **18**, 19–49 (1946); R. R. Riesz and L. Schott, "Visible speech cathode-ray translator," *J.A.S.A.*, **18**, 50–61 (1946); H. Dudley and O. O. Gruenz, Jr., "Visible speech translators with external phosphors," *J.A.S.A.*, **18**, 62–73 (1946). See also R. K. Potter, U.S. Patent 2,403,997 (1946), and W. Koenig and A. E. Rappel, "Quantitative amplitude representation in sound spectrograms," *Jour. Acous. Soc. Amer.*, **20**, 787–795 (1948).

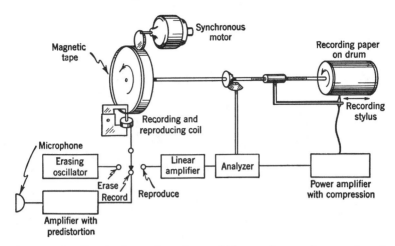

FIG. 12·28 Sketch of speech analyzer which records on a drum a plot of amplitude (which is proportional to the darkness of the trace) on a frequency *vs.* time set of coordinates. (After Koenig, Dunn, and Lacy.[28])

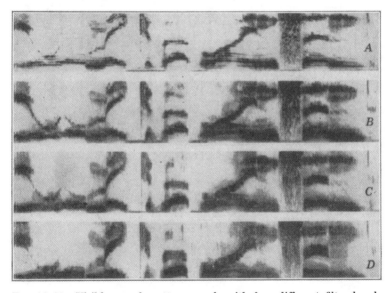

FIG. 12·29 Visible speech patterns made with four different filter bandwidths: (*A*) 90 cps, (*B*) 180 cps, (*C*) 300 cps, (*D*) 475 cps. A low-pitched voice was used. The horizontal axis is time, the vertical axis is a linear scale of frequency from 0 to 3500 cps, and the darkness is proportional to intensity. The dynamic range of darknesses can be as high as 40 db, but for facsimile paper it is little more than 10 db.

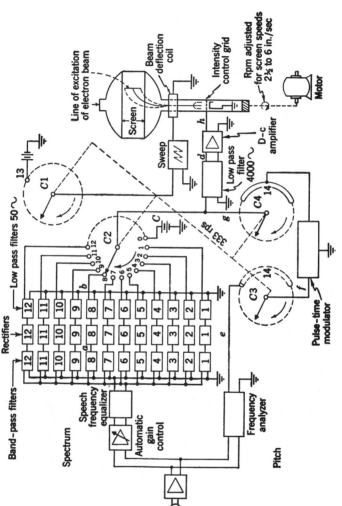

FIG. 12·30   Sound analyzer for portraying speech patterns visibly as a function of time on the face of a rotating cylindrical cathode ray tube.   (After Riesz and Schott.[28])

An alternative arrangement is to have the stylus blacken the drum in proportion to the intensity of the sound. Such an arrangement then gives a pattern like that shown in Fig. 12·29. For this sort of record, facsimile paper is used. This paper blackens in proportion to a potential applied across it, but the dynamic image is quite limited, being little over 10 db.

The second type of analyzer (Fig. 12·30) produces a continuously varying analysis which may be viewed for several seconds after it has been recorded. The speech patterns are portrayed on the screen of a special cathode ray tube shown at the right.

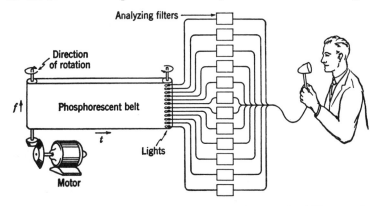

Fig. 12·31   Sketch of an apparatus for portraying speech visibly on a frequency *vs.* time graph. The third dimension of amplitude is obtained by varying degrees of phosphorescent glow on the moving belt. (After Dudley and Gruenz.[28])

The tube rotates about a vertical axis while the electron beam is constrained to move in a fixed vertical plane. The sound to be analyzed passes through a series of band-pass filters and rectifiers, and their outputs are sampled by a rotating switch which is geared to a vertical sweep control. The intensity of the spot on the screen is varied in relation to variations in the d-c voltage at the output of each channel, while the vertical position on the screen corresponds to the position of the commutating switch at that instant. The same sort of patterns is obtained as for the apparatus of Fig. 12·28 except that the analysis is continuously visible.

The third type of analyzer is illustrated in Fig. 12·31, in which speech is analyzed by a set of twelve contiguous filters. The resulting power outputs are conducted to twelve very small "grain-of-wheat" lamps which produce, on the moving belt, strips of corresponding phosphorescence which remain visible for over 1 sec.

It is necessary in the reading of speech patterns that emphasis be placed on the frequency *vs.* time characteristics of speech with less attention being given to the relative intensities among bands. For analysis of other types of sounds it would be desirable to have more positive indication of the relative amplitudes of the waves in the different bands. It is possible that in the continuously readable methods (Figs. 12·30 and 12·31) the dimension of intensity might have to be interjected through the medium of color. Tests on this type of presentation have already been reported by the Bell Laboratories.

12·4 Calibration of Sound Analyzers

Measurements of sound levels may be made to fulfill any one of several objectives. As examples, the conventional sound level meter[29] is designed to read numbers bearing some relation to the loudness of the sound energizing the microphone. Recently an apparatus for determining the loudness of continuous spectrum sounds more accurately has been proposed.[6] In other cases one wishes to determine whether or not a wanted signal can be perceived in the presence of an interfering noise. There is also a proposal in the literature[30] that an equipment be designed to measure a "speech interference level" which would correlate well with the interfering effect of noise on the intelligibility of speech. At other times, accurate measurement of individual components is desired in order to determine what effect changes in the design of a noisy machine might have on certain components of the noise. It is not a purpose of this section to decide the detailed specifications which a sound analyzer should meet to accomplish any one of these particular objectives. That problem is the responsibility of the psychophysicist and the user. Here we shall, however, discuss electronic and acoustic calibration techniques suitable for accurate determination of those parameters of

[29] "American standard for noise measurement," Z24.2 (1942), and "American standard for sound level meters for measurement of noise and other sounds," Z24.3 (1944), American Standards Association, New York, New York.

[30] L. L. Beranek, "Airplane quieting II—specification of acceptable noise levels in flight," *Trans. A.S.M.E.*, **69**, 97–100 (1947). See also, "Sound control in airplanes," *Jour. Acous. Soc. Amer.*, **19**, 357–364 (1947).

analyzing instruments which we believe are pertinent to the analysis of steady, transient, or random sounds.

When we calibrate a sound analyzer, the principal datum we generally desire is either the *level of a pure tone* which will produce the same meter indication on the analyzer as does the unknown noise, or the *spectrum level of a random noise* which will produce the same meter indication as does the unknown noise.   To ascertain either of these quantities we must measure the response characteristics of the bands of the sound analyzer.   To obtain these response characteristics we may use either a pure tone source or a random noise source of sound during calibration. In some cases it is relatively easy to calculate the random noise response characteristic if the pure tone response is available, though it is never possible to do the opposite.

Elaborating further, we generally wish (1) to determine the average response within each pass band (often both before and after insertion of the filter); (2) to ascertain the cutoff frequencies f_a and f_b of each pass band, where f_a and f_b are defined as the limiting frequencies of an ideal pass band which would, when measuring random noise, give the same meter reading as does the actual pass band under test (this definition of f_a and f_b assumes that the average response in the pass band of the actual filter is set equal to the response of the ideal filter in its pass band); (3) to find the mean frequency f_0 of each pass band; (4) to measure the residual noise level in each pass band, because this factor determines the weakest signals that can be measured; (5) to determine the level at which overload of the system occurs, because this factor determines the strongest signals that can be measured; and (6) to determine the attenuation in the regions outside each pass band, which in turn determines the ratio of noise power passed by the filter outside the band to that passed inside the band.   This ratio sets the accuracy with which the level of the noise included within the band is read.

In addition to those factors just mentioned, we must also know the integrating characteristics of the rectifier associated with the indicating instrument because, when complex waves are being measured, a meter which indicates the average amplitude may read from one to several decibels above or below one which reads rms amplitude.   Methods for determining the integrating properties of indicating instruments are given in Chapter 11 and will not be repeated here.

In *A* through *D* below we shall discuss first an exact means for determination of the average response in a filter band using either a sine wave or random noise and secondly an approximate means for doing this by (*a*) estimating the average level in the band, (*b*) determining the effective cutoff frequencies, and (*c*) determining the geometric mean frequency.

A. Determination of the Average Response of a Filter Band—Exact Procedure

Sine Wave Response of the Band. The first step in the determination of the sine wave response of a pass band is to connect

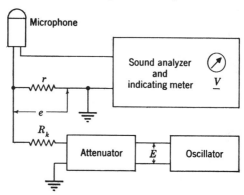

FIG. 12·32   Schematic diagram of the electrical input circuit for calibrating a sound analyzer.   It is assumed that a calibration curve as a function of frequency for the microphone is available.

the analyzer into the circuit of Fig. 12·32.   An insert resistance r is placed in the ground leg of the microphone circuit.*   The acoustic environment of the microphone should be quiet.   An accurately known voltage e, adjustable in magnitude, is produced across the resistance r by means of an oscillator and attenuator. This voltage will cause a deflection V of the analyzer meter in the same manner as that produced when the microphone is excited by sound.

A suitable calibration curve of the microphone should be available.   It must indicate the open-circuit voltage produced as a function of frequency by the microphone for a constant sound pressure.   Either the pressure at the diaphragm, p_d, or the free-field pressure, p_{ff}, or the random-incidence free-field pressure,

---

* The theory of the insert resistor type of test is covered in Chapter 13.

p_{rf}, may be used, depending on what the analyzer is supposed to indicate. The constant sound pressure used during calibration of the microphone is usually chosen to be 1 dyne/cm^2, that is, 74 db *re* 0.0002 dyne/cm^2.

As an example, let us suppose that the calibration curve for the microphone shows the response to be -82 db (*re* 1 volt per dyne/cm^2) at 800 cps. We set the oscillator frequency to 800 cps and e equal to -82 db *re* 1 volt. If the analyzer is in perfect calibration the meter should indicate the number of decibels for which the microphone was calibrated, in this case 74 db. Let us say that instead it reads 67 db at 800 cps. This procedure is repeated at each frequency, the proper value of e being chosen from the microphone calibration curve. If V does not equal the desired reading (74 db) at each frequency checked, a deviation curve in decibels A *vs.* frequency should be prepared like that shown in Fig. 12·33 (lower curve). In this example, the deviation is -7 db at 800 cps, that is, 74 $-$ 67 db.

Alternatively, we can hold e constant during calibration and observe the meter readings V in decibels as a function of frequency. Then, we add to V, in decibels, the deviations of the microphone response curve from the level corresponding to the voltage e. Finally, we subtract 74 db from all readings to get the deviation curve. For example, suppose we hold e constant at -70 db as a function of frequency. Then our meter reading V at 800 cps is 79 db. We add to this the difference between -82 db and -70 db. We get the value 79 $-$ 12 = 67 db. Subtracting 74 db from this gives a deviation of -7 db, the same value we obtained before.

If the analyzer is to be used to measure a pure tone whose frequency is known, the correction datum can be determined directly from Fig. 12·33 for that particular frequency. On the other hand, if we are to measure a pure tone whose frequency lies with equal probability between two limits, say 1000 and 2000 cps, a correction equal to the average area under the deviation curve (plotted on a decibels *vs.* linear frequency scale) divided by the bandwidth should be used. For the curve of Fig. 12·33, an average deviation of -1.0 db is found, which indicates that a correction of $+1.0$ db must be added to the readings. The reading on a pure tone lying between 1000 and 2000 cps after correction will then be correct to within $+1.5$ and -2.0 db, and the probable error will be $+0.5$ and -0.7 db.

550   **Analysis of Sound Waves**

Frequently, continuous spectrum sounds are analyzed in an effort to determine the rms amplitudes within the limits of a set of bands. Unfortunately, it is not possible to apply a single correction to the reading of the meter for all bands, because the correction factor for each band is a function of the shape of the noise spectrum. What we want to determine is the total amount

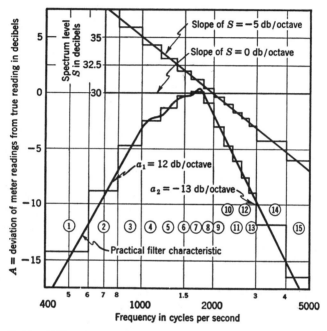

Fig. 12·33 Calibration curves for a sound analyzer. The lower solid line is a calibration curve for a filter band with nominal cutoff frequencies at 1000 and 2000 cps. When a white random noise is passed through this particular filter, the analysis given in the text shows that the effective cutoff frequencies are 940 and 2370 cps and the average insertion loss is −0.5 db.

of energy passed by each band and then to compare that figure with what would have been passed if the band had an ideal shape; that is, vertical sides and a flat top with $A = 0$. One method, applicable to the deviation curve of Fig. 12·33, is to divide the band into a number of intervals and to proceed as described below.

Because the sound energy is assumed to be continuously distributed, we can employ the concept of power $w(f)$ associated with a band 1 cycle in width at a frequency f. This power may be expressed relative to a reference "power per cycle" w_0, where

$$w_0 = \frac{P_0}{\Delta f_0} \qquad (12 \cdot 19)$$

Here, the subscript zero denotes "reference," P_0 is a reference power and Δf_0 the reference bandwidth of 1 cps. For brevity, we call ten times the logarithm of the ratio of $w(f)$ to w_0 the *spectrum level* and give it the symbol S. Hence,

$$S = 10 \log_{10} \frac{w(f)}{w_0} \qquad (12 \cdot 20)$$

and

$$w(f) = w_0 10^{s/10} \qquad (12 \cdot 21)$$

Note that the reference power per cycle w_0 is numerically but not dimensionally equal to P_0.

The total power P_n in any band of $(f_b - f_a)$ cycles may be found by multiplying the average power per cycle w_n by the bandwidth:

$$P_n = (f_b - f_a)w_n \qquad (12 \cdot 22)$$

where n indicates the number of the band being considered. Because we have a number of contiguous bands, the total power P summed over the band is

$$P = P_1 + P_2 + P_3 + \cdots + P_n \qquad (12 \cdot 23)$$

The overall level L due to the power P in the frequency range covered by the bands is

$$L = 10 \log_{10} \frac{P}{P_0} \quad \text{db} \qquad (12 \cdot 24)$$

Now if we assume for the moment that we have an ideal filter with a flat top of zero deviation A and vertical sides at $f_a = 1000$ and $f_b = 2000$ cps, and that we are to measure a white noise whose spectrum level is S decibels, L would be calculated as follows:

$$L = 10 \log_{10} \frac{P}{P_0} = 10 \log_{10} \frac{(f_b - f_a)w}{P_0}$$

$$= 10 \log_{10} (f_b - f_a) + 10 \log_{10} w - 10 \log_{10} P_0 \qquad (12 \cdot 25)$$

where w is given by Eq. (12·21). Now, because w_0 in Eq. (12·21) is equal numerically to P_0 in Eq. (12·25), we get

$$L = 10 \log_{10} (f_b - f_a) + 10 \log 10^{S/10}$$

$$= 10 \log_{10} (f_b - f_a) + S \quad \text{db} \qquad (12·26)$$

Hence, for our ideal filter of this example with a bandwidth of 1000 cps, the level of the noise at the output is simply

$$L = S + 30 \quad \text{db} \qquad (12·27)$$

For the non-uniform filter characteristic of Fig. 12·33, the procedure for determining the power level L at the output of the filter is accomplished by dividing the frequency scale up into n bands and summing the powers in each as follows:

$$L = 10 \log_{10} \sum_n (f_b - f_a)_n w_n - 10 \log_{10} w_0 \qquad (12·28)$$

or

$$L = 10 \log_{10} \sum_n (f_b - f_a)_n 10^{S_n/10} \quad \text{db} \qquad (12·29)$$

Alternatively,

$$L = 10 \log_{10} \sum_n 10^{(S_n + C_n)/10} \quad \text{db} \qquad (12·30)$$

where

$$C_n = 10 \log_{10} (f_b - f_a) \quad \text{db} \qquad (12·31)$$

In Eq. (12·31) the term $(f_b - f_a)$ has been divided by $\Delta f_0 = 1$, so that the argument of the logarithm is dimensionless.

In Fig. 12·33, we have divided the filter band into fifteen bands, thirteen of which are 200 cps in width and two of which are 1000 cps in width. Non-uniform division along the frequency scale is quite feasible, the difference being that the value of C_n is different for each band. The operations called for in Eq. (12·30) are tabulated in Table 12·2. A flat spectrum level is assumed for this calculation, permitting S_n to take any convenient value throughout the summation process. We shall arbitrarily choose $S_n = 30$ db. In this table the quantity A_n is used to designate the average deviation of the level in each band. The use of a figure slightly above the arithmetic average of the deviations in each band is satisfactory because the bands are narrow and the range of the curve in each band is limited.

TABLE 12·2

(S_n is the spectrum level of the noise in the nth band; C_n is the bandwidth expressed in decibels re unit band width; and A_n is the average deviation of the meter reading from true reading for the band in decibels.)

Band	S_n, db	C_n, db	$B_n =$ $C_n + S_n$	A_n, db	$A_n + B_n$	$10^{(A_n+B_n)/10}$
1	30	23	53	−14.2	38.8	0.76×10^4
2	30	23	53	−8.7	44.3	2.69
3	30	23	53	−4.7	48.3	6.76
4	30	23	53	−2.5	50.5	11.22
5	30	23	53	−1.3	51.7	14.79
6	30	23	53	−0.2	52.8	19.05
7	30	23	53	0.2	53.2	20.89
8	30	23	53	−0.8	52.2	16.60
9	30	23	53	−3.0	50.0	10.00
10	30	23	53	−4.8	48.2	6.61
11	30	23	53	−6.1	46.9	4.90
12	30	23	53	−7.6	45.4	3.47
13	30	23	53	−9.0	44.0	2.51
14	30	30	60	−12.	48.	3.02
15	30	30	60	−16.5	43.5	2.24

Total $P/P_0 = 125.51 \times 10^4$

Overall level $= 10 \log_{10} 1.255 \times 10^6 = 61$db

We see from Table 12·2 that when we measure a white noise with the filter characteristic of Fig. 12·33 we obtain a meter reading 1.0 db higher than we would with an ideal filter characteristic having zero deviation extending from 1000 to 2000 cps; see Eq. (12·27) and remember that $S = 30$ db.

If the noise spectrum is continuous but decreases at the rate of 5 db/octave, our ideal filter will read the sum of the powers in bands 4 to 8 respectively in Fig. 12·33. That is, it would read the sum of the powers represented by the $(S_n + C_n)$ values for each band, are $(34.3 + 23)$ db, $(33.1 + 23)$ db, $(32 + 23)$ db, $(31.2 + 23)$ db, $(30.3 + 23)$ db. On taking the antilogarithm of each of these quantities, adding the result, and converting the figure into decibels again, we find that the overall power level is 62.4 db for the ideal filter.

The reading which we would obtain for the fifteen bands of the irregular filter characteristic is calculated as shown in Table 12·3 and is 63.3 db. However, the results of Table 12·3 are not quite correct because the noise spectrum increases on the low frequency side of the band, and more bands below band 1 should have been calculated. If that had been done, a level of about 63.5 db would have been obtained. In conclusion, we see that the corrections to be applied to the readings obtained with the

TABLE 12·3

(S_n is the spectrum level of the noise in the nth band; C_n is the bandwidth expressed in decibels *re* unit bandwidth; and A_n is the average deviation of the meter reading from true reading for the band in decibels.)

Band	S_n, db	C_n, db	$B_n =$ $C_n + S_n$	A_n, db	$A_n + B_n$	$10^{(A_n+B_n)/10}$
1	40.5	23	63.5	−14.2	49.3	0.85×10^5
2	38.	23	61.	−8.7	52.3	1.70
3	36.	23	59	−4.7	54.3	2.69
4	34.3	23	57.3	−2.5	54.8	3.02
5	33.1	23	56.1	−1.3	54.8	3.02
6	32.	23	55.0	−0.2	54.8	3.02
7	31.2	23	54.2	0.2	54.5	2.75
8	30.3	23	53.3	−0.8	52.5	1.78
9	29.7	23	52.7	−3.0	49.7	.93
10	29.0	23	52.0	−4.8	47.2	.52
11	28.2	23	51.2	−6.1	45.1	.28
12	27.7	23	50.7	−7.6	43.1	.20
13	27.1	23	50.1	−9.0	41.1	.13
14	25.8	30	55.8	−10.3	45.5	.35
15	24.0	30	54.0	−16.5	37.5	.06

Total $P/P_0 = 21.30 \times 10^5$

Overall level $= 10 \log_{10} 21.30 \times 10^6 = 63.3$ db

non-uniform filter are $60 - 61 = 1.0$ db for "white" noise and $62.4 - 63.5 = 1.1$ db for a continuous noise whose spectrum level slopes at the rate of -5 db/octave.

Random Noise Response of the Band. Although the method just described will yield corrections for any given filter characteristic and type of noise, it is laborious to carry out if the system consists of a number of electromechanical components connected in tandem, such as is the case for a recording system. Recently a method has been advanced for by-passing much of the labor of calibration of analyzers which are primarily used for measuring random types of sounds.[5] The method comprises four steps:

(1) Apply to the insert resistor of Fig. 12·32 a white electrical noise whose rms spectrum level is 20 $\log_{10} e$, and record the readings V for each setting of the filter bands. Plot these readings at the mean frequencies of each of the bands.

(2) Add the open-circuit calibration curve of the microphone to the measured curve of (1). This operation gives the meter readings which would be obtained if a white acoustic noise had been impressed on the microphone. The spectrum level S (in decibels) of that white acoustic noise is that at which the microphone was calibrated (usually 74 db *re* 0.0002 dyne/cm^2).

(3) Turn off the electrical noise e and pass the unknown acoustic spectrum through the microphone and analyzer.

(4) Determine for each pass band the difference (in decibels) between the meter readings obtained in (2) and (3) above. This result gives spectrum levels of the unknown noise in the various pass bands relative to the spectrum levels of a white noise in the same bands.

(5) Add the curve of (4) to the spectrum level S of (2). This operation gives the spectrum level of the unknown noise as a function of frequency.

Obviously, the microphone calibration would be unnecessary if the white noise were generated acoustically and fed into the microphone. The possibility of doing this acoustically by using pistol shots and condenser discharges as continuous spectrum sources of noise is discussed in Chapter 9.

The rms spectrum level 20 $\log_{10} e$ of the white electrical noise can be measured with a calibrated, narrow-band analyzer. The procedure of calibrating a system by means of a uniform noise spectrum is applicable to a wide variety of instruments. It is relatively foolproof if care is taken not to overload any of the circuit elements, for amplitude distortion would destroy the validity of the method. The procedure is especially useful when the overall response of several successive stages in recording and reproduction of speech or music is desired, each with its own frequency characteristic.

B. Determination of the Average Response of a Filter Band—Approximate Procedure

The approximate procedure for determining the average response in a filter band consists in performing the following steps:

(1) Determine the deviation of the meter readings on the analyzer from the true readings using the circuit of Fig. 12·32 with a pure tone for the voltage E supplied by the test oscillator. The result is plotted on semi-log paper, and it will be a curve like that shown in Fig. 12·33. It is necessary, of course, that the voltage e in the test circuit be that which the microphone would produce if it were excited by a pure-tone sound field whose sound pressure level equals the level that the meter should indicate. For example, suppose that the microphone calibration curve says that at 1000 cps the microphone has a sensitivity of -60 db re 1 volt per dyne/cm^2. Then the voltage e should be set at -60 db re 1 volt (i.e., 1 mv), and the meter should properly read 74 db re 0.0002 dyne/cm^2. If it does not, the deviation of its reading from 74 is plotted as A at 1000 cps in Fig. 12·33.

(2) Determine the "average" response of the pass band. This is done by extending the two sloping cutoffs upward. Then a line is drawn horizontally such that the area between the horizontal line and that part of the A curve lying above it is slightly less than the area between the horizontal line and that part of the A curve lying below it. In both cases the areas considered are bounded by the extensions of the sloping cutoffs. As an example, the horizontal line would be located at about -0.5 db in Fig. 12·33. Let us call the difference between this horizontal line and the zero deviation line of Fig. 12·33 A_{av} db.

(3) Determine the effective cutoff frequencies f_a and f_b by the procedure given in C following. Equations (12·39) and (12·40), used in conjunction with Fig. 12·34, are usually suitable for this purpose. These enable us to calculate the quantity C_n of Eq. (12·31).

(4) Determine the geometric mean frequency f_g of the band where $f_g = \sqrt{f_a f_b}$.

(5) Obtain the spectrum level S_n of the noise being applied to the filter band at the frequency f_g. Let us call this quantity S_{gn}. For example, S_{gn} at 1400 cps for the sloping spectrum of Fig. 12·33 is $+32.5$ db.

(6) Calculate the total power level transmitted by the filter band from the formula

$$L_n = S_{gn} + C_n + A_{av} \quad \text{db} \qquad (12·32)$$

(7) Calculate the total power level that would have been transmitted by an ideal filter band with the *nominal* cutoff fre-

quencies indicated on the filter set of the analyzer. To do this Eq. (12·26) is suitable wherein S is the spectrum level at the nominal mean frequency and f_b and f_a are the nominal cutoff frequencies of the band. Let us call this quantity L_{Nn}, where the N stands for nominal.

(8) Finally, the correction to be applied to the actual filter band readings when measuring continuous spectrum types of noises is

Correction for the nth band $= L_{Nn} - L_n$ db   (12·33)

C. Determination of the Effective Cutoff Frequencies of a Filter Band[31]

Actual filters do not have idealized "vertical" cutoffs, but rather more or less sloping ones. That is, energy will be passed by the filter which lies outside the frequency limits of that flat part of the band. Therefore, we must investigate the transmission of power by a band with "sloping cutoffs." Such a pass band is shown by the solid lines in the lower part of Fig. 12·34. These cutoffs are described in decibels per octave, the number of decibels change in transmission as the frequency is changed by a factor of 2. The filter is assumed to be one whose transmission may be approximated by a flat top from frequencies f_c to f_d, and by cutoffs dropping off a_1 and a_2 db/octave, respectively.

Almost any practical filter has a portion near the top which is fairly flat. When applying our method to these types of filters, we first draw a horizontal line through the average of this flat region. Then we extend the two sloping cutoffs upward until they intersect the horizontal line. These three lines form the idealized filter characteristic.

Now, let us assume that the spectrum level of the noise is represented by a straight line on a linear-log plot (see the upper part of Fig. 12·34) which can be described by the equation

$$\frac{w(f)}{w(f_x)} = \left(\frac{f}{f_x}\right)^{m/3.01} \qquad (12·34)$$

where $w(f)$ is the power per cycle at the frequency f, f_x is any

[31] R. W. Young, "Methods suitable for the calibration and use of an octave-band sound-level meter," Report M32, University of California Division of War Research, at U.S. Navy Radio and Sound Laboratory, San Diego, February 10, 1943.

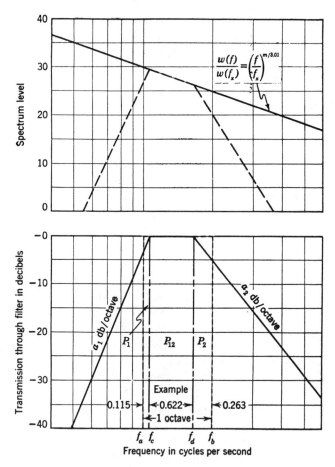

Fig. 12·34 The spectrum level of a sloping band of noise is shown by the solid line in the upper graph, and the dashed lines show the sum of the filter characteristic from the lower graph and the noise spectrum of the upper graph. The short-dashed lines in the lower graph show the frequency limits of an ideal band-pass filter with the same transmission characteristics as those for the filter represented by the solid lines. The ordinate of the graph is logarithmic. (After Young.[31])

arbitrarily selected frequency, and m is the slope of the sound spectrum in decibels per octave.

Our task is to find the flat-topped, "vertical-sided" pass band indicated by the dotted lines f_a and f_b in the lower part of Fig. 12·34 which is equivalent to the sloping-sided filter. This is accomplished by summing the total power passed by the filter.

Divide the total power transmitted by the sloping-sided filter into three parts: P_{1-2}, the power passed between frequencies f_c and f_d; P_1, the power passed at frequencies below f_c; and P_2, the power passed at frequencies above f_d. We get

$$P_{1-2} = \int_{f_c}^{f_d} w(f)\, df = \int_{f_c}^{f_d} w(f_c) \left(\frac{f}{f_c}\right)^{m/3.01} df$$

$$= f_c \left[\frac{3.01 \left(\dfrac{f_d}{f_c}\right)^{(m+3.01)/3.01} - 3.01}{m + 3.01}\right] w(f_c) \quad (12 \cdot 35)$$

Obviously, if $m = $ exactly -3.01 db/octave, this integral assumes a log form.

$$P_1 = \int_0^{f_c} w(f_c) \left(\frac{f}{f_c}\right)^{(a_1+m)/3.01} df = f_c \left(\frac{3.01}{3.01+m+a_1}\right) w(f_c) \quad (12 \cdot 36)$$

$$P_2 = \int_{f_d}^{\infty} w(f_d) \left(\frac{f}{f_d}\right)^{(a_2+m)/3.01} df = f_d \left(\frac{-3.01}{3.01+m+a_2}\right) w(f_d) \quad (12 \cdot 37)$$

Note that a_1 is intrinsically a positive quantity whereas a_2 is intrinsically negative.

The total power P passed by the filter band equals

$$P = f_c w(f_c) \times$$
$$\left[\frac{\left(\dfrac{f_d}{f_c}\right)^{(m+3.01)/3.01} - 1}{1 + \dfrac{m}{3.01}} + \frac{1}{1 + \dfrac{m+a_1}{3.01}} - \frac{\left(\dfrac{f_d}{f_c}\right)^{(m+3.01)/3.01}}{1 + \dfrac{m+a_2}{3.01}}\right] \quad (12 \cdot 38)$$

Under the special condition that $m = 0$, this equation says that the power passed by the filter is the same as that which would be passed by a "vertical-sided" filter whose cutoffs are

$$f_b = \frac{f_d}{1 + \dfrac{3.01}{a_2}} \quad (12 \cdot 39)$$

$$f_a = \frac{f_c}{1 + \dfrac{3.01}{a_1}} \quad (12 \cdot 40)$$

where a_1 and a_2 are the slopes of the filter characteristic on either side of the two cutoff frequencies in decibels per octave, and a_2 is intrinsically negative.

For our example of Fig. 12·33, the average horizontal level in the pass band occurs at a value of A equal to about -0.5 db. If the sloping sides are extrapolated so as to intersect the -0.5 db line, we find that $f_c = 1180$ cps and $f_d = 1820$ cps. On applying formulas (12·39) and (12·40), respectively, and noting that $a_1 = 12$ db/octave and $a_2 = -13$ db/octave, we get $f_a = 940$ cps and $f_b = 2370$ cps. The power level passed by this band, assuming $S_n = 30$, would equal $-0.5 - 10 \log_{10} (f_b - f_a) + 30 = 61.0$ db, which is the same figure we arrived at in Table 12·2.

D. Determination of the Mean Frequency of a Filter Band[31]

When we measure a noise with a filter band and convert the reading to a spectrum level we have an "average" figure to deal with. It is necessary to know to what frequency this average corresponds, in order that it may be properly plotted on a frequency scale.

The mean frequency for an ideal filter band will be a function of f_a, of f_b, and of the slope of the noise spectrum m. For a sloping spectrum, the actual spectrum level will be different at each frequency in the band. At some one frequency f_e, however, the power per cycle will equal an average value $w(f_e)$, such that for a "vertical-sided" band

$$P_{1-2} \equiv w(f_e)(f_b - f_a) \quad \text{watts} \quad (12·41)$$

The power P_{1-2} is calculated from the equation

$$P_{1-2} = \int_{f_a}^{f_b} w(f)\, df = w(f_x) \int_{f_a}^{f_b} \left(\frac{f}{f_x}\right)^{m/3.01} df \quad (12·42)$$

where the value of $w(f)$ is found from Eq. (12·34). When $m = -3.01$, this integral must assume a log form. Integrating we get

$$P_{1-2} = w(f_x)f_x \left[\frac{3.01}{m + 3.01}\right] \left[\left(\frac{f_b}{f_x}\right)^{1+(m/3.01)} - \left(\frac{f_a}{f_x}\right)^{1+(m/3.01)}\right] \quad (12·43)$$

where, as before, f_a and f_b are the effective cutoff frequencies of the filter, f_x is any reference frequency, and m is the slope of the

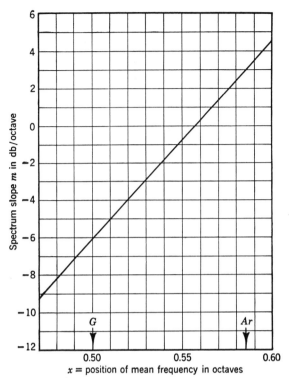

FIG. 12·35   The position of the mean frequency of a perfect octave-band filter when a random noise with a spectrum slope m is passed through it. The abscissa is expressed in octaves above the lower cutoff frequency. For example, if the noise has a spectrum slope of -6 db/octave, the mean frequency will lie one-half an octave above the lower cutoff frequency. This corresponds to the geometric (G) mean frequency. The letters Ar correspond to the arithmetic mean frequency. (After Young.[31])

spectrum in decibels per octave. Now, by substituting f_e for f_x and substituting for P_{1-2} from Eq. 12·41, we get

$$f_e = \left[\frac{3.01}{m + 3.01}\right]^{3.01/m} \left[\frac{f_b{}^{1+(m/3.01)} - f_a{}^{1+(m/3.01)}}{f_b - f_a}\right]^{3.01/m} \quad (12\cdot44)$$

For the particular case of *an octave band*, $(f_b - f_a) = f_a$,

$$f_e = f_a \left[\frac{3.01}{m + 3.01} \left(2^{(3.01+m)/3.01} - 1\right)\right]^{3.01/m} \quad (12\cdot45)$$

For the octave band, let us express the mean frequency f_e as a certain fraction of an octave above the lower cutoff frequency

562   **Analysis of Sound Waves**

f_a. This fraction of an octave is

$$x = \log_2 \frac{f_e}{f_a} = \frac{10}{m} \log_{10} \left[\frac{3.01}{m + 3.01} \right] [10^{(3.01+m)/10} - 1] \quad (12\cdot46)$$

This function is plotted in Fig. 12·35 showing the mean frequency of the octave for various slopes of spectra. If the spectrum

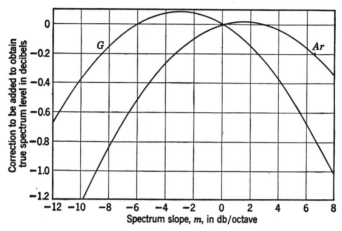

Fig. 12·36 This graph shows the corrections to the error in band reading (in decibels) which will result from multiplying the spectrum power per cycle at either the geometric or the arithmetic mean frequency by the effective bandwidth to obtain the total power passed by a perfect filter band. (After Young.[31])

slopes downward at 6 db/octave ($m = -6$), the geometric mean ($f_e = f_g = \sqrt{f_a f_b} = 1.41 f_a$) of the octave is the correct mean frequency to use. On the other hand, if the spectrum slopes upward by 3 db/octave ($m = 3$), the arithmetic mean [$f_e = f_{Ar} = (f_b + f_a)/2 = 1.5 f_a$] is the correct mean frequency.

The correction needed to compensate for the error that will result when the geometric ($\sqrt{f_a f_b}$) or arithmetic [$(f_a + f_b)/2$] mean frequency is used when plotting $w(f_e)$ is indicated in Fig. 12·36. It appears that, for most types of noise spectra encountered, the geometric mean frequency f_g is the more suitable one to use.

E. Conversion from Narrow-Band Levels to Wide-Band Levels

The procedure for converting from sound levels measured with a set of contiguous narrow-band filters to an overall (wide-band) level was discussed in A of this section of the chapter in connection with determining corrections for non-ideal filter characteristics. An example will be carried through here to show explicitly the method for accomplishing this conversion. Let us consider that the noise spectrum of Fig. 12·37 had been measured in the frequency range of 300 to 9600 cps by using five octave filter bands. The power per cycle which would be passed by each of

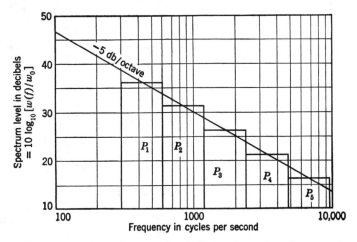

FIG. 12·37 Analysis with octave-band filters of a noise whose spectrum level slopes at the rate of −5 db/octave. The P's represent the power contributed by each band. The effective spectrum level for each band is determined by the intersection of the sloping spectrum with the geometric mean frequency for that band. (After Young.[31])

the filter bands can be calculated from Eq. (12·41), which becomes, when expressed in decibels.

$$10 \log_{10} \frac{P_n}{P_0} = 10 \log_{10} \frac{w_n(f_g)}{w_0} + 10 \log_{10} (f_b - f_a) \quad (12\cdot47)$$

where $w_n(f_g)$ is the spectrum power per cycle at the geometric mean frequency f_g. Or, because $P_0 = w_0$ in magnitude,

$$10 \log_{10} \frac{P_n}{P_0} = B_n = S_n + C_n \quad (12\cdot48)$$

where B_n is the power level in decibels at the output of the nth band, S_n is the spectrum level in decibels in that band, and C_n is given by Eq. (12·31).

For octave-band filters, the term C_n can be found directly in terms of the geometric mean frequency f_g from Fig. $12 \cdot 38$.

To complicate the problem further, let us assume that the microphone and amplifying circuit have the response characteristic of Fig. $12 \cdot 39$. In each of the bands we draw a line at what

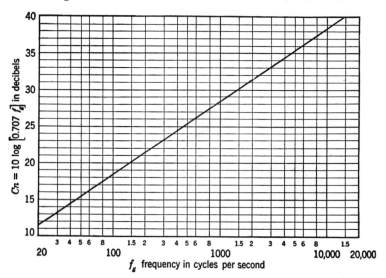

FIG. $12 \cdot 38$ Relation between C_n and the geometric mean frequency for bands which are 1 octave in width.   (After Young.[31])

we estimate is the average response.   The power level for each band now becomes

$$L_n = S_n + C_n + A_n = B_n + A_n \qquad (12 \cdot 49)$$

The overall power level passed by the analyzer is calculated as shown in Table $12 \cdot 4$.

TABLE $12 \cdot 4$

Band	S_n	C_n	B_n	A_n	L_n	$Antilog_{10}\ (L_n/10)$
1	36.2	24.8	61	-2.5	58.5	7.08×10^5
2	31.2	27.8	59	0.5	59.5	8.91×10^5
3	26.2	30.8	57	9.0	66.0	39.81×10^5
4	21.2	33.8	55	9.5	64.5	28.12×10^5
5	16.2	36.8	53	6.5	59.5	8.91×10^5

Total $P/P_0 = 92.83 \times 10^5$

Overall level $= 10 \log 9.28 \times 10^6 = 69.7$ db

Direct Addition of Levels.   With the help of Fig. $12 \cdot 40$, we can go directly from the L_n's to the overall power level without

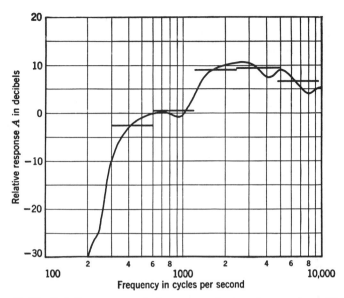

FIG. 12·39   Relative response A of an assumed microphone and amplifying circuit. The horizontal lines are drawn through the estimated average response for each of 5 octave bands lying between 300 and 9600 cps.

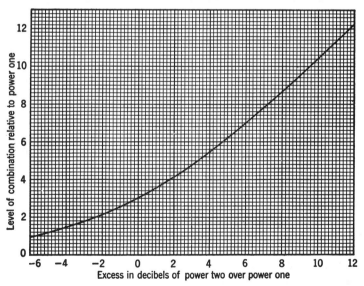

FIG. 12·40   Chart for converting two powers, each given in decibels, over to their sum in decibels. Example: Assume two powers with levels 6 and 12 db *re* 1 watt, respectively. Their sum will be 13 db *re* 1 watt.

going through the conversion to anti-logarithms indicated in Table 12·4. In the example we are using, upon starting with the lowest L_n (L_1 = 58.5 db; see Table 12·4), we observed that the L_2 is 59.5 or 1 db higher. From Fig. 12·40, we find that for a difference of 1 db the combination will have a level 3.5 db higher than L_1, etc. The detailed operations for this example are

$$
\begin{aligned}
L_1 = 58.5 &\leftarrow \text{compare } 59.5 = L_2 \\
\underline{3.5} & \\
62.0 &\leftarrow \text{compare } 66.0 = L_3 \\
\underline{5.4} & \\
67.4 &\leftarrow \text{compare } 64.5 = L_4 \\
\underline{1.8} & \\
69.2 &\leftarrow \text{compare } 59.5 = L_5 \\
\underline{0.5} & \\
69.7 &\leftarrow \text{Total level}
\end{aligned}
$$

F. Conversion from Wide-Band Levels to Spectrum Levels

Sound levels measured with wide-band filters are converted to spectrum levels by the exact reverse of the process described in the preceding section. The procedure follows.

(1) Determine the equivalent "vertical-sided" filter by using the techniques of part C of this section. Equations (12·39) and (12·40), used in conjunction with Fig. 12·34, are usually satisfactory for this purpose. This gives us the effective upper and lower cutoff frequencies f_a and f_b of the pass band.

(2) Determine the conversion term C_n for each band from the formula

$$C_n = 10 \log (f_b - f_a) \quad \text{db} \qquad (12·50)$$

(3) Determine the geometric mean frequency, f_g, for each band by performing the following operation:

$$f_g = \sqrt{f_a f_b} \qquad (12·51)$$

If f_b is very nearly $2f_a$, then $f_g = 1.41 f_a$.

(4) Determine the correction A_n for each band, that is, the average gain or loss in decibels of each of the pass bands. See Fig. 12·39 as an example.

(5) Determine the spectrum level S_n for each band from the equation

$$S_n = L_n - C_n - A_n \quad \text{db} \quad (12 \cdot 52)$$

where L_n is the level in decibels measured with the wide band.

(6) Plot S_n in decibels at those frequency points corresponding to f_g for each band.

G. Determination of Residual Noise

We frequently use sound level meters in airplanes, railroad passenger cars, factories, and so on. In these locations the noise and vibration levels are often high and frequently have very non-uniform spectra. Wrong meter indications will result if the instrument responds to noise or vibration other than through the microphone itself. Indications of the instrument which arise from such causes are called microphonic readings. Even in vibration-free locations there is a lower limit to the sound levels that can be measured. This lower level is established by thermal and shot effect noises in the instrument and is known as the residual noise level.

As an example of the manner in which microphonic readings might be determined, a paragraph is quoted from a recent specification:[32] "The microphone shall be immersed in a noise field of 40 decibels pressure level and the meter reading noted. The microphone shall then be disconnected and an equivalent dummy impedance substituted. The meter shall then be placed in a sound field having a sound pressure level of 130 decibels and the reading noted. Finally, the meter shall be subjected to a sinusoidal vibration of 0.005 inch double amplitude at frequencies from 10 to 50 cycles per second and the meter reading noted. In neither of the latter two cases shall the reading exceed that obtained when the microphone was immersed in the original noise field."

Residual noise is loosely expressed in terms of the meter reading that it produces when the instrument is placed in a quiet location. More accurately, let us define "equivalent self-noise level" as that sound level which would be required to produce the same meter reading as is produced by the residual noise.

[32] "Noise measuring equipment," Army-Navy Aeronautical Specification No. AN-N-7, written during World War II.

H. Determination of Point of Overload

The point of overload is generally determined by applying a pure-tone sound field to the microphone (or alternatively a sine wave voltage e across the insert resistor) and plotting the output level as a function of the input level. The level of the sound field (or the voltage level) at which the input-output characteristic becomes non-linear is the point of overload. This measurement is usually carried out at a number of frequencies.

I. Determination of the Errors Caused by Inadequate Attenuation in the Non-pass Band

An important consideration for any type of analyzer, but especially for the constant-bandwidth type, is the need for adequate

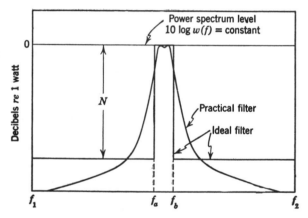

Fig. 12·41   Curves showing the difference between a practical filter and an ideal filter. The ideal filter has zero decibel attenuation inside and N-db attenuation outside the pass band. f_a and f_b are the effective cutoff frequencies, and f_1 and f_2 are the limits of the noise band presented to the filter.

attenuation in the non-pass bands of the filter (or filters). For example, let us assume that the *electrical noise spectrum is "white"* with a power spectrum w watts per unit bandwidth. (See Fig. 12·41.) In the general case, w is a function of frequency, but here it is equal to a constant, say, w_0. The total power P in a frequency band of width $f_b - f_a$ is

$$P = \int_{f_a}^{f_b} w \, df = w_0(f_b - f_a) \tag{12·53}$$

The ratio of the power of the noise lying outside the pass band to that lying within is given by

$$\text{Power ratio} = \frac{\int_{f_1}^{f_2} w(f)\, df - P}{P} = \frac{f_2 - f_1}{f_b - f_a} - 1 \quad (12\cdot54)$$

where f_1 and f_2 are the frequency limits of the total noise band. Now if our analyzer is to indicate the power level of the sound lying within the pass band of the filter $(f_b - f_a)$ with an accuracy of a specified fraction of a decibel, Δ, the attenuation in the non-pass regions of the filter must be at least n db greater than the number of decibels represented by the power ratio given in Eq. $(12\cdot54)$, where n for desired values of Δ is given in Table $12\cdot5$.

TABLE $12\cdot5$

(Table showing the number of decibels, n, by which the power transmitted in the attenuating region of an ideal band-pass filter must lie below that in the band-pass region if the error in the power indicated in the pass band is to be Δ db.)

Δ, decibels	n, decibels
2	2.3
1	5.9
0.5	9.1
0.4	10.2
0.3	11.4
0.2	13.3
0.1	16.3
0.05	19.4

As an illustrative example, assume that an ideal filter (see Fig. $12\cdot41$) of bandwidth Δf is to be used to measure a noise which has a uniform spectrum between 20 and 10,000 cps. The attenuation outside the pass band should be not less than

Attenuation outside pass band, in decibels

$$= 10 \log_{10} \left[\frac{(10^4 - 20)}{\Delta f} - 1 \right] + n \quad \text{db} \quad (12\cdot55)$$

The first term of this equation is evaluated for various values of Δf in Table $12\cdot6$, and n is obtained from Table $12\cdot5$.

Practical filters do not have the simple, easily calculable shape of the ideal filter. If a more exact evaluation of the error in the reading of a power meter connected to the output of the filter is desired, the following procedure should be used.

(1) Assume a noise spectrum which has a constant power per 1-cps band, w_0. Add it (in decibels) to the filter characteristic (in decibels). Convert the decibel values to power per cycle and plot *vs.* frequency on linear-linear graph paper.

(2) Determine the total area below this curve. The result will be power in watts, W. The power ratio W/P_0 may also be determined by a technique similar to that used for Table 12·4.

(3) Calculate from Eq. (12·53) the power passed between the nominal cutoff frequencies $(f_b - f_a)$ and call it P in watts.

TABLE 12·6

(Table showing the number of decibels attenuation that the non-pass-band region must have for a filter of bandwidth Δf if the power passed outside the band is to be equal to that inside the band.)

Δf, cps	$10 \log \left[\dfrac{(10^4 - 20)}{\Delta f} - 1 \right]$, db
1	40
5	33
20	27
100	20
200	17
500	13

(4) Calculate the ratio of the power passed by the filter outside the pass band to that passed inside by the relation

$$\text{Power ratio} = \frac{W - P}{P} \qquad (12·56)$$

In cases where the noise spectrum is not "flat," that is, slopes upward or downward or is irregular, the plot on the linear-linear paper should be multiplied at each frequency by the ratio of the spectrum power at that frequency to the spectrum power at the mean frequency of the pass band. The value of W is then determined as before.

Constant Bandwidth Filter. Figures 12·42 and 12·43 indicate the non-pass attenuation, with n assumed equal to 15 db, for ideal filters required for noises which slope off at rates of 6 and 12 db/octave, respectively. Here, Δf = the width of the pass band in cycles per second. For a flat spectrum the required non-pass attenuation is found by adding 15 db to the values given in Table 12·6.

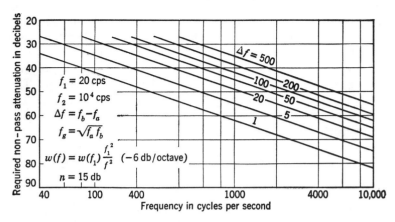

FIG. 12·42 Required non-pass-band attenuation for an ideal constant bandwidth filter to produce a difference between pass-band and non-pass-band attenuation of $n = 15$ db. A noise spectrum sloping at -6 db/octave extending from 20 to 10,000 cps is assumed.

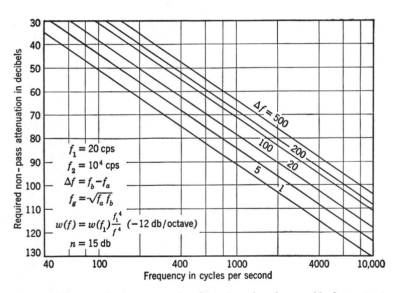

FIG. 12·43 Required non-pass-band attenuation for an ideal constant bandwidth filter to produce a difference between pass-band and non-pass-band attenuation of $n = 15$ db. A noise spectrum sloping at -12 db/octave extending from 20 to 10,000 cps is assumed.

As an example of the need for greater non-pass-band attenuation, the constant bandwidth analysis in Fig. 12·2a approaches an ultimate level of about 65 db because of inadequate attenuation on the lower side of the cutoff frequency. The spectrum being analyzed slopes off at a rate of about 12 db/octave. The result is that, when the mean frequency of the band is high, the energy transmitted by the filter below the lower cutoff frequency exceeds that transmitted in the pass band itself.

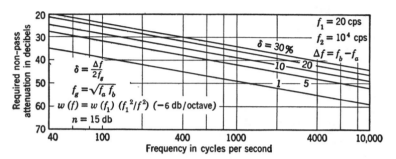

Fɪɢ. 12·44   Required non-pass-band attenuation for an ideal constant-percentage bandwidth filter to produce a difference between pass-band and non-pass-band attenuation of $n = 15$ db. The half-bandwidth of the filter equals δ times the geometric mean frequency. A noise sloping at -6 db/octave extending from 20 to 10,000 cps is assumed.

Constant-Percentage Bandwidth Filter. An example of the required non-pass attenuation for an ideal filter whose bandwidth is equal to $2\delta f_g$, where f_g is the mean frequency and δ is a constant percentage, are shown by the equation below. A random noise is assumed.

Required non-pass attenuation for *flat* random noise spectrum
$$= 10 \log_{10} \left[\frac{(f_2 - f_1)}{2\delta f_g} - 1 \right] + n \quad \text{db} \quad (12·57)$$

where f_1 and f_2 are the lower and upper limits of the noise spectrum, respectively, and n is obtained from Table 12·5.

For random noises which slope off at the rate of 6 db and 12 db/octave, the required non-pass attenuation is shown in Figs. 12·44 and 12·45, respectively. In them, n is assumed to be 15 db.

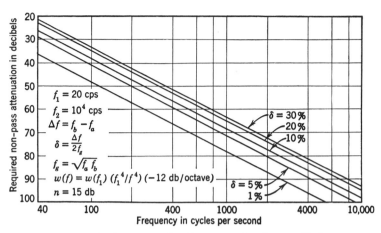

Fig. 12·45 Required non-pass-band attenuation for an ideal constant-percentage bandwidth filter to produce a difference between pass-band and non-pass-band attenuation of $n = 15$ db. The half-bandwidth of the filter equals δ times the geometric mean frequency. A noise sloping at -12 db/octave extending from 20 to 10,000 cps is assumed.

J. Determination of the Dynamic and Rectifying Characteristics of the Indication

In the previous chapter we discussed tests for determining the rectifying characteristics of indicating meters and recorders. In addition to that information, we need to know the speed of indication and the degree of damping of the overall system.

Customary tests for the speed of indication of a meter or recorder are made by applying a train of sinusoidal waves of various lengths and noting the shortest impulse necessary to send the pointer to its maximum deflection. The damping of the meter is judged by the amount of overswing of the indicating needle following the sudden application of a sine wave. For example, one specification written in recent years reads: "The deflection of the indicating instrument for a constant 1000 cps sinusoidal input to the sound level meter (1) shall be equalled by the maximum deflection of the indicating instrument for an input to the sound level meter consisting of the same input signal impressed upon the instrument for any duration lying above 0.2 second; (2) shall be not more than one decibel greater than the maximum deflection of the indicating instrument for an input to the sound level meter consisting of the same input signal impressed upon the instrument for a duration of 0.1 second; and

(3) shall be exceeded by not more than one decibel by the maximum deflection of the indicating instrument obtained upon the sudden application of the constant input."

We cannot apply the same tests to graphic level recorders because the recording stylus operates much more slowly than does a meter needle.   Usually the quantity desired is the number of decibels change in needle position per second following a sudden change in amplitude of the input signal.   This test is performed simply by applying a pure tone suddenly to the input of the recorder and measuring the number of decibels traversed by the recording stylus per second of elapsed time.

12·5   Presentation of Data

The method chosen for presentation of the results of an analysis of a sound depends, of course, on the purpose for which the data were taken.   Although it is generally true that each situation requires different handling, the author has found certain rules helpful in making his own analyses easy to refer to at later times. It is also believed that the principles presented here are adhered to, at least in part, by many other experimenters.

Three types of sound spectra are encountered in practice, namely, (a) line spectra, (b) continuous spectra, and (c) combinations of continuous and line spectra.   We shall give illustrations of methods for plotting the data from an analysis of each of these kinds of spectra.

A. Graphs of Line Spectra

Sounds with line spectra can be analyzed with any type of analyzer which has sufficient resolution.   The meter readings obtained for the different analyzers will be alike provided the instruments are properly calibrated.   The data may either be tabulated or they may be plotted in the form of a bar diagram with a linear or logarithmic frequency base (see Fig. 12·46). If the sound contains widely spaced components, a logarithmic frequency scale is preferable.   If it contains a number of components within a relatively narrow frequency range a linear scale is preferable.

B. Graphs of Continuous Spectra

Continuous spectra noises (no prominent components at discrete frequencies) are generally analyzed with any one of the three common types of analyzers, namely, contiguous-band, constant bandwidth, and constant-percentage bandwidth.

For purposes of comparison of results obtained with these different types of analyzers, the observed data should be reduced

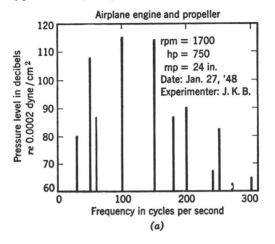

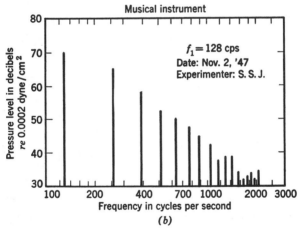

FIG. 12·46 Two typical methods for portraying the results of an analysis of a noise with a line spectrum. (a) Linear frequency abscissa. (b) Logarithmic frequency abscissa.

to *spectrum* levels, defined as the level in decibels of the effective sound pressure (or effective voltage if the output of an electrical source is being analyzed) in bands 1 cycle in width. To reduce a measured level L db, taken by a filter band with a width Δf

cps, to spectrum level S db, the following operation is performed:

$$S = L - 10 \log_{10} \Delta f \quad \text{db} \qquad (12 \cdot 58)$$

The spectrum level S is plotted at the geometric mean frequency $f_g = \sqrt{f_a f_b}$ of the band. As an example, suppose that an airplane noise was analyzed with an octave-band filter set and the data obtained are those given in the first two columns of Table 12·7. The conversion to spectrum level is shown in the third

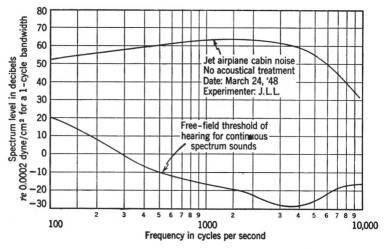

Fig. 12·47 Typical method for portraying the spectrum level of a continuous spectrum noise. The frequency scale is logarithmic, and the ordinate expresses the spectrum level in decibels with respect to a reference power for a 1-cycle bandwidth.

and fourth columns, and the geometric mean frequency is shown in the fifth.

Spectrum levels should preferably be plotted on semi-logarithmic paper, with frequency along the abscissa and decibels along the ordinate. The data of Table 12·7 are shown plotted in Fig. 12·47 as an example. If the elevation of the noise above the normal free-field threshold of hearing is desired, the threshold should also be reduced to its *spectrum level*. The proper threshold for continuous spectrum noises expressed in decibels for unit bandwidth is shown at the bottom of Fig. 12·47. Obviously, the function $10 \log_{10} \Delta f$ will be a constant for a heterodyne-type analyzer, and it will increase in magnitude by 3 db for each doubling of frequency for a constant-percentage bandwidth

TABLE 12·7

1	2	3	4	5
Octave Band, cps	*Observed level, L db*	$10 \log_{10} \Delta f$, *db*	*Spectrum level, S db*	*Geometric Mean Frequency, f_0 cps*
37.5–75	66	15.7	50.3	52
75–150	72	18.7	53.3	110
150–300	78	21.7	56.3	210
300–600	84	24.7	59.3	420
600–1200	91	27.7	63.3	850
1200–2400	95	30.7	64.3	1700
2400–4800	95	33.7	61.3	3400
4800–9600	83	36.7	46.3	6800

filter. It is the author's opinion that all measurements of continuous spectra noise should be reduced to spectrum level. In this way maximum ease of comparison of data obtained by different laboratories is possible.

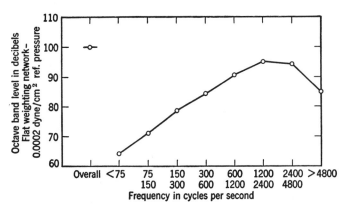

Fig. 12·48 Typical method for plotting data taken with a contiguous-band analyzer. If the bands are octave or partial-octave multiples of each other, their mean frequencies space themselves along the ordinate logarithmically. If the mean frequencies do not come out this way directly, the points should be so spaced horizontally that they do fall logarithmically along the abscissa.

Sometimes it is more convenient to portray contiguous-band data as they were taken. In these cases, plots should not be made on semi-logarithmic graph paper, but rather in the style shown by Fig. 12·48. This type of portrayal clearly shows that the levels pertain to bands of the width and frequency limits shown at the bottom, and equal emphasis is given to each band on the graph. Furthermore, the distinctive appearance of the type of graph shown in Fig. 12·48 prevents any confusion with data that have been reduced to spectrum levels. Note that here the spacing of the frequencies along the scale is logarithmic. This feature should be preserved even if the bands do not double in width each time a new one is switched in.

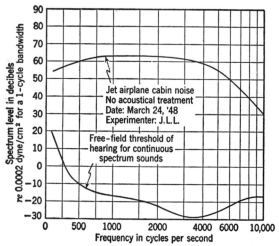

Fig. 12·49   A graph paper suggested by the Bell Telephone Laboratories for approximating the pitch scale (mels).[35]   The paper is linear below 1000 cps and is logarithmic above.   The advantage is a compression of the range of frequencies below 500 cps relative to what would occur if log paper were used.   See Fig. 12·47 for comparison.

Occasionally specialized types of graph paper such as those used for plotting articulation index[33] or loudness functions[34] are required. The end result demands these specialized plots, and no suggestions regarding their use is necessary here. One interesting example of a specialized graph paper which is an easy compromise between ordinary graph papers and one with a frequency scale corresponding to that required for articulation index has been offered by the Bell Telephone Laboratories. It consists of a linear frequency scale up to 1000 cps and a logarithmic scale

[33] L. L. Beranek, "Design of speech communication systems," *Proc. Inst. Radio Engrs.*, **35**, 880–890 (1947).

[34] H. Fletcher, "Auditory patterns," *Rev. Mod. Phys.*, **12**, 47–65 (1940).

[35] W. Koenig, "A new frequency scale for acoustic measurements," Bell Laboratories Record **27**, 299–301 (August 1949).

thereafter. An example of this type of graph is shown in Fig. 12·49. The data of Fig. 12·47 have been replotted on it for comparison.

C. Graphs of Combination Line and Continuous Spectra

No well-defined procedure has been advanced for plotting sound spectra of the combination type. The most logical type of plot is one which gives the proper relative weighting of the continuous part of the noise with respect to the discrete components. This weighting would, for sound, be that dictated by the ear.

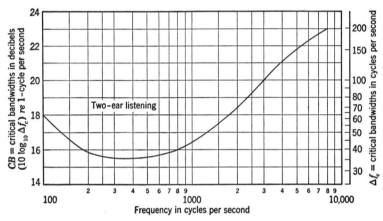

FIG. 12·50 Graph of critical bandwidths (CB) of hearing as a function of frequency. The left-hand ordinate is equal to $CB = 10 \log_{10} \Delta f_c$, where Δf_c is the critical bandwidth in cycles. The right-hand ordinate is Δf_c.

We have already shown in Chapter 5 that the ear seems to analyze continuous spectra sounds as though it contained a set of filter bands with widths equal to critical bandwidths (see Fig. 12·50). The procedure then is to reduce the continuous part of the spectrum as measured by a wide-band filter to levels in *critical bandwidths* L_c by the formula

$$L_c = L - 10 \log_{10} \Delta f + CB \quad \text{db} \qquad (12·59)$$

where L is the level measured by a filter with bandwidth Δf and CB is $10 \log_{10}$ of the critical bandwidth at the geometric mean frequency f_g of the filter band. CB is found from Fig. 12·50. The discrete components are plotted without any change in level. A graph combining the data of Figs. 12·46a and 12·47 is shown in Fig. 12·51.

The graph shown in Fig. 12·51 lends itself to an interesting interpretation. The number of decibels by which a discrete component stands above the critical-band level is exactly the amount by which the level of the discrete component would need to be reduced to make it become inaudible. (This statement holds only if the components are separated by more than a

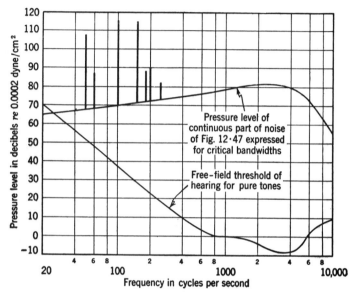

Fig. 12·51 Typical method for plotting a combined continuous spectrum and line spectrum noise. The continuous part of the spectrum is expressed in decibels for critical bandwidths *re* a reference power. The discrete components are plotted directly as measured. The resulting graph yields the number of decibels that any line component must be reduced in level in order that it become inaudible in the presence of the continuous spectrum noise.

critical bandwidth.) It can be said, therefore, that this is a "weighted" plot designed to illustrate how the ear hears the discrete component in the presence of a background noise.

If the amount by which the background noise *or* the discrete components exceed the threshold level is desired, the ordinary free-field threshold may be plotted on the graph as shown at the bottom of Fig. 12·51. This threshold lies above that shown at the bottom of Fig. 12·47 by the critical bandwidths of Fig. 12·50.

13.

Basic Tests for Communication Systems
The Rating of Microphones, Amplifiers,
and Loudspeakers

13·1 Introduction

The telephone, radio, and interphone have become an important part of our way of living. We witness daily a continual flow of intelligence over stationary systems such as our radio and telephone, and over portable systems such as those on railroads, airplanes, and in automobiles. Some systems are operated under favorable conditions such as quiet surroundings and by unhurried users; others are operated in intense noise fields and often under stress of emergency. At one extreme of design we see the modern radio transmitter and home receiver. Each of these units is engineered to transmit and reproduce speech and music with a minimum of distortion in quiet surroundings. At the other extreme, we find the airplane-to-airplane channel with attendant high ambient noise levels, with static (both atmospheric and locally generated), and with stringent requirements on tolerable weight of equipment. It is not surprising, therefore, that with such a wide range of operating conditions much effort has had to be devoted to the development of tests for determining the efficacy of speech-transmitting channels.

A little thought will tell us that our problem can be separated into two parts: (a) The use of psychophysical tests to determine how well the system accomplishes its purpose. Such tests involve the use of the system by humans, and in these tests the procedures and controls of modern experimental psychology must be employed. (b) The use of physical tests from which the performance of the system, as it will be used, can be predicted.

By far the greater part of the American literature dealing with these two types of tests has come from the Bell Telephone Laboratories. They must be credited with developing the articulation test, the repetition count test, and numerous physical

581

tests. They also explored early the properties of hearing and speech and have used that information to assist in the design of effective testing methods. Further significant contributions to the literature were made by the government-sponsored efforts of the Psycho-Acoustic and Electro-Acoustic Laboratories of Harvard University, particularly with regard to communication in high ambient noise levels.

A clear and detailed account of the problem of rating the performance of telephone circuits was given by Martin in 1931.[1] He pointed out that, in carrying on a telephone conversation, three major functions are involved, namely, that of the talker in formulating his ideas and uttering words to convey these ideas, that of the telephone circuit in taking the sounds of these words and reproducing them at another point, and, lastly, that of the listener in hearing and recognizing these reproduced sounds and in comprehending the ideas which they are intended to convey.

There is a great difference between telephoned and direct conversation. Even though we were to produce the same speech spectrum and sound pressure level at the ears of a listener in the two cases, the understandability of the speech would be different for psychological reasons. It has even been found that the vocabulary of telephone conversations differs considerably from that used by writers![2]

Still another and surprising result is that tests which measure quantitatively the number of words that a listener is able to distinguish correctly when his attention is focused on listening yield results which do not correlate too closely with the results of repetition counts made on telephone circuits in normal use. It may be that the listener is less likely to focus his attention on the words during normal use or else that he is careless about holding the telephone instrument in the proper relationship to his ear and mouth. Or, perhaps he asks for repeats merely to make certain that he understood the inflection of what the other person said.

It seems obvious, therefore, that any one test will not be suit-

[1] W. H. Martin, "Rating the transmission performance of telephone circuits," *Bell System Technical Jour.*, **10**, 116–131 (1931).

[2] N. R. French, C. W. Carter, Jr., and W. Koenig, Jr., "The words and sounds of telephone conversations," *Bell System Technical Jour.*, **9**, 290–324 (1930).

able for all our needs. In fact, at least six different types of tests have found considerable use. If we had available the proper facilities, we could perform all these tests on any particular system, and we should find that each gave some information about the efficacy of that system under a certain condition of use. However, some of these tests are more convenient to use than others; some are better suited for precise studies in the laboratory; and some are more economical to perform. These tests yield the six types of results enumerated here:

(*a*) Repetition count, defined as the average number of repetitions occurring per minute over a given two-way telephone system under its normal usage conditions.

(*b*) Articulation score, defined as the average number of speech units correctly recorded by listeners per hundred units read over a communication system.

(*c*) Subjective appraisal, defined as the rank ordering of several communication systems by listeners who are experienced in judging the quality of a speech communication system. Alternatively, the listeners may assign a subjective rating to the quality of speech that they hear.

(*d*) Threshold evaluation, defined as the level at which, under specified conditions, speech is either (1) just detectable, (2) just perceptible, or (3) just intelligible.

(*e*) Orthotelephonic response, defined as the ratio of the loudness or sound pressure produced at the ear of a listener by the communication system to that produced directly by the talker when the two persons are located in an anechoic chamber a distance of 1 meter apart.

(*f*) Electroacoustic response, defined as the ratio of the sound pressure produced by the communication system in an artificial ear or at a specified location to the sound pressure actuating the communication system in a specified manner.

These tests will be discussed broadly in the remainder of this chapter. Detailed instructions for performing an articulation test are given in Chapter 17. Detailed procedures for obtaining electroacoustic response data on the components of a speech communication system will be found in Chapters 14 through 16.

Because of their simplicity, physical methods for obtaining and combining the response characteristics of microphones, amplifiers, and loudspeakers to yield a suitable overall response characteristic of the system are treated in detail at the very beginning of this chapter.

13·2   Physical Response Characteristics

In this chapter the word *response* is used to designate at a single frequency the ratio of a quantity measured at the output terminals (whether electrical or acoustic) to a quantity measured at the input terminals. The words *response characteristic* or *frequency response* are used interchangeably to designate the curve obtained by plotting the response as a function of frequency. The words *gain* and *attenuation* are used interchangeably with *response* when dealing with amplifiers and attenuators, respectively.

When dealing with electroacoustic systems, we often find that we must determine their overall response by combining the response characteristics of the individual components. Indiscriminate addition of individual component curves, however, will lead to incorrect results unless the separate responses have been determined in the proper manner or unless correction factors are devised. It is the purpose of this section to discuss the electrical considerations involved in the measurement and combining of response curves. A new system of rating microphones and loudspeakers is presented which permits direct comparison of units of different electrical impedances. In addition, the concepts of constant power available, open-circuit voltage, and the measurement of the latter by the insert resistor method are explained.

The discussion which follows is divided into four parts, (a) microphone response, (b) amplifier gain, (c) source (loudspeaker or earphone) response, and (d) overall system response.

A. Microphone Response

Equivalent Circuits. A microphone and its terminal connections can be described by equivalent circuit diagrams. For a microphone placed in an anechoic chamber in a plane wave sound field whose sound pressure amplitude before insertion of the microphone was p_{ff}, the circuit of Fig. 13·1 can be drawn. The equations and terminology for that circuit are

$$p_B = (Z_{rad.} + Z_M)U + \tau_{12}i$$
$$e' = \tau_{21}U + (Z_e + Z_L)i$$

$$(13·1)$$

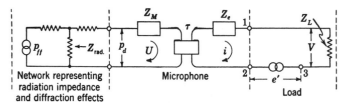

Fɪɢ. 13·1 Equivalent circuit for a microphone placed in a free sound field. p_{ff} = pressure in a free field in dynes per square centimeter; p_d = pressure at the diaphragm in dynes per square centimeter; U = volume velocity of the diaphragm in cubic centimeters per second; Z_M = acoustic impedance of the diaphragm in acoustic ohms; τ = electromechanical coupling constant; Z_e = electrical impedance in abohms measured with the diaphragm blocked; Z_L = load resistor in abohms; i = electrical current in abamperes; V = voltage across the load in abvolts.

where p_{ff} = the free-field sound pressure, i.e., the pressure measured in a free progressive sound wave before insertion of the microphone

p_d = pressure measured at the diaphragm of the microphone when it is in the sound field

p_d' = same as p_d except for the special condition that the electrical terminals are open-circuited

p_B = pressure measured at the diaphragm when it is blocked, i.e., $Z_M \rightarrow \infty$ (In Fig. 13·1, this is "Thévenin's pressure" for the T network to the left of the diaphragm impedance.)

$Z_{\text{rad.}}$ = acoustic impedance of the test chamber viewed from the diaphragm. (This is the so-called radiation impedance when the microphone is driven as a loudspeaker)

Z_M = acoustic impedance of the mechanical moving elements measured when the electrical terminals are open-circuited

U = volume velocity of the diaphragm.

τ_{12}, τ_{21} = electromechanical coupling coefficients in the forward and reverse direction, respectively; $\tau_{21} = -\tau_{12}$ for electromagnetic transducers and $\tau_{21} = \tau_{12}$ for electrostatic transducers. (For carbon-button and other non-linear transducers τ_{21} is not equal in magnitude to τ_{12}.)

Z_e = electrical impedance of the microphone measured with the diaphragm blocked

Z_L = electrical load resistance

e' = voltage inserted for test purposes. (The method by which it is generated will be discussed in detail later.)

i = electrical current.

For simplicity, the mks system of units should be used. If this is done, we have the units of pressure as newtons per square meter, of acoustic impedance as newtons-sec/m^3, of volume velocity as cubic meters per second; and all electrical quantities are in practical units. The number of newtons multiplied by 10^5 gives the number of dynes. The dimensions of τ are webers per meter, where the number of webers per square meter multiplied by 10^4 equals the number of gausses.

If cgs units are used, the electrical quantities must be expressed in abvolts, abamperes, and abohms (see footnote, p. 116).

The open-circuit voltage e_o of the transducer (microphone) placed in a free-field pressure with $e' = 0$ will be equal to

$$e_o = -\tau_{21}U \bigg|_{Z_L = \infty} = \frac{-\tau_{21}}{Z_{\text{rad.}} + Z_M} p_B = \frac{-\tau_{21}}{Z_M} p_d' \quad (13 \cdot 2)$$

The electrical impedance Z_0 of the microphone measured at terminals 1 and 2 when it is placed in an anechoic chamber with $p_{ff} = 0$ is

$$Z_0 = Z_c - \frac{\tau_{12}\tau_{21}}{Z_{\text{rad.}} + Z_M} \quad (13 \cdot 3)$$

Now, Thévenin's theorem says, "any network containing one or more sources of voltage and having two terminals behaves, insofar as a load impedance connected across the terminals is concerned, as though the network and its generators were equivalent to a simple generator having an internal impedance Z and a generated voltage V, where V is the voltage that appears across the terminals when the electric terminals are open-circuited and Z is the impedance that is measured between the terminals when all sources of voltage in the network are short-circuited." We extend this theorem by analogy to mechanical or acoustical systems as well.

Hence, by Thévenin's theorem, we can replace the circuit of Fig. 13·1 by the equivalent circuit of Fig. 13·2.

For a microphone at whose diaphragm the pressure is held constant at a value p_d, the equivalent circuit will be that of Fig. 13·3. The equations are the same as before except that $Z_{rad.} = 0$ and $p_B = p_d$. By the same manipulation, we can obtain the open-circuit voltage e_o' and the impedance Z_0' for a microphone at whose diaphragm the pressure is held constant. They are

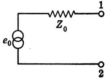

$$e_o' = \frac{-\tau_{21}}{Z_M} p_d = \frac{-\tau_{21}}{Z_M} p_d' \quad (13·4)$$

$$Z_0' = Z_e - \frac{\tau_{12}\tau_{21}}{Z_M} \quad (13·5)$$

FIG. 13·2 Equivalent Thévenin's circuit of the microphone in Fig. 13·1 as viewed from the electrical terminals 1 and 2. e_0 is the open-circuit voltage, and Z_0 is the impedance measured to the left of terminals 1 and 2 with p_{ff} short-circuited.

Note that $p_d = p_d'$ because p_d, in this case, is held constant regardless of whether the microphone is open-circuited or not.

The impedance Z_0' can be measured when the microphone diaphragm is coupled to a tube one-fourth wavelength long, that is, a tube whose input acoustical impedance is zero. Again, for a microphone at whose diaphragm the pressure is held constant regardless of changes in the electrical loading and as a function of frequency, an equivalent circuit like that in Fig. 13·2 can be drawn, with e_0' and Z_0' substituted for e_o and Z_o.

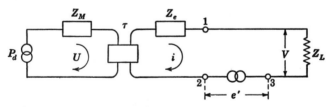

FIG. 13·3 Equivalent circuit for a microphone with a constant pressure held at the diaphragm. Z_M = impedance of the diaphragm in acoustic ohms; p_d = pressure at the diaphragm in dynes per square centimeter; τ = electromagnetic coupling constant; i = current in abamperes; Z_e = electrical impedance in abohms measured with the diaphragm blocked; Z_L = load resistance in abohms.

Let us extend these ideas further to the case of a microphone mounted in one wall of a closed cavity and driven by a transducer operating as a source in the opposite wall. (*Note:* This is a technique common in the pressure calibration of microphones by the reciprocity method. See Chapter 4.) Let us assume that

all wavelengths are large compared with the dimensions of the
cavity. The equivalent circuit will be that of Fig. 13·4, where
p_1 is the force per unit area acting to move the diaphragm of the
source when the diaphragm is blocked; p_c is the sound pressure
in the cavity; $Z_1{}^s$ is the acoustic impedance of the diaphragm
of the source, measured with the electrical terminals short-circuited; C is the acoustic compliance of the cavity; U is the volume
velocity of the diaphragm of the microphone; and the other elements are as before.   If the *source* transducer is driven by a

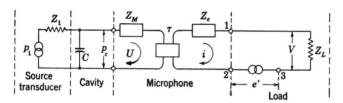

FIG. 13·4 Equivalent circuit for a microphone driven through an inter-
vening cavity by an electrostatic transducer with a constant voltage applied
to the terminals. p_1 = pressure acting to move the diaphragm of the source
transducer, in dynes per square centimeter; Z_1 = acoustic impedance of the
source diaphragm with electrical terminals short-circuited, in acoustic
ohms; C = cavity compliance in centimeters to the fifth power per dyne;
Z_M = impedance of the microphone diaphragm measured with electrical
terminals open-circuited, in acoustic ohms; U = volume velocity, in cubic
centimeters per second; τ = electromagnetic coupling constant; Z_e = electrical impedance measured with the diaphragm blocked, in abohms; Z_L =
load resistance, in abohms.

voltage e_1, the pressure p_1 actuating its diaphragm when the
diaphragm is blocked (i.e., p_1 is Thévenin's pressure) will be

$$p_1 = -\frac{e_1\tau_{12}{}^s}{Z_e{}^s} \qquad (13\cdot6a)$$

where the superscripts s indicate that the quantities apply to the
source transducer.
  The Thévenin mechanical impedance of the source microphone is

$$Z_1{}^s = Z_M{}^s - \frac{\tau_{21}{}^s\tau_{12}{}^s}{Z_e{}^s} \qquad (13\cdot6b)$$

  Thévenin electrical impedance Z_0'' of the receiving microphone
measured at terminals 1 and 2 of Fig. 13·4 is

$$Z_0'' = Z_e - \frac{\tau_{12}\tau_{21}}{Z_M + \dfrac{Z_1}{1 + j\omega Z_1 C}} \tag{13.7}$$

and the open-circuit voltage e_o'' is

$$e_o'' = \frac{\dfrac{e_1\tau_{21}\tau_{12}{}^s}{Z_e{}^s}}{\left(Z_M + \dfrac{Z_1}{1 + j\omega Z_1 C}\right)(1 + j\omega Z_1 C)} \tag{13.8}$$

By Thévenin's theorem we can also represent this type of circuit by an equivalent circuit like that shown in Fig. 13·2 with e_o'' and Z_0'' substituted for e_o and Z_0.

Open-Circuit Voltage. Our next question is: How do we measure the open-circuit voltage produced by a microphone? The most obvious way, of course, is to connect a voltmeter whose impedance is very large compared to Z_0 across the open terminals 1 and 2. The open-circuit voltage may also be measured by the *insert resistor method. Either procedure will give exactly the same results; the choice is a matter of convenience, or necessity.* In the case of carbon microphones, the insert method is often a necessity in order that the d-c flow not be interrupted.

By the insert resistor method, a resistor r is inserted between points 2 and 3 of the circuits above. A voltage is made to appear across this resistor. The proper form of this arrangement is constructed as shown in Fig. 13·5. The insert resistor r is in series with the output of a constant impedance attenuator and a resistor R_k. The attenuator must be terminated both at the input and at the output with impedances equal to its image impedances R_a. This means that R_k plus r must equal R_a. Generally r is made small compared to $Z_e + Z_L$ (see Fig. 13·4), so that the ground side of the microphone or the shielded cable is not raised above ground potential sufficiently to cause spurious readings of the voltmeter due to noise pickup.

A voltage $2E$ is applied as shown in Fig. 13·5. A voltage K_2E will appear across the output terminals, where $K_2 = 10^{-A/20}$ and A is the number of decibels attenuation provided by the attenuator. The voltage appearing across r, when the circuit is that of Fig. 13·5, equals $K_2Er/(r + R_k)$. That is, Thévenin's open-circuit voltage produced at terminals 2-3 by this circuit is

$$e = \frac{Er10^{-A/20}}{r + R_k} \qquad (13 \cdot 9)$$

and the impedance R_a' of the generator producing that voltage is

$$R_a' = \frac{r(R_k + R_a)}{r + R_k + R_a} \qquad (13 \cdot 10)$$

The equivalent circuit may be seen in Fig. 13·5b. Under the special, but *not required*, condition that $r \ll R_k + R_a$, we will have $R_a' = r$.

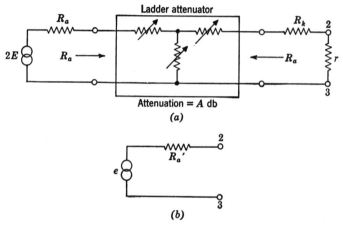

FIG. 13·5 (a) Arrangement for producing a known insert voltage in a microphone circuit. The ladder attenuator has constant resistance R_a looking into either pair of terminals if it is terminated in R_a ohms at each end. (b) Equivalent Thévenin circuit of (a).

Now, if the equivalent circuit of Fig. 13·2 is combined with that of Fig. 13·5b, the circuit of Fig. 13·6 will be obtained. (Note that e_o and Z_0 are replaced by e_o' and Z_0' for the case of Fig. 13·3 and e_o'' and Z_0'' for the case of Fig. 13·4.) If the vacuum tube voltmeter has finite impedance it must be considered as part of Z_L.

The following procedure is necessary in measuring the open-circuit voltage of the microphone. First, we make $e = 0$ and expose the microphone to the sound field. The voltage e must be reduced to zero by short-circuiting $2E$ in Fig. 13·5 without disturbing the value of R_a'. The equivalent voltage e_o produced by the microphone will give an indication, say V, on the vacuum tube voltmeter (VTVM). Next, the sound field is turned off (i.e., $e_o = 0$), and e is turned on. Then the attenuation A is adjusted until the same reading V is obtained on the vacuum tube voltmeter as before. Inspection of the circuit of Fig. 13·6 shows that under these circumstances $e = e_o$. The voltage e is then calculated from Eq. (13·9). It is apparent that R_a' can have any value whatever provided $r + R_k = R_a$.

The open-circuit voltage e_o of the microphone equals the insert voltage e only if the same value Z_0 is in the circuit when the insert voltage was applied as was there when the sound field was operating. This is obvious from inspection of Fig. 13·6.

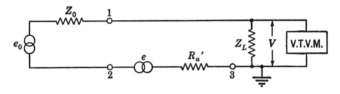

Fig. 13·6 Combination of equivalent Thévenin circuits for the microphone and for the insert resistor arrangement. This circuit should be compared with that of Fig. 13·1, for which it is an equivalent.

As can be seen from Eq. (13·3), or, analogously, Eqs. (13·5) and (13·7), this requirement means that $Z_{rad.}$ of Fig. 13·1 [or $Z_1/(1 + j\omega Z_1 C)$ of Fig. 13·4] must be the same whether e or e_o is acting. We might ask ourselves under what condition $Z_{rad.}$ would not be the same for the two parts of the test. Let us take the case of Fig. 13·4 as an example. Assume that we excite the source transducer with a constant voltage e_1 from a generator of zero impedance. Then we remove the electrical generator leaving the terminals of the source transducer *open-circuited*. By this maneuver, we introduce an infinite electrical impedance in series with Z_e^s of Eq. (13·6b) which was not there when the electrical generator was connected. A change in Z_1 causes a change in Z_0'' as can be seen from Eq. (13·8). Hence, the circuit impedance of Fig. 13·6 differs when e is operating from that when e_o is operating and, for the same reading V, e cannot equal e_o. Obviously, we should have *short-circuited* the terminals of the source transducer when we removed the electrical generator from the circuit.

Another case in point arises in the everyday use of a standard microphone whose calibration curve is given as "open-circuit volts for a sound pressure at the diaphragm of 1 dyne/cm.^{2}" The part of the expression within the quotation marks is equal to the quantity $-\tau_{21}/Z_M$ of Eqs. (13·2) and (13·4). Hence, when we measure the open-circuit voltage of the standard microphone when it is immersed in a given sound field, we do not determine p_d, the pressure at the diaphragm for any condition of electrical loading, but rather p_d', the pressure that exists at the diaphragm when the electrical terminals are *open-circuited*. Remember that, unless $Z_{\text{rad.}} = 0$ [or $Z_1/(1 + j\omega Z_1 C) = 0$], p_d is not equal to p_d'.[3]

Open-Circuit Free-Field Response. Most laboratory or studio-type microphones are calibrated in terms of their open-circuit voltage for a given sound pressure existing in a plane wave sound field before insertion of the microphone. The response characteristic is usually a plot in decibels of the quantity given in the equation below as a function of frequency in cycles:

$$\text{Response in decibels} = 20 \log_{10} \frac{e_o}{p_{ff}} + 20 \log_{10} \frac{p_{\text{ref.}}}{e_{\text{ref.}}} \quad (13\cdot11)$$

where e_o is the open-circuit voltage produced by a free-field pressure p_{ff}, and $e_{\text{ref.}}$ and $p_{\text{ref.}}$ are reference voltages and pressures, respectively. In many cases we choose $e_{\text{ref.}} = 1$ volt and $p_{\text{ref.}} = 1$ dyne/cm^2, so that

$$\text{Response in decibels} = \rho_m = 20 \log_{10} \frac{e_o}{p_{ff}} \quad (13\cdot12)$$

and we say that the response ρ_m is in decibels *re* 1 volt per dyne/cm^2.

Open-Circuit Pressure Response. The open-circuit pressure response differs from the open-circuit free-field response only in that the sound pressure is measured at the diaphragm of the microphone rather than in the sound field before insertion of the microphone. If the dimensions of the microphone are very small compared to a wavelength, the two responses will be approximately equal. However, if diffraction effects are observable,

---

[3] M. S. Hawley, The substitution method of measuring the open circuit voltage generated by a microphone," *Jour. Acous. Soc. Amer.* **21**, 183–189 (1949). See also, R. K. Cook, "Measurement of electromotive force of a microphone," *Jour. Acous. Soc. Amer.*, **19**, 502–504 (1947).

the two will differ appreciably. The circuit applicable to the case of a constant pressure at the diaphragm is that of Fig. 13·3. The equations are the same as above, except that p_{ff} is replaced by p_d'.

Response for a Specified Load Impedance. Occasionally it is more convenient to give the response of the microphone in terms of the voltage V it produces across a specified load resistor (Z_L of Figs. 13·1 through 13·6). The voltages obtained across a load impedance will be less than the open-circuit voltages unless the load impedance should happen to resonate with the microphone impedance. We have

Response in decibels

$$= 20 \log_{10} \frac{V}{p_{ff}} \left(\text{or } 20 \log_{10} \frac{V}{p_d} \right) re \text{ 1 volt per dyne/cm}^2 \quad (13·13)$$

B. Amplifier Response

An amplifier can be represented by a simple four-terminal network (see Fig. 13·7) having the impedances Z_{in} and Z_{out} and a gain measured by one of the methods described below. We shall confine our discussion here to the determination of only the magnitude of the

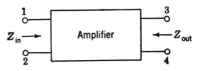

Fig. 13·7 Block diagram of an amplifier.

gain. The ideas can be extended, however, to a determination of phase shifts if necessary.

Power Gain. The power gain of an amplifier is determined by performing two of the three measurements indicated in Fig. 13·8. First, the input to the amplifier is connected to a generator e with an impedance R_1 and the output to a load Z_2. If no other conditions dictate a choice, R_1 and Z_2 are resistors whose values are equal, respectively, to the magnitudes of Z_{in} and Z_{out}. The voltage e_2 is measured. Secondly, the generator is connected directly to the load resistance (Fig. 13·8b), and the voltage e_2' is measured.

The power gain at any frequency is given by the formula

$$\text{Power gain in decibels} = 20 \log_{10} \frac{e_2}{e_2'} \quad (13·14)$$

If R_1 is not equal to Z_2 and if the amplifier is supposed to perform the function of impedance transformation (wherein no power gain actually takes place), the comparison circuit (b) is usually modified as shown in Fig. 13·8c, where the square of the

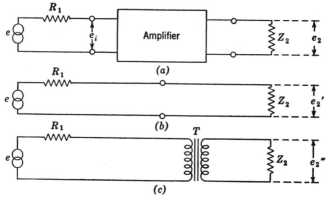

FIG. 13·8   Circuits for measuring the power gain of an amplifier. The power gain is equal to either $(e_2/e_2')^2$ or $(e_2/e_2'')^2$ depending on whether the amplifier is supposed to serve an impedance transformation function or not.

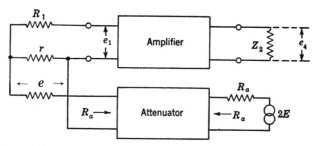

FIG. 13·9   Schematic diagram of an arrangement for measuring the insert-resistor response of an amplifier.

turns ratio of the transformer T is equal to the ratio of the resistance R_1 and the magnitude of the impedance Z_2.   In this case,

$$\text{Power gain} = 20 \log_{10} \frac{e_2}{e_2''} \qquad (13·15)$$

Voltage Gain.   The voltage gain of an amplifier is determined simply by taking the ratio of e_2 to e_i in Fig. 13·8a:

$$\text{Voltage gain in decibels} = 20 \log_{10} \frac{e_2}{e_i} \qquad (13·16)$$

Strictly speaking, *decibels* can never be used to represent voltage gains unless the impedances are alike. However, the practice has become popular.

Insert-Voltage Gain. The insert-voltage gain is obtained by performing the test indicated in Fig. 13·9. It is

$$\text{Insert-voltage gain in decibels} = 20 \log_{10} \frac{e_4}{e} \quad (13 \cdot 17)$$

where e is given by Eq. (13·9) and $r + R_k = R_a$.

C. Loudspeaker or Earphone Response

The sound pressure produced by a loudspeaker or earphone can be measured in any one of the many ways discussed in detail

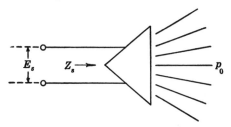

FIG. 13·10   Block diagram of a loudspeaker.

in Chapters 15 and 16. In this section we shall concern ourselves only with listing the various electrical connections that might be used during the experiment. The sound pressure which the loudspeaker produces will be designated arbitrarily as p_0 regardless of how or in what environment it is measured. Also to avoid repetition of the words loudspeaker and earphone we shall designate them generically as loudspeakers.

Voltage Response. The voltage response of a loudspeaker is determined by the simple experiment of Fig. 13·10:

Voltage response in decibels

$$= 20 \log_{10} \frac{p_0}{E_s} - 20 \log_{10} \frac{p_{\text{ref.}}}{e_{\text{ref.}}} \quad (13 \cdot 18)$$

Generally, $p_{\text{ref.}}$ is taken as 0.0002 dyne/cm^2 and $e_{\text{ref.}}$ as 1 volt. Hence, we get

$$\text{Voltage response in decibels} = 20 \log_{10} \frac{p_0}{E_s} + 74$$

$$\text{in decibels } re \text{ 0.0002 dyne/cm}^2 \text{ and 1 volt} \quad (13 \cdot 19)$$

Constant Power Available Response. For many applications it is desired to predict the performance of a given loudspeaker which is energized from an amplifier whose output impedance is nearly resistive. In this and other cases, the concept of *constant power available* from the generator is of basic importance.

The amplifier can be represented, according to Thévenin's theorem, as a generator having a power capacity corresponding to a voltage e_s and an internal resistance R_s, both constant with frequency, as shown in Fig. 13·11a. If the load resistance is

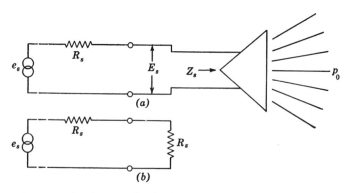

Fig. 13·11 (a) Equivalent circuit of a loudspeaker driven from a constant maximum power available source; (b) circuit for obtaining maximum power available from a generator of impedance R_s.

made equal to R_s (see Fig. 13·11b) a condition of matched impedances obtains, and the *maximum power available* from the generator is equal to $e_s^2/4R_s$. During the test of a loudspeaker, e_s is held constant as a function of frequency. The assumption is thereby made that the output impedances of most amplifiers are nearly resistive in the frequency range of interest. Since they generally are, this test is of practical utility.

The constant power available response is defined as follows:

Constant power available response in decibels

$$= 20 \log \frac{p_0}{p_{\text{ref.}}} + 10 \log \frac{W_{\text{ref.}}}{\dfrac{e_s^2}{4R_s}} \quad (13\cdot20a)$$

where $p_{\text{ref.}}$ is a reference pressure and $W_{\text{ref.}}$ is a reference power. Usually, $p_{\text{ref.}}$ is chosen as 0.0002 dyne/cm^2, and $W_{\text{ref.}}$ is made equal to 1 mw.   Hence, we get

$$\text{Constant power available response} = 10 \log \frac{p_0{}^2}{\dfrac{e_s{}^2}{4R_s}} + 44$$

$$\text{in decibels } re \ 0.0002 \text{ dyne/cm}^2 \text{ and } 1 \text{ mw} \quad (13 \cdot 20b)$$

In practice, amplifiers generally do not match the rated impedance of the loudspeakers connected to them.   A recent proposal
for a standard attempts to take this fact into account by requiring
that the test generator have an impedance which is greater than
that of the loudspeaker.   Then, instead of speaking of constant
power available *from the generator*, one speaks of constant power
available *to the loudspeaker*.   The power available to the loudspeaker becomes $(e_s{}^2/R_s') \ R_s'^2/(R_s' + R_s)^2$, where R_s' is the
rated impedance of the loudspeaker, and e_s and R_s are the voltage
and resistance of the generator, respectively.   The *regulation* of
the generator N is then given by the expression

$$N \quad (\text{db}) = 20 \log_{10} \left(1 + \frac{R_s}{R_s'} \right) \qquad (13 \cdot 21a)$$

When this method of measuring response curves is used, the
regulation of the generator must be specified along with the
response curve.   We then have

Constant power available response (N db regulation)(db)

$$= 20 \log \frac{p_0}{p_{\text{ref.}}} + 10 \log \frac{W_{\text{ref.}}}{\dfrac{e_s{}^2}{R_s'}} + N \quad (13 \cdot 21b)$$

For a constant power available response of the type described in
$(13 \cdot 20a)$, $N = 6$ db; for a voltage response of the type in $(13 \cdot 18)$,
$N = 0$ db.

D. Overall System Response

The response of an overall system can be measured directly
by a procedure similar to that used for measuring the power gain
of amplifiers.   For example, suppose that the frequency response
of a system composed of a microphone, amplifier, and loudspeaker
is desired.   Then the two experiments of Fig. 13·12 might be
performed.   First, the free-field pressure p_{ff} would be deter-

mined at a given distance, say 10 ft, from the test source in chamber A. Then the microphone M of the sound system would be inserted in the sound field at exactly the same point at which p_{ff} had been measured. The loudspeaker S would be placed in a second anechoic chamber. The pressure p_0 produced by the overall system would be measured at the given distance (10 ft) from the loudspeaker. The overall gain of the system would be equal to the ratio of p_0 to p_{ff} or $p_0{}^2$ to $p_{ff}{}^2$, depending on whether pressure or intensity gain is desired. The same standard micro-

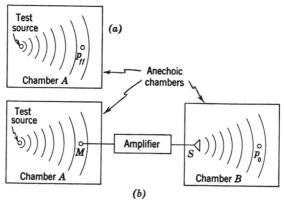

FIG. 13·12   Method for measuring the power gain of a communication system.   (a) The output of the test source is first measured.   (b) Then the output of the communication system is measured. The power gain equals $(p_0/p_{ff})^2$.

phone would be used for measuring p_0 and p_{ff}, so that its calibration need not be known. Of course, p_0 can be measured in other ways, as discussed in Chapter 15. The experiment of Fig. 13·12 would, for one thing, require two adjacent anechoic sound chambers—a luxury literally not in existence at this writing. Usually, therefore, the responses of the components are determined separately and then added together to get the overall response.[*] The purpose of this section of the chapter is to present

*Several organizations promulgate audio system testing standards:

(a) Standard IHF–A–202, 1978, "Measurement of audio amplifiers," Inst. of High Fidelity, 489 Fifth Ave., New York, NY 10017

(b) Standard IEEE 219–1975, "Recommended practice for loudspeaker measurements," IEEE, 345 E. 47th Street, New York, NY 10017

(c) International Standard IEC 268–5–1972, "Measurement of loudspeakers," ANSI, 1430 Broadway, New York, NY 10018

the rules for combining individual responses to obtain the correct overall response.

In order to reduce these difficulties to a minimum, Romanow and Hawley[4] have proposed ratings for microphones, amplifiers, and loudspeakers (or sound sources in general). This method of ratings has advantages over other methods in existence. For example, it yields response characteristics which are indicative of the efficiency of different instruments regardless of their impedance. The overall response can be determined approximately by simply adding together the microphone rating, amplifier rating, and loudspeaker rating (all in decibels) *provided* the impedances of the microphone and loudspeaker are nearly equal to the rated source and load impedances, respectively, of the amplifier. The nominal impedance is often taken as the magnitude of impedance of the device at 1000 ± 100 cps.

Romanow and Hawley, in addition, give formulas and curves from which the exact response of the overall system as a function of frequency can be determined, provided the electrical impedances of all the components are known as a function of frequency.

Before describing in detail their method of rating instruments, let us list those cases wherein the exact responses of the overall system may be obtained by direct addition of the component response curves.

Direct Methods. CASE I. Pressure Response. Impedance of test generator R_1 for amplifier test equals Thévenin's impedance of microphone Z_0. Load impedance for amplifier test Z_2 equals impedance of loudspeaker Z_s.

To obtain the overall response at any given frequency, perform the following addition:

$$20 \log_{10} \frac{p_0}{p_{ff}} = \rho_m + (13 \cdot 17) + (13 \cdot 19) - 74 \quad \text{db} \quad (13 \cdot 22)$$

where ρ_m = the open-circuit, free-field response of the microphone in decibels (see Figs. $13 \cdot 1$ and $13 \cdot 2$)

$$\rho_m = 20 \log_{10} \frac{e_0}{p_{ff}} \qquad (13 \cdot 12)$$

[4] F. F. Romanow and M. S. Hawley, "Proposed method of rating microphones and loudspeakers for systems use," *Proc. Inst. Radio Engrs.*, **35**, 953–960 (1947).

(13·17) = the equation for the insert-voltage gain of the amplifier in decibels, i.e., it equals (see Figs. 13·5 and 13·9)

$$20 \log_{10} \frac{e_4}{e} \qquad (13·17)$$

(13·19) = the equation for the voltage response of the loudspeaker in decibels, i.e., it equals (see Fig. 13·10)

$$20 \log_{10} \frac{p_0}{E_s} + 74 \qquad (13·19)$$

The distance at which and the conditions under which p_0 was obtained must be specified.

CASE II. Pressure Response. Impedance of test-generator for amplifier test R_1 equals Thévenin's impedance of microphone Z_0. Load impedance Z_2 for amplifier test equals the pure resistance of test generator for loudspeaker test R_s. R_s equals Z_{out} of amplifier. Z_{out} is purely resistive. The open-circuit voltage e_s of the test generator for the loudspeaker test equals twice the voltage which the amplifier produces across its load $Z_2 = R_s$.

To obtain the overall response at any given frequency, perform the following addition:

$$20 \log_{10} \frac{p_0}{p_{ff}}$$
$$= \rho_m + (13·17) + (13·21) - 10 \log_{10} R_s - 44 \quad \text{db} \quad (13·23)$$

where ρ_m and (13·17) = (see case I and Fig. 13·9)

(13·21) = the equation for the constant power available response of the loudspeaker in decibels, i.e., it equals (see Fig. 13·11)

$$10 \log_{10} \frac{p_0{}^2}{\dfrac{e_s{}^2}{4R_s}} + 44 \qquad (13·21)$$

The distance at which and the conditions under which p_0 was obtained must be specified.

CASE III. Pressure Response. Specified load resistance for microphone test Z_L equals Z_{in} for amplifier. Load impedance for amplifier test Z_2 equals impedance of loudspeaker Z_s.

To obtain the overall response at any given frequency, perform the following addition:

$$20 \log_{10} \frac{p_0}{p_{ff}} = (13 \cdot 13) + (13 \cdot 16) + (13 \cdot 19) - 74 \quad \text{db} \quad (13 \cdot 24)$$

where $(13 \cdot 13)$ = equation for voltage produced by the microphone across a specified load resistance Z_L, i.e., it equals (see Fig. $13 \cdot 1$)

$$20 \log_{10} \frac{V}{p_{ff}} \qquad (13 \cdot 13)$$

$(13 \cdot 16)$ = equation for voltage gain of the amplifier in decibels, i.e., it equals (see Fig. $13 \cdot 8$)

$$20 \log_{10} \frac{e_2}{e_i} \qquad (13 \cdot 16)$$

$(13 \cdot 19)$ = (see case I).

The distance at which and the conditions under which p_0 was obtained must be specified.

CASE IV. Pressure Response. Specified load resistor for microphone test Z_L equals Z_{in} for amplifier. Load impedance for amplifier test Z_2 equals the pure resistance of test generator for loudspeaker test R_s. R_s equals Z_{out} of amplifier. Z_{out} is purely resistive. The open-circuit voltage E_s of the test generator for the loudspeaker test equals twice the voltage which the amplifier produces across its load $Z_2 = R_s$.

To obtain the overall response at any given frequency, perform the following addition:

$$20 \log_{10} \frac{p_0}{p_{ff}} = (13 \cdot 13) + (13 \cdot 16)$$
$$+ (13 \cdot 21) - 10 \log_{10} R_s - 44 \quad \text{db} \quad (13 \cdot 25)$$

where $(13 \cdot 13)$ and $(13 \cdot 16)$ = (see case III)
$(13 \cdot 21)$ = (see case II).

The distance at which and the conditions under which p_0 was obtained must be specified.

Romanow-Hawley Method. By this method we confine our attention to the basic circuit of Fig. $13 \cdot 13$. The various voltages and impedances which are shown in that figure plus those which will be used later are defined as follows:

e = open-circuit voltage produced by Thévenin's generator used to obtain amplifier response (Fig. $13 \cdot 8$)

e_2 = voltage produced by an amplifier across a load resistance

e_i = voltage across input of the amplifier

e_o = open-circuit voltage produced by the microphone when it is in a free field

e_{out} = open-circuit voltage produced by the amplifier

e_s = open-circuit voltage produced by Thévenin's generator used to obtain the loudspeaker response (Fig. 13·11)

E_s = voltage appearing across the terminals of the loudspeaker (Fig. 13·11)

G = power gain of the amplifier

p_{ff} = free-field pressure measured at microphone position before inserting it into the sound field (The average pressure over the diaphragm p_d may also be used if desired. In this case a different response curve will result whenever diffraction occurs around the microphone.)

p_0 = pressure, in dynes per square centimeter, produced by the loudspeaker

R_1 = resistance which equals the magnitude of rated input impedance of the amplifier (Fig. 13·8)

R_2 = resistance equal to the magnitude of the rated load impedance of the amplifier (Fig. 13·8)

R_0 = resistance equal to the nominal microphone impedance (usually at 1000 $\pm$ 100 cps)

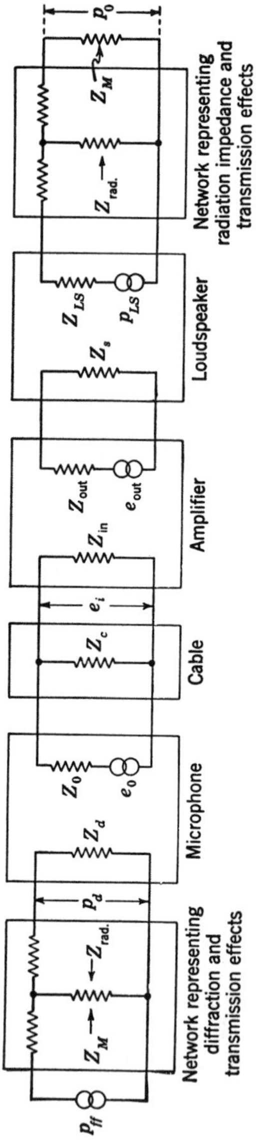

Fig. 13·13   Overall block diagram representing the combination of microphone, cable, amplifier, loudspeaker, and the acoustic media.

R_s = resistance whose magnitude equals the nominal impedance of the loudspeaker (Fig. 13·11) (usually at
1000 ± 100 cps)

$W_2 = e_2^2/R_2$ = power, in watts, delivered by the amplifier to
its rated load resistance R_2

$W_a = e^2/4R_1$ = maximum power available to the amplifier, in
watts, from a Thévenin's generator of internal impedance R_1 and an open-circuit voltage e (see Fig. 13·8)

$W_{as} = e_s^2/4R_s$ = maximum power available, in watts, from a
Thévenin's generator used to drive the loudspeaker
(The generator open-circuit voltage is e_s, and the
resistance is R_s; see Fig. 13·11.)

$W_m = e_0^2/4R_0$ = maximum power available from the microphone, in watts

W_s = total acoustic power output from the loudspeaker, in watts

Z_2 = impedance terminating the amplifier   (In measuring the
gain of the amplifier, Z_2 is equal to R_2 (see Fig. 13·8.)

Z_c = shunt impedance of cable   (This impedance is generally
that of a pure capacitance and is negligibly high for
low impedance microphones.)

Z_{in} = input impedance of the amplifier

Z_{LS} = acoustic impedance looking into the loudspeaker
diaphragm

Z_M = acoustic impedance in the chamber at the point where
the test microphone is located

Z_0 = complex electrical microphone impedance with unblocked
diaphragm (Fig. 13·13)

Z_{out} = output impedance of the amplifier

$Z_{rad.}$ = radiation impedance viewed from microphone diaphragm

$Z_{RAD.}$ = radiation impedance viewed from loudspeaker diaphragm

Z_s = electrical impedance of the loudspeaker (Fig. 13·10)

ρ_m = open-circuit free-field response of the microphone in
decibels re 1 volt per dyne/cm^2; eq. (13·9).

The pressure response S_p in decibels of the overall system (Fig.
13·13) may be expressed by the formula

$$S_p = 20 \log_{10} \frac{p_0}{p_{ff}}$$

$$= 10 \log_{10} \left(\frac{W_m}{p_{ff}^2}\right)\left(\frac{W_a}{W_m}\right)\left(\frac{W_2}{W_a}\right)\left(\frac{W_{as}}{W_2}\right)\left(\frac{p_0^2}{W_{as}}\right) \quad (13·26)$$

This equation can be broken up into five separate terms:

$$S_p = SR_m + CF_{in} + G + CF_{out} + SR_{sp} \qquad (13\cdot27)$$

where each term is defined as follows:

MICROPHONE SYSTEM RATING (SR_m).

$$SR_m \text{ (db)} = 10 \log \frac{W_m}{p_{ff}{}^2}$$

$$= 10 \log \frac{e_0{}^2}{4R_0} - 20 \log p_{ff} + 10 \log \frac{p_{ref.}{}^2}{W_{ref.}} \qquad (13\cdot28)$$

$$= \rho_m - 10 \log R_0 - 50 \quad \text{db} \qquad (13\cdot29)$$

where $W_m = e_0{}^2/4R_0$, $p_{ref.} = 0.0002$ dyne/cm^2, $W_{ref.} = 1$ mw, and where the terminology (SR_m) means system rating of the microphone.

INPUT COUPLING FACTOR (CF_{in}).

$$CF_{in} \text{ (db)} = 10 \log \frac{W_a}{W_m}$$

$$= 10 \log \frac{R_0}{R_1} + 20 \log \left| 1 + \frac{R_1}{Z_{in}} \right|$$

$$- 20 \log \left| 1 + \frac{Z_0}{Z_{in}} + \frac{Z_0}{Z_c} \right| \qquad (13\cdot30)$$

where Z_c = shunt impedance of microphone cable. (For low impedance microphones, $Z_0/Z_c \ll Z_0/Z_{in}$. For high impedance microphones, $Z_c \doteq -j/C_c\omega$, where C_c is the capacitance of the cable.)

AMPLIFIER GAIN RATING (G).

$$G \text{ (db)} = 10 \log \frac{W_2}{W_a}$$

$$= 10 \log W_2 - 10 \log W_a \quad \text{db} \qquad (13\cdot31)$$

where $W_2 = e_2{}^2/R_2$, and $W_a = e^2/4R_1$. Note that W_a is the available power input to the amplifier.

OUTPUT COUPLING FACTOR (CF_{out}).

$$CF_{out} \text{ (db)} = 10 \log \frac{W_{as}}{W_2} \qquad (13\cdot32)$$

where $W_{as} = e_s{}^2/4R_s$.

$$CF_{out} = 10 \log \frac{R_2}{4R_s} + 20 \log \left| 1 + \frac{R_s}{Z_s} \right| + 20 \log \left| 1 + \frac{Z_{out}}{R_2} \right|$$
$$- 20 \log \left| 1 + \frac{Z_{out}}{Z_s} \right| \quad \text{db} \quad (13 \cdot 33)$$

SOURCE (LOUDSPEAKER) SYSTEM RATING (SR_{sp}).

$$SR_{sp} = 10 \log_{10} \frac{p_0{}^2}{W_{as}} + 10 \log \frac{W_{\text{ref.}}}{p_{\text{ref.}}{}^2}$$

$$= 20 \log p_0 - 10 \log \frac{e_s{}^2}{4R_s} + 10 \log W_{\text{ref.}} - 10 \log p_{\text{ref.}}{}^2$$

$$= 20 \log \frac{p_0}{e_s} + 10 \log R_s + 50 \quad \text{db} \quad (13 \cdot 34)$$

where $W_{\text{ref.}}$ is 1 mw, and $p_{\text{ref.}}$ is 0.0002 dyne/cm^2, and the terminology (SR_{sp}) means "system rating of the source when the sound pressure output is measured." One standard now in preparation specifies that the sound pressure p_0 should be stated as though it were measured in an anechoic room at 30 ft from the source.

For the reproduction of sound *indoors*, the acoustic power output of the loudspeaker generally is of more interest than the acoustic pressure p_0. If the power output is measured, the loudspeaker rating may be defined instead as

$$SR_{sw} = 10 \log \frac{W_s}{W_{as}} + 44 \quad \text{db} \quad (13 \cdot 35)$$

where W_s = total acoustic power output from the loudspeaker in watts, and the terminology (SR_{sw}) means "system rating of the source when the acoustic power output is measured."

For this case, Eq. (13·26) will have to read

$$S_w = 10 \log_{10} \frac{W_s}{p_{ff}{}^2} \quad (13 \cdot 36)$$

CALCULATION OF INPUT AND OUTPUT COUPLING FACTORS.   Most of the terms in Eqs. (13·30) and (13·33) are of the form

$$20 \log \left| 1 + xe^{j\theta} \right| \quad (13 \cdot 37)$$

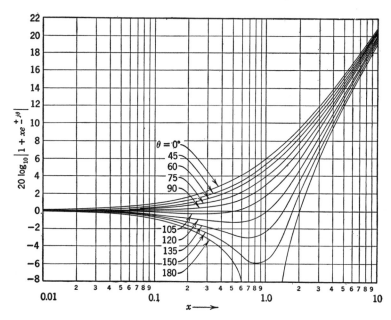

FIG. 13·14   Chart for calculating the coupling factors.   The chart yields $20 \log_{10} |1 + xe^{\pm j\theta}|$ as a function of x.

To facilitate calculation of the coupling terms, the graph of Fig. 13·14 may be used.

EXAMPLE OF ROMANOW-HAWLEY METHOD.[4]   Assume the system to be as follows:

Microphone

Condenser with capacitance of 50×10^{-12} farad

$\rho_m = -50$ db *re* 1 volt per dyne/cm^2 (assume flat response)

Z_0 (100 cps) $= 31.8 \times 10^6 \underline{/-90°}$

Z_0 (1000 cps) $= 3.18 \times 10^6 \underline{/-90°}$

Z_0 (10,000 cps) $= 0.318 \times 10^6 \underline{/-90°}$

R_0 (nominal impedance) $= 3.18 \times 10^6$ ohms

Cable

None

Amplifier

G (100 cps) $= 100$ db

G (1000 cps) $= 102$ db

G (10,000 cps) $= 95$ db

Z_{in} (100 cps) $= 30.3 \times 10^6 \underline{/-72°}$

Z_{in} (1000 cps) $= 3.18 \times 10^6 /\underline{-88°}$
Z_{in} (10,000 cps) $= 0.318 \times 10^6 /\underline{-90°}$
$R_1 =$ (rated input impedance) $= 10^5$ ohms
$Z_{out} = 3$ ohms resistive
$R_2 =$ (rated load impedance) $= 12$ ohms

Loudspeaker

Moving coil:

$SR_{sp} = 68$ db *re* 0.0002 dyne/cm^2 and 1 mw, measured in an anechoic
    chamber, 30 ft from source (assume flat response)
Z_s (100 cps) $= 11 /\underline{-20°}$
Z_s (1000 cps) $= 14 /\underline{30°}$
Z_s (10,000 cps) $= 43 /\underline{48°}$
R_s (nominal impedance) $= 14$ ohms

The microphone system rating SR_m is found from Eq. (13.29).
Substituting, we get

$$SR_m = -50 - 65 - 50 = -165 \quad \text{db } re \text{ 0.0002 dyne/cm}^2 \text{ and 1 mw}$$

The input coupling factors CF_{in} are calculated from Eq. (13·30).
Substituting, we get

$$CF_{in} \text{ (100 cps)} = 10 \log \frac{3.18 \times 10^6}{10^5} + 20 \log \left| 1 + \frac{10^5}{30.3 \times 10^6 /\underline{-72°}} \right|$$

$$-20 \log \left| 1 + \frac{31.8 \times 10^6 /\underline{-90°}}{30.3 \times 10^6 /\underline{-72°}} \right|$$

$$= +15 + 0 - 6.2 = 8.8 \quad \text{db}$$

$$CF_{in} \text{ (1000 cps)} = +15 + 0 - 6.0 = 9.0 \quad \text{db}$$

$$CF_{in} \text{ (10,000 cps)} = +15 + 0.3 - 6.0 = 9.3 \quad \text{db}$$

The output coupling factors CF_{out} are calculated from Eq. (13·33).
Substituting, we get

$$CF_{out} \text{ (100 cps)} = 10 \log \frac{12}{4 \times 14} + 20 \log \left| 1 + \frac{14}{11 /\underline{-20°}} \right|$$

$$+ 20 \log \left| 1 + \frac{3}{12} \right| - 20 \log \left| 1 + \frac{3}{11 /\underline{-20°}} \right|$$

$$= -6.7 + 6.8 + 2.0 - 1.9 = 0.2 \quad \text{db}$$

$$CF_{out} \text{ (1000 cps)} = -6.7 + 5.6 + 2.0 - 1.5 = -0.6 \quad \text{db}$$

$$CF_{out} \text{ (10,000 cps)} = -6.7 + 2.0 + 2.0 - 0.4 = -3.1 \quad \text{db}$$

The pressure response S_p is given by Eq. (13·27). Substituting yields

$$S_p \ (100 \text{ cps}) = -165 + 8.8 + 100 + 0.2 + 68$$

$$= +12 \text{ db}$$

$$S_p \ (1000 \text{ cps}) = -165 + 9.0 + 102 - 0.6 + 68 = +13.4 \text{ db}$$

$$S_p \ (10{,}000 \text{ cps}) = -165 + 9.3 + 95 - 3.1 + 68 = +4.2 \text{ db}$$

One of the principal advantages of the Romanow-Hawley method is that a rating in decibels is obtained for each component, the microphone, amplifier, and loudspeaker. If the rated source and rated load impedances of the amplifier are approximately equal to the impedances of the microphone and loudspeaker, respectively, the three ratings may be added together directly. Such direct addition is fairly accurate for moving-coil microphones and loudspeakers or earphones whose electrical impedances are nearly constant as a function of frequency. For systems that use crystal microphones with long leads or condenser microphones, the coupling factors are appreciable and must be included to obtain the rating of the system. Other cases for which the coupling factors are large are for systems in which the amplifier is improperly terminated, that is, when the ratios R_0/R_1 and R_2/R_s are much different from unity.

Since the microphone rating is expressed in terms of available output power, it is a figure of merit whereby the efficiencies of microphones of different electrical impedances may be compared. Similarly, since the loudspeaker ratings are expressed in terms of available input power they permit the comparison of loudspeakers of different electrical impedances.

Although the coupling factors which we have given here are derived for a system having a single microphone and a single loudspeaker, they are equally applicable to systems with a plurality of microphones and loudspeakers. In these cases, Z_c of Eq. (13·30) should include the parallel impedance of the additional microphones, and Z_s of Eq. (13·33) should include the parallel impedance of the additional loudspeakers.

We have just discussed methods of determining the overall response of a system from the separate physical response curves obtained on individual components. Speech communication systems are coupled to real ears and real voices, however, and, for precise measurement of their overall response characteristics, tests must be employed involving humans as part of the measuring system.   In the next section, we shall discuss the concept of *orthotelephonic response*, which is a response measured while the system is "coupled" in a suitable manner to a talker and a listener.

13·3   Orthotelephonic Response

A speech transmission system must include all components beginning with the vocal cords of the talker and continuing through to the eardrum of the listener.   For example, the system starting with an announcer in a radio studio and continuing through to the ear of a listener in a living room of a home involves the components shown in Fig. 13·15.   The driving generator

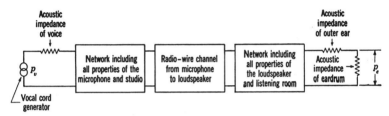

FIG. 13·15   Block diagram representing an overall speech communication system.

is the pair of vocal cords, and the receiving mechanism is the eardrum.   To characterize accurately the complete system in between, we would need to determine the ratio of p_e/p_v and the values of the acoustic impedances of the voice and ear.   Such a determination would be hopelessly difficult.   However, an acceptable compromise is to determine the *orthotelephonic response* of the system as a function of frequency.

Before defining orthotelephonic response let us first establish a definition of a basic reference communication system.   Although subject to proof by test, it is obvious that two people with normal speech and hearing could understand each other nearly perfectly if placed in an absolutely quiet room, free from reflecting surfaces and facing each other at a meter distance apart.   With this condition as a reference, it can be said that a nearly perfect communication system is one which produces exactly the same sounds at the ear of a listener as would be produced in the above-described situation.

Obviously, the same talker and listener would need to be used in both cases.   The case of transmission over a 1-meter air path is called the direct or "ortho" system, and it will serve as the standard of reference.   When we come to test a communication (i.e., telephonic) system its response will be expressed in terms of the response of the basic reference system.

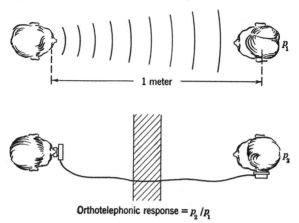

Orthotelephonic response = p_2/p_1

Fig. 13·16   Measurement of the orthotelephonic response of a speech communication system.   The orthotelephonic response equals p_2/p_1, where p_1 is the pressure produced by a talker at the ear of a listener and p_2 is the pressure produced by the system at the same point.   A quiet, anechoic chamber is assumed as the environment for the measurements.

Orthotelephonic[5] response can be defined as follows:

$$\text{Orthotelephonic response} = 20 \log_{10} \frac{p_2}{p_1} \qquad (13 \cdot 38)$$

where p_1 is the pressure measured at the eardrum of a listener seated facing a talker in an anechoic chamber at a distance of 1 meter, and p_2 is the pressure measured at the same point produced by the communication system under test (see Fig. 13·16).   It is the practice of some observers to measure the pressure at the eardrum subjectively, that is, by the *loudness* which it produces. Other observers have measured the pressure at the eardrum objectively by using a small probe microphone.

It will be noticed that no mention has been made of the phase relations between the pressures at the eardrum and those at the vocal cords.   Fortunately, the ear seems to pay little atten-

[5] A. H. Inglis, "Transmission features of the new telephone sets," *Bell System Technical Jour.*, **17**, 358–380 (1938).

tion to phase, at least so far as the intelligibility of speech is concerned; consequently we choose to disregard it here. A more important factor, however, is that there seems to be some psychological difference among the ear's responses to sounds which are presented to it in various ways. Experiments performed in several laboratories indicate that the ear judges a given sound pressure *measured at the eardrum* to be louder if it is presented through the open air than if it is presented by an earphone held in a cushion against the head or the pinna. The difference in loudness is not uniform as a function of frequency and is of the order of 5 **or so** db. The result of this intriguing discrepancy is that a different orthotelephonic response will be obtained if pressures are measured at the eardrum than if loudnesses are measured. Until this difficulty is resolved, techniques are available for obtaining consistent results in the calculation of articulation scores, provided the particular technique used in determining the orthotelephonic response is clearly stated.[6]

The orthotelephonic response does not take into account the effects of time delays or reverberation on the performance of the system. For that reason, it is usually measured for communication systems with close-talking microphones and earphones.

In practice, we generally find it simpler to measure the orthotelephonic response in several steps; that is, we measure the real-voice response of the microphone, the power gain of the electrical system, and the real-ear response of the earphone. Methods for performing real-voice and real-ear calibrations will be described in Chapter 16.

13·4 Repetition Count

From the standpoint of the users of a telephone system, the transmission performance is measured by the success which they have in carrying on conversations over the circuit. Different degrees of success are indicated by the number of failures to understand the ideas transmitted over the telephone and by the amount of effort required on the part of the users to impart and receive these ideas.

The repetitions required in a conversation can be counted, but a determination of the effort factor presents difficulties. Martin[1] concludes that the effort in general increases as the diffi-

[6] L. L. Beranek, "The design of speech communication systems," *Proc. Inst. Radio Engrs.*, **35**, 880–890 (1947).

culty of conversing becomes greater and, hence, bears a relation to the increase in repetitions. So, it is perhaps legitimate to use the rate of occurrence of repetitions requested by the users of a telephone circuit as a direct measure of the service performance of that circuit.

To determine the performance of a telephone circuit by this method, it must be monitored and the number of repetitions and the total length of a conversation noted. If the test is to be significant, a large number of observations will need to be made involving a variety of talkers and listeners. The Bell Telephone Laboratories engineers[7] found it desirable to establish a reference telephone system. They chose telephone instruments and a length of line which were in common use at that time. They state that as conditions changed another reference standard might have to be chosen.

The next step in their line of reasoning was to find some number which could be used to specify the performance of the system under test relative to that of the reference system. In setting up their number for rating systems in this manner, they gave weight to a consideration that is peculiar to line telephone systems. This consideration is that the principal factor affecting the understandability of speech in most offices and homes is the level at which it is delivered to the listener's ear. In other words, the principal factor is the ratio of signal level to background noise level. The background noise could arise on the telephone line, at the listener's position, or in his own ear (the threshold of hearing is sometimes thought of as being set by background noise in the ear).

The procedure used, then, is to determine the number of repetitions per minute for the standard system as a function of the attenuation in decibels inserted into the connecting line. Then the repetition rate for the system under test is determined. By comparing this repetition rate with that obtained for the standard, the system can be stated as being so many decibels better or worse than the standard system.

Such a means of characterizing the performance of a system is not good if the important variable of frequency response of the system plays its full part. For example, in airplane-to-airplane

[7] F. W. McKown and J. W. Emling, "A system of effective transmission data for rating telephone circuits," *Bell System Technical Jour.*, **12**, 331–346 (1933).

systems where the ambient noise is very high, either increasing or decreasing the gain of the standard system may under some conditions cause a loss of intelligibility of the transmitted speech. The only way in which improvement is possible is by changing the relative frequency response of the system. For such an environment a change in gain of the standard cannot be used as a characterization of the performance of the system under test.

The repetition count, however, should still be a legitimate measure of the efficacy of the system even though an equivalent decibel rating is not possible. Colpitts[8] suggests a logarithmic relationship which agrees with the decibel characterization described above over a limited range. There is no reason why the concept could not be extended to be a general expression for the performance of one system with respect to another. The relationship is

$$\text{Repetition level} = 50 \log_{10} \frac{R_1}{R_2} \qquad (13 \cdot 39)$$

where R_1 and R_2 are the repetition rates for two systems under comparison. The use of the word "decibels" has been avoided because the repetition level is equal to the improvement in decibels only in limited cases.

13·5 Articulation Tests

A. General Considerations

A quantitative measure of the intelligibility of speech may be obtained by counting the number of discrete speech units correctly recognized by a listener. The procedure by which this quantitative measure is obtained is an *articulation test*. Typically, an announcer reads lists of syllables, words, or sentences to a group of listeners, and the percentage of items correctly recorded by these listeners is called the *articulation score*. This percentage is taken as a measure of the intelligibility of speech.

The articulation test as a means of testing telephone instruments was first described by Campbell[9] in 1910. More refined procedures for performing articulation tests can be found in

---

[8] E. H. Colpitts, "Scientific research applied to the telephone transmitter and receiver," *Bell System Technical Jour.*, **16**, 251–274 (1937).

[9] G. A. Campbell, "Telephonic intelligibility," *Phil. Mag.*, **19**, 152–159 (1910).

articles by Fletcher and Steinberg and by Castner and Carter.[10] Basing their work on these excellent contributions, Egan and his colleagues[11] at the Psycho-Acoustic Laboratory at Harvard advanced the science of articulation testing substantially. The material in this section and in Chapter 17 is drawn almost entirely from their work.

Articulation-testing methods may be used as tools in the solution of many problems of communication. First among these is the comparison of communication systems or components. For example, the effect of frequency and amplitude distortion introduced by transducers or amplifiers may be determined. The effect of ambient noise and the protection against it by microphones and earphones may be evaluated.

Static and man-made interference are further hazards to communication. The detrimental effects of these noises and the degree to which they may be tolerated in a radio circuit can be determined and evaluated. A comparison of the effectiveness of various types of noises by articulation-testing methods has important applications in the "jamming" of enemy messages.

Large differences exist between the basic intelligibility of words and commands. Communication can be made more effective by selecting those words and phrases which can be heard either above the din of noise or over systems which distort the sounds of speech. In military applications, articulation tests provide the tool for selecting military vocabularies.

Articulation tests have been applied to the rating and training of communication personnel. Because listeners may be tested by these methods in relatively large numbers, the articulation test may be used to provide a practical and accurate rating of listening ability.

The articulation test differs from repetition counts in that it is under laboratory control. Carefully selected words are usually used. The talkers and listeners are trained to listen attentively or to speak with constant voice levels. Changes in the system under test can readily be made, and the ambient noise is always controllable. The test does not, of course, allow for inattentive-

[10] H. Fletcher and J. C. Steinberg, "Articulation testing methods," *Bell System Technical Jour.*, **8**, 806–854 (1929); T. G. Castner and C. W. Carter, Jr., "Developments in the application of articulation testing," *Bell System Technical Jour.*, **12**, 347–370 (1933).

[11] J. Egan, "Articulation testing methods, II," O.S.R.D. Report No. 3802, November 1, 1944.

ness, carelessness in enunciation, groping for hidden meanings in the other man's words, and other such factors which come about in normal telephone conversations. It cannot be said, therefore, that the articulation test is a replacement for other types of tests, such as repetition counts, but it is a powerful aid in the development of new equipment.

B. Significance of Articulation Scores

The chief fact which should be recognized about an articulation score is that it is not an absolute quantity. In other words, for any given communication system the articulation score is a function of at least the following items:

(a) Choice of sounds used (words, sentences, syllables, etc.).

(b) Selection of testing personnel.

(c) Training of personnel.

(d) Manner in which the sounds are presented.

(e) Spectrum and level of ambient noise.

(f) Manner in which the communication equipment is used.

(g) Dozens of small factors such as voice quality, regional pronunciation, interaction between the sounds and the testing personnel, etc.

We conclude that *all articulation scores are relative scores.* Little trust can be placed in absolute statements about articulation, especially if such statements are based on tests with different voices and different listeners. However, if items (a) to (g) above are carefully controlled, it has been well established that the articulation test reliably rank-orders different communication systems.

The types of sounds used affect the results in great measure. Words are more easily understood than syllables, and sentences even more so. The accent given a word may aid the listener in discriminating between two such meaningful words as *ex'-it* and *ex-ist'*, even though the final consonant or consonant compound is not heard. Scores obtained with polysyllables are affected more by these psychological factors than are those obtained with monosyllables. Figure 13·17 shows a relationship between the number of words correctly recorded and the number of sounds contained in the words. Short words which provide less opportunity for the operation of such factors as inflection and meaning are usually missed more frequently than long words.

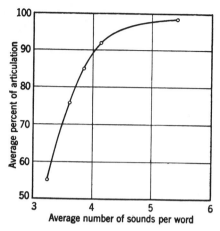

FIG. 13·17   The improvement of articulation as the number of sounds per word is increased. Five groups of 20 words, having different average numbers of sounds per word, were read 20 times to a group of listeners. (After Egan.[11])

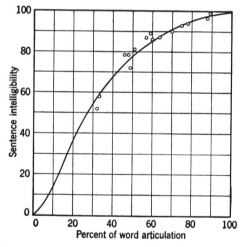

FIG. 13·18   Relation between sentence intelligibility and word articulation measured under a wide variety of conditions. (After Egan.[11])

When sentence lists are scored in terms of the meaning conveyed, these psychological factors are still more important. For this reason, sentence articulation is typically higher than word or syllable articulation. One such relationship between word and sentence articulation is shown in Fig. 13·18.

Of equal significance is the choice of announcers and listeners for the tests. When tests are made under very easy conditions, such as very low ambient noise, even poor announcers and listeners will produce articulation scores that are only slightly different. As the test conditions become more difficult, however, the differences in vocal quality and listening ability become more significant, and the differences in articulation scores become greater. Figures 13·19 and 13·20 illustrate the differences

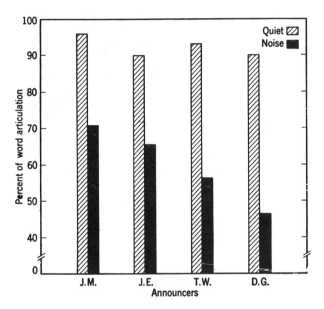

FIG. 13·19   Bar graph showing the differences in word articulation scores obtained with four different announcers. (After Egan.[11])

among announcers and listeners which may be expected. For any given crew of announcers and listeners, however, reliable rank-ordering of several systems is possible (see Fig. 13·21).

Articulation scores obtained with inexperienced listeners show improvement with practice. A typical curve of improvement for a crew of 10 listeners is given in Fig. 13·22. First there is a gradual rise in the curve, then it flattens off. After the stable level of performance is reached, improvement may continue at a very slow and uniform rate, so that retesting of a standard reference system at regular intervals is indicated.

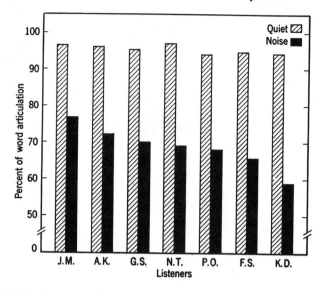

FIG. 13·20 Bar graph showing the differences in word articulation scores obtained with a typical group of listeners. (After Egan.[11])

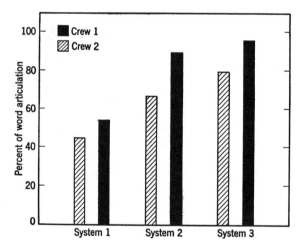

FIG. 13·21 Rank-ordering of three communication systems by two different articulation crews. Crew 1 was a trained laboratory testing crew. Crew 2 consisted of eight military servicemen. (After Egan.[11])

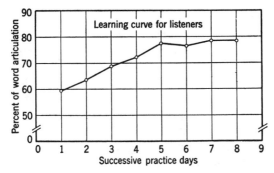

Fɪɢ. 13·22 Typical learning curve obtained for a test crew with the same speech communication system. Each point on the curve represents the average score on 12 tests for a crew of 10 listeners. The tests were read over the interphone system by three well-practiced announcers. (After Egan.[11])

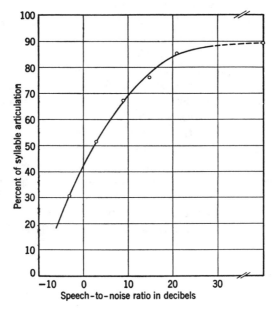

Fɪɢ. 13·23 Curve showing the effect of ambient noise on the syllable articulation score. The speech level at the listeners' ears was held constant at a level of about 103 db. A "white" noise was mixed electrically with the speech. Measurements were made with a *VU* meter. (After Egan.[11])

13·6 Objective Speech Transmission Meter

A recent international draft standard[12] has proposed an objective method for obtaining the equivalent of the result of a PB-word articulation score using an objective measuring system.[13] The result of a test using this method leads to a single number that can be related to the PB-word intelligibility score, called the "RASTI" value, where RASTI stands for "Rapid Speech Transmission Index".

The method, including basic assumptions, is as follows:

(a) The two most significant octave bands in determining the intelligibility of speech are those centered on 500 Hz (350–700 Hz) and 2000 Hz (1400–2800 Hz). In fact, the three basic formants of speech, formed by the resonant passages of the throat, mouth, and lips, are generally just below 500 Hz, and near 1500 and 2500 Hz.

(b) The second assumption is that for the most part speech intelligibility is carried in the random noise component of speech rather than in the voiced portion. Thus a source of "pink" random noise (sloping at -3 dB per octave) is supplied to these two bands as the "carrier frequencies". The sound pressure levels of these bands, as radiated by a built-in loudspeaker on the apparatus, are 59 dB in the 500 Hz band, and 50 dB in the 2000 Hz band, measured at 1 meter distance, which levels equal the long-time average levels in normal speech.

(c) The next assumption is that the intelligibility in speech is carried in low-frequency modulations of the "carrier frequency," that is to say, the ligature fluctuations in the signal that are imposed on the carrier frequencies by the motions of the tongue, lips, and jaw. To simulate these fluctuations, the standard has chosen four modulation frequencies for the 500 Hz band, namely, 1, 2, 4, and 8 Hz, and for the 2000 Hz band, 0.7, 1.4, 2.8, 5.6, and 11.2 Hz.

---

[12]International Standard IEC Draft Publication 268, Part 16 (1987).

[13]H. J. M. Steeneken and T. Houtgast, "A physical method for measuring speech-transmission quality," J. Acoust. Soc. Am. **67**, 318–326 (1980).

13·7 The RASTI Method

When conducting a test in an auditorium, the two modulated noise bands are radiated to the microphone of the sound system under test, or into the room without amplification, either through the mouth of a manikin (see Chaps. 9 and 16), or directly from the built-in loudspeaker. The "listening" apparatus consists of a microphone and a signal-processing apparatus which is moved about the auditorium. That apparatus determines the reduction in percent modulation for each of the nine low frequencies caused by both the reverberation and the ambient noise in the auditorium and calculates the RASTI value.

In Fig. 13·24, these concepts are shown. The transmitted signal is shown in the upper left. The modulation in the received signal is reduced, by comparison, owing to reverberation and noise in the room. This reduction in modulation is called the Modulation Transfer Function (MTF) and is defined as the modulation reduction factor expressed as a function of modulation frequency.

Figure 13·25 shows the effect of the S/N ratio, in dB, and the reverberation time on the modulation transfer function. If the predominant factor in reducing the modulation component is the (S/N) ratio, all of the nine frequencies will be affected in the

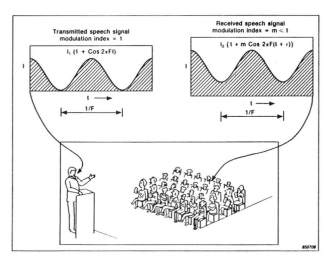

FIG. 13·24 Illustration of the reduction in modulation of a speech signal caused by background noise and reverberation. (Courtesy of Bruel & Kjaer.)

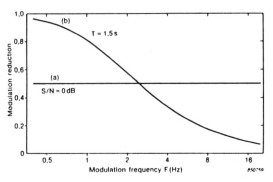

FIG. 13·25   The Modulation Transfer Function for two cases: (a) no reverberation and S/N = 0 dB; (b) no background noise and reverberation time (early) = 1.5 s. (Courtesy of Bruel & Kjaer.)

same way. For S/N = 0 dB, the MTF is 0.5. If room reverberation is the reason for the reduction in modulation, the modulation transfer function for each low frequency will decrease with increasing frequency. The reason for this is that rapid fluctuations in the random noise envelope become more blurred as a result of reverberation as compared to slower fluctuations. The reduction in modulation is therefore greater at higher modulation frequencies.

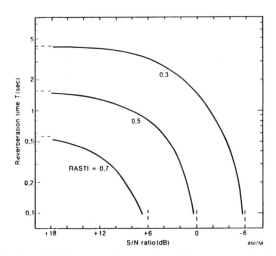

FIG. 13·26   Iso-RASTI curves showing how different combinations of S/N and reverberation time result in the same RASTI value. (Courtesy of Bruel & Kjaer.)

Because both the S/N ratio and reverberation reduce the modulation, there is a "tradeoff" in contribution to RASTI, as shown by Fig. 13·26.

The MTF is calculated at each modulation frequency from a knowledge of the reverberation time, T in sec, and the signal-to-noise ratio, S/N in dB,

$$m_i(f_i) = \cfrac{1}{\sqrt{1 + \left(2\pi f_i \cfrac{T}{13.8}\right)^2 \left(1 + 10 \cfrac{-S}{N} \cfrac{1}{10}\right)}} \qquad (13\cdot40)$$

where $m_i(f_i)$ is the reduction in modulation at the modulation frequency f_i, and T refers to the early part of the sound decay curve.

For each of the nine modulation frequencies, f_i, a transformation is made by Eq. (13·40) to a RASTI value, X_i,

$$X_i = 10 \log\left(\frac{m_i}{1 - m_i}\right) \qquad (13\cdot41)$$

where, X_i is the apparent signal-to-noise ratio, in dB, corresponding to the measured modulation reduction factor, m_i.

The X_i values are truncated at ± 15 dB, i.e., if X_i is greater than 15 dB, than X_i is taken to be $+15$ dB. If it is less than -15 dB, than it is taken to be -15 dB.

The arithmetic average of the nine values of X_i is taken and normalized to yield an index that ranges from 0 to 1.0.

$$\text{RASTI value} = \frac{(\overline{X}_i + 15)}{30} \qquad (13\cdot42)$$

The receiver makes these calculations automatically.

13·8 Relation of RASTI to PB word intelligibility

By repeated articulation tests, Steenchen and Houtgast[13] have produced a relation between RASTI values and PB word intelligibility that is expressed, practically, by:

Subjective intelligibility scale	RASTI value
Bad	0 to 0.3
Poor	0.3 to 0.45
Fair	0.45 to 0.6
Good	0.6 to 0.75
Excellent	0.75 to 1.0

14.

Tests for Laboratory and Studio Microphones

14·1 Introduction

Laboratory and studio microphones are generally called upon to serve a wide variety of purposes. They may be used to pick up music, speech signals, pure tones, or noise of various kinds, or any combination of these sounds. They may be used to measure the sound pressure or particle velocity, or, in some cases, the intensity at a point in a closed acoustical system or in free space. No one microphone can be universally used for all these types of measurement, as shown in Chapter 5, and the selection of an instrument for a given purpose must depend on certain physical characteristics. The following characteristics are required to specify the performance of a given microphone:

(a) *The frequency response characteristic* is the function by which the electrical output of the microphone, with a given constant acoustical input, is related to the frequency. The electrical output may be in terms of open-circuit voltage, or the voltage or power developed in a specified load. The acoustical input may be in terms of sound pressure at the diaphragm of the microphone, or of sound pressure, particle velocity, or intensity of a specified sound field in free space.

(b) *The directional characteristic* is the function by which the electrical output of the microphone, when placed in a specified freely traveling sound field, is related to the angle between the principal axis of the microphone and the direction of propagation of the sound field. It is usually a plot on polar paper of the ratio (expressed in decibels) of the response at angle θ to that at $\theta = 0$. The directional characteristic is different at different frequencies. However, a single number at each frequency, called the *directivity index*, may be derived from the polar plot, so that the complete directional characteristics of the microphone can be indicated by a plot of directivity index *vs.* frequency.

(*c*) *The power efficiency* is a function by which the power available at the electric terminals is related to the acoustic power available directly from a sound field to the microphone. The *available power* from a source is defined as the power which the source can deliver to a resistive load equal in size to the modulus of the microphone impedance at a frequency of 1000 cps (or other specified frequency).

(*d*) *The distortion characteristic* is a function by which the total non-linear distortion in the output signal, for a specified acoustical input signal, is related to frequency. Various ways of expressing the total distortion may be used. The most common are the *rms harmonic distortion* and the *intermodulation distortion*. In the former, a pure tone signal is applied, and the distortion is expressed as the ratio of the effective amplitude of the harmonics in the output to the effective value of the total output (fundamental plus harmonics). In the latter, two (or more) pure tones of different frequencies are applied, and the distortion is expressed as the ratio of the effective amplitude of specified sum or difference tones in the output to the effective value of the two fundamentals in the output.

(*e*) *The impedance characteristic* is a function by which the complex electrical impedance of the microphone, measured at the output terminals, is related to frequency. The acoustic load on the diaphragm of the microphone must be specified.

(*f*) *The fidelity of reproduction of complex signals*, particularly those of highly transient character is sometimes of importance. Basically, the fidelity is a function of the frequency response and phase shift *vs.* frequency characteristics, the latter of which is difficult to determine. If these and the waveform of the transient are known, the waveform of the corresponding electrical output can be predicted. There is no standardized test at present for indicating the performance of a microphone with transient acoustic signals.

(*g*) *The dynamic range* of a microphone is the range of levels of input signal which can usefully be transduced by the instrument. It is bounded at low levels by the inherent thermal noise generated in the microphone resistance and is limited at high levels by the amount of distortion which can be tolerated in the transduced signal, or, in some cases, by the point of failure of the mechanical system of the instrument under large applied forces.

The basic procedure for absolute calibration of a primary standard microphone has been discussed in detail in Chapter 4. The material to be presented in the present chapter concerns the secondary calibration of various types of microphones by comparison of their performance with that of a primary standard. It is assumed in the discussions which follow that such a primary standard microphone is available for use in measuring the sound field which is applied to the microphone under test.

14·2   Frequency Response Characteristic

The open-circuit free-field response of a microphone at a given frequency is defined by the relation

$$\rho_m = 20 \log_{10} \frac{e_o}{p_{ff}} \qquad (14\cdot1)$$

where e_o is the open-circuit voltage generated by the microphone, as measured at its accessible terminals, when placed in a progressive plane wave sound field of sound pressure p_{ff} (see Chapter 13). The value of p_{ff} is that which exists prior to the introduction of the microphone. To be of general use, a statement of the value of ρ_m must be accompanied by a statement of the impedance of the microphone, since ρ_m is in terms of open-circuit voltage. Unless otherwise stated, the symbol ρ_m will be taken to mean the response of the instrument to sound for which the direction of propagation is perpendicular to the diaphragm or ribbon, or is along an axis which may be called the axis of normal usage of the microphone.

In the experimental determination of the field response, factors which may affect the results, and therefore need serious consideration, are (a) the sound source, (b) the location of the microphone with respect to the sound source, (c) the acoustical nature of the environment in which the measurement is made, and (d) the voltage-measuring system.

A. Sound Source

The first and most obvious requirement of the sound source is that it must be capable of producing sufficiently high sound levels to cover the useful operating range of the microphone. In particular, it must be able to produce signal levels which are high enough above the ambient noise so that noise does not contribute significantly to the output of the microphone. A signal level of 30 db or more above the noise should be satisfactory.

The second important requirement of the sound source is that the signal it produces shall be suitably low in distortion. It is not practical to specify a given maximum of distortion, because the effect on the test results is strongly dependent on the shape of the frequency response characteristic of the microphone and on the nature of the distortion. For example, if the microphone under test has a uniformly rising response with increasing frequency, the second, third, fourth, etc., harmonics in the signal from the sound source will be increasingly emphasized in the microphone output as the order of the harmonic increases. A tentative recommendation is that the distortion products in the signal should be held to such a value that their contribution to the measured response will be less than 0.2 db (2 percent). If it is not possible to use a source which meets this requirement, filters may be used in the electrical equipment with which the output of the microphone is measured. The filters should be such as to pass only the fundamental component of the signal. There is, of course, a practical limit to the amount of harmonic distortion which can be tolerated in the signal when filters are used, since the distortion products should obviously not be sufficiently large to overload the microphone when the fundamental does not.

The sound source must also be capable of producing an essentially plane wave at the microphone position, over an area which is several times the area of the microphone face. If the wave is not plane, variations in measured response of the microphone may arise from uncontrollable variations in its position in the sound field when repeated measurements are made. Discrepancies from this cause will be most important at high frequencies, where the diffraction of sound around the microphone depends most strongly on the shape of the wave front.

The use of random noise as a signal, rather than pure tones, is discussed in some detail in Chapter 15 with respect to tests of loudspeakers. There is usually less reason to use this type of signal for free-field calibration of microphones than for loudspeakers, since microphone response is usually a smoother function of frequency. However, if one wishes to obtain the diffuse-field response (see discussion of diffusion rooms below), it is practically mandatory that a random noise source be used.   In that case the signal voltage may be amplified thermal noise from a resistance or electrical noise from a gas tube. Either of two procedures (or a combination) might be used: (1) a wide-band noise signal covering the frequency range to which the microphone responds is produced in the room, and the voltage output of the microphone is analyzed by a narrow-band analyzer (bandwidth of 15 to 60 cps) as a function of frequency; or (2) a narrow band of random noise is produced and the output of the microphone measured as a function of frequency as the mean frequency of the noise band is swept slowly through the frequency range of interest.   The sound pressure level produced by either of the two sources is measured by a similar procedure by a primary standard microphone, whose diffuse-field response must be known. Some thought must be given to the transient characteristics of the filters and analyzer used in either method.

B. Location with Respect to Sound Source

In principle, the secondary calibration of a microphone is obtained by measuring the free-field sound pressure "at a point" in the sound field with a primary standard microphone and then determining the output of the unknown microphone when placed "at the same point." Since microphones vary considerably in size and shape, and, since some have relatively large screens or grilles surrounding or covering the active elements, it is necessary to specify the means of locating the microphone with respect to the sound source.

A tentative convention for location of the microphone suggested by B. B. Bauer* is illustrated in Fig. 14·1. The basic principle is that the microphone shall be placed in the sound field so that the diaphragm, or the acoustically sensitive inlet, is located at the specified distance d from the source.   In Fig. 14·1 several types of microphones are shown, located coaxially with their sources at the left-hand side of the drawing, in accordance with this convention. The acoustically sensitive surfaces or inlets are indicated by means of arrows in each case. A and B are pressure microphones in which the diaphragms are essentially open to the air, and the distance d is measured to the diaphragm. Microphone C has a cavity of appreciable size in front of the diaphragm, so the distance d is measured to the outer edge of the

*Now deceased. In 1949 he was at Shure Bros., 225 West Huron Street, Chicago.

cavity which is the acoustical inlet. Microphone D is a pressure microphone with an attached probe tube, the distance d being measured to the open end of the probe tube. Microphones E and F are combination instruments in which the acoustically sensitive elements are surrounded by a screen or open grille on all sides; the distance d is measured to the geometrical mid-point

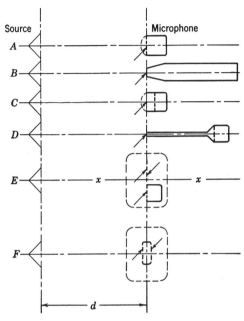

Fig. 14·1 Suggested standard methods for specifying the distance d between the source and microphone. A and B, pressure microphones with essentially exposed diaphragms; C, microphone with acoustic networks but single opening; D, probe tube microphone; E, cardioid microphone; F, velocity microphone. In each case the arrows indicate the position of the "diaphragm" of the microphone. (Courtesy B. B. Bauer.)

of the various sound-sensitive elements and openings within the screen or case.

Another problem which arises in connection with the relative locations of microphone and sound source is that of obtaining an essentially plane wave at the microphone position. Since it is hardly possible to construct a sound source which will produce a true plane wave over a sufficiently large area for the entire audio range, a practical compromise must be effected. The usual procedure is to employ a source which produces a divergent wave, and to locate the microphone at a sufficient distance, so that the curvature of the wave front at the microphone position is insignificantly small. A criterion for this condition, which has been suggested by L. J. Anderson,* is that the distance of the microphone from the sound source d shall not be less than

$$d = \frac{350}{f} \qquad (14\cdot2)$$

where d is in feet, and f is the signal frequency in cycles. Furthermore, in no case shall d be less than four times the maximum

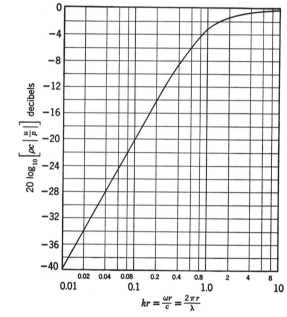

Fig. 14·2 Magnitude of ratio of particle velocity to pressure times ρc expressed in decibels as a function of kr; where k = wave number and r = distance from the center of a spherical source.

dimension of the microphone. If the source produces a divergent wave, it is particularly important to have a sufficient distance between it and a velocity microphone undergoing calibration. The output of a velocity microphone is proportional to the particle velocity in a sound wave. However, the calibrating sound field is usually measured by a standard microphone the output of which is proportional to the sound pressure. Hence, if we

* RCA-Victor Engineering Laboratories, Camden, N. J.

are to obtain a calibration of the velocity microphone in terms of free-field plane wave sound pressure, it must be measured in a sound field in which the ratio of particle velocity to pressure is constant at all frequencies. In a plane wave, this is true. In a spherical wave, however, this is not true in the region near the source, and, also, the particle velocity and sound pressure are not in phase in that region. As the distance from the source becomes greater or the frequency higher, the ratio of particle velocity to pressure becomes more nearly constant with frequency, as shown by Fig. 14·2, and the phase angle between pressure and velocity approaches a value of zero at all frequencies, as indicated in Fig. 2·13 (Chapter 2). Thus, at a sufficiently great distance from the source, a spherical wave field is practically equivalent to a plane wave field.

C. Acoustic Environment for Tests

There are four general types of "environment" in which secondary calibrations of microphones may be made: (a) closed coupler, for pressure calibration of microphones with high diaphragm impedance; (b) anechoic chamber, for free-field calibrations; (c) outdoors, for free-field calibrations; and (d) diffusion room, for random-field calibrations.

Closed Coupler. There are three desirable requirements for a closed coupler used for pressure calibrations, as has been pointed out in the discussion of the reciprocity method for primary calibration in Chapter 4. First, the volume of the coupling chamber should preferably be large enough so that its acoustic impedance is small relative to that of the microphone being calibrated and that of the standard microphone also. This is in order that the sound pressure within the coupler be the same for both microphones. Otherwise, the difference between the shunting effects of the diaphragms must be taken into account explicitly. Second, the linear dimensions of the coupling cavity should be sufficiently small so that standing waves do not occur at any frequency within the range in which calibration is to be made. If this is not true, a cavity must be selected in which explicit account is taken of wave motion. Third, it is desirable to make the ratio of surface area to volume of the cavity as small as possible in order to minimize heat transfer from the gas in the chamber to the coupler.

The first and third of these requirements are in direct opposition to the second, and a compromise must be effected. With regard to the first requirement, it should be noted that, if the primary standard microphone and the microphone to be calibrated are of identical, or nearly identical, acoustic impedance, it should be possible to use a smaller coupling chamber than if they are widely different. The point of importance is that the acoustic impedance into which the sound source works should ideally be the same with either microphone in place. The second requirement, that the linear dimensions of the cavity be small to avoid wave motion, may be made easier to meet if the proper gas is introduced into the cavity. The wavelength of sound in the gas should be substantially larger than that in air. Hydrogen and helium are possibilities, as the ratios of wavelengths in them to those in air are about 3.8 and 2.9, respectively.

Anechoic Chamber. A first requirement for an anechoic chamber is, of course, that the sound pressure level at the microphone due to sound reflected from the walls (or from equipment in the chamber) shall be well below that due to direct transmission of sound from the source. Some observers have suggested that the sound pressure due to reflected waves should be at least 20 db below that due to sound transmitted directly from the source. The magnitudes of such reflected waves may be determined with the aid of a highly directional microphone placed at the calibrating position. They may also be estimated by examining the manner in which sound pressure varies along a line between a point source and the calibrating position. If reflections are negligible, the sound pressure will vary inversely as the square of the distance from the acoustic center of the source. A criterion that is frequently used as a measure of satisfactoriness of the sound field is that the sound pressure near the calibrating point shall not deviate from the inverse square law by more than ± 1.0 db. A directional type of sound source will assist in minimizing the effects of reflections.

It should be noted that the anechoic chamber must be large enough so that the requirements for distance of the microphone from the sound source, as discussed in the preceding section are satisfied.

Outdoors. When a satisfactory anechoic chamber is not available, calibrations may be made outdoors. The requirements for reflected sound which were considered in the previous paragraph must be met. Two types of procedure have been used. The sound source may be mounted on the ground, pointing upward, and the microphone suspended over it from a boom on a tower. Or, the source may be mounted on a tower or other structure with its axis horizontal and the microphone suspended at a point on the axis of the source from a horizontal boom. As in any free-field measurement, the distance between source and microphone must be sufficiently great to avoid errors due to the shape of the wave front. The practical difficulties which arise in outdoor calibrations are usually those due to wind, weather, and ambient noise. If wind noise is encountered, a suitable windshield may be used. Several constructions for windshields are given in Chapter 5, pp. 258–261.

It has been suggested that the total voltage output of the microphone being calibrated because of extraneous causes should be at least 20 db below the voltage developed by the acoustic signal. Such extraneous causes include wind, stray electromagnetic and electrostatic fields, ambient noise, and vibration of the microphone as a whole.

Diffusion Room. It is frequently desirable to know the average response of a microphone to a diffuse (random-incidence) sound field. A diffuse sound field may be defined as one in which the probability that sound will arrive at the microphone from a given direction is the same for all directions, and in which the sound waves from all directions are equal in amplitude and random in phase at the position of the microphone. It is hardly possible to realize such a field experimentally, but a reasonably close practical approximation may be achieved by proper design of the room in which such calibrations are to be made. In an ordinary rectangular room, the sound pressure level due to a source in the room varies widely from point to point, owing to the standing waves set up between the walls. Furthermore, the sound arrives at the point where the microphone is placed from only certain specific directions which are determined by the geometry of the room and the locations of the source and the point of measurement. However, by making the wall surfaces highly irregular and by introducing reflecting objects of various sizes and shapes into the room, the standing wave patterns may be broken up considerably. The number of directions from which reflected sound arrives at a point may thus be increased tremendously. As a result, the sound field at a point will approach the diffuse field defined above, making dependable calibrations possible.

The relative degree of diffusion of the sound field depends on the size and nature of the irregularities, such as bumps or curvatures in the wall surfaces. In general, such irregularities will act best as diffusers for sounds of wavelength not greater than about twice the dimension of the irregularity.[1] Many rooms of this type which have been built to date have "polycylindrical" walls and ceilings.[2, 3] In these, each wall surface consists of parallel sections of cylinders of various diameters and chord

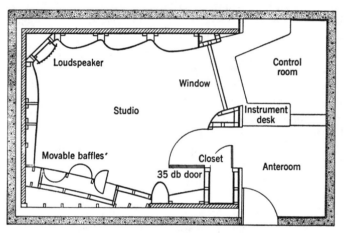

Fig. 14·3   Drawing of the interior of a small studio with irregular surfaces for producing a diffuse sound field.   (Courtesy Acoustics Laboratory of the Massachusetts Institute of Technology.)

lengths, the order of sizes along a given wall being random. The axes of the cylinders on any one wall are laid perpendicular to those on adjacent walls to increase the diffusion. Another construction leading to the same acoustical results may be achieved as shown in Fig. 14·3.

If a pure tone source is used in such a room and the sound pressure is measured at various points, it is found that there are still some variations in pressure from point to point, although they

[1] P. M. Morse and R. H. Bolt, "Sound waves in rooms," *Rev. Mod. Physics*, **16**, 69–150 (1944).

[2] J. E. Volkmann, "Polycylindrical diffusers in room acoustic design," *Jour. Acous. Soc. Amer.*, **13**, 234–243 (1942).

[3] C. P. Boner, "Performance of broadcast studios designed with convex surfaces of plywood," *Jour. Acous. Soc. Amer.* **13**, 244–247 (1942).

are very much less than for a room with plane walls. However, if a source which produces a fairly narrow band of random noise is used, the variations of total level of the noise may be made quite small. Similarly, with such a source, if the microphone is placed at a fixed point in the room and the mean frequency of the noise band is varied, the variations in sound pressure at the microphone will be small. Rudmose has shown that with a random noise band 15 to 60 cps in width the variation of sound pressure level with frequency at a point can be as little as ± 2 db.[4]

D. Voltage-Measuring System

As stated in Section 13·2 (Chapter 13), the open-circuit voltage of a microphone may be measured by means of a voltmeter whose impedance is very high in comparison with that of the microphone, or the insert-voltage method may be used. In the latter case, the resistance of the insert-voltage source is usually made small in comparison with that of the microphone, although such a condition is not mandatory.

The type of signal produced by the insert-voltage source should be the same as that supplied to the sound source during calibration, that is, pure tone, or band of random noise, as the case may be. If random noise is used as the signal, and a high impedance voltmeter is used instead of an insert voltage, the meter must be either an rms type or a linear type. If a linear type is used 1 db must be added to its readings (see Chapter 10).

Noise voltages produced at the output meter of the voltage-measuring system due to noise inherent in the system should be at least 20 db below the signal voltage produced there by the microphone output.

14·3 Directivity of Microphones

The free-field response of a microphone is generally dependent on the direction from which the sound is incident upon it. The amount and nature of the variation of response with direction is a function of the size, shape, and manner of construction of the instrument. The characteristics of several present-day types of microphones have been discussed briefly in Chapter 5. One characteristic by which the directional properties may be indi-

---

[4] H. W. Rudmose, "The acoustical performance of rooms," *Jour. Acous. Soc. Amer.*, **20**, 225 (1948).

cated is the *directivity factor* $Q(f)$, which is defined as the ratio of two electrical powers W_2 to W_1 delivered to a resistor by two microphones located in a diffuse (random-incidence) sound field, where W_1 is the power delivered to the resistor by the microphone under test, and W_2 is the power delivered to the resistor by a non-directional microphone whose response is equal to the principal-axis response of the microphone under test.

Baumzweiger [Bauer][5] has proposed a graphical method whereby the directivity factor of a microphone may be determined directly from the polar response pattern (directional characteristic) plotted on special paper. This method applies only to the common case of a microphone having a response pattern which is substantially symmetrical about an axis which is usually perpendicular to the plane of the diaphragm or to the plane of the ribbon.

First, the directional characteristics of the microphone are determined by measuring the response at each of a number of frequencies as a function of angle of incidence. The complete range of angles from 0° to 180° is covered. The directivity factor at the frequency f is given by the formula

$$\text{Directivity factor} = Q(f) = 2 \left[\int_0^\pi f^2(\theta) \sin \theta \, d\theta \right]^{-1} \quad (14 \cdot 3)$$

where $f(\theta) = E(\theta)/E(0)$ = fractional response at the angle θ; $E(\theta)$ is the rms voltage output at angle θ; and $E(0)$ is that at zero angle of incidence.

By the graphical method, the fractional response $f(\theta)$ is plotted as a function of θ on the special graph paper shown in Fig. 14·4. The enclosed area is measured with a planimeter, and the ratio of this area to the area of the square in the upper right-hand corner of the figure is determined. The quotient of 25 and this quantity is the directivity factor $Q(f)$. Another possibility is to cut out the pattern and the square and to weigh each. The ratio of their weights divided into 25 is the directivity factor. Equation (14·3) and Fig. 14·4 give the correct directivity factor provided the microphone is symmetrical about the zero axis. For nearly all microphones this is true. A more general equation for calculating this quantity when the microphone has no axis of

[5] B. B. Baumzweiger [Bauer], "Graphical determination of the random efficiency of microphones," *Jour. Acous. Soc. Amer.*, **11**, 477–479 (1940).

symmetry is given in Chapter 15, Eq. (15·13).   Characteristics
for a typical pressure microphone at frequencies of 1000, 2000,
4000, and 8000 cps are shown in Fig. 14·5, along with the computed values of directivity factor $Q(f)$.   From this graph one

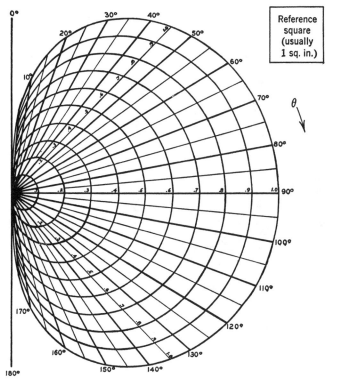

Fig. 14·4   Special graph paper for determining the directivity factor $Q(f)$
of a microphone.   The ratio of the output voltage $E(\theta)$ at an angle θ to the
voltage $E(0)$ on the axis of symmetry ($\theta = 0$) is plotted as a function of θ.
The ratio of the area enclosed by this plot to the area of the reference square
is determined.   The value of $Q(f)$ is obtained by dividing 25 by this number.
Note that the area inside the outer curve marked 1.0 is equal to 25 times
that of the reference square.   Hence, for it, $Q(f) = 1$.

may also deduce the ratios of "front random" response to "total
random" response, which represent the ratio of the response of
the microphone to random sound through a hypothetical hemisphere at the front of the microphone to the total random response.
That is to say, the "front random" response is obtained from the
area enclosed by the curve between 0° and 90°.

Another way to indicate the directional properties of a microphone is by the *directivity index*. This is simply the directivity factor, as defined above, expressed in decibels. It is the ratio, in decibels, of the power which would have been delivered by the

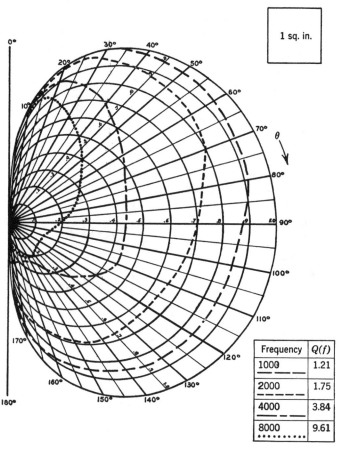

Frequency	Q(f)
1000	1.21
2000	1.75
4000	3.84
8000	9.61

FIG. 14·5 Sample calculation of directivity factor at four frequencies for a typical semi-directional pressure microphone. (After Baumzweiger [Bauer].[4])

microphone if it were perfectly non-directional to the power it actually delivers, when subjected to a diffuse (random-incidence) sound field. The directivity index is expressed mathematically as

$$DI = 10 \log_{10} Q(f) \qquad (14·4)$$

Oftentimes we desire to know the *random incidence response characteristic* of a microphone. This characteristic is the ratio (in decibels) as a function of frequency of the output voltage to the random incidence sound pressure measured before the microphone is placed in the sound field. The random incidence response characteristic is obtained by subtracting at each frequency the directivity index from the free-field response in decibels. The same physical axis of the microphone is assumed for both the directivity index and the response.

14·4 Power Efficiency of Microphones

From a practical viewpoint, the voltage response of a microphone, that is, the open-circuit voltage developed by the instrument when a specified sound pressure is applied to it, is a universally useful quantity. However, from a fundamental viewpoint, we may also be interested in the efficiency of conversion of acoustical power into electrical power by the microphone. Massa has proposed the following basic definition of microphone efficiency: "The efficiency of a microphone is the ratio of the maximum electrical power that can be delivered by a microphone into a pure resistance load to the acoustic power which is intercepted by the diaphragm when immersed in a plane wave with the normal axis of the diaphragm perpendicular to the wave front."[6] It is to be noted that in this case he speaks of the energy intercepted by the diaphragm rather than the energy actually absorbed. Thus, if the mechanical impedance of the instrument is such that it cannot easily absorb energy from the medium, its failure to do so is accounted for as a loss in efficiency, which seems proper.

A mathematical expression for the efficiency based in this concept can be derived in terms of the constants of the microphone and the medium. When the microphone is placed in a free plane wave, the acoustical power intercepted is

$$W_a = \frac{p^2 A}{10 \rho_0 c} \quad \text{microwatts} \qquad (14 \cdot 5)$$

where p is the free-field sound pressure, in dynes per square centimeter; A is the area of the diaphragm, in square centimeters; ρ_0 is the density of the medium, in grams per cubic centimeter;

[6] F. Massa, "Microphone efficiency: A discussion and proposed definition," *Jour. Acous. Soc, Amer.*, **11**, 222–224 (1939).

and c is the velocity of sound in the medium, in centimeters per second. The microphone will deliver maximum electrical power, at a given frequency, to a resistive load R, of the same magnitude as the absolute value of the microphone impedance at that frequency. If the microphone impedance is a function of frequency, a single average value, say at 1000 cps, is generally chosen. Under optimum load conditions, then, the electrical power delivered by the microphone is

$$W_e = \frac{V^2}{R} \quad \text{microwatts} \tag{14·6}$$

where V is the voltage in millivolts across the load resistor, and R is the load resistor in ohms, equal to the absolute value of the microphone impedance. The efficiency of the microphone is, therefore,

$$\text{Efficiency} = \frac{10\rho c}{RA} \left(\frac{V}{p}\right)^2 \times 100 \quad \text{percent} \tag{14·7}$$

For air under average conditions, a freely traveling plane wave still being assumed, this becomes

$$\text{Efficiency} = \frac{41500S^2}{RA} \quad \text{percent} \tag{14·8}$$

where S is the terminal voltage developed across the load resistor in millivolts per dyne per square centimeter of sound pressure, R is the load resistor in ohms, and A is the area of the diaphragm in square centimeters.

Massa observes that the efficiency of most commercially available microphones for airborne sound, computed on the above basis, is surprisingly low, of the order of 1 percent or less. The loss of efficiency may be due to either or both of two things, the mismatch between the acoustic impedances of the diaphragm and the medium, and low efficiency of conversion of mechanical power to electrical power in the electromechanical system of the instrument.

Baerwald, in a paper on noise level of microphones, has developed an expression for the "absolute efficiency" of a microphone.[7] He considers the acoustic noise generated by thermal

[7] H. G. Baerwald, "The absolute noise level of microphones," *Jour. Acous. Soc. Amer.*, **12**, 131–139 (1940).

agitation of molecules in the medium, the electrical noise voltage generated by thermal agitation of the electrons in the resistance of the microphone, and the response of the microphone. The open-circuit thermal noise voltage e_o, generated in a frequency band 1 cycle wide, in a microphone circuit is[8]

$$e = \sqrt{4KTR(f)} \qquad (14 \cdot 9)$$

where K is the Boltzmann constant equal to 1.37×10^{-23} joule per degree Kelvin

T is the absolute temperature, in degrees Kelvin

$R(f)$ is the effective resistive component of the microphone circuit at the frequency f.

We have the response of the microphone

$$\rho_m(f) = 10 \log \frac{e_o{}^2}{p_{ff}{}^2} \quad \text{in decibels } re \text{ 1 volt per dyne/cm}^2 \quad (14 \cdot 10)$$

The sound pressure level of an ambient acoustical noise which would produce a voltage at the microphone terminals equal to the resistance noise can be determined. This equivalent noise pressure level for a 1-cycle bandwidth will be called the *noise spectrum level* of the microphone, and will be denoted by $B(f)$:

$$B(f) = 10 \log 4KT + 10 \log R(f) - \rho_m(f) - 20 \log p_{\text{ref.}}$$

$$= 10 \log R(f) - \rho_m(f) - 124$$
$$\text{in decibels } re \text{ 0.0002 dyne/cm}^2 \quad (14 \cdot 11)$$

at ordinary room temperature. As in Chapter 13, $p_{\text{ref.}}$ is the reference pressure, 0.0002 dyne/cm^2.

If the microphone were "ideal," it would be completely loss-free in its electrical circuit except for the reflected acoustic radiation resistance. The equivalent noise level of such a microphone, which will be denoted by $B_0(f)$, thus represents the lowest limit of noise spectrum level which can possibly be approached by the microphone. From the requirement of thermodynamical equilibrium between the acoustical and electrical sides of the instrument, Baerwald derives a general relation for $B_0(f)$ for a microphone:

[8] J. B. Johnson and F. B. Llewellyn, "Limits to amplification," *Bell System Technical Jour.*, **14**, 85–96 (1935).

$$B_0(f) = 10 \log \left[\frac{4KT'}{p_{\text{ref.}}^2} \times 10^7 \right] + 10 \log \overline{A \cdot H_s}$$

$$= -53.9 + \log \overline{A \cdot H_s} \quad \text{in decibels } re \ 0.0002 \ \text{dyne/cm}^2$$

$$(14 \cdot 12)$$

The area of the diaphragm is represented by A, and H_s is the real part of the specific acoustic radiation impedance of the microphone diaphragm. The quantity $\overline{A \cdot H_s}$ denotes a weighted average which depends on the mode of motion of the diaphragm. If the diaphragm moves uniformly as a piston, this quantity is a simple product. The natural efficiency of a microphone per cycle of bandwidth may then be represented by the quantity

$$\eta(f) = 10^{-(B-B_0)/10} \qquad (14 \cdot 13)$$

From Eqs. $(14 \cdot 11)$ to $(14 \cdot 13)$, this may be written

$$\eta(f) = F(kL) \frac{1}{RA} \left(\frac{e_o}{p_{ff}} \right)^2 \qquad (14 \cdot 14)$$

where e_o denotes the open-circuit voltage corresponding to the sound pressure p_{ff}, and $F(kL)$ is a factor of proportionality and is a function of $k = 2\pi/\lambda$, the wave number, and L, the average width of the microphone.

As Baerwald points out, there are two essential differences between this definition of efficiency and that proposed by Massa in Eq. $(14 \cdot 7)$. In Massa's definition, the factor of proportionality $F(kL)$ and the microphone resistance $R(f)$, both functions of frequency, are replaced by the characteristic impedance of the medium ρc, and by a resistance R. Since $F(kL)$ is a complicated function, very difficult of determination, especially in the upper frequency range, the assigning of a fixed value to it, as in Massa's definition, seems to be a practical compromise. However, Baerwald considers the use of a resistance R equal to the average of the microphone impedance, rather than to the resistive component, to be unsatisfactory. This follows because it is the resistive component rather than the magnitude of the impedance which determines both the power of thermal agitation per cycle of bandwidth and the maximum power per cycle of bandwidth deliverable into a matched electric load, that is, quantities to which the efficiency is naturally related.

14·5   Non-linear Amplitude Distortion

When the output voltage (or current) of a microphone is not directly proportional to the input sound pressure of a pure tone at a given frequency, the waveform of the signal is not reproduced exactly, and *amplitude distortion* is said to occur. Amplitude distortion may be caused by non-linear mechanical, electrical, or electromechanical elements in the microphone. When a signal which has suffered non-linear distortion is analyzed, it is found to consist of a fundamental voltage, of the same frequency as the signal, plus a series of voltages of frequencies which are integral multiples of that of the original signal, the so-called harmonics. The harmonic distortion is expressed quantitatively as a percentage, according to the relation

Percentage of rms harmonic distortion

$$= \sqrt{\frac{E_2{}^2 + E_3{}^2 + E_4{}^2 + \cdots}{E_1{}^2 + E_2{}^2 + E_3{}^2 + E_4{}^2 + \cdots}} \times 100 \quad (14\cdot15)$$

where E_1 is the fundamental voltage appearing in the output of the microphone, and E_2, E_3, E_4, etc., are the voltages of the harmonics, which are of frequencies 2, 3, 4, etc., times that of the fundamental. By measuring the rms harmonic distortion at a number of different signal frequencies, data may be obtained for a plot of distortion *vs.* frequency.

Obviously, if distortion measurements are to be meaningful, the sound signal which is used must be very pure and free from distortion in itself. Phelps has suggested a method whereby a sound field of a high degree of purity can be obtained at a wide variety of levels and frequencies.[9] The equipment is shown schematically in Fig. 14·6. In brief, it consists of an iron tube, 8 ft long and 10 in. in diameter. The sound signal is produced by a loudspeaker which closes the pipe at one end. The microphone under test is inserted into the tube from the side or is supported from the right-hand variable piston. It is desirable that the inner surface of the pipe be smooth. The tube can be made to resonate at desired frequencies by adjustment of the position of either the left- or right-hand piston within the tube. At reso-

[9] W. D. Phelps, "A sound source for investigating microphone distortion," *Jour. Acous. Soc. Amer.*, **11**, 219–221 (1939).

nance, there is a standing wave pattern along the length of the tube such that there is a velocity maximum at a quarter-wave-length from the right-hand piston, and a pressure maximum at a half-wavelength. Similarly, there is a velocity minimum at a half-wavelength and a pressure minimum at a quarter-wave-length from the right-hand piston. All resonant frequencies of the system do not have pressure of velocity nodes at these places. For a pressure microphone, any single harmonic can be nearly completely eliminated from the sound field without eliminating the fundamental by moving the microphone to a quarter-wave-length point for that harmonic. For a velocity microphone, the half-wavelength point is used. Phelps estimates that for a loudspeaker input voltage having as much as 2 or 3 percent of

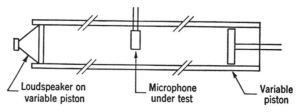

| Loudspeaker on variable piston | Microphone under test | Variable piston |

Fig. 14·6   Resonant tube used for selectively suppressing harmonics of a resonant fundamental.

a particular harmonic, the sound field at the microphone can be made free of that harmonic to within a few hundredths of a percent.

Another type of distortion measurement which may be made on microphones is the measurement of intermodulation products. If the microphone is non-linear, and if two or more pure tones are applied to it simultaneously, the output will contain, in addition to voltages of the same frequencies as the signals, a number of voltages of frequencies which are the sums and differences of the signal frequencies and their harmonics. Usually two signal tones are used, and the principal distortion products generated are then of frequencies $f_2 - f_1$, for the first-order intermodulation product, and $2f_2 - f_1$ and $2f_1 - f_2$ for the second-order products. The percentage of first-order intermodulation ID_1 distortion is given by

$$\text{Percentage of } ID_1 = \frac{E_{(f_2-f_1)}}{\sqrt{E_{f_1}{}^2 + E_{f_2}{}^2}} \times 100 \qquad (14\cdot16)$$

The percentage of second-order distortion ID_2 is the rms sum of

$$\frac{E_{2f_1-f_2}}{\sqrt{E_{f_1}^2 + E_{f_2}^2}} \times 100 \quad \text{and} \quad \frac{E_{2f_2-f_1}}{\sqrt{E_{f_1}^2 + E_{f_2}^2}} \times 100 \quad (14\cdot17)$$

where the values of E are voltages of frequencies indicated by the subscripts, as measured in the output of the microphone.

As in the measurement of rms harmonic distortion, purity of the signals is of paramount importance. In the measurement of intermodulation distortion, the problem is made more difficult by the use of two tones, each of which must be very free of distortion. Unfortunately, no apparatus has been proposed for giving a suitably strong sound field when testing studio types of microphone. One apparatus, suitable for testing close-talking microphones, is described in Chapter 16, pp. 715–717.

In measuring either type of distortion, the harmonic or intermodulation voltages are measured with the aid of a wave analyzer, by means of which the amplitude of each distortion product voltage, as well as the fundamental voltages, can be determined separately.

For a general discussion of procedures and of the meaning of the results of the two kinds of distortion measurement, the reader should refer to Chapter 15, Section 15·5. Most of the comments made there regarding distortion in loudspeakers apply equally well to distortion in microphones.

14·6   Electrical Impedance of Microphones

The frequency response characteristic of a laboratory microphone is usually given in terms of the *open-circuit* voltage it develops. In practical use of microphones, for example, in broadcast studios, the operation is likely to be into a load which is not infinite in impedance, hence the impedance of the microphone must be known in order to compute its performance with any given load. The impedance can be measured by conventional means with any good impedance bridge. The signal level applied should be equivalent to a sound pressure at the diaphragm within the operating range. A characteristic curve of impedance *vs.* frequency may be plotted.

In the case of a microphone which has been calibrated in a free sound field, the impedance should be measured with the microphone diaphragm open to free space, as in the calibration.

Usually, an adequate approximation to free space is that there be no objects in the room nearer than several feet.   When the microphone has been calibrated in terms of sound pressure at the diaphragm, the diaphragm should be terminated in a zero acoustic impedance.   This may be done by coupling it to a tube one-quarter wavelength long.   These conditions of acoustic termination of the microphone are necessary when accurate results are desired.

14·7   Transient Response of Microphones

The fidelity with which the waveform of a given acoustic transient is reproduced in the voltage waveform of the output of a microphone is dependent on its frequency response characteristic and its characteristic of phase-shift *vs* frequency.   The frequency characteristic must be uniform for the range of component frequencies in the transient, and the phase shift must be uniformly zero or be proportional to frequency in that range, if the waveform of the signal is to be maintained.   Microphones are used primarily in the transmission and reproduction of speech and music, both of which are highly transient in nature; therefore it is important that both of the above requirements be met, within certain limits.   If the phase shift does not meet the requirement, some of the components will be delayed more than others.   A common example may be found in the transmission of speech over loaded electrical lines, or lines having low pass filters in them, in which cases the high frequencies are usually delayed more than the low frequencies.   When the delay is severe, the late-arriving high frequency components of the signals give rise to "tweets" or "birdies" at the end of words.   Published results of listening tests[10, 11] indicate that tolerable limits on delay distortion are about 8 milliseconds at the high frequencies and about 15 milliseconds at 100 cps, both relative to the delay at 1000 cps.

Wiener[12] has measured the delay characteristics of a number of commercial microphones.   A miniature condenser microphone

[10] F. A. Cowan, R. G. McCurdy, and I. E. Lattimer, "Engineering requirements for program transmission circuits," *Bell System Technical Jour.*, **20**, 235–249 (1941).

[11] J. C. Steinberg, "Effects of phase distortion on articulation," *Electrical Engineers' Handbook* (Communication and Electronics), 3rd edition, pp. 9–32 to 9–35, John Wiley & Sons, Inc. (1944).

[12] F. M. Wiener, "Phase distortion in electroacoustic systems," *Jour. Acous. Soc. Amer.*, **13**, 115–123 (1941).

was first calibrated as a standard of reference by determining its response and phase characteristics by a reciprocity technique. The characteristics of the other microphones were then found by comparison with the standard, either by substitution for the standard in a known sound field, or by direct simultaneous comparison with the standard in a given sound field. Two condenser microphones, one dynamic microphone, two crystal microphones (one sound-cell and one diaphragm type), and a ribbon velocity microphone were tested. Typical data are reproduced in this book in Chapter 5.

14·8 Dynamic Range of Microphones

The dynamic range of a microphone is usually bounded at high levels of input signal by the amount of distortion which can be tolerated in the output voltage. Most laboratory microphones have reasonably linear input-output characteristics for signals below a certain level. Above this level the distortion increases with increasing signal input. The allowable amount of distortion depends on the duty the microphone is to perform. The point at which a given amount of distortion occurs is inherent in the mechanical and electrical design of the instrument.

The dynamic range is bounded at low levels by the amount of thermal noise voltage which is generated in the microphone and its load. This voltage is given by Eq. (14·9) as before except that R is now the parallel combination of a resistive microphone and a resistive load.

From the frequency-response characteristic and the noise voltage spectrum, the input sound pressure of noise which is equivalent to this noise voltage can be determined. This equivalent input noise sound pressure may aptly be called the "threshold pressure" for the microphone, since it is representative of the lowest level of signal which can usefully be picked up by the microphone. The voltage produced at the output of the microphone by acoustic signals of levels below the threshold pressure will generally be masked by the noise voltage developed in the microphone and its load.

As an example, consider a resistive microphone of resistance r operating into an amplifier with a matched resistive input impedance r.[13] The noise voltage per unit bandwidth across the

[13] E. Dietze, "Threshold pressure," unpublished memorandum of Bell Telephone Laboratories, Murray Hill, New Jersey (1941–1945).

parallel combination, which is applied to the input grid of the amplifier, is [see Eq. (14·9)]

$$v_n = \sqrt{\frac{4KTr}{2}} \qquad (14 \cdot 18)$$

Since the input and the microphone resistances are equal, the open-circuit voltage developed by the microphone when an acoustic signal is applied is twice that which appears across the input resistor. Thus, if the noise voltage v_n is multiplied by 2, it can be thought of as the equivalent of an open-circuit signal voltage which we shall call v_{no}:

$$v_{no} = 2\sqrt{\frac{4KTr}{2}} = \sqrt{2}\,\sqrt{4KTr} \qquad (14 \cdot 19)$$

From this quantity and from the response of the microphone ρ_m, we can compute the equivalent threshold sound pressure as follows. First, note that

$$\rho_m = 20 \log \frac{e_o}{p_{ff}} = 20 \log e_o - 20 \log p_{ff} \qquad (14 \cdot 20)$$

and therefore

$$20 \log p_{ff} = 20 \log e_o - \rho_m \qquad (14 \cdot 21)$$

re 1 volt per dyne/cm^2. Substituting v_{no} for e_o, we have a quantity which we shall call the threshold pressure level:

$$\text{T.P.L.} = 20 \log \sqrt{2} + 20 \log \sqrt{4KT} + 20 \log \sqrt{r} - \rho_m \qquad (14 \cdot 22)$$

in decibels *re* 1 dyne/cm^2. At $T = 20°C$,

$$\text{T.P.L.} = 10 \log r - 121 - \rho_m \qquad (14 \cdot 23)$$

in decibels *re* 0.0002 dyne/cm^2. It is to be noted from this equation that an increase of a given number of decibels in the microphone sensitivity, with its electrical resistance remaining constant, decreases the threshold pressure by the same number of decibels and extends the dynamic range by a corresponding amount.

15.

Tests for Loudspeakers

15·1 Introduction

In the United States, the loudspeaker has become a common adjunct to our way of living. It is the means for converting electrical currents from our radio or TV into intelligence. We also encounter loudspeakers in the theater and at most public gatherings. Whether they are used for serious purposes or for entertainment, the requirements for loudspeakers are generally the same, namely, speech should be intelligible in the presence of varying background noises and music should sound natural. Therefore, when selecting physical tests to determine the performance of a loudspeaker we must keep these basic requirements uppermost in our minds. These two factors are closely allied to the properties of hearing, so it is suggested that the reader acquaint himself with the material in Chapter 5, Section 5·4A, "The Ear." In particular, we need to know those psychological attributes of hearing called pitch, loudness level, and critical bandwidths if we are to appreciate all the material in this chapter.

At least seven different physical characteristics are required to specify fully the performance of a loudspeaker. With the data from these tests, we can estimate loudness, quality, or speech intelligibility under many conditions of use. These seven characteristics follow.

(a) *The frequency response characteristic* is a measure of the sound pressure amplitude produced on a designated axis and at a specified distance as a function of frequency for a constant electrical input. The acoustic environment may either be an anechoic chamber, the outdoors, or a reverberant room. A different response curve is generally obtained for each type of environment selected. The electrical input may either be a constant voltage, constant current, or constant available power.

The results obtained for each type of source will be different. Also they will vary depending on whether the source generates a sine wave, random noise, or a warble tone.

(*b*) *The directional characteristic* is a plot at any given frequency on polar paper (if necessary in three dimensions) of the sound pressure level as a function of angle from the principal axis of the loudspeaker. This measurement is generally made at a number of selected frequencies. The several curves so obtained can be combined into a single curve yielding a *directivity index* as a function of frequency.

(*c*) *The efficiency characteristic* is a plot as a function of frequency of the ratio of the total acoustic power output to the maximum power available from the generator.

(*d*) *The distortion characteristic* is a plot as a function of the total non-linear distortion for a stated electrical input signal. Different distortion characteristics will be obtained for different power levels. The distortion may be rated in a number of ways such as: (1) rms harmonic distortion, (2) the ratio of the arithmetic sum of the harmonic amplitudes to the amplitude of the fundamental, and (3) the ratio of the rms average of the amplitudes of the sum or difference tones to the rms amplitude of two pure tones. In cases (1) and (2) single sine wave excitation is used. In case (3) two sine waves drive the loudspeaker.

(*e*) *The impedance characteristic* is a plot as a function of frequency of the complex electrical impedance measured at the input terminals of the loudspeaker. The acoustic loading conditions must be specified. Generally the measurement is made in an anechoic chamber or outdoors, although for loudspeakers of low efficiency, it may be made in an ordinary room, separated a few feet from other objects.

(*f*) *The rated power-handling capacity* is the maximum available electrical power of speech or music which can be supplied to the loudspeaker over long intervals of time without mechanical failure. In some cases, the rated power-handling capacity is stated as the maximum electrical power from a sinusoidal source which can be supplied to the loudspeaker before the non-linear distortion exceeds some specified percentage.

(*g*) *The transient properties* of a loudspeaker may be described by measuring the rate of growth and decay of transients supplied electrically and reproduced acoustically. For example, trains of sine waves of various durations and frequencies may be applied to the loudspeaker, and the rate of decay of the acoustic output measured as a function of time following the completion of each wave train. Or, the accuracy of reproduction of square waves may be measured. No standardized tests are in use it this time, but possible procedures of measurement are described in this chapter.

15·2 Frequency Response

The most commonly portrayed property of a loudspeaker is its frequency response characteristic. It is from these data that we are generally able to predict the loudness of transmitted speech or music, the quality of reproduction, and the ability of the loudspeaker to produce intelligible speech in any given acoustic environment. Unfortunately, however, no standardized procedures have come into common use for performing this measurement, although action along that line is now in progress.[1] As a result, different test laboratories customarily select different electrical or acoustical conditions during test, and the frequency response curves which result from their measurements differ by 10 to 15 db in various parts of the acoustic spectrum.[2] The applicability of these various test methods can be determined only if we know the use which is to be made of the loudspeaker. First, let us consider the factors governing the choice of an electrical source.

A. Electrical Source

The electrical impedance of a loudspeaker is complex and is generally irregular as a function of frequency primarily because of the reflected mechanoacoustic impedance involved. Because of this irregularity, the frequency response characteristic of the loudspeaker will depend on the impedance of the electrical generator. One of two methods is commonly selected for supplying electrical energy to the voice coil. The first of these methods requires that the voltage across the voice coil be held constant while the frequency response curve is being taken. This type of response curve can be added (in decibels) directly to the voltage response of the amplifier, provided the amplifier response was taken with a load impedance equal to that of the loudspeaker

[1] "Standards Proposal No. 197," Radio Manufacturers Association (1947).

[2] *Loudspeaker frequency-response measurements*, Technical Monograph Number One, Jensen Manufacturing Company, Chicago, Illinois (1944).

(see Chapter 13).   By the second and more common method, the response of the amplifier is expressed in terms of the power which it delivers to a resistor whose value is equal to the magnitude of the rated impedance of the loudspeaker.   If the internal resistance of the amplifier is also equal to the rated resistance of the loudspeaker, the power delivered to the load is the *maximum power available* from the amplifier.*   Hence, when testing a loudspeaker we can simulate the amplifier by the circuit of Fig. 15·1.

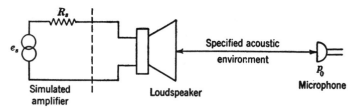

Fᵢɢ. 15·1   Electrical circuit used for testing loudspeakers.   The value of R_s is often made equal to the rated impedance of the loudspeaker.   The maximum power available from the simulated amplifier is $e_s^2/4R_s$.

The *constant power available response* of the loudspeaker at any particular frequency is then given by the equation

Constant power available response (in decibels)

$$= 20 \log_{10} \frac{p_0}{p_{\text{ref.}}} - 10 \log_{10} \frac{W_s}{W_{\text{ref.}}} \quad (15 \cdot 1a)$$

where p_0 is the sound pressure in a specified acoustic environment and location; $p_{\text{ref.}}$ is a reference pressure, usually 0.0002 dyne/cm^2; W_s is the maximum power available from the electrical source; $W_{\text{ref.}}$ is a reference power.   Also,

$$W_s = \frac{e_s^2}{4R_s} \quad (15 \cdot 1b)$$

where e_s is the source voltage and R_s is the source resistance. Equation (15·1) says that the response is proportional to the ratio (in decibels) of the square of the sound pressure to the maximum electrical power available.

When R_s is not made equal to the rated resistance of the loud-

---

* Further discussion of the electrical circuits for measuring the response of loudspeakers and amplifiers may be found in Chapter 13.   The reader should bear in mind that the rated load impedance of an amplifier is frequently not equal to its internal impedance.

speaker, R_s', we speak of the response for a source of a given regulation N as follows:

Constant power available response (N db regulation)

$$= 20 \log \frac{p_0}{p_{\text{ref.}}} - 10 \log \frac{\dfrac{e_s^2}{R_s'}}{W_{\text{ref.}}} + N \quad \text{db} \quad (15 \cdot 2a)$$

where N is the *source regulation*, defined as

$$N = 20 \log_{10} \left(1 + \frac{R_s}{R_s'} \right) \quad \text{db} \qquad (15 \cdot 2b)$$

As before, R_s is the resistance of the source, and R_s' is the rated resistance of the loudspeaker. For the case of Eq. (15·1), the regulation is 6 db; for constant voltage across the loudspeaker terminals, the regulation is 0 db.

Once the test circuit for calibrating our loudspeaker has been selected, we still have a choice of type of source voltage, e_s. For tests by design engineers where a knowledge of resonant peaks in the loudspeaker is of importance, e_s should be a sine wave voltage. However, for tests from which the loudness of reproduced speech, music, or noise is to be calculated, it seems more logical that the test source should produce voltages at a great many frequencies—preferably a continuous spectrum such as is produced by random noise. This statement is based on a property of the ear which causes it to resemble an analyzer. As discussed in Chapter 5, the ear, when perceiving random noises with a spectrum whose amplitude does not change too abruptly as a function of frequency, acts as though it were a series of contiguous band-pass filters having band widths of about 40 cps (for two-ear listening) at frequencies below 1000 cps and gradually increasing in width up to 200 cps at 8000 cps.[*] That is to say, within any one of these *critical bands*, the ear responds to the total rms sound pressure level.

Several observers have shown[3–5] that the use of random noise

---

[*] The absolute values of these bandwidths are not clearly established; the relative values as a function of frequency are fairly definite, however.

[3] F. H. Brittain and E. Williams, "Loud speaker reproduction of continuous-spectrum input," *Wireless Engineer*, **15**, 16–22 (1938).

[4] B. Olney, "Experiments with the noise analysis method of loudspeaker measurement," *Jour. Acous. Soc. Amer.*, **14**, 79–83 (1942).

[5] H. W. Rudmose, "The acoustical performance of rooms," *Jour. Acous. Soc. Amer.*, **20**, 225 (1948) (abstract).

in tests of loudspeakers is effective in smoothing out the sharp peaks and valleys introduced into the response curves in indoor measurements by the room, provided the normal modes of vibration of the room are not too widely separated. Warble-tone and multi-tone* sources have also been used with some success, although, for those cases, a continuous distribution of energy throughout a frequency band is not achieved. Rudmose[5] showed that bands of random noise ranging in width between 15 and 60 cps gave a good averaging of the sharp and closely spaced peaks and valleys in the loudspeaker response characteristic without disguising the principal variations. Olney[4] believes if a wide enough band of noise is used to smooth out room peaks, significant peaks and dips in loudspeaker response are also smoothed out. Olney's conclusion has largely been that of commercial laboratories in the United States, so that pure tones and anechoic rooms (or outdoors) are commonly used for frequency response measurements. The difference between Rudmose's and Olney's opinions arises largely from the meaning of "significant peaks and dips." Until psychological experiments are performed to establish "significance," a definitive answer to which type of source voltage should be used cannot be given.

B. Microphone

The ear is a pressure-operated device; hence it seems logical that the microphone used should also measure pressure. Pressure gradient microphones have been used in the past, but, unless free-field conditions obtain, the results are not directly explainable in terms of the properties of hearing. The use of a pressure-actuated microphone has the disadvantage that it is a "monaural" (one-ear) device, whereas we ordinarily listen to sounds "binaurally" (two ears). The very simple experiment of plugging one ear while listening in a reverberant room will reveal the difference between binaural and monaural listening. We must expect, therefore, that our "monaurally" measured response curve will not bear an exact relationship to what a listener would perceive if he were put in the same location as the microphone.

C. Indicating Instrument

The indicating instrument should be a graphic level recorder in order to supply the maximum amount of detail in the measure-

* The theory of warble-tone and multi-tone sources is given in Chapter 18.

ments for a minimum of effort. If the output of the loudspeaker is measured with a heterodyne-type analyzer, the recorder and the analyzer will need to be geared together.

The integrating characteristics of the rectifier are also of importance. It has been partially established that the ear responds to rms pressure amplitude if the sound is not too intense. This fact would indicate that a square-law type of meter should be used. We may see from Chapter 10 that a meter with a linear rectifying characteristic will read 1 db below a square-law meter when we are measuring random noise or inharmonically related tones provided both meters are calibrated to read alike on pure tones. This relationship will hold even though the noise spectrum deviates greatly from uniformity. It appears, therefore, that a linear instrument is generally as acceptable as a square-law instrument because the response of a loudspeaker is always expressed as the ratio of the output to the input, and the same meter can be used to determine both quantities so that the 1 db difference cancels out. This will not always be the case, however, if waves that can be analyzed into a harmonic series are applied to the input terminals, because then the readings of the two types of instruments will not differ by a constant value of 1 db if there is either phase or frequency distortion or both in the loudspeaker. In fact, the difference may vary over a wide range of values. Hence, for a number of harmonically related sine waves only square-law meters should be used. If single sine wave inputs are applied, linear, square-law or peak-indicating instruments can be used interchangeably provided the nonlinear distortion produced by the loudspeaker is less than a few percent.

To recapitulate, both psychological and physical considerations suggest that the procedure used for measuring a frequency response curve probably should be as follows: A "white" random source of noise voltage should be used to excite the loudspeaker undergoing test. The acoustic output of the speaker should be measured with a pressure-sensitive microphone connected through an amplifier and an analyzer into a graphic power level recorder. The analyzer should be of the constant bandwidth type with a bandwidth of between 15 and 40 cps. The rectifier in the recorder or other indicating instrument should have either a linear or square-law characteristic. However, until more definite psychological measurements have been performed to establish this procedure, the conventional method of pure-tone excitation will continue to be used.

D. Acoustic Environment

Outdoors. Essentially three arrangements of apparatus have been used outdoors for measuring the response of loudspeakers. With one,[2] the loudspeaker and microphone are suspended from a long boom projecting from a tower on top of the corner of a tall building. The loudspeaker is pointed diagonally away from the building and is located 5 ft or so out from the corner of the building. The microphone is a pressure-actuated type and is located on the boom 5 to 20 ft out from the loudspeaker. In the second arrangement,[6] the loudspeaker is mounted at the top of a tall tower outdoors pointing horizontally. The microphone is located on a movable tower of variable height. With this method, a pressure-gradient type of microphone is often employed with its null plane oriented so that it discriminates against the principal ground reflection. With the third arrangement,[7] the loudspeaker (or the microphone) is mounted on the ground, and the sound is measured by suspending the microphone (or loudspeaker) directly above it between two poles. The disadvantage of locating the loudspeaker on the ground is that the directivity pattern is changed unless the loudspeaker would normally be used in the equivalent of an "infinite" baffle. In that case, the loudspeaker under test would be mounted flush with the ground. The disadvantage of locating the loudspeaker in the air is that reflections from the ground may modify the acoustic impedance into which the horn radiates.

In addition to difficulties from spurious reflections, all outdoor methods suffer disadvantages over indoor methods such as inclement weather, background noise, and annoyance to other people working or living in the vicinity.

Anechoic Chambers. Indoor free-field measurements require an anechoic chamber. The principal deterrent to indoor tests is the cost of constructing a chamber large enough to test large loudspeakers such as those used with theater sound systems. Two anechoic chambers of considerable size have been described

---

[6] C. P. Boner, "Acoustic spectra of organ pipes," *Jour. Acous. Soc. Amer.*, **10**, 32–40 (1938).

[7] E. W. Kellogg, "Loud speaker sound pressure measurements," *Jour. Acous. Soc. Amer.*, **2**, 157–200 (1930).

recently.[8, *] If chambers of this quality are available, the response curves measured on a loudspeaker in different laboratories should be identical provided the same distance between loudspeaker and microphone is maintained. It was shown in Chapter 3 that different response curves will often be obtained at different distances from a loudspeaker because of diffraction around the case or baffle.

Reverberant Chambers. Loudspeakers are customarily listened to in reverberant rooms. It has frequently been argued, therefore, that frequency response curves should be obtained under conditions closely simulating those of the average home or theater. Response curves measured indoors in reverberant enclosures differ principally in two ways from those measured outdoors. First, there is an increase in low frequency response relative to the high frequency response, and, secondly, the resonances of the room introduce irregularities into the curves. The enhancing of the low frequency response indoors is easily explained in terms of the directional characteristics of the loudspeaker. In a free field, the very low frequency sounds radiate in all directions just as though the loudspeaker were a point source. The larger the loudspeaker, the lower in frequency one will have to go to observe this effect. At high frequencies, however, the sound is focused in a beam. Hence, the intensity of the sound at a point along the axis will be higher for a given total radiated power at high frequencies than at low. Indoors, however, the walls of the room reflect the sound, so that the total energy radiated at any one frequency tends to become distributed uniformly throughout the room. Therefore, that part of the radiated power which outdoors would not get to the microphone is reflected around the room and contributes indoors to the microphone reading. A relative enhancement of the low frequencies with respect to the high frequencies, therefore, occurs. We will illustrate these differences by comparing indoor with outdoor measurements a little later.

If *rectangular enclosures* are employed for indoor measurements an important consideration is the location of the loudspeaker in

[8] L. L. Beranek, and H. P. Sleeper, Jr., "Design and construction of anechoic sound chambers," *Jour. Acous. Soc. Amer.*, **18**, 140–150 (1947).

* Bell Telephone Laboratories, Murray Hill, N. J. This chamber is essentially similar to that of Ref. 8. Comparative data have not been published.

the room. If no diffusing members have been introduced into the room to break up normal resonant conditions, appreciable differences in the low frequency response of a loudspeaker will be observed, especially for certain loudspeaker positions. These positions are (*a*) in a corner of the room at floor level, (*b*) in the middle of one wall at floor level, (*c*) in the middle of one wall halfway between the floor and ceiling, and (*d*) in the exact center of the room halfway between floor and ceiling.

In order to understand the reasons for differences at these four positions, we must turn to the normal mode theory of room acoustics. Morse,[9] Maa,[10] and Bolt[11] have all shown that a rectangular room may be considered an assemblage of resonators. Some of these resonators (called normal modes of vibration) may be excited only at the corners of a room, others may be excited at the corners and at edges of the room, still others may be excited at corners, edges, or in the center of the room. This fact was shown experimentally by Hunt[12] and by workers in other countries. Morse[9] shows that all modes of vibration are excited at a corner; one-half are excited at position (*b*) above; one-fourth at position (*c*); and one-eighth at position (*d*). If the elementary assumption is made that at low frequencies the square of the effective sound pressure in the room is proportional to the number of modes of vibration that are excited, we can see that the response will decrease by 3 db for each change of speaker location starting with (*a*) and continuing through (*d*). This assumption will be nearly correct for cases in which the acoustic radiation impedance of the loudspeaker is low, that is, where the loudspeaker is small compared to a wavelength.

Data demonstrating that this qualitative statement is approximately true are shown in Fig. 15·2, for conditions (*a*) to (*c*). At frequencies above 500 cps, no difference is found among the curves, both because irregularities in the shape of the room introduce diffusion and the simple normal mode picture breaks down,

---

[9] P. M. Morse, *Vibration and Sound*, Second Edition, Chapter VIII, McGraw-Hill (1948).

[10] D. Y. Maa, "Distribution of eigentones in a rectangular chamber at low frequency range," *Jour. Acous. Soc. Amer.*, **10**, 235–238 (1939).

[11] R. H. Bolt, "Frequency distribution of eigentones in a three-dimensional continuum," *Jour. Acous. Soc. Amer.*, **10**, 228–234 (1939).

[12] F. V. Hunt, "Investigation of room acoustics by steady-state transmission measurements," *Jour. Acous. Soc. Amer.*, **10**, 216–227 (1939).

and because the loudspeaker approaches a wavelength in size so that its radiation impedance becomes high.

As for the location of the microphone in the room, the same arguments apply. If a reading proportional to the total radiated

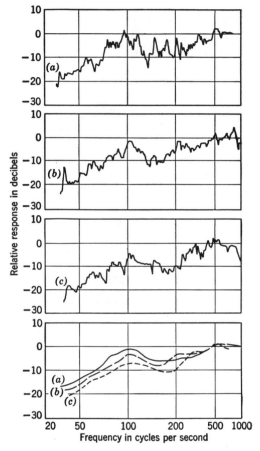

FIG. 15·2 Loudspeaker frequency response for locations: (a) at corner of a rectangular room; (b) at center of one wall at floor level; (c) at center of one wall halfway between floor and ceiling. The lower graph shows smoothed versions of these three curves. (From Ref. 2.)

power is desired, the microphone should be located in a corner of the room either at floor or ceiling level. Oftentimes, in an effort to obtain smoother response curves, some observers employ a number of microphones placed throughout the room. The outputs of these microphones are fed to a rapidly operating commutator at the input of the measuring system. Curves showing the difference between a single microphone and an array of eight microphones are shown in Fig. 15·3. Equally smooth or perhaps smoother response curves could be obtained by using a single microphone placed at the corner of the room and exciting the loudspeaker with a narrow band of random noise continuously variable along the frequency scale. This type of source voltage has been discussed earlier.

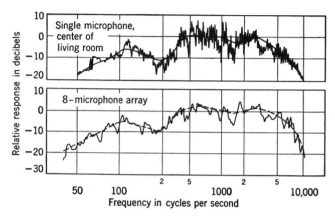

FIG. 15·3 Curves showing that a smoother frequency response characteristic will be obtained if the outputs of a number of microphones are commutated instead of using a single microphone. The smoothed line drawn through the center of each curve is nearly the same. (From Ref. 2.)

Although rectangular rooms yield response curves which are useful if suitably interpreted, the smoothness of the resulting response curves and the ease of their interpretation is greatly enhanced if *irregularly shaped test chambers* are employed. If the chamber is sufficiently reverberant as well as irregular, the sound radiated from any source contained in it will be diffused uniformly throughout it. Under such conditions, the properties of the sound field may be calculated with the aid of the classical theory of room acoustics. Let us now see what effect such a diffuse-sound chamber will have on the effective sound pressure level at various distances from a loudspeaker placed in it.

In a reverberant room with irregular surfaces, a sound wave radiated by a loudspeaker strikes the walls and is reflected in random directions. This reflected sound in turn strikes other surfaces and is reflected repeatedly. On each reflection a portion of the incident energy is removed from the sound wave, and, in time, a state is reached where the sound level is steady and the energy lost at the boundaries is just equal to that radiated by the loudspeaker. At any point in the room, the effective sound pressure will be made up of two parts, the direct and the reverberant sound.

From the classical theory of room acoustics[13] it is known that the average energy density $\rho_{av.}$ at any point within such an enclosure is given by

$$\rho_{av.} = \frac{p^2}{\rho_0 c^2} = \frac{E}{4\pi c}\left[\frac{Q}{r^2} + \frac{16\pi}{R}\right] \quad (15\cdot3)$$

where p = effective sound pressure at the point in dynes per square centimeter

E = rate of emission of sound from the source, in ergs per second

ρ_0 = density of air in grams per cubic centimeter

c = velocity of sound, in centimeters per second

Q = directivity factor = ratio of the intensity on the designated axis of the loudspeaker at a stated distance r to the intensity that would be produced at the same position by a point source if it were radiating the same total acoustic power (a free sound field is assumed)

$\Omega = 4\pi/Q$ equivalent solid angle of radiation in steradians

r = distance along the designated axis between the microphone and the effective center of the source, in centimeters

$R = \alpha S/(1 - \alpha)$ = room coefficient, in square centimeters

α = average energy absorption coefficient of the surfaces of the room

S = total area of the boundaries of the room, in square centimeters

The first term in the brackets of Eq. (15·3) is related to the direct sound and the second to the reverberant sound.

Beginning with this equation, Hopkins and Stryker[14] have developed a method for a quantitative evaluation of the effect of enclosures, the results of which are given here in the form of

[13] W. C. Sabine, *Collected Papers on Acoustics*, Harvard University Press (1927).

[14] H. F. Hopkins and N. R. Stryker, "A proposed loudness-efficiency rating for loudspeakers and the determination of system power requirements for enclosures," *Proc. Inst. Radio Engrs.*, **36**, 315–335 (1948).

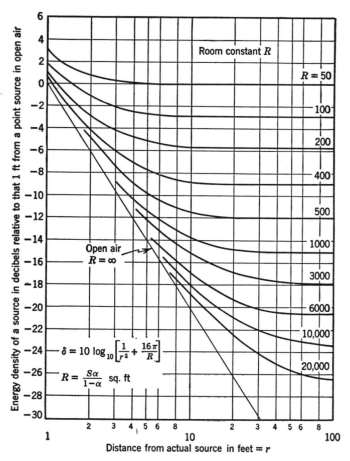

Fig. 15.4   Chart for calculating the ratio, expressed in decibels, of the energy density produced in a large irregular enclosure by a loudspeaker with unity directivity factor to that produced by a point source at a distance of 1 ft. A free sound field and the same total sound power emission for each loudspeaker are assumed. The energy density is proportional to the mean square sound pressure, and, hence, the ordinate applies to readings of pressure-actuated microphones. (After Hopkins and Stryker.[14])

charts. These charts (Figs. 15·4 and 15·5) show the manner in which the average energy density varies with distance from the source in chambers having various room coefficients. They give the *ratio* (using English units) of the average energy density $\rho_{av.}$ produced in the enclosure by a loudspeaker with a directivity factor Q to that produced in free space by a point source ($Q = 1$)

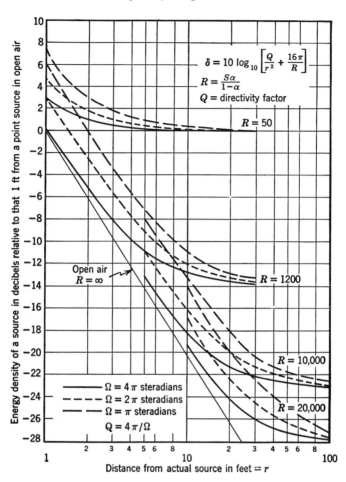

Fig. 15·5 Chart for calculating the ratio, expressed in decibels, of the energy density produced in a large irregular enclosure by a loudspeaker with a directivity factor Q to that produced by a point source at a distance of 1 ft. The chart applies to points along the axis relative to which Q was calculated. A free sound field and the same total sound emission for each loudspeaker are assumed. The energy density is proportional to the mean square sound pressure and, hence, the ordinate applies to readings of pressure-actuated microphones. (After Hopkins and Stryker.[14])

at unit distance ($r = 1$ ft) with the same total acoustic emission
E. This ratio, expressed in decibels, is

$$\delta \text{ (in decibels)} = 10 \log_{10}\left[\frac{Q}{r^2} + \frac{16\pi}{R}\right] \qquad (15 \cdot 4)$$

In English units r is expressed in feet and R in square feet.

Equation ($15 \cdot 4$) for a point source radiator ($Q = 1$) is plotted
in Fig. $15 \cdot 4$ for various values of the room coefficient. The
same equation for three values of Q and four values of R is plotted
in Fig. $15 \cdot 5$. One important fact is observable from Fig. $15 \cdot 5$,
namely, that at distances of 30 ft or more from the loudspeaker
the direct sound is negligible compared to the reverberant sound,
and the effects of directivity of the loudspeaker have largely dis-
appeared. Actual measurements show that beyond 10 ft in
small rooms and 30 ft in large rooms, the energy density is constant and is due entirely to reverberant sound. These facts suggest that a distance of 30 ft should be used as a reference. Then
if the sound pressure produced by a loudspeaker is measured at 30
ft (or the results extrapolated to that distance), *a room gain factor
K_2* may be calculated for any room with non-uniform boundaries.

The *room gain factor K_2* is defined as 20 $\log_{10}$ of the ratio of the
effective sound pressure level that would exist in an enclosure
(because of the presence of the loudspeaker) relative to that
which would be measured in an open air at a distance of 30 ft
from a point source for the same total acoustic power output.
Values of K_2 (*using English units*) are calculated approximately
from the following equation, in which an exponential term has
been replaced by the first two terms of its equivalent series:

$$K_2 \text{ (in decibels)} \doteq 10 \log_{10}\left[\frac{Q}{r^2} + \frac{1000T}{V\left[1 + \frac{0.05V}{2ST}\right]}\right] - L_0 \quad (15 \cdot 5)$$

where Q = directivity factor
r = distance between loudspeaker and microphone, in feet
T = reverberation time, in seconds
V = volume of room, in cubic feet
S = total surface area of room, in square feet
L_0 = $20 \log_{10} \frac{1}{30}$ = -29.5 db. This correction term is
necessary because the reference distance for Eq.
($15 \cdot 4$) was 1 ft instead of 30 ft.

The actual room gain K_2', which is defined as $20 \log_{10}$ of the ratio of the effective sound pressure measured 30 ft from the loudspeaker in a diffuse-sound room to that measured 30 ft from

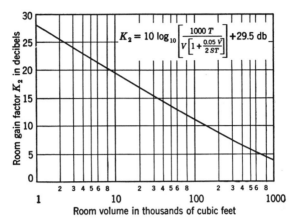

FIG. 15·6   Plot of room gain factor K_2 as a function of room volume. K_2 is defined as the ratio (expressed in decibels) of the effective sound pressure level that would exist in an enclosure (because of the presence of the loudspeaker) to that which would be measured in open air at a distance of 30 ft from a point source for the same total power output.   The reverberation times of Fig. 15·7 were used, and it was assumed that the term (Q/r^2) of Eq. (15·5) was negligible compared to the second term in the argument of the logarithm.   Also S, the surface area, was assumed to equal six times the two-thirds power of the volume.   (After Hopkins and Stryker.[14])

the same loudspeaker in a free field for a constant power available, is equal to

$$K_2' = K_2 - DI(f) \quad \text{db} \qquad (15·6)$$

where

$$DI(f) = 10 \log_{10} Q(f) \quad \text{db} \qquad (15·7)$$

$DI(f)$ is called the directivity index at any frequency f.   For most practical loudspeakers Q varies between 1 and 20 as a function of frequency.   A chart giving K_2 as a function of room volume for $(S \doteq 6V^{2/3})$, assuming the reverberation times of Fig. 15·7 at 512 cps, is shown in Fig. 15·6.

The considerations which we have stated show clearly that the same response curve should be obtained in a diffuse-sound room as in a free-field provided the directivity of the loudspeaker is the same at all frequencies.   Otherwise the relative differences between the responses as a function of frequency will vary as

10 $\log_{10} Q(f)$, where $Q(f)$ is a frequency-dependent directivity factor.

Comparison of Environments. In the light of the considerations of the previous section, it is of interest to compare free-field and reverberant chamber response curves for a practical loudspeaker. Boner *et al.*[15] measured the response of a horn loudspeaker in five different-sized rooms and outdoors. The horn was 28 in. long and had a mouth opening 22 in. by 30 in. The

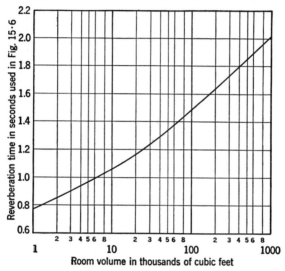

Fɪɢ. 15·7   Plot of reverberation times at 512 cps used in preparing Fig. 15·6. These reverberation times are somewhat higher than the values given in standard references for studios or for auditoriums designed for speech. (After Hopkins and Stryker.[14])

dimensions of the five rooms in feet and their reverberation times at 500 cps were as follows: room I: 9 by 20 by 12, 5 sec; room II: 23 by 33 by 12, 8 sec; room III: 24 by 33 by 12, 0.6 sec; room IV: 42 by 48 by 23, 1 sec; room V: volume equals 1,000,000 cu ft, 5 sec.

The results of the tests are given in Fig. 15·8. All data are plotted relative to the free-field data except that the 1000 cps points on all curves were first arbitrarily brought into coincidence. In general, all the curves have the same shape as the free-field

[15] C. P. Boner, H. Wayne [Rudmose] Jones, and W. J. Cunningham, "Indoor and outdoor response of an exponential horn," *Jour. Acous. Soc. Amer.*, **10**, 180–183 (1939).

curve between 600 and 4000 cps. Below 600 cps the curves for all rooms rise above the free-field curve in about the same manner, indicating that the rise is to be attributed to a property of the horn and not the rooms. This phenomenon is in complete agreement with our statement in the previous section that the relative indoor and free-field response curves will differ if the directivity index is a function of frequency. Because of the size of the mouth of the horn, its directivity factor ought to be

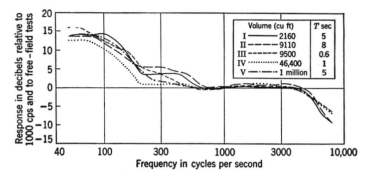

Fig. 15·8 Response of a loudspeaker in five rooms relative to its response in open air. All curves have been adjusted vertically on the page to bring their 1000-cps values into coincidence. (After Boner et al.[15])

about unity at frequencies below 100 cps. Hence, we can calculate the value of the directivity factor Q from the relation

$$Q(f) = \log^{-1}\left[\frac{L_{50} - L_f}{10}\right] \qquad (15\cdot8)$$

where L_{50} (in decibels) is the average difference between the indoor and the free-field measurements in the vicinity of 50 cps, and L_f is that average difference at frequency f. Such a calculation is shown in Fig. 15·9. Above 4000 cps (see Fig. 15·8) the difference between the indoor and free-field measurements may be caused in part by an increase of Q for the loudspeaker, but it is more likely caused by an increase in Q for the moving-coil microphone used—a factor which was not taken into account in the original paper.

Conclusions. In conclusion, it is believed that the following steps solve the problem of a suitable environment for loudspeaker tests: (a) determine the axial frequency response characteristic in a free field and express it in decibels as a function of frequency;

(*b*) measure the directional characteristic at each of a number of frequencies; (*c*) combine these directional characteristics to produce a plot of directivity index $DI(f)$ as a function of frequency expressed in decibels, as given by Eq. (15·7); (*d*) convert the axial frequency response characteristic to the frequency response characteristic in any specified environment indoors (wherein the acoustical conditions can be approximated by the Norris-Eyring reverberation formula) with the aid of Eq. (15·6) and Fig. 15·6. If these data are taken one will know the response outdoors on the axis from (*a*); the response outdoors at any angle off the axis

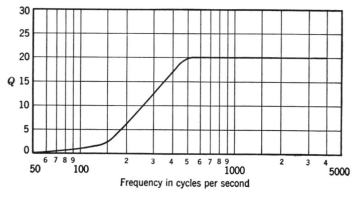

Fig. 15·9   Value of directivity factor Q as a function of frequency as computed from data of Fig. 15·8.

from (*b*); and the response indoors in any specified environment from (*d*).

In conclusion to this section, we should note that the use of the physical characteristics of a loudspeaker in practical applications must be made with an eye on the psychological factors involved. One possible way of converting physical ratings to a psychological rating is given in Section 15·9 of this chapter.

15·3   Directivity

The directional characteristic of a loudspeaker is always determined in a free field in the same manner as is the axial response characteristic. The only difference is that the frequency is held constant and either the loudspeaker is rotated about some selected vertical axis or the microphone is moved around the loudspeaker about that same axis. The directional character-

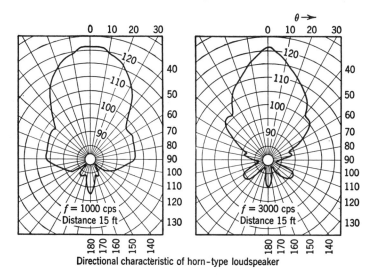

Directional characteristic of horn-type loudspeaker

FIG. 15·10   Typical directional characteristics obtained at two frequencies for a horn-type loudspeaker. The microphone was separated 15 ft from the assumed center of the horn. The graph is a plot of the sound pressure level in decibels *re* 0.0002 dyne/cm^2 as a function of θ. Because the horn is symmetrical, the level is not a function of ϕ. The maximum power available from the electrical source was 250 watts.

istics of a loudspeaker are usually plotted in some such form as that shown in Fig. 15·10.

Once the directional characteristics at a number of frequencies for a loudspeaker are determined we are generally interested in deriving the *directivity indexes* $DI(f)$ in decibels, where

$$DI(f) = 10 \log_{10} Q(f) \tag{15·7}$$

$Q(f)$ is the directivity factor at a frequency f and is equal to the ratio of the intensity on the designated axis of the loudspeaker at a stated dis-

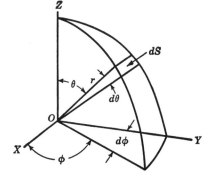

FIG. 15·11   Sketch showing the coordinate system used in calculating the directivity factor $Q(f)$. Area of surface element dS equals $r^2 \sin \theta \, d\theta \, d\phi$.

tance r to the intensity that would be produced at the same position by a point source radiating the same acoustic power.

To determine $Q(f)$, refer to Fig. 15·11. Consider the center of the radiating area to be at the origin O. At a sufficiently large distance r, in a free field, the effective pressure p and the particle velocity u are in phase and are related to each other by the relation $p = \rho c u$, where ρc is the characteristic impedance of the medium. The power radiated from a source whose effective center is at the origin O, is $p^2/\rho c$ per unit area of the spherical surface. That is to say, the power dP transmitted through any unit area dS is

$$dP = \frac{p^2}{\rho c} dS \qquad (15·9)$$

From Fig. 15·11, we see that the elemental spherical surface dS is

$$dS = r^2 \sin\theta \, d\theta \, d\phi \qquad (15·10)$$

The total power P at any given frequency passing through the spherical surface is given by

$$P = \frac{r^2}{\rho c} \int_0^{2\pi} \int_0^{\pi} p^2(\theta, \phi) \sin\theta \, d\theta \, d\phi \qquad (15·11)$$

where $p(\theta, \phi)$ was measured at a constant distance r from the assumed center of the loudspeaker as a function of θ and ϕ at a given frequency. The directivity factor Q at the frequency f is given by

$$Q(f) = \frac{4\pi p_{ax.}^2}{\displaystyle\int_0^{2\pi} \int_0^{\pi} p^2(\theta, \phi) \sin\theta \, d\theta \, d\phi} \qquad (15·12)$$

where $p_{ax.}$ is the pressure measured axially for the loudspeaker at the given frequency f. Usually the denominator is calculated from experimental data by substituting a series for the integrals:

$$\int_0^{2\pi} \int_0^{\pi} p^2(\theta, \phi) \sin\theta \, d\theta \, d\phi$$

$$\doteq \sum_{m=1}^{2\pi/\Delta\phi} \sum_{n=1}^{\pi/\Delta\theta} p^2(\theta_n, \phi_m) \sin\theta_n \, \Delta\theta \, \Delta\phi \qquad (15·13a)$$

where $p^2(\theta_n, \phi_m)$ is assumed to be constant within the intervals $\Delta\theta$ and $\Delta\phi$. Frequently, the loudspeaker and its housing are symmetrical, and Eq. (15·13a) is only a function of one variable. In that case,

$$\int_0^{2\pi}\int_0^{\pi} p^2(\theta,\phi)\sin\theta\,d\theta\,d\phi \doteq 2\pi\sum_{n=1}^{\pi/\Delta\theta} p^2(\theta_n)\sin\theta_n\,\Delta\theta \quad (15\cdot13b)$$

As an example of a case where $p(\theta,\phi)$ is known and where the integration of Eq. (15·12) can be accomplished analytically, let us consider the case of radiation from a rigid disk set in an infinite baffle. Take the Z axis normal to the face of the disk, and locate the origin of coordinates at its center. Because the disk is symmetrical, p will only be a function of θ. It is known that the variation of p as a function of θ for distances that are greater than 10 times the radius of the disk is given by

$$p(\theta) = \frac{2p_{\text{ax}}.J_1(ka\sin\theta)}{ka\sin\theta} \quad (15\cdot14)$$

in which J_1 = Bessel function of first order
k = wave number = ω/c
a = radius of the disk.

Substituting (15·14) in (15·12), assuming radiation over a hemisphere and integrating,[16] gives

$$Q(f) = \frac{(ka)^2}{\left[1 - \dfrac{J_1(2ka)}{ka}\right]} \quad (15\cdot15)$$

In the case where $p(\theta,\phi)$ has been measured, but an analytical expression is not possible, we must use Eq. (15·13). For example, from Fig. 15·10 let us calculate the directional characteristic at 1000 cps. We note that $p(\theta,\phi)=p(\theta)$ because the loudspeaker is symmetrical about the Z axis. If $\Delta\theta = 10°$, then Eq. (15·12) becomes

$$Q(f) = \frac{4\pi p_{\text{ax}}.^2}{2\pi\sum_{n=1}^{18} p^2(\theta_n)\sin\theta_n\dfrac{\pi}{18}} \quad (15\cdot16)$$

or, inverting,

$$\frac{1}{Q(f)} = \frac{\pi}{36}\sum_{n=1}^{18}\frac{p^2(\theta_n)}{p_{\text{ax}}.^2}\sin\theta_n \quad (15\cdot17)$$

[16] N. W. McLachlan, *Bessel Functions for Engineers*, p. 90, Oxford University Press (1934).

The numerical values needed to solve this equation are tabulated in Table 15·1. Column 3 gives the number of decibels that the sound pressure level at θ_n lies below that at $\theta = 0$. The magnitude of $Q(f)$ at 1000 cps is equal to 36.1.

A graphical method has been devised for accomplishing the operations shown in Table 15·1 by Bauer.[17] The method is described in the preceding chapter of this text, and it makes use of a distorted set of polar coordinates. Data like those of Fig. 15·10 are plotted directly on the distorted coordinate system, and the value of Eq. (15·12) for a symmetrical loudspeaker (p not a function of ϕ) is determined with the aid of a planimeter or by cutting out the plotted directivity characteristic and weighing it on a sensitive balance. This weight is related to the weight of a unit area of the paper.

15·4 Power Efficiency

The power efficiency of a loudspeaker is equal to the ratio of the total acoustic power radiated to the electrical power supplied. Generally, the power supplied is not measured directly, but rather the maximum available power from a resistance generator is used. It is then called the available power efficiency. A plot of the power efficiency *vs.* frequency is called the *efficiency frequency characteristic*.

If both the axial frequency response and the directivity factor $Q(f)$ have been determined, and if the loudspeaker is driven from a constant power available generator, then, at each frequency,

$$\text{Percentage of available power efficiency} = \frac{I_{\text{ax.}} S_s}{Q W_{as}} \times 100 \quad (15·18a)$$

where $I_{\text{ax.}}$ is the axial intensity, in ergs per second per square centimeter (or watts per square centimeter); S_s is the area, in square centimeters, of the sphere whose radius, in centimeters, is equal to the distance at which the intensity was measured; Q is the directivity factor; and W_{as} is the maximum available electrical power, in ergs per second (or watts).

Expressed in decibels, and substituting English units for distance, this formula becomes

[17] Benjamin Baumzweiger [Bauer], "Graphical determination of the random efficiency of microphones," *Jour. Acous. Soc. Amer.*, **11**, 477–479 (1940).

Available power efficiency level (db)

$$= L_{\text{ax.}} + 20 \log_{10} r - DI - 10 \log_{10} W_{as} - 119.5 \quad (15 \cdot 18b)$$

where $L_{\text{ax.}}$ is the free-field axial sound pressure level, in decibels *re* 0.0002 dyne/cm^2; r is the distance of the microphone from the source, *in feet; DI* is the directivity index; W_{as} is the available electrical power, in watts; and 119.5 db is the value of the numerical constants figured for $\rho c = 41.4$ rayls.

TABLE 15·1 CALCULATION OF $Q(f)$ FOR LOUDSPEAKER WHOSE DIRECTIVITY PATTERN AT 1000 CPS AND 15 FT IS GIVEN IN FIG. 15·10

θ_n	$\sin \theta_n$	$10 \log \left[\dfrac{p(\theta_n)}{p_{\text{ax.}}} \right]^2$	$\left[\dfrac{p(\theta_n)}{p_{\text{ax.}}} \right]^2$	$\left[\dfrac{p(\theta_n)}{p_{\text{ax.}}} \right]^2 \sin \theta_n$
5	0.0872	0 db	1.000	0.0872
15	0.259	−3.5	0.446	0.1156
25	0.423	−8.0	0.159	0.0672
35	0.574	−14.0	0.040	0.0230
45	0.707	−22.5	0.006	0.0042
55	0.819	−24	0.004	0.0033
65	0.906	−24	0.004	0.0036
75	0.966	−24	0.004	0.0039
85	0.996	−24	0.004	0.0040
95	0.996	−27	0.002	0.0020
105	0.966	−29	0.001	0.0010
115	0.906	−31	0.001	0.0009
125	0.819	−33	0.001	0.0008
135	0.707	. . . . . .	. . . . . .	. . . . . .
145	0.574	−37	. . . . . .	. . . . . .
155	0.423	−35	. . . . . .	. . . . . .
165	0.259	−34	. . . . . .	. . . . . .
175	0.0872	−30	0.001	. . . . . .
			Sum	0.3167

$$Q(f) = \frac{36}{\pi} \times \frac{1}{0.3167} = 36.1$$

$$DI(f) = 10 \log_{10} 36.1 = 15.6 \quad \text{db}$$

As an example, let us determine the percentage available power efficiency at 1000 cps for the horn whose directional pattern at 1000 cps is given in Fig. 15·10. The intensity level on the axis at a distance of 15 ft is 121 db *re* 10^{-16} watt/cm^2. This gives us $I_{\text{ax.}} = 1.26 \times 10^{-4}$ watt/cm^2. The area S_s equals $4\pi \times (15)^2 \times$

$(30.5)^2 = 2.633 \times 10^6$ cm^2; and the power available was 250 watts.

Percentage of available power efficiency

$$= \frac{2.633 \times 1.26 \times 10^4}{36.1 \times 250} = 3.68 \text{ percent} \quad (15\cdot19)$$

15·5 Non-Linear Distortion

Non-linear distortion (amplitude distortion) in loudspeakers refers to the deviation from correspondence between the acoustic output wave and the electrical input wave that results from non-linear elements or effects in the loudspeaker system. This distortion is regarded as distinct from the effects on the waveform of a non-uniform frequency characteristic (frequency distortion) and a non-linear phase characteristic (phase distortion). Of the many possible ways of measuring this non-linear distortion only two distinct methods are at present in general use. These are the harmonic distortion and the intermodulation distortion methods.

The *harmonic distortion* method is the more conventional of the two and requires the excitation of the speaker by an electrical sine wave of negligible harmonic content. The acoustic output of the loudspeaker is measured with a calibrated microphone, and the resultant electric wave is analyzed by a wave analyzer (see Chapter 12) or a distortion meter.[18] This test determines the relative magnitudes of the harmonic components produced by the non-linearity in the loudspeaker. Subharmonic components should also be measured, as they frequently occur in direct-radiator types of loudspeakers.

The *intermodulation distortion* method has come into use relatively recently. By this method we excite the loudspeaker by an electrical wave consisting of two inharmonically related sine waves. The resultant electrical wave from the pickup microphone is analyzed for the relative magnitudes of the various distortion components whose frequencies are sums and differences of integral multiples of the input frequencies.

Before discussing these two systems, further certain requirements for the measuring equipment that the two have in common can be outlined. Just as in the other measurements outlined

---

[18] A. E. Thiessen, "Audio-frequency distortion and noise measurements," *General Radio Experimenter* **22**, 5–7 (December, 1947).

in this chapter, it is essential that the measuring setup and procedure do not in themselves significantly determine the results of the test. Thus, obviously, no element in the system other than the loudspeaker under test should be operated under conditions that introduce appreciable distortion components into the analyzing system. Fortunately, for this class of measurement, the measuring elements in the setup can be made relatively distortion-free. The usual possible source of trouble is the power stage and output transformer of the driven amplifier, and these should

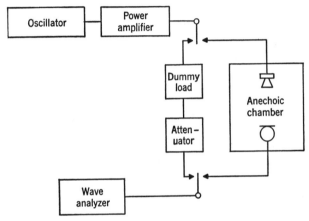

FIG. 15·12   Block diagram of an arrangement for determining the additional non-linear distortion introduced by inserting the loudspeaker and microphone into the electrical circuit.

be carefully checked independently. This could readily be done as an overall check by replacing the acoustic transducers with a suitable attenuator and performing an overall electrical measurement (see Fig. 15·12). Furthermore, the acoustic environment should ideally be an anechoic chamber. Although one might conceive of doing this measurement in a reverberant room, the reinforcement of some harmonics in preference to others by the resonant conditions existing in the room would preclude an accurate answer unless data were taken at a great many points in the room and the results averaged.

In the conventional method for measuring non-linear distortion[19] the loudspeaker is driven from a constant power available sinusoidal source, and the amplitude of all harmonic components

[19] *Standard on Electroacoustics*, The Institute of Radio Engineers (1938).

is measured. The total distortion is occasionally expressed as the ratio (in percent) of the arithmetic sum of the pressure amplitudes of the higher harmonics to the amplitude of the fundamental. More often it is expressed as the rms ratio of the amplitudes of the harmonics to those of the fundamental, plus harmonics, given by

$$\text{Rms distortion (in percent)} = 100 \sqrt{\frac{p_2{}^2 + p_3{}^2 + p_4{}^2 + \cdots}{p_1{}^2 + p_2{}^2 + p_3{}^2 + \cdots}}$$

$$(15 \cdot 20)$$

where p_1, p_2, p_3, etc., are the pressure amplitudes of the harmonic components in the output. p_1 is understood to be the amplitude of the fundamental.

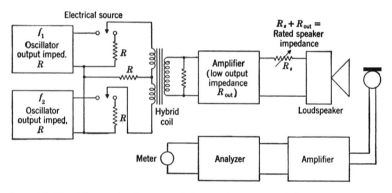

Fig. 15·13 Schematic diagram of the equipment needed to measure the intermodulation distortion produced by a loudspeaker. The hybrid coil prevents interaction between the two oscillators.

A block diagram showing the arrangement of a suitable apparatus for determining intermodulation distortion[20–22] is shown in Fig. 15·13. The loudspeaker is excited by two sine waves of different frequency. These two frequencies are passed through a mixing stage and thence to the loudspeaker. The loudspeaker

[20] G. L. Beers and H. Belar, "Frequency-modulation distortion in loud speakers," *Proc. Inst. Radio Engrs.*, **31**, 132–138 (1943).

[21] J. K. Hilliard, "Distortion tests by the intermodulation method," *Proc. Inst. Radio Engrs.*, **29**, 614–620 (1941).

[22] F. M. Wiener *et al.*, "Response characteristics of interphone equipment," O.S.R.D. Report No. 3105, January 1, 1944. This report may be obtained in photostat form from the Office of Technical Services, Department of Commerce, Washington, D. C. Request PB No. 22889.

and standard microphone are located in an anechoic chamber. The output of the microphone is analyzed by a narrow-band wave analyzer.

Let us assume that the two oscillators are adjusted to produce two sine waves, f_1 and f_2. If the loudspeaker is not strictly linear, various sum and difference frequencies (i.e., intermodulation frequencies) will be produced; as, for example, $f_2 - f_1$, $f_2 + f_1$, $2f_1 - f_2$, $2f_1 + f_2$, $2f_2 - f_1$, $2f_2 + f_1$, etc. Also, harmonic frequencies, $2f_1$, $2f_2$, $3f_1$, $3f_2$, etc., will appear. In general, as much information is contained about the non-linearity of the loudspeaker in the difference components as in the summation components, so that only the difference components are measured. Also, it is generally sufficient to measure the second-order $(f_2 - f_1)$ and the third-order $(2f_2 - f_1)$ and $(2f_1 - f_2)$ components without bothering with the higher orders, although under special conditions the next two orders may also be significant.

Fundamentally, the intermodulation test differs from an rms harmonic distortion test in several respects. First, if f_1 and f_2 are properly selected, it indicates the relative amplitude of combination tones which are generated within the pass band of the transmitting system. In speech transmission systems, for example, non-linear distortion of certain types acts as though it were a masking ambient noise. However, it is only those unwanted components which lie between 500 and 3000 cps that have any appreciable effect on the intelligibility of speech. Harmonic distortion measurements for fundamentals located above 2000 cps will show low distortions if the system cuts off, say, at 3500 cps, whereas intermodulation distortion measurements with proper selection of frequencies will yield numbers more nearly related to the interfering effect of the distortion. On the low frequency end of the spectrum the rms distortion is again misleading. If the fundamental is located below the lower cutoff frequency of the system, abnormally large rms distortions will be measured. Again the intermodulation distortion test will yield better results. Moreover, within the pass band of the system, a fairly satisfactory correlation between rms and intermodulation distortion can be established if the nature of the non-linear distortion is known.[23]

[23] W. J. Warren and W. R. Hewlett, "An analysis of the intermodulation method of distortion measurement," *Proc. Inst. Radio Engrs.*, **36**, 457–466 (1948).

The percentage of first-order intermodulation distortion is calculated from

$$\text{Percentage of } (f_2 - f_1) \text{ distortion} = \frac{p_{2-1}}{\sqrt{p_1{}^2 + p_2{}^2}} \times 100 \quad (15\cdot21)$$

Similarly, the percentage second-order intermodulation distortions are calculated from

$$\text{Percentage of } (2f_1 - f_2) \text{ distortion} = \frac{p_{(2.1)-2}}{\sqrt{p_1{}^2 + p_2{}^2}} \times 100$$

$$(15\cdot22)$$

$$\text{Percentage of } (2f_2 - f_1) \text{ distortion} = \frac{p_{(2.2)-1}}{\sqrt{p_1{}^2 + p_2{}^2}} \times 100$$

$$(15\cdot23)$$

where the p's indicate the sound pressure. Some observers plot the larger of $(15\cdot22)$ and $(15\cdot23)$ at each frequency. Others take the rms average. The values are usually plotted at the geometric frequency $f_m = \sqrt{f_1 f_2}$ in cases where f_1 and f_2 are not widely separated.

Differences of opinion exist as to what are suitable values for f_1 and f_2 and what the amplitudes p_1 and p_2 should be. Hilliard[21] has prescribed that tests should be performed with f_1 equal to either 40, 60, or 100 cps and f_2 equal successively to 1000, 7000, and 12,000 cps. He also specified that the ratio of the amplitude of the sine wave with frequency f_1 should be four times that with frequency f_2. This selection is based on the premise that the principal source of annoying distortion in a sound system is that produced by intermodulation between the intense low frequency and the weaker high frequency components of music. However, where the effect of distortion on speech intelligibility is desired, the frequencies of the two sine waves should not be separated nearly so widely and should be of more nearly equal amplitude. Many experimenters are taking data both ways, namely, with widespread frequencies of different amplitudes and with closer spaced frequencies of the same amplitude because each type of measurement yields results of use in judging the quality of a sound system. Results of intermodulation tests for a magnetic-type earphone are shown in Fig. $15\cdot14$.

Hilliard[21] and Roys[24] have advocated a simplified apparatus for the measurement of intermodulation distortion. Their apparatus supplies two test frequencies to the input of the audio device under test. The frequencies are those advocated by Hilliard and mentioned in the paragraph above. The output of the amplifier will contain sum and difference frequencies, as well as harmonic frequencies of the tones under test. Because the test tones are so widely separated in frequency, a low pass filter may be used to eliminate the lower frequencies, leaving only the high frequency signal (carrier) plus side bands (intermodulation

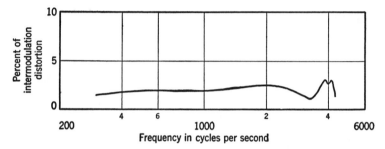

FIG. 15·14 Percentage of intermodulation distortion measured on a magnetic-type earphone (ANB-H-1). The power available to the earphone was 83.4 mw, and the distortion was measured in a 6-cc coupler. The input electrical signal consisted of two sine waves of equal amplitude with a constant frequency difference of 100 cps. The points were plotted at

$$f_m = \sqrt{f_1 f_2}.$$

components). The resulting wave is then rectified and passed through a low pass filter. The magnitude of the envelope is proportional to the intermodulation distortion. In studying this method, Warren and Hewlett conclude that the presently accepted value of 4:1 for ratio of the amplitude of the low to the high frequency signal is a good compromise. This ratio gives a high intermodulation percentage accompanied by reasonable values of carrier and side-band voltages for detection and measurement. They also conclude that the detector and the meters used to measure the amplitude of the carrier and of the intermodulation components should be a linear or square-law type and not a peak type (see Chapter 11).

[24] H. E. Roys, "Intermodulation distortion analysis as applied to disk recording and reproducing equipment," *Proc. Inst. Radio Engrs.*, **35**, 1149–1152 (1947).

Interesting comments on the material of this section of the chapter were received from Dr. H. C. Hardy, of the Armour Research Foundation in Chicago, in a letter dated February 7, 1949. He says:

Throughout this chapter the intermodulation distortion has been defined as "the ratio of the effective amplitude of specified sum of difference tones in the output to the effective value of *the two fundamentals in the output.*" Referring to the level of the *two* fundamentals is inconvenient and probably does not properly describe the phenomena. For instance, with an 80-cps and a 1000-cps note, we believe that the psychological effect is that the intermodulation products 840, 920, 1080, 1160, 1840, 1920, etc., mask and "muffle" the 1000-cps note and do not affect appreciably the sensory impression of the 80-cps note. It is our firm opinion that, when the frequencies are widely separated, they should be expressed as a percentage of the effective value of the higher frequency tone. There is another important advantage of this standardization. The intermodulation in loudspeakers, where the motion at high frequencies is linear and the motion at low frequencies is not, gives the interesting result that the *percentage* intermodulation distortion is proportional to the level of the low frequency component. The percentage is independent of the high frequency component over any dynamic range the loudspeaker would normally be used. Of course, this rule is true only by our method of computing the percentage.

In conclusion we emphasize that adequate psychological tests have not been performed to validate or invalidate the procedures for measuring and specifying amplitude distortion as presented in this chapter.

15·6 Electrical Impedance

The electrical impedance may be measured by a conventional one-to-one impedance bridge. The bridge should be capable of supplying a fair amount of power to the loudspeaker, and the input power used should be specified along with the impedance characteristic. In those cases where the electrical impedance varies with power input a family of impedance characteristics with power input as the parameter should be determined. The impedance should be measured when the loudspeaker is located in the same acoustic environment as used for the response characteristic. For low efficiency loudspeakers, the measurement may be made in an ordinary room several feet away from other objects without noticeably affecting the results.

In cases where only the magnitude of the impedance is desired, a fair approximation may be obtained by connecting a variable resistance box in series with the loudspeaker and driving the two from an audio-frequency oscillator. The magnitude of the impedance is taken to be the value of the resistor box at the time that the voltage across the loudspeaker terminals is equal to that across the resistance.

15·7   Power-Handling Capacity

Every loudspeaker has a maximum power-handling capacity. The value of this capacity is determined to provide the user with a rating available power such that use below that level will ensure reliable and normal operation. This limit may be set by the temperature rise in the voice coil, by failure of the vibrating mechanism, or by the permissible distortion generated. An input limitation set by distortion may be determined by methods described in Section 5 of this chapter. Tolerable distorton might also be determined by listening tests. There appears to be no commonly accepted procedure for determining the safe operating point from the standpoint of mechanical failure.

It is useful to employ a VU meter for the measurement to correlate with usage. However, it must be remembered that dangerous peaks may exceed VU meter readings by 5 to 15 db, depending on the signal. Thus the power-handling capacity depends on the type of program material, type of limiting amplifier, and sometimes on the transient response of the system (high accelerations).

A technique used by the Bell Telephone Laboratories[14] is as follows: "For direct-radiator devices, a uniform sweep-frequency band from 50 to 1000 cycles is applied to the loudspeaker set up in the recommended operating condition. The power capacity of the loudspeaker is then considered to be the maximum available power at which no failures occur in a continuous testing period of 100 hours. No ambient temperature is specified except where special applications are involved. For horn-driver units, a sweep frequency 2000 cps wide whose lowest frequency is 100 cycles below the resonant frequency of the loudspeaker is used. This assumes that the unit is equipped with a recommended horn." There is a growing tendency to extend the upper frequency region of the uniform sweep frequency band to 2000 cps to take account of the large peaks in orchestral energy delivered from many systems not using a limiter.

15·8   Transient Response

The response of loudspeakers to transient sounds has received relatively little attention in the United States. McLachlan[25] and Mott[26] have devoted effort toward determining the response of loudspeakers in a free field and earphones in couplers to a square-fronted impulse and to square waves of various repetition frequencies. Obviously the microphone and measuring equipment must be selected to have a minimum of transient distortion themselves. The chief disadvantage of the pulse method is that it cannot be easily interpreted if the response does not extend down to near-zero frequency. The method will show the frequency, decay constant, and number of more prominent modes of vibration, but little more.

A more fruitful approach was described by Helmhold.[27]   He excited the loudspeaker under test in a free field with an interrupted sine wave of a certain frequency and observed the response during the build-up period. He expressed the duration of the transient as the number of oscillations the sound pressure executed before the envelope fell within ± 20 percent of its steady-state value. The number so obtained was given a negative sign if the pressure overshot its final value before reaching it, and a plus sign if it did not. When the resulting "transient times" were plotted as a function of frequency, the curve bore a close relationship to the steady-state response curve; that is, for the most part the smoother portions of the steady state curve were associated with low transient times. He also showed that the build-up transient can be predicted with fair accuracy by analyzing the steady-state response into amplitude and phase as a function of frequency. The results obtained by this method are more easily interpreted than those from square-wave excitation.

Shorter[28] takes exception to the conclusions of Helmhold. He argues that the decay time following the train of waves and

---

[25] N. W. McLachlan, *Loudspeakers*, Oxford University Press, 1934.

[26] E. E. Mott, "Indicial response of telephone receivers," *Bell System Technical Jour.*, **23**, 135–150 (1944).

[27] See Reference 28.

[28] D. Shorter, "Loudspeaker transient response," *BBC Quarterly*, **1**, October (1946).

not the build-up time is the more important phenomenon to study. He considers the loudspeaker, its baffle, and its cabinet as an assemblage of resonators, each having its own characteristic frequency. The situation is analogous to that of a room in which there are a great many modes of vibration, each with its

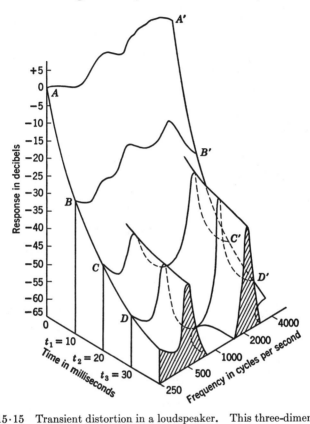

Fig. 15·15 Transient distortion in a loudspeaker. This three-dimensional plot shows the persistence of sound as a function of time after the driving sinusoidal voltage is removed. Presumably, for best quality, all tones should decay rapidly and at the same rate. (After Shorter.[28])

own normal frequency. Now, in addition, each of these normal modes has its own decay constant, and, because some modes decay more slowly than others, the response of the loudspeaker during decay will be a function of the interval of time that has elapsed after the tone was interrupted. Shorter illustrates this phenomenon by a three-dimensional plot of the type shown in

Fig. 15·15. As examples, two slowly decaying modes occur at 600 and 2100 cps.

To perform tests of this type, an anechoic chamber with low ambient noise is necessary if smooth decay curves and quiet are to be achieved. Shorter applied an interrupted train of waves for $\frac{1}{20}$ sec and turned it off for $\frac{1}{20}$ sec. The acoustic output was conducted from the microphone to a cathode ray oscilloscope, the time base being synchronized to the interruption frequency to give a stationary display of the decay envelope. Shorter found that a simple apparatus, making use of the discriminating properties of the eye, was the least troublesome to use. The

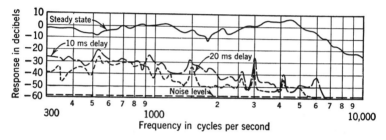

Fig. 15·16 Transient distortion measurements for a loudspeaker. The curves show the rate at which the sound decays after the pure tone source is turned off. (After Shorter.[28])

frequency dial on the heterodyne oscillator which produced the basic frequency of the interrupted tone was mechanically coupled to the paper drum on an automatic power level recorder. The frequency was changed manually. A translucent mask, having a single, narrow vertical slit, partially obscured the face of the cathode ray tube. The horizontal location of this slit was adjusted at the beginning of each run so that it lay above the point on the time axis at which the envelope amplitude was to be plotted. During the run, the envelope amplitude as observed through the slit was set to a certain height by adjusting the bias to the vertical plates with a hand control. This hand control also supplied an alternating input to the power level recorder and thereby located a point on the paper graph.

A typical set of curves, obtained by Shorter, on a commercial loudspeaker with an elliptical cone is shown in Fig. 15·16. On some loudspeakers the higher frequencies decay much more rapidly than the lower.

15·9   Loudness Efficiency Rating

A. Derivation

This section has to do with a method for converting the physical response curve of a loudspeaker into a single number which relates to the psychological effect which music or speech transduced by it produces on a listener.   Loudspeakers are used primarily for the production of speech and music.   Tests have shown that our ability to understand these two forms of intelligence is closely related to the loudness of the reproduced spectrum at the ear of the listener.   This follows because the background noise at the listener's ear is often high enough that unless the reproduced speech or music is sufficiently loud it will be unintelligible.   Methods for the calculation of loudness have been published elsewhere (see chapter 5), and the simplification of this process by the use of filter bands whose cutoff frequencies were chosen from a pitch scale is treated briefly in Chapter 12.   More pertinent, however, to the immediate problem of specifying the performance of loudspeakers is the establishment of a *loudness efficiency rating*, defined as the ratio of the total "effective" acoustic power produced by the loudspeaker to the available electrical power.   Here, the total "effective" acoustic power is so measured that it is nearly proportional to the loudness produced by the loudspeaker in a free field.

The concept of loudness efficiency rating has been discussed by Hopkins and Stryker,[14] and the treatment here is entirely theirs.   The first step in deriving such a rating is to form plots of the percentage of intensity* and loudness below any given frequency f as a function of f.   (See Fig. 15·17.)   Average curves are also given in that figure which are sufficiently representative for either speech or music.   It is apparent that the average curve for loudness differs greatly from that for intensity.   The intensity of any part of a sound spectrum, $\Delta f = f_2 - f_1$, is equal to the product of the intensity per cycle within that band and Δf.   Hence, for a flat spectrum, equal frequency increments contribute equal portions to the total intensity.   This means that equal

---

* *Intensity* is used advisedly here because the data are expressed for a free field.   When these formulas are used indoors, however, the word "intensity" must be interpreted as meaning $p_e^2/\rho c$, where p_e is the effective sound pressure.

frequency increments of a flat spectrum do not yield numbers proportional to equal loudness increments if the curves of Fig. 15·17.
are to be believed.   Instead, the frequency bands in Table 15·2
(read from the average loudness curve of Fig. 15·17) contribute
equally to the loudness, and they include 96 percent of the loudness spectrum.   If a white noise is passed through these bands,
the level of the noise in each, relative to the spectrum level,
would be that indicated in the fourth column of Table 15·2.

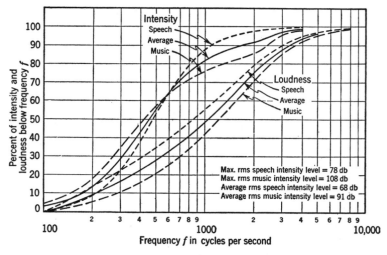

FIG. 15·17   Percentage of intensity and loudness below any frequency in
the spectrum for speech or music.   The maximum rms intensity level occurring in 0.25-sec intervals and the long time rms intensity level are indicated.
The instantaneous peaks of speech occur about 10 db above the maximum
            rms level indicated.   (After Hopkins and Stryker.[14])

Because each of the frequency bands in Table 15·2 is supposed to
make an equal contribution to loudness, we can obtain a number
proportional to overall loudness from an intensity measurement
using random noise as source, provided the noise spectrum is so
tailored that the intensity in each of these bands is the same.
If the levels in the bands are to be alike, say 22 db above the
spectrum level, the spectrum level of the noise must be increased
(algebraically) at the mean frequency of each band by the number
of decibels shown in the fifth column.   Hopkins and Stryker give
the circuit drawn in Fig. 15·18 for accomplishing this equalization approximately.   Now let us see how we may use such a
tailored spectrum to obtain loudness efficiency ratings.

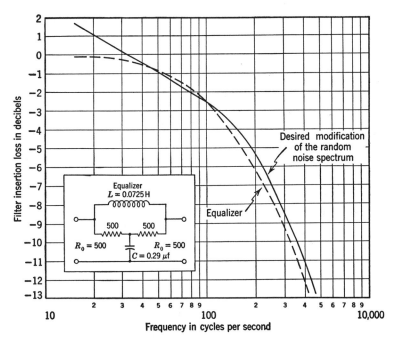

FIG. 15·18 Electrical network designed to tailor the spectrum of a random noise to produce readings from a constant bandwidth analyzer as a function of frequency which are about proportional to the loudness contributed by each band of noise. (After Hopkins and Stryker.[14])

Assume that the loudspeaker is a point source located in a free field. A source of random voltage *with a spectrum tailored according to Fig. 15·18* is supplied to the electrical input. For

TABLE 15·2 BANDS OF SPEECH OR MUSIC OF EQUAL LOUDNESS

Band No.	Frequency Limits	Mean Frequency	10 log Δf, db	22 −10 log Δf, db
1	100– 210	160	20.42	1.58
2	210– 360	280	21.76	0.24
3	360– 540	450	22.67	−0.67
4	540– 780	660	23.61	−1.61
5	780–1050	900	24.31	−2.31
6	1050–1360	1200	24.91	−2.91
7	1360–1770	1570	26.13	−4.13
8	1770–2300	2000	27.25	−5.25
9	2300–3300	2750	30.00	−8.00
10	3300–6000	4400	34.31	−12.31

a maximum electrical power available (see Chapter 13) of W_R watts, the effective sound pressure measured on the axis of the loudspeaker at a distance of 30 ft will be p_{ax}. dynes/cm^2. The sound intensity in watts per square centimeter at that distance is

$$I_{ax.} = \frac{p_{ax.}^2}{\rho c} \times 10^{-7} \qquad (15 \cdot 24)$$

The intensity level $L_{ax.}$ in a free field is equal to the sound pressure level re 0.0002 dyne/cm^2 and is given by

$$L_{ax.} = 20 \log p_{ax.} + 74 \quad \text{db} \qquad (15 \cdot 25)$$

The total radiated acoustic power in watts, for this loudness-weighted source of noise assuming a *non-directional* loudspeaker, is the product of the intensity $I_{ax.}$ times the area S_s of a sphere with a radius of 30 ft. The electroacoustic efficiency of the loudspeaker is the ratio of the total effective acoustic power in watts to the available electrical power in watts:

$$\text{Electroacoustic efficiency} = e = \frac{I_{ax.}S_s}{W_R} \qquad (15 \cdot 26)$$

Now, let us define an efficiency level L_e equal to $10 \log_{10} e$. This will be

$$L_e = 10 \log_{10} I_{ax.} + 10 \log_{10} S_s - 10 \log_{10} W_R$$

$$= 20 \log_{10} p_{ax.} - 86.2 + 70.2 - k \qquad (15 \cdot 27)$$

$$= 20 \log_{10} p_{ax.} - 16 - k$$

where $k = 10 \log_{10} W_R$, and W_R equals the maximum electrical power available in watts.

Equation (15·27) is valid only for a point source. As we have already seen, the total acoustic power radiated from a loudspeaker will be less at any given frequency than that indicated by Eq. (15·26) by the directivity factor $Q(f)$; see Eq. (15·7). Accordingly, the efficiency level L_e must be modified to include the effect of speaker directivity. The modification to L_e which we want is called the *loudness directivity index* and is equal to $10 \log_{10}$ of the average of the *directivity factors* for the ten mid-frequencies of equal loudness and is expressed as follows:

$$K_1 = 10 \log_{10} \left\{ \frac{Q(f_1) + Q(f_2) + \cdots + Q(f_{10})}{10} \right\} \qquad (15 \cdot 28)$$

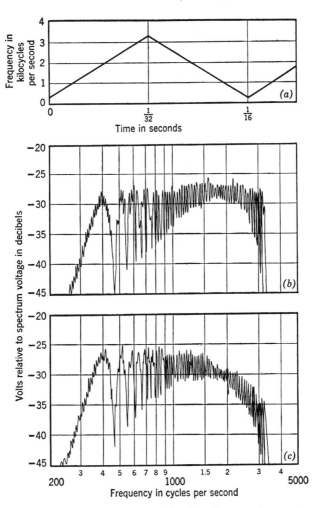

FIG. 15·19   (a) Frequency vs. time relation for a linear reciprocating sweep;
(b) envelope of the components of the sweep band of (a); (c) envelope of the
components of the sweep band of (a) with loudness-weighting equalization.
(After Hopkins and Stryker.[14])

where $Q(f)$ is the directivity factor at the frequency f.   Loudness
directivity indexes for a number of types of horns have been calculated by Hopkins and Stryker.[14] L_e, the efficiency level in
decibels, now becomes

$$L_e = 20 \log_{10} p_{\mathrm{ax.}} - 16 - k - K_1 \qquad (15 \cdot 29)$$

A loudness efficiency factor LR in percent has been selected as a suitable factor for rating the loudness of a loudspeaker. It is equal to

$$LR = 100e = 100 \times 10^{L_e/10} \quad \text{percent} \quad (15 \cdot 30)$$

It should be noted that this factor is obtained from a simple measurement of the axial sound pressure in a free field using a random noise with a loudness-tailored power spectrum as an electrical source. From *LR* the amplifier power and the number of loudspeakers required for a specified sound system installation can be calculated as we shall see shortly.

For those cases where a random noise source is not available, a sweep frequency of the form shown in Fig. 15·19a may be used.[14] The envelopes of the spectrum produced by such an electrical source before and after equalization are shown in Figs. 15·19b and 15·19c. Although a sweep frequency generator may be more available in some laboratories than a random noise generator, its frequency range is limited to between about 400 and 3000 cps, and gaps exist in the spectrum below 1000 cps.

B. Application to Sound System Design

If we are to use data measured in this way for the design of sound systems, we must have a relationship between the loudness

TABLE 15·3   SOUND LEVELS FOR SPEECH AND MUSIC IN DECIBELS
re 0.0002 DYNE/CM²

Type of Sound	Levels at 30 Ft in Free Field		Desired Levels within Enclosure	
	Max. rms levels in ¼-sec intervals	Volume indicator reading long rms	Recommended for the amplifier design	Volume indicator reading
Conversational speech				
Men	56.5	46.5		
Women	54.5	44.5	78	68
Music				
1 voice	87	77	87	77
100 voices	107	97	107	97
75-piece orchestra	106	96	106	96
18-piece orchestra	96	86	96	86

efficiency factor LR and the required amplifier power and number of loudspeakers in any enclosure. For speech and music, the maximum rms power in any one-fourth second interval is about 10 db above the level indicated by a sound level meter or VU

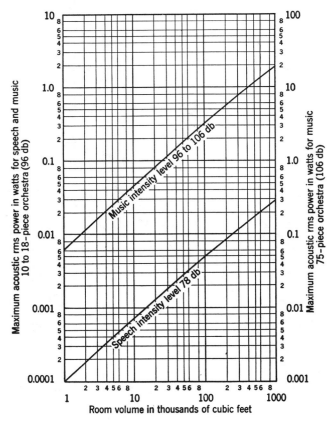

F<small>IG</small>. 15·20 Graphs showing the levels produced by small and large orchestras and by the human voice as a function of room volume. (After Hopkins and Stryker.[14])

meter. Amplifier design is usually based on the maximum rms power needed. Values of sound levels in decibels for speech and music measured in a free field, 30 ft from the source, are given in Table 15·3. The desired levels in any enclosure are shown in the last two columns in terms of both the VU meter readings and the values recommended for amplifier design.

Earlier in the chapter we showed that the acoustic power radi-

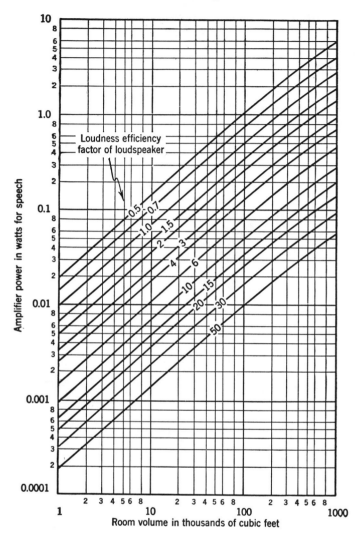

Fig. 15·21   Amplifier power required for successful reproduction of speech as a function of room volume for various loudness efficiency factors of loudspeakers.   (After Hopkins and Stryker.[14])

ated by a loudspeaker is enhanced by the room in which it is located.   In Eq. (15·5) we defined a *room gain factor* K_2 which will, when combined with the sound levels from Table 15·3, give us the maximum acoustic power P_2 necessary to produce the desired levels of speech and music for any room volume having

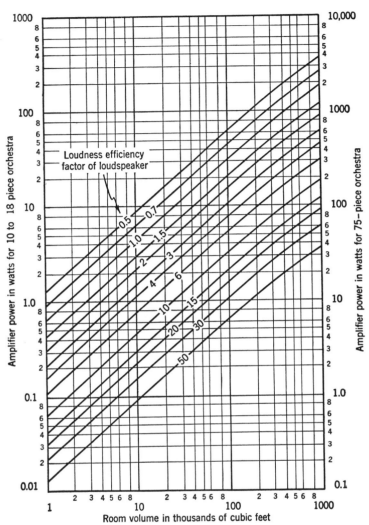

FIG. 15·22 Amplifier power required for successful reproduction of small and large orchestras as a function of room volume for various loudness efficiency factors of loudspeakers. (After Hopkins and Stryker.[14])

an optimum reverberation time. The value of P_2 is calculated from

$$P_2 = P_1 \, 10^{-K_2/10} \qquad (15·31)$$

where P_1 equals the maximum rms acoustic power derived from the sound levels in the fourth column of Table 15·3, and K_2 is given by Fig. 15·6.　Values of P_2 are plotted in Fig. 15·20 as a function of room volume for the three special cases of conversational speech, an 18-piece orchestra, and a 75-piece orchestra.

The amplifier capacity required for various enclosures is determined from the two charts of Figs. 15·21 and 15·22. They show the use of the loudness efficiency factor LR.　The number of loudspeakers required is determined by dividing the required amplifier power by W_R, the power-handling capacity of the loudspeaker.

16.

Testing of Communication System Components

16·1 Introduction

This chapter presents techniques for testing earphones, bone-conduction phones, earphone cushions, and hearing aids. The research which led to the test procedures reported here was conducted largely in two places, the Bell Telephone Laboratories and the wartime Electro-Acoustic Laboratory at Harvard. The Bell Telephone Laboratories were primarily concerned with the testing of telephone equipment which is used in locations where reasonably low background levels and speech levels prevail. On the other hand, the Electro-Acoustic Laboratory was interested in communication in aircraft where high background levels, high speech levels, and low ambient pressures and temperatures are the rule.

Fortunately, many of the test procedures used in the testing of telephone instruments were also adaptable to the testing of aircraft microphones and earphones. As an example, the Western Electric 640-AA condenser microphone was adopted early by the Army and Navy air branches as a standard laboratory microphone. Other examples are the 6-cc coupler for testing earphones and one of the procedures for testing carbon microphones.

16·2 Real·Voice Testing of Microphones

A. Air Microphones (Refer also to Chapter 9, Section 1B)

The usual procedure for calibration of microphones which are used in close proximity to the lips involves an *artificial voice* whose acoustic output at a reference point is known from measurement. The microphone to be calibrated is placed at the reference point in the sound field of the artificial voice, and its voltage output is measured as a function of frequency. The frequency response characteristic is expressed in terms of either the open-circuit voltage or the voltage produced across some stated load for a given sound pressure level input to the microphone. In some procedures, the stated sound pressure level is that actually existing at the face of the microphone; in others, it is the sound pressure existing in open air at the point where the microphone is to be placed. Procedures of this general type will be discussed in the next section.

The artificial-voice type of test is very useful for the calibration of certain kinds of microphones, especially when testing of large numbers of production samples for conformance to type requirements is concerned, or when the performance characteristics of a number of reasonably similar units are to be compared with each other. The validity of the procedure as a basic standard of measurement, however, depends entirely on the degree to which the performance of the combination of artificial voice and microphone simulates that of the human voice and microphone. Also, the problems of calibration of a unit such as a throat microphone, or a microphone in combination with a noise shield or oxygen mask, cannot readily be solved by the artificial-voice method. It is important, therefore, to have available a method by which the microphone is tested with a person as the source of sound.

The real-voice test for a microphone makes use of the apparatus[1] shown in Fig. 16·1. The test is carried out in two steps. For step A the person doing the talking is placed in an anechoic chamber. A laboratory standard microphone is placed in front of the talker at a meter's distance. With a suitable set of parallel filters, the speech signal is divided into a number of frequency bands. The output of each band is connected to an integrating circuit,[2] and the average sound pressure is determined over any desired time interval.

The second part (step B) requires that the talker hold the microphone under test in its normal operating position and that he repeat the speech material used in the first part of the test.

[1] L. L. Beranek, "Design of speech communication systems," *Proc. Inst. Radio Engrs.*, **35**, 880–890 (1947).

[2] H. W. Rudmose, K. C. Clark, F. D. Carlson, J. C. Eisenstein, and R. A. Walker, "Voice measurements with an audio spectrometer," *Jour. Acous. Soc. Amer.*, **20**, 503–512 (1948).

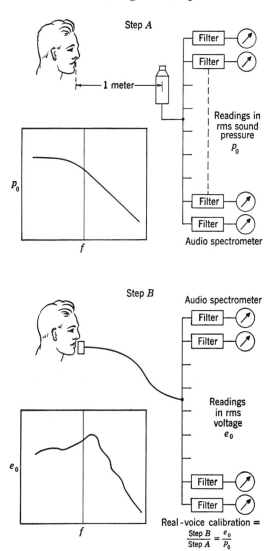

FIG. 16·1 The two steps necessary to obtain the real-voice calibration of a microphone. Step A: determination of the speech spectrum. Step B: determination of output voltage spectrum of the microphone using same speech material as for step A. (After Beranek.[1])

The output of the microphone is connected to the analyzer in place of the laboratory standard. Obviously, the same voice level is used, as before.

From step A we obtain the average sound pressure produced by the talker in each band. From step B we obtain the average voltage produced by the microphone in each band. The ratio of the output voltages of step B to the corresponding sound pressures of step A yields the real-voice calibration. Because the same filter bands are used for the two parts of the test, the calibration is reasonably independent of bandwidth provided no peaks and dips exist in the microphone response. Hence, curves obtained by this method may be compared directly with those using an artificial voice with pure-tone excitation. As discussed in Chapter 13 the output voltage may be given either as the open-circuit voltage or as the voltage across a stated load. The open-circuit voltage is the more basic quantity, because it and the internal electrical impedance of the microphone fully specify the microphone's performance under any condition of loading. In either case, the real-voice response is given by

$$\text{Real-voice response (db)} = 20 \log_{10} \frac{e}{p_{ff}} + 20 \log_{10} \frac{p_{\text{ref.}}}{e_{\text{ref.}}} \quad (16\cdot1)$$

where e = output voltage   (The nature of the voltage measured, open-circuit or across a load, must be specified.)

p_{ff} = free-field sound pressure 1 meter from the talker's lips

$p_{\text{ref.}}$ = reference sound pressure, usually 1 dyne/cm^2

$e_{\text{ref.}}$ = reference voltage, usually 1 volt.

Obviously, the results obtained from a real-voice test will have to be analyzed from a statistical viewpoint. Speech levels vary rapidly with time, and the voices of different talkers may be greatly different. The degree to which any one response curve obtained corresponds to the way the microphone would respond on the average in actual use depends on several factors. These factors include (a) the stability of the microphone under test, (b) the speech material used, (c) the number of talkers used, (d) the number of repeats used for each talker, and (e) the care exercised by the talkers in holding their voice levels and rates of talking constant.

Instability of carbon microphones can arise from several considerations. These include "breathing," incorrect shaping of the carbon granule housing, and aging of the carbon granules. These factors have been discussed in Chapter 5.

The speech sample used should contain all the sounds of speech and should cover a wide frequency range. One sentence which contains most of the important speech sounds in reasonable proportion and which has been used with success is

> "Joe took father's shoe bench out; she
> was waiting at my lawn."

Obviously, the speech sample should provide speech energy in each of the frequency bands in order that a meaningful calibration result. If a speech sample were used which had all its energy concentrated in a limited frequency region, the microphone response in other regions would be indeterminate. For this reason, the relatively long speech sample about "Joe" is satisfactory.

A third factor which affects the degree of validity of the data is the talking rate. Constant talking rate can be maintained by providing a timing device that flashes every time the speech material is to be repeated. The talker soon learns to adjust his rate and pauses so that he is just ready to repeat the test sentence when the light flashes.

A fourth factor which affects the variability of the results is the ability of the talker to hold his voice constant from one sample to another. Constancy of both the rate of talking and the speech level are involved. One way to monitor the speech level is to mount a reference microphone in the anechoic chamber near the talker and to connect the output of it to a meter which the talker can observe. It is found that the overall speech level at a point in front of the talker is not appreciably altered when a hand-held or similar type of microphone is held in front of the lips.

Monitoring of the voice level when testing mask-enclosed microphones is somewhat more difficult, however. It might seem at first thought that a throat microphone could be used for the purpose. Studies have shown, however, that the mask enclosure reacts on the vocal cord mechanism, and changes in level of the output of the throat microphone of several decibels occur when the mask is placed over the talker's mouth. In this case, the talker might be instructed to do his best to hold his voice at what he considers a constant level. It will be found, however, that he will automatically raise his voice level several decibels because it sounds weaker to him with the mask in place. Hence, such a procedure will usually make the microphone appear more sensitive than it actually is.

One other method of holding the voice level constant was employed by Rudmose et al.[2] in studies of the variation of the human voice with altitude. Their procedure follows: The talker is equipped with a throat microphone connected to a VU meter which is placed in plain sight of the talker. He is then asked to say the test sentence at the maximum effort he can sustain without becoming hoarse and to determine his voice level on the meter. Then he reduces the attenuation in the electrical circuit by 6 db and during the experiment he repeats the test sentence at the meter reading he obtained when speaking at maximum effort. This means that his voice level is 6 db down from what it was at maximum effort.

For any given talker, the maximum level achievable is found to be repeatable to within a decibel or so. When mask microphones are being tested, a separate determination of the meter reading should be made with and without the mask in place. If this is done, presumably the same effort is being expended before and after the mask is added.

The number of talkers and the number of repeats per talker which one must use depends on the variance* of the data, that is, the spread of the data. The larger the variance is, the greater the number of talkers and repeats that must be used in order that a value approaching the mean for a very large number of talkers and conditions be obtained.

Other factors affecting the validity of the results are: distortion of the speech signals by the microphone, extraneous noise caused by the breath blown against the microphone, and vibration caused by handling.

The problem of calibration of a microphone which produces a high degree of distortion of the signals presented to it is the same for the real-voice procedure as for the artificial-voice or any other type of method. It is difficult in any case to establish a meaningful or useful definition of the response, since application of a signal at one frequency produces output voltages at several frequencies.

Suitable types of integrating circuits following the filters have been discussed in Chapters 11 and 12. For real-voice calibra-

* Square of the standard deviation. See Chapter 10.

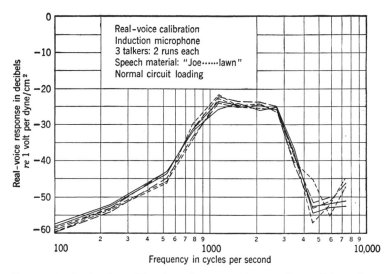

FIG. 16·2   Real-voice calibration of a magnetic-type close-talking microphone.   Total of 3 talkers; 2 runs each.   (After DiMattia *et al.*[4])

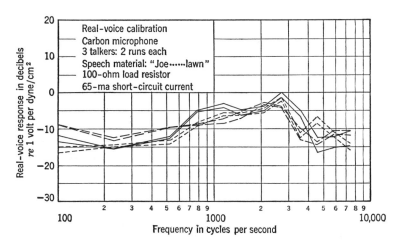

FIG. 16·3   Real-voice calibration of a carbon-button microphone.   Total
of 3 talkers; 2 runs each.   (After DiMattia *et al.*[4])

tions contiguous-band integrative analyzers having either linear or square-law rectifier characteristics are suitable.[2]   The filter bandwidths should probably be chosen on a constant-pitch-interval basis rather than on any other because close-talking microphones are generally used with equipment involving human listeners.[3]

Typical real-voice data taken on two types of close-talking microphones are shown in Figs. 16·2 and 16·3.[4]

B. Throat Microphones

Throat microphones present a somewhat different problem than do other types of microphones.   Many of the speech sounds are produced by air rushing by the teeth or between the lips. These speech sounds contribute greatly to the intelligibility of speech although the total amount of energy associated with them is small.

When a calibration curve is obtained for a throat microphone by the real-voice technique, its shape will depend on the speech sound uttered.   For example, the three curves of Fig. 16·4 indicate the different real-voice response curves yielded by the use of "SHHH," "EE," and "OO" as the speech sample.[4]   The high frequency components of the vowel sound "OO" are passed well by the microphone because they originate almost entirely in the voice box.   "SHHH," on the other hand, is attenuated by 20 db at frequencies above 1000 cps because its components originate at the lips and must travel back down the throat to get to the microphone.

Satisfactory correlation of real-voice response curves on throat microphones with articulation data has never been made.   As a result the relative weighting that must be given to a group of such curves taken for different sounds to yield a meaningful average curve is not known.   It is fairly obvious, however, that the test sentence about "Joe" will not be adequate.   This follows because a very small amount of energy is contained in the unvoiced sounds as compared to the voiced sounds, although the unvoiced sounds are important to the intelligibility of speech.

---

[3] S. S. Stevens, J. P. Egan, and G. A. Miller, "Methods of measuring speech spectra," *Jour. Acous. Soc. Amer.*, **19**, 771–780 (1947).

[4] A. L. DiMattia, J. P. Lienesch, and R. A. Walker, "Real-voice response of microphones," Section G-I, Report No. PNR-6, Electro-Acoustic and Psycho-Acoustic Laboratories, Harvard University (1946).

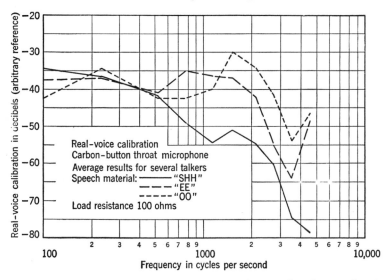

Fig. 16·4   Typical real-voice response curves for a carbon-button throat microphone. The curves are for three different types of speech sounds, "SHHH," "EE," and "OO."   (After DiMattia *et al.*[4])

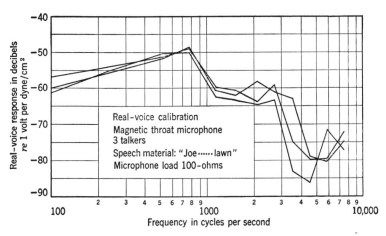

Fig. 16·5   Differences in real-voice response curves obtained with 3 talkers for a throat microphone.   (After DiMattia *et al.*[4])

Hence, a curve obtained with this sentence as speech material will not show the degradation of speech intelligibility which results because of the microphone's insensitiveness to the unvoiced sounds in speech.

The differences among response curves for a throat microphone taken with several talkers may be seen from Fig. 16·5.[4]

16·3   Artificial-Voice Testing of Microphones

Close-talking types of microphones can be divided into two categories: (1) carbon instruments, and (2) induction instruments.   The first type is the more difficult to test because of the instability of the carbon button.   The frequency response curve obtained is a function of at least the following factors:

(a) Previous handling.

(b) "Conditioning" method used to remove the effects of previous handling.

(c) Sound pressure level of the signal or speech used to actuate the microphone.

(d) Ambient noise conditions under which the microphone is tested.

(e) "Agitation" method used to simulate the effect of ambient noise conditions.

In actual use, the "conditioning" is provided by the talker who picks up the microphone (thereby shaking up the carbon granules) and shakes it occasionally as it is being used.   This sort of handling must be simulated during test.

"Agitation" of the carbon granules during artificial-voice measurements is also necessary.   Apparently, the carbon granules will pack together to some extent under the influence of a pure tone or when standing with no tone applied.   When the real voice is used, this difficulty does not arise because speech fluctuates rapidly in both frequency and intensity, thereby keeping the carbon granules continually agitated so that no packing occurs. Ambient noise also serves the purpose of keeping the carbon granules agitated.

Four methods have found considerable use in the testing of carbon microphones using artificial voices as sources of sound. The names given to the methods are not in common use but are adopted here for convenience.

A. Reference Method

The reference method[5] was developed under the premise that any carbon microphone should be tested at signal levels and under ambient noise conditions approximating as closely as possible those under which the microphone is to be used. Carbon microphones frequently are operated in the high ambient noise levels of airplanes, locomotives, and automobiles. For telephones also, it has been shown that significant ambient noises frequently exist.[6] The experimental apparatus for the reference method is shown in diagrammatic form in Fig. 16·6. During

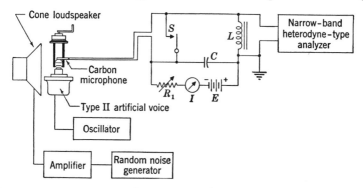

Fig. 16·6   Arrangement of apparatus and test circuit for artificial-voice testing of close-talking microphones.   (After Rudmose *et al.*[5])

tests the microphone is mounted in a fixture so that it is axially positioned in front of a cone loudspeaker unit and at a distance of one-fourth inch from the opening of a 1949 type II artificial voice.*   The cone loudspeaker is used to produce the ambient noise field while the artificial voice produces the test tone.   The noise is obtained from a random noise generator.   Its spectrum

[5] H. W. Rudmose, F. M. Wiener, R. B. Newman, R. H. Nichols, Jr., L. L. Beranek, "Response characteristics of interphone equipment, No. 3," O.S.R.D. Report 1095, March 1, 1943.   This report may be obtained in photostatic or microfilm form from the Office of Technical Services, Department of Commerce, Washington, D. C.

[6] D. F. Seacord, "Room noise at subscribers' telephone locations," *Jour. Acous. Soc. Amer.*, **12**, 183–187 (1940).   Approximate average noise levels quoted are: residences, 43–50 db; small stores, 54 db; large stores, 61 db; small offices, 54 db; medium offices, 58 db; large offices, 65 db; factory offices, 62 db; factories, 77 db.

*The 1949 type II artificial voice consisted of a W.E. 555 unit fitted with a special mouth opening, as shown in Fig. 16·7.

is tailored so that the noise at the microphone resembles that which would surround the microphone in actual use. The output of the artificial voice is adjusted to produce a sound pressure level at the center of the grid (the opening where the sound enters the microphone) equal to the overall level which the voice will produce there in actual use. This level is about 100 db in quiet locations and 120 db in noisy ones.

The carbon microphone is connected into a suitable test circuit such as that shown in Fig. 16·6. If the open-circuit voltage is desired, an inductance whose reactance $L\omega$ is very large compared to the impedance of the microphone may be used. If the voltage across some particular load resistance is desired, a resistor R_2 is substituted for L. The open-circuit voltage may also be measured by the insert-resistor method (see Chapter 13), although fluctuations of the carbon-button resistance lead to results which are not so repeatable when pure tones are employed. The resistance R_1 should be adjusted to provide the normal current through the microphone, and E should be the same size of battery that would be found in the actual installation. The capacitance C should be large enough that its reactance is small compared to R_1. Generally, it is easier in production testing to set the current to a value I with the switch S shorting the microphone. This current I is then called the *short-circuit current*. The current will drop, of course, to a lower value when S is opened.

The artificial-voice response of a microphone is defined in this chapter as

Artificial-voice response (db)

$$= 20 \log_{10} \frac{e}{p_G} + 20 \log_{10} \frac{p_{\text{ref.}}}{e_{\text{ref.}}} \quad (16\cdot2)$$

where e = output voltage   (It must be specified whether the voltage is the open-circuit voltage or the voltage across a load resistor.)

p_G = sound pressure measured one-fourth inch in front of the artificial voice at the center of a small baffle which simulates the microphone housing

$p_{\text{ref.}}$ = reference sound pressure, usually 1 dyne/cm^2

$e_{\text{ref.}}$ = reference voltage, usually 1 volt.

To "condition" the microphone, it is shaken vigorously in all directions before it is placed in the fixture. After the microphone is in place, the random noise field and the test tone are applied simultaneously. The open-circuit voltage as a function of frequency is read on a narrow-band, heterodyne-type analyzer which is tuned to the frequency of the test tone. It is generally found that the signal-to-noise ratio at the output of the analyzer is of the order of 20 db so that no particular difficulty caused by fluctuation of the noise is encountered in taking the readings.

B. Bell Telephone Laboratories Method

The Bell Telephone Laboratories method[7] of testing close-talking microphones differs from the preceding in that the "agitation" is provided just before the data are taken, but during the test only pure tones are applied. The electrical circuit is the same as that of Fig. 16·6 except that a vacuum tube voltmeter may be substituted for the wave analyzer. As before, the inductance L may be replaced by a resistor R_2 if the voltage across a load resistor of a certain size is required instead of the open-circuit voltage.

During the test a fixture like that shown in Figs. 16·7[5] and 16·8[8] is used. To calibrate the artificial voice, the standard microphone F surrounded by a baffle E (upper part of Fig. 16·7) is mounted on the fixture. The baffle may have the same shape as that of the microphone to be tested. The distance between the mouth opening B and the front of the microphone F is made to be 0.25 in. With this setup, the voltage across the voice coil of the artificial voice which will produce a constant pressure at the grid of the standard microphone F over the desired frequency range is first determined. Next the standard microphone is removed and replaced with the microphone under test D. The distance between its grid and the mouth opening is made 0.25

---

[7] The Bell Telephone Laboratories method is contained in Army Air Forces and Bureau of Aeronautics specifications covering the procurement and testing of carbon microphones. During the war it was called the "JRB method."

[8] F. M. Wiener, H. W. Rudmose, R. H. Nichols, Jr., R. L. Wallace, Jr., R. J. Marquis, R. B. Newman, A. S. Filler, A. I. Stieber, W. G. Wiklund, P. S. Veneklasen, A. L. DiMattia, H. F. Dienel, C. T. Morrow, D. B. Feer, and L. L. Beranek, "Response characteristics of interphone equipment IV," O.S.R.D. Report No. 3105, Electro-Acoustic Laboratory, Harvard University, January 1, 1944. Photostatic or microfilm copies of this report may be obtained from the Office of Technical Services, Department of Commerce, Washington, D. C. Ask for PB 22889.

in.   When the voltages just determined are applied to the voice coil, the pressure produced at the grid should be nearly constant as a function of frequency.   The amount by which it differs from that measured with the standard microphone is dependent on the ratio of the acoustic impedances at the grids of the standard and test microphones.

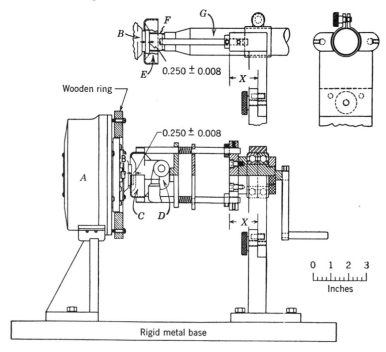

FIG. 16·7   Drawing of fixture and type II artificial voice for the testing of close-talking microphones.   (After Rudmose et al.[5])

To "condition" the carbon microphone, it is rotated (with its face vertical) in its fixture about the axis of the microphone through an arc of approximately 270° and back to its original position two times at a uniform rate of approximately 1 second per rotation.   The purpose of "conditioning" is to remove the effects of previous standing or handling of the microphone. Next the switch S is opened (see Fig. 16·6), and a pause of approximately 3 sec is allowed for the carbon current to stabilize. The oscillator is swept through the 1000 to 3000 cps audio range three times at a rate of approximately one complete sweep (1000–3000–1000) in 2 sec.   This provides acoustical agitation of the carbon.   The input to the source is controlled in such a manner that the sound pressure applied to the microphone unit during the application of the sweep band is, on the average, approximately 124 db and is at no frequency in the band less than 120 db.

Fɪɢ. 16·8   Photograph of a mounting for the microphone fixture and type II artificial voice which allows testing of close-talking microphones at different orientations in space.   (After Wiener *et al.*[8])

At the conclusion of the third sweep cycle, the oscillator is shut off in such a manner as not to disturb the previous conditioning and agitation.   Then the test tone is turned on after one or two seconds' delay, and the response curve is taken point by point. It is necessary that the total time for taking the response curve not exceed 2 or 3 min, in order that the carbon button may not completely lose its conditioning.

C. Random Noise Method

The random noise method[5,] * of testing close-talking microphones employs the same apparatus as that shown in Fig. 16·6. Only one source of sound, the artificial voice, is used. The voice is driven from a random noise generator, and its output is carefully tailored to produce at the grid of the microphone a noise, the spectrum level of which is uniform with frequency. After the spectrum has been adjusted to have the proper shape, the microphone under test is mounted in the fixture. The output voltage as a function of frequency is then measured with a narrow-band-heterodyne type of analyzer. As before, the microphone should have been shaken thoroughly in all directions at the start to "condition" it. Even if the noise spectrum produced by the artificial voice is not strictly flat, satisfactory results will be obtained by taking the ratio of the microphone voltage to the sound pressure level in any band at a given frequency.

D. "Knocking" Method

The "knocking" method[5] differs from the previous methods in that the agitation is provided mechanically. In this case, the microphone is mounted on a rocker arm about 7 in. in length. Before each datum is taken, the rocker arm is rotated in a vertical plane so that the microphone is lifted a distance of about ½ in. Then the arm is released, the microphone and arm drop ½ in. and come to rest against a soft rubber stopper. This method is adaptable to use in altitude and low temperature chambers, because an electromagnet can be used to rotate the rocker arm. The same test circuit is used as before except that a vacuum tube voltmeter can be substituted for the wave analyzer. The microphone should be conditioned before test by shaking it thoroughly in all directions.

E. Comparison of Data Taken by the Different Methods

Agreement among the data taken by the Bell Telephone Laboratories and reference methods is shown in Fig. 16·9. To

---

* The random noise method was first suggested to the author in 1941

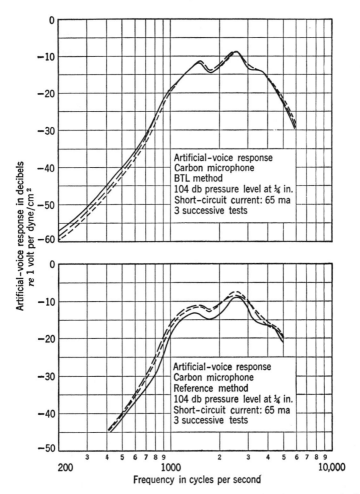

Fɪɢ. 16·9 Comparison of data taken by BTL and reference methods. The upper graph shows curves obtained from three different runs using BTL method; the lower shows the same for reference method. (After Rudmose *et al.*[5])

obtain this agreement the test tone level had to be greater than 105 db in order to simulate the peak levels of the human voice. The effect of using too low a level of test tone is shown in Fig. 16·10. The "knocking" method yielded the same results as the reference method.

by the late Stuart Ballantine. Similar methods have been used on the European Continent.

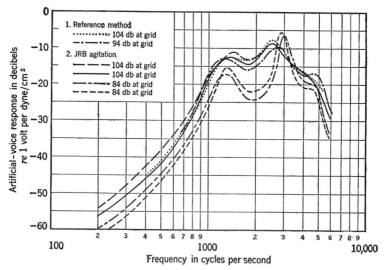

F<small>IG</small>. 16·10   Comparison of response curves obtained with two methods of agitation and three signal levels.   For low signal levels the response curves lie low on the graph.   (After Rudmose *et al.*[5])

F. Method for Differential Microphones

We find in aircraft, tanks, locomotives, and so on, that the ambient noise levels are so high as to nearly obscure speech.   A partial remedy which results in an increase of 5 to 15 db in speech-to-noise ratio is the use of a differential "pressure-canceling" microphone.   This instrument operates as follows: Two openings located a few millimeters apart communicate with the two sides of a diaphragm.   Sound coming from a distance will arrive essentially in-phase at the two sides and will produce no voltage at the output.   Sound arriving from a source closely adjacent to one of the holes, however, will produce a sizable output because of the pressure gradient in a spherical wave near the source (see Chapter 2).

Two characteristics of this instrument are of interest; its frequency response and its noise-cancellation characteristic.   The frequency response may be measured by the techniques described above, but the noise-cancellation characteristic requires special consideration.   One experimental arrangement designed for use in industrial testing is shown in Fig. 16·11.[9]

[9] R. H. Nichols, Jr., and J. P. Lienesch, "Test methods and equipment for differential (noise-cancelling) microphones," Part M, Report No. PNR-6,

In Fig. 16·11, the microphone is seen directly in front of the type II artificial voice and beneath and on the axis of a large cone loudspeaker. The box surrounding the equipment is designed to be closed during test so that the test tones will not interfere with other activities in the room, and it is lined with acoustical material to reduce standing waves. Thereby a fairly uniform noise field is provided in the space around the microphone.

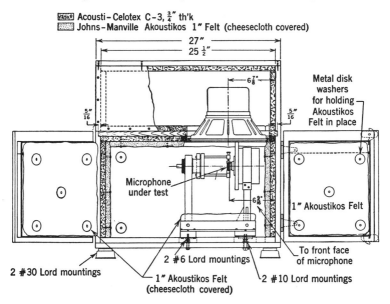

FIG. 16·11 Apparatus for testing signal-to-noise ratio of noise-canceling microphones. Two sources of sound are used: one for supplying ambient noise; the other for the equivalent of a speech signal. (After Nichols and Lienesch.[9])

The procedure for performing the frequency response calibration is the same as that for the Bell Telephone Laboratories method above except that no baffle is necessary around the standard microphone for calibrating the artificial voice. The noise-canceling characteristic is measured by determining the signal-to-noise ratio S/N of the output voltages which result from the application of: (1) a simulated speech signal (by the artificial voice), and (2) an ambient noise (by the cone loudspeaker). The speech and noise signals are applied separately

Psycho-Acoustic and Electro-Acoustic Laboratories, Harvard University, July 1, 1945.

and not simultaneously. The speech and noise spectra can be made of tailored random noise spectra or of line spectra. Two types of line spectra which have been used successfully to represent the normal speech spectrum and airplane noise are given in Table 16·1.

TABLE 16·1 FREQUENCIES AND RELATIVE LEVELS OF PURE TONES SELECTED TO SIMULATE THE SPECTRA OF THE HUMAN VOICE AND OF NOISE IN AN UNTREATED AIRPLANE

Frequency, cps	Speech Spectrum Level, db	Airplane Noise Spectrum Level, db
40	. . .	0
70	. . .	0
130	0	0
250	+6	−4
430	+8	−8
650	+8	−10
780	+7	−11
1500	0	−15
2500	−5	−18
3500	−8	−20

The electrical circuit used is the same as that of Fig. 16·6 except that the wave analyzer is replaced by a vacuum tube voltmeter. After suitable conditioning (rotation through 270° and back twice) the "speech" signal is applied at an overall level of about 115 db for a few seconds to agitate the carbon granules acoustically. The "speech" signal is turned off, and the "noise" signal is turned on at an overall level of 115 db. The overall "noise" voltage output N is read on the vacuum tube voltmeter. During this reading it is advisable to short-circuit the voice coil of the artificial voice. Next the "noise" signal is turned off, the speech signal is turned on, and the overall voltage S is read. The difference in decibels between the voltage levels S and N is called the signal-to-noise ratio S/N. When measured as a function of frequency, it is called the *noise-cancellation characteristic*.

Very little data have been taken relating the noise-cancellation characteristic of a microphone to the intelligibility of speech for it, although some were reported by Nichols and Lienesch.[9] Twelve microphones whose S/N ratios ranged from 9.4 to 25.6 db were tested by J. Egan at the Psycho-Acoustic Laboratory at Harvard. He used standard articulation-test procedures. The response characteristics of the twelve instruments were quite similar. Their data indicate that articulation scores increase with increasing values of S/N, at least over a range of 0 to 15 db.

G. Methods for Induction-Type Microphones

We may test moving-coil or magnetic types of microphones with the same apparatus as that just described. The differences are that no carbon current need be provided and no agitation or conditioning is required. Because the output levels of these instruments are lower than those of a carbon microphone, precautions to shield the electrical circuits properly and additional amplification may be necessary.

H. Non-linear Distortion

We are particularly interested in knowing the non-linear distortion characteristics of carbon-type microphones. To do this, the apparatus for the production of large sound pressures described in Chapter 9 may be used. As described there, that apparatus will produce, at the face of a microphone with *large* diaphragm impedance, sound pressures of the order of 130 db or more with distortions of less than a few percent rms harmonic content.

Two types of distortion may be measured, harmonic distortion and intermodulation distortion. Harmonic distortion is measured by applying a pure-tone sound field at the face of the microphone and measuring the amplitudes of the harmonic frequencies in the electrical output. From these data the percentage rms distortion is given by

Percentage of rms harmonic distortion

$$= 100 \times \frac{\sqrt{E_2^2 + E_3^2 + E_4^2 + \cdots}}{\sqrt{E_1^2 + E_2^2 + E_3^2 + \cdots}} \qquad (16\cdot3)$$

where E_1 is the amplitude of the fundamental and E_2, E_3, etc., are the magnitudes of the respective harmonics.

Intermodulation frequencies are those sum and difference frequencies which result when two or more inharmonically related tones are used to excite a microphone. For example, the principal difference frequencies generated by two tones of frequencies f_1 and f_2 are $f_2 - f_1$, $2f_2 - f_1$, $2f_1 - f_2$. The intermodulation distortion method yields at least the following quantities:

$$\text{Percentage of im distortion} = \frac{E_{1-2}}{\sqrt{E_1^2 + E_2^2}} \times 100 \quad (16\cdot4)$$

or

$$= \frac{E_{(2,1)-2}}{\sqrt{E_1^2 + E_2^2}} \times 100 \quad (16\cdot5)$$

or

$$= \frac{E_{(2,2)-1}}{\sqrt{E_1^2 + E_2^2}} \times 100 \quad (16\cdot6)$$

where E_{1-2} is the amplitude of the output voltage component of frequency $f_1 - f_2$; $E_{(2,1)-2}$ is that of frequency $2f_1 - f_2$; $E_{(2,2)-1}$

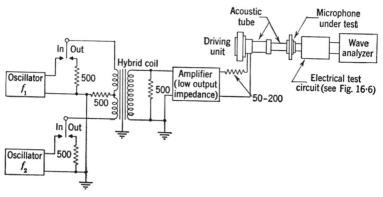

Fɪɢ. 16·12   Typical test circuit for determining the intermodulation distortion produced by close-talking microphones. The acoustic part of the circuit was discussed in Chapter 9. If only one oscillator is used, the harmonic distortion may also be determined. (After Wiener *et al.*[8])

is that of frequency $2f_2 - f_1$, and E_1 and E_2 are the amplitudes of the output voltages due to the two applied tones. The total intermodulation distortion would equal the rms sum of all the components of the types shown in Eqs. (16·4 to 16·6) above.

When determining the distortion as a function of frequency, each of the orders of distortion from Eqs. (16·4–6) may be plotted as a function of f_m where

$$f_m = \sqrt{f_1 f_2} \quad (16\cdot7)$$

We generally do not need to measure the summation components because they usually do not contribute any new information of significance. Furthermore, it seems to be characteristic of carbon microphones that the component of frequency $f_1 - f_2$ is always larger than that of frequency $f_1 + f_2$.

The circuit used for calibration is shown in Fig. 16·12.[8]   One possible set of frequencies for the tube of Fig. 9·49 (Chapter 9) is:

f_1	f_2
200	530
530	825
1220	1500
1500	1800
2550	2800
3270	3580
3580	3860
4210	4520

I. Effect of Current and Position on Carbon Microphone Performance

The sensitivity of a carbon microphone is related to the direct current which flows through the button.   A typical example of

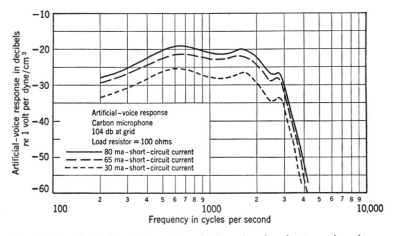

Fig. 16·13   Typical variation of sensitivity of carbon-button microphone with change of direct current.   (After Wiener *et al.*[8])

the variation is shown in Fig. 16·13.   In every carbon instrument, with no signal applied, there is present a certain amount of noise which has its origin in the individual contacts between the carbon granules.   It is commonly called *burning noise*.   It seems that there is no optimum carbon current for which the burning noise is a minimum.   The burning noise is, moreover, generally a function of the position in which the microphone is held.

Since the carbon granules are not packed very tightly, their relative position and contact pressure are functions of the shape of the carbon chamber and its position with respect to the direction of the gravity force vector. With inferior microphone and carbon chamber design, the frequency response and other characteristics of the microphone may be strong functions of position. There is indication that the effects of position on response are more readily revealed with the Bell Telephone Laboratories method than with the reference method.

16·4 Real-Ear Testing of Earphone

Although artificial ears are available and will be described shortly, we find that real ears possess properties which are difficult to simulate. For example, the impedance of the eardrum and of the side walls of the ear canal is not easily determined or duplicated. Nor can we take into account artificially the effect of the pinna on the response of earphones contained in large cushions. A further difficulty lies in the fact that there are wide differences among human ears, and the effects of these differences on the output of an earphone can be determined by no way except with humans. So, we must often resort to the real ear as a means to test an earphone, or to establish the validity of using an artificial ear in any particular instance.

We can choose from at least three methods for measuring the response of earphones on the human ear.[10] One might be called the *eardrum pressure method*. It consists in determining the sound pressure produced at the eardrum for a given power available to the earphone. The second might be called the *outer ear canal method*. In this case the pressure produced beneath the earphone cushion is measured. The third might be called the *equal-loudness method*. It comprises a determination of the pressure in a free field which will produce the same loudness at the ear of a subject as does the earphone for a given electrical power available.

Unfortunately, the equal-loudness method does not appear to yield the same answer as the sound pressure method. Even

---

[10]F. M. Wiener and A. S. Filler, "The response of certain earphones on the ear and on closed couplers," Report PNR-2, Psycho-Acoustic and Electro-Acoustic Laboratories, Harvard University, December 1, 1945.

when the effects of diffraction around the head and resonance in the ear canal are corrected for, there still remain discrepancies. It appears that for a given pressure *measured in both tests at the eardrum* a free-field wave produces a loudness greater by 5 or so dB than that produced by an earphone bearing against the pinna. The nature of this difference is not understood, but it seems to be a physiological or psychological phenomenon. It has been observed by several laboratories, and it may be part of the reason for the difference between the minimum audible field and minimum audible pressure threshold curves currently published.[11] Until the validity of one or the other of the measurements is established, the one used for obtaining the real-ear response should be clearly stated when data are presented.

A. Eardrum Pressure Method

In this method the ear is used only as a passive acoustic impedance for terminating the earphone. The pressure is measured directly at the eardrum by means of a small, flexible probe tube attached to the input of a pressure microphone.[10,12] Details on two metal probe tubes, one commercially available, are in Figs. 16·14 –16·18.[12,13] Associated with it is a mechanism for clamping and supporting the head of the subject and the microphone preamplifier. One possible arrangement is shown in Fig. 16·16.[10]

The probe tube is calibrated by terminating it in a small chamber coupled to the diaphragm of a calibrated standard (see Fig. 16·17).[12] The coupler shown there is cylindrical and has a volume of about 3 cc. One of the condenser microphones acts as a sound source. The calibration is done as follows: The pressure produced with the coupler is first measured with the standard microphone. Then the standard microphone is removed, and

---

[11]S. S. Stevens and H. Davis, *Hearing* (Wiley, New York, 1938). The observations referred to above were made in the Bell Telephone Laboratories and at the Electro-Acoustic and Psycho-Acoustic Laboratories at Harvard.

[12]R. H. Nichols, Jr., R. J. Marquis, W. G. Wiklund, A. S. Filler, D. B. Feer, and P. S. Veneklasen, "Electro-acoustical characteristics of hearing aids," O. S. R. D. Report 4666, Electro-Acoustic Laboratory, Harvard University, May 1, 1945. This report is not available to the public.

[13]"Horn-coupled probe microphone, Type 4170, 6.5 in. long, coupled to 0.5 in. condenser microphone," (1986), Bruel & Kjaer Instruments, Inc., 185 Forest Street, Marlborough, MA 01752.

the probe tube, mounted as shown in the right-hand part of Fig. 16·17, is inserted in its place.

For very small-sized probe tubes (inside diameter = *ca.* 0.025 in.), the pressure in the cavity will remain unchanged when the substitution is made. If desired, we can determine approximately the difference in the pressure (if any is measurable) before and after the substitution by means of a third probe tube and microphone inserted permanently into the side of the coupler.

The correction which must be subtracted from the pressure response of the 640-AA is shown in Fig. 16·15. The overall frequency response for a commercially available probe tube, 6.5 in. long and 0.05 in. i.d. connected by a 0.5 in. horn to a 0.5 in. condenser microphone is given in Fig. 16·18.[13]

Measurement of pressure at the eardrum is accomplished with the apparatus of Fig. 16·16. The 3 in. length of tubing shown in Fig. 16·14 is extended by adding it to a 2 in. length of flexible plastic tubing of about 5/64 in. outer diameter.[10] To

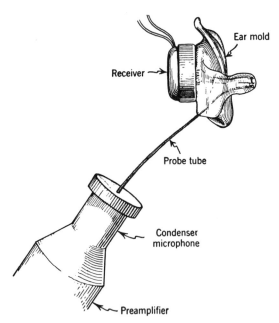

FIG. 16·14   Probe tube suitable for determining the sound pressure produced by a hearing-aid earphone near the eardrum (After Nichols *et al.*[12]).

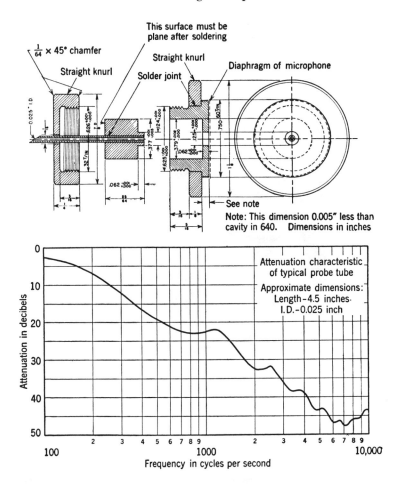

FIG. 16·15   (*Above*) Attachment for joining probe tube to standard 1.0 in. condenser microphone (After Nichols *et al.*[12]). (*Below*) Probe tube calibration to be subtracted from pressure response curve of 640-AA.

permit easy and accurate insertion of the probe tube into the ear canal, the microphone holder must be mounted on a special adjustable carriage. The one shown in Fig. 16·16 is designed to permit vertical adjustment by means of a lead screw, lateral adjustment roughly parallel to the length of the ear canal by means of a rack and pinion, and motion approximately perpendicular to the ear canal by means of another lead screw. The

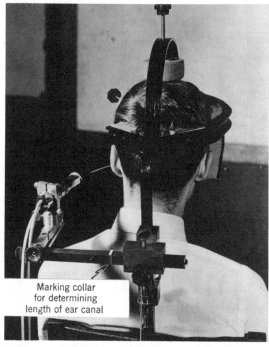

Marking collar
for determining
length of ear canal

FIG. 16·16   Head clamp and microphone with flexible probe tube for sound pressure measurements in the ear canal under an earphone cushion (After Wiener and Filler.[10]).

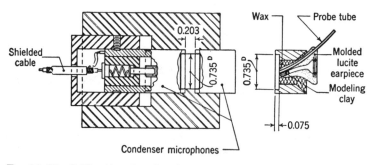

FIG. 16·17   Calibrating chamber for a probe tube of very small diameter. The sketch at the left shows a condenser microphone being used to measure the pressure in a cavity. This pressure is produced by a second condenser microphone driven as a source. After the pressure is determined, the right-hand microphone is removed from the cavity and the probe tube and its holder are inserted (After Nichols *et al.*[12]).

carriage is anchored to the main rod supporting the head clamp. The end of the probe tube is located near the eardrum by advancing it cautiously into the auditory canal until the person reports an auditory sensation approximating a dull thud. After a slight withdrawal, the sound pressure is measured as a function of frequency.

B. Outer Ear Canal Method

For safety, we usually measure the sound pressure in the outer ear and convert it to pressure at the eardrum. For earphones fitted to cushions that bear against the ear, the probe tube is located as follows: The end of the probe tube is pushed through the rubber walls of the eardrum cushion (see Fig. 16·19) and is adjusted so that its tip lies in a plane through the face of the earphone and near its center.[10] In earphones with rubber tips that extend part way down into the ear canal, the end of the probe tube is made to coincide with the plane through the end of the tip.

For changing from pressures measured at the cushion to pressures at the eardrum, the curve given in Fig. 16·20 may be used.[10] Sometimes, the ratios of the pressures in a free sound field to those generated at the person's eardrum after he enters the

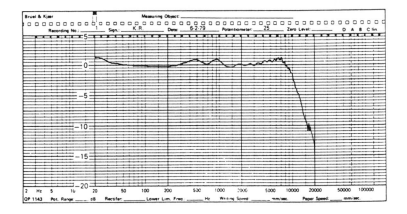

FIG. 16·18 Overall response of horn-coupled probe microphone with preamplifier. The probe tube, 6.5 in. long and 0.05 in. internal diameter, is connected to 0.5 in. condenser microphone by a horn 0.5 in. long. An acoustic matching-impedance in the microphone end of the horn equalizes the frequency response of the assembly (Courtesy of Bruel & Kjaer).

sound field are desired. A conversion curve for this purpose is shown in Fig. 5·12 of Chapter 5.[14]

Typical results of real-ear tests are shown in Figs. 16·21 and 16·22.[10] A difficulty is encountered when attempting to present such sound pressure data. The average value of the distribution of the datum points is easily computed and useful to a certain

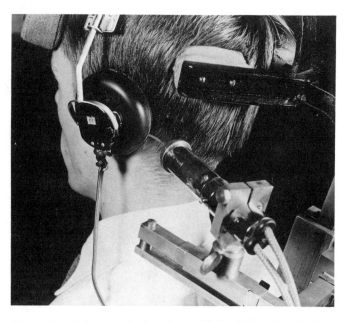

Fig. 16·19   Head clamp and microphone with flexible probe tube for sound pressure measurements in the ear canal under an earphone cushion. The sound pressure in this case is determined at a position a few millimeters away from the face of the earphone. (After Wiener and Filler.[10])

extent, but the average response characteristic computed on that basis has a tendency to obscure the fine structure of the individual response characteristics. If, for example, an earphone exhibits a peak in a certain frequency region, whose magnitude is constant but whose frequency varies from person to person, the average response characteristic may not show this significant peak at all.

In the data of Figs. 16·21 and 16·22, Wiener made an attempt

[14] F. M. Wiener and D. A. Ross, "The pressure distribution in the auditory canal in a progressive sound field," *Jour. Acous. Soc. Amer.*, **18**, 401–408 (1946).

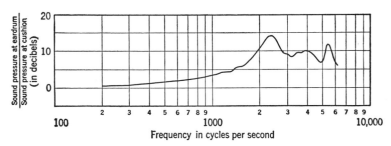

Fig. 16·20 Typical curve for the conversion of sound pressures at the cushion over to sound pressures at the eardrum. This curve was obtained for the particular earphone and cushion shown in Fig. 16·19. (After Wiener and Ross.[14])

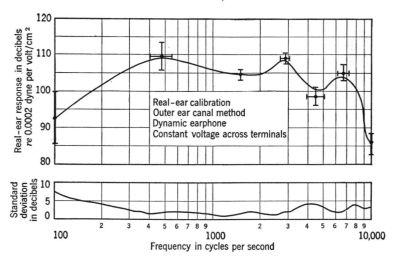

Fig. 16·21 Typical sound pressure data measured beneath the cushion for a dynamic-type earphone. The average level and the average frequency of each characteristic peak are shown as solid circles on the curve. The standard deviations of the levels and the standard deviations of the frequencies of the peaks are shown as bars on the curve. The lower curve shows the standard deviations for the average levels. The measurements were made on 11 ears. (After Wiener and Filler.[10])

at a somewhat different method of averaging. The set of individual response characteristics for a given microphone was inspected, and certain characteristic points, such as peaks and valleys on *all* curves, were selected. The ordinates and abscissas for these points were tabulated from the individual curves, averaged, and the standard deviations in both directions computed.

The averages and the standard deviations are plotted as solid dots and bars, respectively, on the same graph with the conventional averages.   The lower curve of Fig. 16·21 is the standard deviation for the average curve.   The range is also plotted in Fig. 16·22.   Inspection of such graphs enables us to draw conclusions about the variability of the earphone and of the seal obtained with a given cushion for various ears.

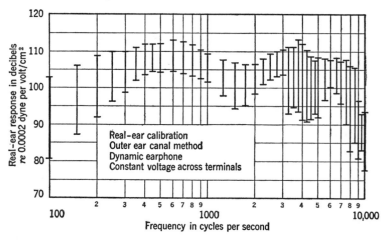

Fig. 16·22   The range of the data obtained on 11 ears for the earphone of Fig. 16·21.   (After Wiener and Filler.[10])

C. Equal-Loudness Method

The equal-loudness method of obtaining a real-ear calibration of an earphone is illustrated in Fig. 16·23.[1, 12, 15]   In step A, a loudspeaker, located at a distance of 1 meter (or other stated distance) from a standard microphone, is energized by an oscillator whose output voltage is adjusted to a value of E_1 for which a convenient sound level is indicated by the microphone.   Next, a high fidelity earphone, known as the transfer standard, is placed over one ear of an observer whose head replaces the microphone.   In step B the switch is thrown to connect the transfer standard to the output of the attenuator, and the voltage E_1 is reduced by an attenuation of A_1 db until the earphone produces a sound which the listener judges to be as loud as that produced by the loudspeaker with a voltage E_1 across it.   Then, in step

[15] F. F. Romanow, "Methods for measuring the performance of hearing aids," *Jour. Acous. Soc. Amer.*, **13**, 294–304 (1942).

C, the earphone under test is placed on the opposite ear and the attenuator A_2 is adjusted until the same loudness is produced by the unknown as by the transfer standard. During all these steps the frequency of the oscillator is held constant. Automatic, frequent switching of the voltage E_1 between the two sources of sound being compared in each of the two cases leads to results which are repeatable to a satisfactory degree. For

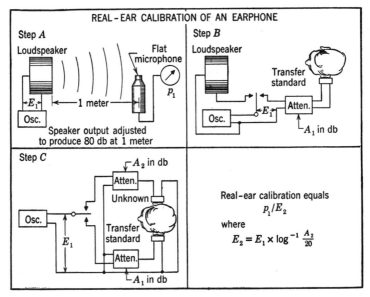

FIG. 16·23 Equal-loudness method for measuring the real-ear response of an earphone. (After Beranek.[1])

results typical of a population, a number of human subjects must be used and the data averaged at each frequency. The real-ear calibration is then expressed as the voltage required to produce the same loudness at the ear as is produced by the sound field measured before the listener enters it.

16·5 Artificial-Ear Testing of Earphones

An ideal artificial ear for earphone testing would fulfill the following requirements:

1. It would present to the earphone under test the same acoustic impedance as the average normal ear over the significant frequency range.

2. It would adequately simulate the effect of leakage between earphone and ear.

3. By means of a suitable microphone, it would permit the measurement of the sound pressure at a point in the artificial ear which gives a one-to-one correspondence with the sound pressure developed in the human ear over the significant frequency range.

4. Its performance would be stable.

A. Artificial Ears

Six artificial ears have been standardized.[16–18]

1. National Bureau of Standards 9A Audiometric Earphone Coupler[*,16]

The NBS 9A coupler was described in Chap. 8, Section 8·2 and Fig. 8·3. This coupler is used for the calibration of audiometers in the USA. It has a volume of about 5.6 cm^3, which is approximately the volume enclosed by a supra-aural earphone on the human ear.

2. American Standard Type 1 Earphone Coupler[16]

The Type 1 earphone coupler has a volume of approximately 6 cm^3 and is a made of a massive nonmagnetic material such as brass (Fig. 16·24). The base of the cavity is terminated by a 1 in. condenser microphone. This coupler was designed for testing telephone receivers that are held flat against the pinna. The earphone cap can form part of the basic shape.

The shape was designed to reduce resonance effects to a minimum and certainly to a lesser amount than the 9A coupler. This particular shape tends to equalize the acoustic pressure rise associated with longitudinal resonance and the pressure drop due to transverse resonance. Therefore, the coupler is free from resonance effects from 0 to nearly 6000 Hz. When hard-faced earphones are used, a tight seal is maintained by using

*CHABA Committee, "Earphones in Audiometry," J. Acoust. Soc. Am. **83**, 1688–1689 (1988).

[16]American National Standard, ANSI S3.7-1973, "Method for coupler calibration of earphones," Acoustical Society of America.

[17]American National Standard, ANSI S3.25-1979, "For an occluded ear simulator."

[18]International Standard, "An IEC artificial ear, of the wide band type, for the calibration of earphones used in audiometry," IEC 318 (1970).

petroleum jelly between the coupler and the earpiece, otherwise leakage will cause a drop in response at frequencies below, say, 400 Hz.

For microphones having equivalent volumes between 0.05 cm^3 and 0.15 cm^3, a nominal value of 0.10 can be assumed. The capillary tube (with inserted wire) that is used to equalize the static pressure inside with that outside is held in place in such a way that leakage occurs only through the inner bore. Above 100 Hz, the capillary leak affects response less than 0.1 dB.

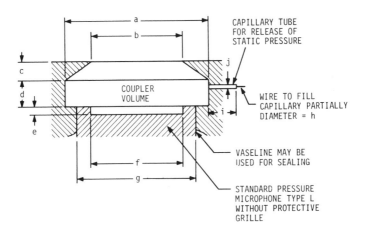

Dimensions			
	in	cm	Comment
a	1.188 ± 0.001	3.018 ± 0.0025	Diameter
b	0.750 ± 0.001	1.905 ± 0.0025	Diameter
c	0.142 ± 0.001	0.361 ± 0.0025	—
d	0.205	0.521	Nominal
e	0.077	0.196	Nominal
f	0.728	1.849	Nominal diameter
g	0.938 ± 0.0006	2.383 ± 0.0015	Diameter
h	0.020	0.051	Wire diameter
i	0.3	0.8	Minimum
j	0.024	0.061	Diameter

FIG. 16·24 American Standard Type-1 earphone coupler for earphones with flat face, i.e., without a solid or soft earcap. An indented face may become part of the coupler volume. (see Ref. 16).

When comparisons between real-ear and coupler calibration of telephone earphones were made on a number of persons, the results of Fig. 16·25 were obtained. The real-ear measurements were made using the probe tube arrangement of Fig. 16·15 (above) inserted through a hole in the moulded cap. The low frequency droop is caused by highly-variable air leaks between the ear and earphone.

3. IEC Coupler for Supra-Aural Earphones[18]

The IEC earphone coupler, like the NBS 9A, is intended for the calibration of earphones used on audiometers. It differs in a very significant way, however, in that it simulates the acoustic input impedance of the average human ear when certain types of supra-aural earphones are connected to it. The simulation is not perfect, and it still is necessary to make subjective transfer data tests as described in Chap. 8 for each type of earphone used.

The IEC artificial ear has incorporated three basic cavities, V_1, V_2, and V_3, as shown in Fig. 16·26, with respective volumes of 2.5, 1.8, and 7.5 cm^3. This sketch shows one specific design, using a 0.5 in. diameter condenser microphone, which is more common today in laboratories. The volumes V_2 and V_3 are circumferential. A slot, e, connects V_2 with V_1, and three adjusting screws set the flow resistance through the slot to the prescribed value. Four holes, H_1, connect V_3 with V_1. One hole, H_2, equalizes the pressure between the interior of the coupler and the exterior ambient pressure.

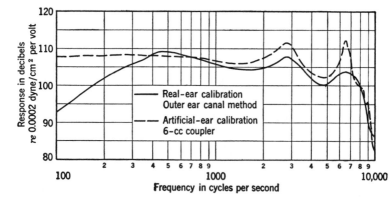

FIG. 16·25   Comparison of real-ear and coupler calibrations of a dynamic earphone unit. Eleven cars were used for the real-ear test.

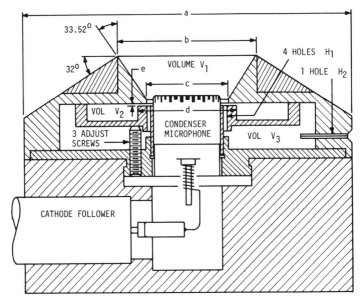

NOTES:
(1) The three adjusting screws are set so that the corresponding flow resistance is 6.5 × 10⁶ Nsm⁻⁵.
(2) The condenser microphone has 0.5-in (1.27-cm) diameter.

	cm		Dimensions cm³		cm	
a	5.995					
b	2.5	V_1	2.5	H_1 (hole)	0.045	Diameter
c	1.49	V_2	1.8		0.38	Length
d	1.75	V_3	7.5	H_2 (hole)	0.03	Diameter
e	0.01				0.90	Length

FIG. 16·26 One specific design of the IEC coupler designed for supra-aural earphones such as are used on audiometers. (see Ref. 16).

The driving acoustic impedance at the face of the artificial ear is specified to have the real and imaginary parts shown in Figs. 16·27 and 16·28. This impedance can be represented by the equivalent circuit of Fig. 16·29.

4. IEC/American Standard Type-2, 2 cm³, Earphone Coupler
In Ref. 16, a coupler is described that is intended to be used in the testing of earphones that are commonly used with hearing aids. Such earphones are inserted into the ear canal and do not entail the large volume formed by the pinna/earphone cap of a

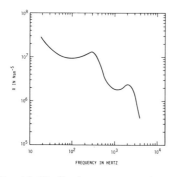

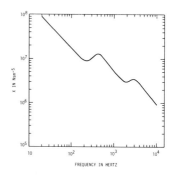

FIG. 16·27   Real component of the acoustic driving point impedance of the IEC coupler for supra-aural earphones. (see Ref. 16).

FIG. 16·28   Imaginary component of the acoustic driving point impedance of the IEC coupler for supra-aural earphones. (see Ref. 16).

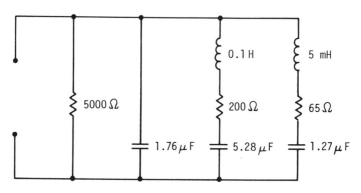

FIG. 16·29   Lumped-parameter electrical analog of the acoustic driving-point impedance of the IEC coupler for supra-aural earphones. (see Ref. 16).

NOTE: In this analog, one electrical ohm corresponds to 10^5 Nsm^{-5}.

telephone earphone. The basic configuration of the Type-2 coupler is shown in Fig. 16·30. The volume, V, shown there is about 2 cm^3, and the coupler is designed to use a 1.0 in. condenser microphone.

The Type-2 coupler is primarily useful in maintaining quality control in production manufacturing, because earphone responses on this coupler and real ears may be quite different.

The Standard contains drawings on how to adapt the coupler to accommodate various types of insert phone, including those

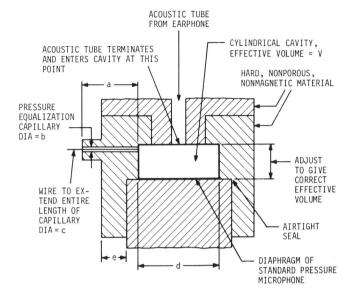

FIG. 16·30   Basic configuration for the IEC/American Standard Type-2, 2-cm³ coupler for insert type earphones.[16]

with 1 in. or longer rigid or flexible tubes between the earphone and the insert device.

5. American National Standard for an Occluded Ear Simulator[17]

This recent Standard for an occluded ear simulator[17] for use with insert earphones was developed to take into account the difference between the sound pressure at the tip of the earphone and the pressure at the eardrum. This difference occurs because of a standing wave at the higher frequencies in the ear canal and because of damping (acoustic resistance) that is present.

a. Four-Branch occluded ear simulator

One version of the Standard occluded ear coupler is given in Fig. 16·31. The "X–X'" plane is intended to pass through the tip of the ear insert (earmold). The portion below the line "X–X'" is the standardized part. That above connects the junction of the concha of the pinna and the outer ear canal with the coupler. Also, if a moulded earpiece loosely fits into the concha, the volume, resistance and leakage can be simulated in the design.

The diagram portrays four acoustic resonators formed by the volumes z_1 to z_4 and the coupling tubes or slots to the simulated ear canal. The microphone is a condenser type, 0.5 in. in diameter. The dimensions of the chambers, connecting tubes and wire mesh screens used for damping are detailed in the standard.

The fundamental specification, however, relates to the transfer impedance, which is determined as follows:

Sound source: The test for compliance with the specification requires a sound source having a high internal impedance, such that it will produce a known constant volume velocity at "X–X'". A 0.5 in. or a 0.25 in. condenser microphone used as a source will produce a constant volume displacement output when driven by a constant voltage. To transfer to constant volume velocity multiply by $2\pi f$.

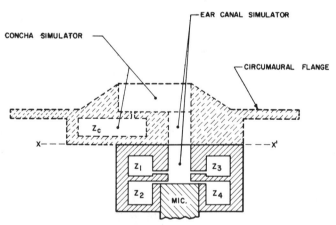

FIG. 16·31 Simplified cross-section diagram of a 4-branch ear simulator for the measurement of insert type earphones. The portion below "X–X'" is the standardized portion; that above must be adapted to the particular geometry and acoustical properties of the insert device. Z_1, Z_2, Z_3, Z_4, and Z_5 and the connecting tubes and slots are acoustic networks comprising acoustic compliance, acoustic mass and acoustic resistance.[17]

Pressure at Microphone: The magnitude and phase of the pressure at the microphone is measured by the 0.5 in. condenser microphone. Recent improvements have been reported to microphones which reduce the phase angle of the output voltage relative to the diaphragm pressure.[19]

Transfer impedance: The transfer impedance is the complex ratio of the pressure at the microphone to the volume velocity at the source. The specified values of the transfer impedance with tolerances are given in Table 16·2.

The tolerances given in Table 16·2 are small compared to the variations in the transfer impedance that would be measured

TABLE 16·2 COMPOSITE OCCLUDED EAR SIMULATOR TRANSFER IMPEDANCE
MODULUS AND PHASE ANGLE TOLERANCES. *

Nominal frequency	Exact frequency	Modulus $(MPa \cdot s/m^3)$	Tolerance $(MPa \cdot s/m^3)$	Phase angle (degrees)	Tolerance (degrees)
100	100.0	175.0	± 8.0	− 88	± 2
125	125.9	140.0	± 6.0	− 87	± 2
160	158.5	110.0	± 6.0	− 86	± 2
200	199.5	87.7	± 4.5	− 86	± 2
250	251.2	69.8	± 4.0	− 85	± 2
315	316.2	56.0	± 3.0	− 85	± 3
400	398.1	44.6	± 2.5	− 84	± 4
500	501.2	35.4	± 3.0	− 80	± 4
630	631.0	27.8	± 2.5	− 74	± 4
800	794.3	21.9	± 3.0	− 66	± 5
1 000	1 000.0	21.3	± 2.0	− 60	± 5
1 250	1 258.9	20.8	± 3.5	− 62	± 3
1 600	1 584.9	18.7	± 2.5	− 66	± 4
2 000	1 995.3	16.6	± 2.0	− 70	± 7
2 500	2 511.9	14.0	± 2.0	− 71	± 5
3 150	3 162.3	11.9	± 2.0	− 72	± 4
4 000	3 981.1	10.5	± 1.5	− 74	± 3
5 000	5 011.9	9.8	± 1.5	− 78	± 3
6 300	6 309.6	10.4	± 1.0	− 84	± 4
8 000	7 943.3	11.0	± 1.5	− 92	± 5
10 000	10 000.0	15.5	± 5.0	− 110	± 16

*See Ref. 17.

[19]E. Frederiksen and O. Schultz, "Pressure microphones for intensity measurements with significantly improved phase properties," Bruel and Kjaer Instruments Inc., 185 Forest Street, Marlborough, MA 01752.

on the ears of a group of people. Alternate constructions to that shown in Fig. 16·31 are permitted by the Standard, provided the transfer impedance falls with the indicated tolerances.

b. Two-branch occluded ear simulator

The Standard gives the construction details for a two-branch simulator that meets the requirements of Table 16·2.

The construction, which is shown in Fig. 16·32, involves two side branches which comprise separately sealed volumes arranged circumferentially and concentrically with the canal, connected to the canal by two and four tubes, respectively. The two smaller tubes form the resistance for the low frequency branch. The resistance for the other branch is formed from layers of screencloth, specified in detail in the Standard. A 0.5 in. condenser microphone is used.

B. Measurement of Non-linear Distortion

Two simple procedures for determining the non-linear distortion produced by earphones have been employed. One uses a single-frequency input, and the other uses two single-frequency signals of equal intensity, spaced by about 100 cps in frequency. In both cases, the artificial ear (coupler) and the electrical con-

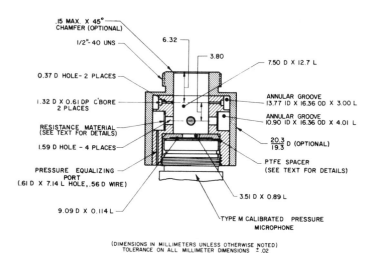

(DIMENSIONS IN MILLIMETERS UNLESS OTHERWISE NOTED)
TOLERANCE ON ALL MILLIMETER DIMENSIONS ± .02

NOTE: DOTS INDICATE FIGURES OF REVOLUTION

FIG. 16·32   Construction details for a two-branch occluded ear simulator meeting the specifications for the American National Standard for an occluded ear simulator.[18]

nections are the same as those used for obtaining the response characteristic. If a single frequency input is used, we measure the harmonics of the acoustic output generated by the earphone in the coupler by means of a standard microphone whose output is amplified and analyzed by a narrow-band wave analyzer. The total rms harmonic distortion is given by

$$\text{Rms harmonic distortion} = 100 \, \frac{\sqrt{p_2^2 + p_3^2 + p_4^2 + \cdots}}{\sqrt{p_1^2 + p_2^2 + p_3^2 + \cdots}} \tag{16.8}$$

If an input signal consisting of two frequencies is used, not only harmonics but also modulation products will be generated. For simplicity we usually refer to this type of distortion as intermodulation distortion. In particular, $f_1 - f_2$, $2f_1 - f_2$, and $2f_2 - f_1$ are singled out for measurement with the wave analyzer, where f_1 and f_2 are the two input frequencies. These are the most important difference tones. The summation tones of equal order are usually not measured because they generally contribute no new information of significance.

The electrical circuit is shown in Fig. 16.33. The following three percentage distortion coefficients are measured and plotted as a function of $f_m = \sqrt{f_1 f_2}$.

$$\text{Percentage of IM distortion} = \frac{p_{1-2}}{\sqrt{p_1^2 + p_2^2}} \times 100 \tag{16.9}$$

or

$$= \frac{p_{(2,1)-2}}{\sqrt{p_1^2 + p_2^2}} \times 100 \tag{16.10}$$

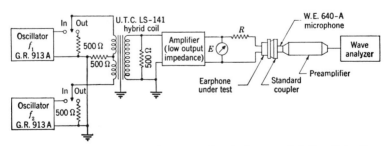

FIG. 16.33 Electrical circuit for measuring the intermodulation distortion produced by earphone in a coupler. (After Wiener et al.[8])

or

$$= \frac{p_{(2,2)-1}}{\sqrt{p_1{}^2 + p_2{}^2}} \times 100 \qquad (16\cdot11)$$

The p's are the sound pressures of the frequencies $f_1 - f_2$, $2f_1 - f_2$, and $2f_2 - f_1$, respectively.

16·6 Artificial-Mastoid Testing of Bone-Conduction Vibrators

Bone-conduction vibrators are commonly used on hearing aids. The problem of testing such units is similar to that of testing earphones, namely, it is necessary to terminate the vibrating part of the unit in a suitable mechanical impedance. Under no-load conditions a bone-conduction vibrator may exhibit large resonant peaks which are damped out when used on a human being. We call a device, which properly terminates a bone-conduction vibrator and which measures the vibrating output in a suitable manner, an *artificial mastoid*.

One type of commercially available artificial mastoid was

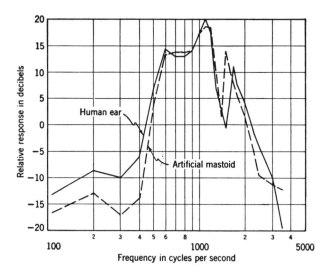

Fig. 16·34   Comparison of response curves for a bone-conduction vibrator measured on a human being by a real-ear technique and on an artificial mastoid. The positions of the two curves on the page are adjusted to bring about coincidence at 1000 cps (After Inglis *et al.*, B.S.T.J., 1932.)

described in Chap. 8, Section 8·2·E and Fig. 8·8.[20] The surface against which the bone vibrator makes contact is a domed metal mass, covered with a neoprene-rubber pad and covered again with a butyl-rubber pad. Imbedded in the butyl pad is a "loading mass". These four elements are vulcanized together to form an integral unit. The force transducer, a piezo-electric disk, is mounted between the domed mass and 3.5 kg inertial mass. This arrangement simulates the complex mechanical impedance of the skin as measured at the mastoid of a number of people.

16·7 Ear Cushion Attenuation

At least five methods have been proposed for the measurement of the attenuation of noise provided by the presence of an earcover cushion (mounted on a headband) over the ear. Two of these tests are psychological in nature, and three are purely physical. The tests are performed about as follows:

A. Psychological Tests

Threshold Method. In this test, a listener is seated in a puretone sound field. With the cushions off, he adjusts the pressure level of the sound until it is just audible. Then, the cushions are placed over the ears, and the pressure level is readjusted until the sound is again just audible. The change in level of the sound, in decibels, is the attenuation provided by the cushion.

Loudness-Balance Method. The same procedure is followed here as for the threshold method, except that the sound level is well above the threshold level. The listener adjusts the attenuation until the sound is equally loud with and without the cushions in place.

B. Physical Tests

Insertion-Loss Method. The ratio of the sound pressure in the concha with the cushion off the ear to the sound pressure at the same point with the cushion on the ear is determined. The result is expressed in decibels.

Orthotelephonic method. By this method the ratio of the sound pressure at the position of the center of the head (prior to

[20]"Types 4930 and 3505, artificial mastoid, artificial mastoid with calibrator," Bruel and Kjaer Instruments, Inc., 185 Forest Street, Marlborough, MA 01752.

the insertion of the head in the sound field) to the sound pressure in the concha with the cushion covering the ear is determined. Normally, we measure the level of noise spectra in the absence of disturbing objects, such as the head, and the orthotelephonic method allows us to use such noise measurements directly in the calculation of pressures in the concha or at the eardrum, using Fig. 5·12 for conversions.

Manikin Method:[21] This method uses a manikin equipped with a head that has a "normal" pinna, concha and outer ear canal. The inner ear canal is part of the occluded ear simulator, described in 16·5·5 of this chapter. The measurement is the same as for the interaction loss or orthotelephonic methods just discussed.

Another variable is the manner in which the noise is presented. For example, a band of random diffuse noise (random in time and striking the head at random angles of incidence) might be used as the sound field. Or, a plane wave sound field might be employed, either with the listener's face or one ear facing the source of the wave. The results will be different at the higher frequencies because of the diffracting characteristics of the head. It seems advisable that the sound field chosen for the measurement approximate that which will be encountered in actual use.

Although the same probe tube might be employed for the modified telephonic method used for the real-ear response measurements, the simpler arrangement of Fig. 16·35 has been used. The cushions may contain earphones mounted on a headband or simply be used on a headband to eliminate loud noise.

Typical results for four different cushions using the modified orthotelephonic method and the threshold method are shown in Figs. 16·36 and 16·37, respectively. These two tests were not strictly comparable because the pure-tone source of sound was located at the side of the head in one case and at the front in the other. In both tests the opposite ear was plugged to prevent any pickup of sound by it. If the curves of Fig. 16·36 are averaged and those of Fig. 16·37 are averaged and corrected to correspond to the condition of the source at the side, the two types of measurement (physical and psychological) may be compared.

---

[21]American National Standard, ANSI S3.36-1985, "Specification for a manikin," Acoustical Society of America.

This comparison appears in Fig. 16·38. The surprising result obtained is that the two curves lie about 7 dB apart. This situation apparently arises from the same factors that caused the pressure and the loudness-balance real-ear response tests to differ by 5 or so dB.

The important precaution must always be taken, therefore, that the response and cushion attenuation curves should be determined alike, that is, either both by a subjective method or both by a pressure method, if the data are to be used in the design of speech communication systems.[1]

16·8 Hearing Aids

Ideally, the performance of a hearing aid as measured by physical laboratory tests should represent identically the performance of the aid when worn by an average person. Hearing aids are small enough that, generally, they either rest behind

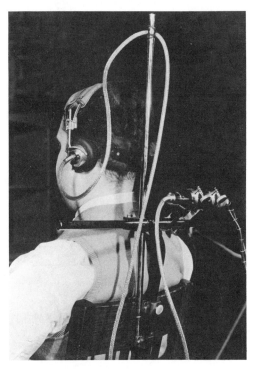

FIG. 16·35 Arrangement for measuring the sound pressure under an earphone cushion due to an external source.

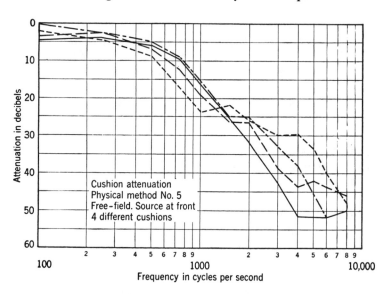

FIG. 16·36 Cushion attenuation curves measured by the procedure illustrated in Fig. 16·36. A pure-tone source of sound was located in front of the observer. The modified orthotelephonic method was used.

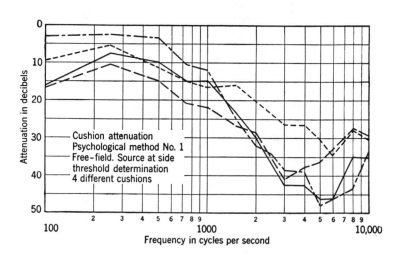

FIG. 16·37 Cushion attenuation curves measured by a psychological method. The threshold method was used.

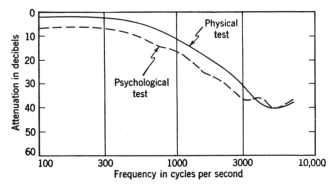

FIG. 16·38 Comparison of results of psychological and physical tests for determining cushion attenuation. The averages of the curves in Fig. 16·36 and of those in Fig. 16·37 were first made. Then a correction for diffraction was made to one of the sets of data. The two resulting curves are plotted here.

the outer ear (pinna) or are placed inside the concha of the pinna. Although an earlier American Standard is still in force[23] that permits free-standing hearing aids to be tested in anechoic space or in a sound-absorbent enclosure, the trend is toward placing them on a carefully designed manikin[21,22] and making the test in a free sound field. The head and torso of the standardized manikin provide acoustic diffractions similar to those measured around a person with median head and torso dimensions. Of particular interest are the shape and dimension for the pinna as shown in Fig. 16·39.

An occluded ear simulator, discussed in Section 16·2·E and Figs. 16·31 and 16·32, is mounted inside the head simulator in accordance with Fig. 16·31. In particular, the ear canal extension, an 8.8 mm-long circular cylinder having a diameter of 7.5 mm, starts from the "X–X'" reference plane and ends at the concha. The intent is that the sound pressure measured by the microphone in the "occluded" ear simulator (without the hearing aid) should be the same as that measured at the eardrum of a person of median build when either stands in the same sound field, without regard to the angle of arrival of the sound wave at the head. Parenthetically, the surface material of the head and torso must be nonporous, with an acoustic impedance that is large compared to that of air; the pinnae and their immediate surroundings are made of a flexible and resilient material.

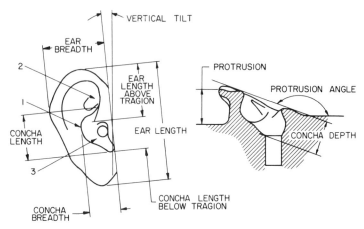

FIG. 16·39   Definitions and dimensions of manikin pinna: (1) antihelix; (2) crus of helix; and (3) concha. (see Ref. 21).

A. Free-Field–Manikin tests

The purpose of this recent Standard[22] is to describe test methods that *include* the acoustical effects of a simulated median adult wearer on the performance of a hearing aid.

In making the frequency response measurements, the sound source must be so controlled that either (a) it produces a constant SPL at the head position without the manikin present, or (b) it produces a constant SPL in the ear simulator with the manikin present (without the hearing aid). Either source control will yield the same results if the hearing aid is operating as a linear device. The method used must be stated.

However, at frequencies where ear canal resonance occurs, the sound pressure levels will be much higher at the input to the hearing aid for method (a) than for method (b).

The recent Standard[22] recommends the following tests:

Insertion gain frequency response: The difference between (i) the sound pressure level (SPL) produced by the hearing aid in the manikin ear simulator and (ii) the SPL produced in the simulator with the hearing aid absent. This, and the following measurements, are made over a frequency range of 200–6000

[22]American National Standard, ANSI S3.35-1985, "Measurements of hearing aids under simulated *in-situ* working conditions, Acoustical Society of America.

Hz. The source level must be the same for the two tests, whether method (*a*) or method (*b*) is used.

Full-on insertion gain frequency response: The insertion gain frequency response with the gain control at maximum and at stated settings of the other hearing aid controls.

Full-on insertion gain frequency response with high input SPL: This test is made as a function of frequency with the source producing the same sound as was required to hold the SPL equal to 90 dB at all frequencies, using method (*a*) or (*b*) according to what was used above.

Directional response: The insertion directional frequency responses, in dB, determined as follows: Measure the frequency response, without the hearing aid, at each angle of incidence and subtract from these the frequency response at $\theta = 0°$ and $\phi = 0°$. Repeat the test with the hearing aid on the manikin. The two frequency responses are subtracted to obtain the insertion directional frequency response for the hearing aid. The aximuth angle, θ, equals zero when the manikin faces the sound source, 90° when the ear with the hearing aid faces the source and 270° when the opposite ear faces the source. The elevation angle, ϕ, equals zero when it lies in a horizontal plane passing through the simulated ear canals. It is positive above the reference plane, and negative below.

The sound source is one meter from the center-point of the manikin head. No clothing or wig is to be used on the manikin. The hearing aid is mounted on the manikin in a position of normal use.

A typical hearing aid with an earhook and a flexible tube connecting to a moulded insert is assumed in the test setup of Fig. 16·40. The reference plane is the "*X–X'*" plane of the occluded ear simulator. Rather than using an actual earmold, the earmold simulator shown may be substituted.

B. Free-field or highly absorbent chamber pressure tests

In the older Standard[23], a pressure calibration of the hearing aid is permitted. That is to say, the SPL in the coupler is determined as a function of frequency with the SPL at the acoustic port in the unit held at a stated value. The input SPL is measured at the acoustic port in the unit (Figs. 16·41 and 16·42).

[23]American National Standard, ANSI S3.22-1982, "Specification of hearing aid characteristics," Acoustical Society of America.

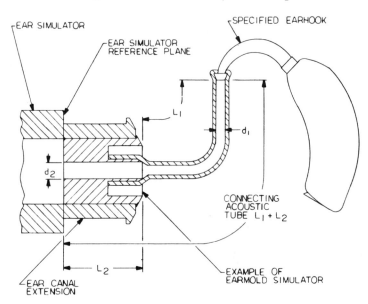

FIG. 16·40   Permitted connection of the hearing aid sound outlet to the ear simulator. (see Ref. 22).

C. Recommended measurements, specifications and tolerances

The new Standard[22] does not make recommendations for acceptable insertion gain frequency response, tolerances thereto, directivity, harmonic distortion, residual noise, etc. for the use in writing purchase specifications or for tests after delivery. Perhaps, the recommendations contained in the old Standard[23] were thought to carry over. Assuming that to be true, the remainder of this section is taken from the old Standard.

Here, it is assumed that *either* of the following is true:
(1) The SPL in the free-field without the manikin or the hearing aid present is held constant, (this is the same as method (a) above), or,
(2) The SPL at the entrance port to the microphone of the hearing aid is held constant (as specified in Ref. 22) (Fig. 16·41).

I. Saturation insertion level gain (SSPL90) Curve: With the gain control full-on and with basic settings of controls, measure the insertion level gain, using (1) or (2) above with the source SPL held constant at 90 dB.

II. Normal frequency response curve: Repeat "A" with the SPL held constant at 60 dB. Plot "A" and "B" as shown in Fig. 16·42.

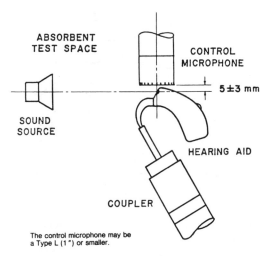

ABSORBENT
TEST SPACE

CONTROL
MICROPHONE

5±3 mm

SOUND
SOURCE

HEARING AID

COUPLER

The control microphone may be
a Type L (1") or smaller.

FIG. 16·41 Measurement configuration[23] for a non-directional microphone. For a directional microphone the two input ports should be in line
with the axis of the source. The control microphone is located about 12 mm
from that line and halfway between the two ports. (see Ref. 23).

III. Setting the gain control to the "reference test position":
Using the high-frequency average level curve (measured in the
earphone coupler) with 90dB input, determine "Maximum
SSPL90" as shown in Fig. 16·42. The *reference gain control position* (with the input SPL equal to 60 dB) is set so that the high-
frequency average, HFA = $(R_1 + R_2 + R_3)/3$ for the response
curve is equal to $(S_1 + S_2 + S_3)/3 - 17$ dB.

IV. Reference test gain: With the gain control set at the reference test position, the reference test gain is:

(HFA-SSPL90-17) − 60 dB .

V. Stated frequency range: The manufacturer's stated frequency range for the hearing aid is determined as follows: Using the frequency response curve with the gain control set at
the reference test position, (*a*) determine HFA = $(R_1 + R_2 + R_3)/3$ dB (Fig. 16·42). Then (*b*) subtract 20 dB. (*c*) Draw a
horizontal line parallel to the bottom of the graph paper at the
reduced level. (*d*) Note the lower frequency f_1 and the upper
frequency f_2 at which the horizontal line intersects the response curve. The stated frequency range is between f_1 and f_2.

VI. Tolerances: The frequency response curve is divided into
two regions, the first between either $1.25f_1$ or 200 Hz (which

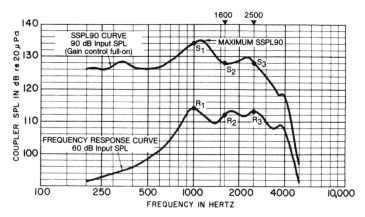

Fig. 16·42   Example of the Saturation SPL (90 dB input and gain control full-on) frequency response curve (above) and the 60 dB input frequency response curve with gain control set at its reference test position as described in the text (below), measured in the earphone coupler. The High-Frequency Average (HFA) is equal to the average sound pressure levels at 1000, 1600, and 2500 Hz. (see Ref. 23).

ever is higher) and 2000 Hz, and the second between 2000 Hz and either 4000 Hz or $0.8f_2$ (whichever is lower). In the first region the tolerance is 4 dB and in the second region 6 dB.

VII. Total harmonic distortion: With the gain control in the reference test position and with an input sound pressure level of 70 dB at 500 and 800 Hz and 65 dB at 1600 Hz, record the total harmonic distortion in the coupler output for each of the above frequencies. The manufacturer should state the values of the H.D. that his model of hearing aid should not exceed.

VIII. Equivalent input noise level: With the gain control in the reference test position and the input signal at 60 dB, determine the high frequency average level (HFA), L_{av}. Then turn off the input source and measure the total noise, L_2 produced in the coupler. The equivalent input noise level, L_n, is given by $L_n = L_2 - (L_{av} - 60)$ dB.

IX. The old Standard[23] has many alternatives for hearing aids with automatic gain controls, high frequency directionality, inadequate dynamic range, battery current, ambient magnetic field, allowable tolerances in the measuring system, and other variations. The user must read all three standards[21-23] to gain full utilization of the Standards.

17.

Articulation Test Methods

17·1 Introduction

In Chapter 13 we described some of the general characteristics of the articulation test. In this chapter we shall present what amounts to an instruction manual for conducting such a test. The procedures described here are taken entirely from ANSI S3.2-1960 and from Egan *et al.*[1] The object of the test is to assess the relative effectiveness of a communication system in transmitting speech when there is ambient noise of arbitrary level at one or more parts of the system.

Since human factors are involved, the results obtained are subject to considerable variability. Special precautions must therefore be taken to keep the effects of individual differences at a minimum without increasing inordinately the amount of testing necessary. The method of testing described here was designed particularly to increase the precision of the comparisons and to minimize the effort involved in conducting such tests.

Furthermore, the method of analysis described here was designed to extract the maximum amount of information from the data, not only about the relative effectiveness of the systems being compared, but also about the adequacy with which the comparisons were made.

---

[1]American National Standard, ANSI S3.2-1960 (R1971), "Method for measurement of monosyllabic word intelligibility," Acoustical Society of America. J. P. Egan *et al.*, "Articulation testing methods II," OSRD Report No. 3802 (1944), and "Procedures for measuring the intelligibility of speech," Report No. PNR-33 (1947), Psycho-Acoustic Laboratory, Harvard University.

17·2 Reference Systems

Since articulation testing yields relative rather than absolute values, two "standard" communication systems are usually tested simultaneously with the particular equipment being evaluated. The two standards serve to "calibrate" the talkers and the listeners (who are in fact the measuring instruments) upon the particular occasion of the tests. The two standard systems might be: (1) a high fidelity system consisting of a condenser microphone and moving-coil earphones held in modern ear cushions, or, alternatively, face-to-face communication without a system, and (2) a system whose characteristics are about the same as those systems which are likely to be tested in the future. The amplifier in the high fidelity system should show a uniform frequency response characteristic ($\pm$ 2 dB) between 100 and 5000 cps. Below 100 and above 5000 cps, the response of the amplifier may fall off rapidly or may remain uniform, but not rise.

17·3 Choice of Ambient Noise Conditions

Everyday experience shows that communication is difficult when the environment is noisy. In most communication systems ambient noise enters the communication circuit in one or more of three ways:

(1) It is picked up by the microphone. The amount and the type of ambient noise which enters the system by this means depend on three main factors: the intensity and spectrum of the ambient noise; the amount of acoustic shielding provided by the construction and mounting of the microphone; and the response characteristics of the microphone itself.

(2) It may also enter a communication circuit by way of acoustic leaks in or around the earphone. The efficiency of the acoustic seal provided at the ear by different earphones varies over a wide range.

(3) Line noise or static may be of a sharp "crashing" sort or of a random type.

If the communication system is typically used in a noisy environment, articulation tests designed to measure the intelligibility provided by that system should be conducted with the talker or listeners or both in the same degree of noise. We have already seen in Chap. 13 that differences among talkers and among listeners are magnified when communication is attempted in noisy surroundings. Another important reason for using noise is that the articulation scores will not be too high and therefore too closely bunched for the three different systems. Differences among systems will be much more readily observable if the articulation scores are made to fall nearer 50 percent than 100 percent.

A convenient way of generating noise is by electronic means. In order that the same noise field exist at the positions of all the observers, it is important that the walls and ceiling of the room have low absorption and reflect sound diffusely. (Many types of noise are possible, but typical spectra of noise suitable for these tests are shown in Fig. 17·1.)

17·4 Testing Crew

The subjects selected as talkers for articulation testing should not have obvious speech defects or strong regional or national accents. The subjects selected as listeners should each have a hearing level (loss) averaging no more than 10 dB at 250, 500, 1000, 2000, and 4000 Hz with no more than 15 dB at any one of those frequencies as measured with a Standard audiometer (Chap. 8) conforming to ANSI S3.6-1969. For adequate testing, a minimum of four talkers and six listeners is needed. More

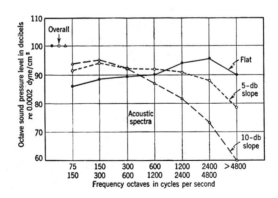

Fig. 17·1   Examples of noise spectra suitable for use when testing the performance of speech communication systems. The overall level of the noise may be adjusted upward or downward. (After Egan et al.[1])

may be used if desired, although any increase in the number of talkers will increase the complexity of the testing method. It is important that the talkers not be used as listeners and that both groups be naïve with respect to the qualities of the systems under test. On the other hand, the opinion they form of a system after testing with it for some time may, along with the test scores, be very useful in evaluating the system.

It cannot be assumed that normal hearing, normal speech, and naïvete on the part of the testing crew will ensure adequate articulation testing. Probably more important than any of these factors is the morale of the testing crew. Without active cooperation by listeners and talkers, the results of a series of tests can be entirely useless. Uncritical selection of testing personnel must be avoided; their educational level must be high enough to ensure familiarity with most of the words on the test lists; they must be intelligent enough to understand the general purpose and method of testing and the necessity of obtaining unbiased results; and, finally, they must be sufficiently motivated to endure a great deal of monotonous and uninteresting testing without becoming bored and uncooperative.

17·5 Training Procedures

A considerable practice period must precede the formal testing of the new equipment. In order to familiarize the testing crew thoroughly with the testing situation and the exact procedure, the high fidelity system (1) should be used first. Testing should continue with this system until it has become entirely routine, and until the mean articulation score of the listening crew shows no further systematic improvement over a series of five or six tests. Then the reference system (2) may be introduced into the testing. Another training period will be required before the mean scores obtained on this system also become stable. It is suggested that a number of tests with the high fidelity system (1) be interspersed among the tests with this system. When a stable difference has been established between the mean scores obtained on the high fidelity system and those obtained on the No. 2 system, the new system to be evaluated can be introduced. Since the new system may introduce some new type of distortion, a short practice period may be necessary to achieve reasonably stable mean scores on the new system. The crew is now ready for a series of formal tests.

17·6 Testing Procedure

To be of any value in comparing communications systems, the measures of effectiveness obtained on the systems must be unbiased measures; that is, no one system may be tested under more favorable circumstances than any other system. When the measures in question are physical, the precautions needed to avoid bias are fairly obvious; when the measures are the results of articulation tests, the precautions necessary are both less obvious and more elaborate.

The use of a large crew of listeners and of talkers is, for the most part, a protection against bias. Even after the listeners and the talkers have undergone considerable training, a small but steadily rising trend is likely to be found in their scores. During a day's testing the scores may show a slight downward trend due to fatigue of the listeners or the talkers or a slow change in the characteristics of the noise. Other factors may cause a rise in the scores during the day, or from one day to the next. Much of the time, effective but irrelevant factors inherent in the method may tend to cancel one another, but many times these factors produce spurious estimates of the differences among systems. At all times they will increase the variability of the obtained scores.

For subsequent analysis of the data it is necessary that the unavoidable variability due to irrelevant factors be distributed randomly over all the tests. Probably the most satisfactory method of achieving this is to perform the tests in random order. It is not, however, necessary or desirable to perform all the tests of a series in random sequence. A series of tests can be most conveniently broken down into several *blocks* of tests within which the testing order is random. In each block of tests each system is tested once by each talker. A complete series of tests evaluating one new system will then consist of one or more such blocks of tests. Since a whole block must be run off in sequence with no long waits between tests, and since a block of twelve tests will take somewhat less than two hours with an experienced crew, a block makes a convenient temporal unit for planning a series of tests.

Order of testing within a block can best be arranged by means of a table similar to Table 17·1.

The test numbers for the first block, 1 to 12, are inserted *at random* in the columns labeled block 1, and the test numbers for

TABLE 17·1 TEST NUMBERS FOR A SERIES OF TWENTY-FOUR TESTS

Block	1				2				3			
Talker	A	B	C	D	A	B	C	D	A	B	C	D
System												
1. High fidelity	12	2	9	7	17	24	22	20				
2. Reference	8	5	11	4	13	18	15	23				
3. New type	6	10	1	3	19	14	21	16				

the second block, 13–24, are inserted *at random* in the columns labeled block 2. If a third block is wanted, the numbers 25–36 can be inserted *at random* in the columns labeled block 3. It is evident that such a table can be extended to include any number of systems and any number of blocks of tests, as well as any number of talkers. In practice, however, a block of more than 16 tests is rather lengthy. In addition, it is not advisable to increase greatly either the number of talkers or the number of systems tested. It would be perfectly consistent with this plan to run each block of tests with an entirely different set of talkers in order to use a more representative sample of voices, but the time necessary for training even one group of talkers makes it inadvisable to increase their number except under rather special circumstances. This question will be taken up later in Section 17·9.

The testing order of the first twenty-four tests of the series as determined from Table 17·1 would be:

	Block 1			Block 2	
Test No.	Talker	System	Test No.	Talker	System
1	C	3	13	A	2
2	B	1	14	B	3
3	D	3	15	C	2
4	D	2	16	D	3
5	B	2	17	A	1
6	A	3	18	B	2
7	D	1	19	A	3
8	A	2	20	D	1
9	C	1	21	C	3
10	B	3	22	C	1
11	C	2	23	D	2
12	A	1	24	B	1

One of the most critical factors determining the scores on an articulation test is the voice level used by the talker. For testing of this sort, it is necessary to keep the range of voice levels within reasonable limits. Probably the most satisfactory method of controlling the voice level in these tests is by "side-tone monitoring," since it is the talker's side tone (what he hears over his own earphones) that will determine the voice level employed by a talker in actual practice. The talker, wearing the same kind of headset as the listeners, hears in his phones just what they hear. He is simply instructed to "make himself intelligible." With further instructions not to shout and to maintain the same level as nearly as possible, most talkers soon become quite adept at maintaining a consistent, high voice level without straining themselves or blasting the listeners' ears (or their own).

In reading aloud the test words, the talker must learn to relax and speak fairly rhythmically. Each word is read in a carrier sentence: "Would you write . . . now," at intervals of three to five seconds, depending on the capacity of the listeners.

17·7 Test Lists

Experience has shown that there are four main categories of useful test materials: (1) nonsense syllables, (2) monosyllabic words, (3) spondiac words, (4) sentences.

A. Nonsense Syllable Lists

When it is desired to determine accurately the effectiveness of a device in transmitting particular speech sounds, nonsense syllables are superior to words or sentences as test items. Articulation scores obtained with lists of nonsense syllables may be made to represent the number of phonemes* actually heard by the listener. Furthermore, since lists of nonsense syllables are constructed by combining into syllables the fundamental speech sounds, the relative frequency of occurrence of these speech sounds can be adjusted as desired. On the other hand, the use of nonsense syllables as test items requires that the testing crew be thoroughly trained. The announcer must pronounce the speech sounds correctly, and the listeners must record in phonetic symbols the sound they hear.

---

*A group of variants of a speech sound usually spelled with the same letter and commonly regarded as the same sound, but varying somewhat with the same talker according to different phonetic conditions, i.e., the *l* sounds in *leave, feel, truly, solely*; the *t* sounds in *ten, stay, try, bottle, cotton, city.*

Four lists of syllables containing eighty-four items each are given below. It is recommended that each list be employed as an indivisible unit for purposes of articulation testing, and that the order in which the syllables are presented be changed at random from reading to reading.

The key for the pronunciation of the sounds follows:

VOWELS

Long
ā (*as in* take *or* face)
a (*as in* father *or* arm)
o (*as in* orb *or* wall)
ō (*as in* boat *or* low)
ē (*as in* team *or* feet)
ū (*as in* boot *or* glue)

Short
a' (*as in* tack *or* cat)
e (*as in* let *or* fed)
i (*as in* lit *or* sin)
u' (*as in* run *or* sun)
u (*as in* could *or* put)

Diphthongs
ī (*as in* bite *or* lime)
ow (*as in* cow *or* ouch)
oi (*as in* coil *or* boy)
ew (*as in* pew *or* cute)

CONSONANTS

Voiced Stops
b (*as in* bold)
d (*as in* dent)
j (*as in* joke)
g (*as in* gold)

Voiced Fricatives
z (*as in* zone)
v (*as in* vow)
zh (*as in* azure)
th' (*as in* then)

Transitional
y (*as in* you)
w (*as in* will)
h (*as in* hot)
wh (*as in* what)

Unvoiced Stops
p (*as in* poor)
t (*as in* tent)
ch (*as in* choke)
k (*as in* cold)

Unvoiced Fricatives
f (*as in* face)
s (*as in* soup)
sh (*as in* shine)
th (*as in* thin)

Semi-vowel
l (*as in* loaf)
r (*as in* root)
m (*as in* men)
n (*as in* never)
ng (*as in* wrong)

The successful use of these syllable lists requires a thorough training of both the announcers and the listeners.

1. *S Master List A*

1 dū	15 che	29 thow	43 ye	57 ūch	71 ewsh
2 da'	16 vū	30 lū	44 ud	58 a'ch	72 oth
3 bo	17 va'	31 la'	45 owd	59 av	73 ith
4 bi	18 zē	32 ro	46 ēb	60 īv	74 ul
5 gā	19 zew	33 ri	47 ewb	61 āz	75 owl
6 goi	20 th'o	34 mā	48 ag	62 oiz	76 ēr
7 ju'	21 th'i	35 moi	49 īg	63 ōzh	77 ewr
8 pu	22 fa	36 nu'	50 ōj	64 ezh	78 am
9 pow	23 fī	37 hu	51 ej	65 uth'	79 īm
10 tē	24 sā	38 how	52 u'p	66 owth'	80 ōn
11 tew	25 soi	39 hwē	53 āt	67 u'f	81 en
12 ka	26 shō	40 wa	54 oit	68 ūs	82 ūng
13 kī	27 she	41 wī	55 ok	69 a's	83 a'ng
14 chō	28 thu	42 yō	56 ik	70 ēsh	84 u'

2. *S Master List B*

1 du	15 chu'	29 lu	43 yu'	57 uch	71 a'sh
2 dow	16 va	30 low	44 ed	58 owch	72 uth
3 bū	17 vī	31 rū	45 ewd	59 u'v	73 owth
4 ba'	18 zu	32 ra'	46 ab	60 ōz	74 ēl
5 go	19 za'	33 mo	47 īb	61 ez	75 ewl
6 gi	20 th'ē	34 mi	48 ōg	62 āzh	76 ar
7 jā	21 th'ew	35 nā	49 eg	63 oizh	77 īr
8 joi	22 fu'	36 noi	50 u'j	64 oth'	78 ōm
9 pē	23 sō	37 hē	51 āp	65 ith'	79 em
10 pew	24 se	38 hew	52 oip	66 āf	80 u'n
11 ta	25 shā	39 hwa	53 ot	67 īf	81 āng
12 tī	26 shoi	40 hwī	54 it	68 es	82 oing
13 kō	27 tho	41 wō	55 ūk	69 ēws	83 u
14 ke	28 thi	42 we	56 a'k	70 ush	84 ow

3. *S Master List C*

1 dē	15 choi	29 lē	43 yoi	57 ēch	71 owsh
2 dew	16 vu	30 lew	44 ad	58 ewch	72 ūth
3 bu	17 vow	31 ru	45 id	59 ōv	73 a'th
4 bow	18 za	32 row	46 ōb	60 ev	74 al
5 gū	19 zī	33 mū	47 eb	61 u'z	75 īl
6 ga'	20 th'ū	34 ma'	48 u'g	62 ozh	76 ōr
7 jo	21 th'a'	35 no	49 āj	63 izh	77 er
8 ji	22 fō	36 ni	50 oij	64 āth'	78 u'm
9 pa	23 fe	37 ha	51 op	65 oith'	79 ān
10 pī	24 su'	38 hī	52 ip	66 ēf	80 oin
11 tō	25 sho	39 hwō	53 ūt	67 ewf	81 ong
12 te	26 shi	40 hwe	54 a't	68 as	82 ing
13 ku'	27 thā	41 wu'	55 uk	69 īs	83 ē
14 chā	28 thoi	42 yā	56 owk	70 ush	84 ew

4. *S Master List D*

1 da	15 chi	29 la	43 yi	57 ach	71 īsh
2 dī	16 vō	30 lī	44 ōd	58 īch	72 āth
3 bē	17 ve	31 rē	45 ed	59 ēv	73 oith
4 bew	18 zu	32 rew	46 u'b	60 ewv	74 ōl
5 gu	19 zow	33 mu	47 āg	61 iz	75 el
6 gow	20 th'a	34 mow	48 oig	62 oz	76 u'r
7 jū	21 th'ī	35 nū	49 oj	63 u'zh	77 ām
8 ja'	22 fē	36 na'	50 ij	64 ūth'	78 oim
9 pō	23 few	37 hō	51 ūp	65 a'th'	79 on
10 pe	24 so	38 he	52 a'p	66 ōf	80 in
11 tu'	25 si	39 hwu'	53 ut	67 ef	81 īng
12 kā	26 shu'	40 wā	54 owt	68 us	82 ewng
13 koi	27 thū	41 woi	55 ēk	69 ows	83 ā
14 cho	28 tha'	42 yo	56 ewk	70 ash	84 oi

B. Monosyllabic Lists

The lists given in this section are monosyllabic in structure and are specified in the Standard (20 PB lists are given).[1] They cover a range of difficulty and suit most types of system comparisons. The spread of difficulty is approximately the same in each list, and each list has nearly the same average difficulty. Furthermore, all the lists have a phonetic composition quite similar to that of the English language. Rare and unfamiliar words have been avoided as much as possible. If the experimental conditions are so chosen that the whole group of lists yields an average articulation score of about 50 percent, very few of the words will be extremely easy or extremely difficult to understand. Each of the lists contains fifty words, the smallest number that will satisfy the requirements just mentioned.

In order to avoid any difficulty with those words which will inevitably prove unfamiliar to some listeners, it is recommended that the listeners be made familiar with the meaning and spelling of all the words in the lists before testing is begun.

PB-50 List 1		*PB-50 List 2*	
1 are	26 hunt	1 awe	26 nab
2 bad	27 is	2 bait	27 need
3 bar	28 mange	3 bean	28 niece
4 bask	29 no	4 blush	29 nut
5 box	30 nook	5 bought	30 our
6 cane	31 not	6 bounce	31 perk
7 cleanse	32 pan	7 bud	32 pick
8 clove	33 pants	8 charge	33 pit
9 crash	34 pest	9 cloud	34 quart
10 creed	35 pile	10 corpse	35 rap
11 death	36 plush	11 dab	36 rib
12 deed	37 rag	12 earl	37 scythe
13 dike	38 rat	13 else	38 shoe
14 dish	39 ride	14 fate	39 sludge
15 end	40 rise	15 five	40 snuff
16 feast	41 rub	16 frog	41 start
17 fern	42 slip	17 gill	42 suck
18 folk	43 smile	18 gloss	43 tan
19 ford	44 strife	19 hire	44 tang
20 fraud	45 such	20 hit	45 them
21 fuss	46 then	21 hock	46 thrash
22 grove	47 there	22 job	47 vamp
23 heap	48 toe	23 log	48 vast
24 hid	49 use (yews)	24 moose	49 ways
25 hive	50 wheat	25 mute	50 wish

PB-50 List 3

1	ache	26	muck
2	air	27	neck
3	bald	28	nest
4	barb	29	oak
5	bead	30	path
6	cape	31	please
7	cast	32	pulse
8	check	33	rate
9	class	34	rouse
10	crave	35	shout
11	crime	36	sit
12	deck	37	size
13	dig	38	sob
14	dill	39	sped
15	drop	40	stag
16	fame	41	take
17	far	42	thrash
18	fig	43	toil
19	flush	44	trip
20	gnaw	45	turf
21	hurl	46	vow
22	jam	47	wedge
23	law	48	wharf
24	leave	49	who
25	lush	50	why

PB-50 List 4

1	bath	26	neat
2	beast	27	new
3	bee	28	oils
4	blonde	29	or
5	budge	30	peck
6	bus	31	pert
7	bush	32	pinch
8	cloak	33	pod
9	course	34	race
10	court	35	rack
11	dodge	36	rave
12	dupe	37	raw
13	earn	38	rut
14	eel	39	sage
15	fin	40	scab
16	float	41	shed
17	frown	42	shin
18	hatch	43	sketch
19	heed	44	slap
20	hiss	45	sour
21	hot	46	starve
22	how	47	strap
23	kite	48	test
24	merge	49	tick
25	move	50	touch

PB-50 List 5

1	add	22	mast
2	bathe	23	nose
3	beck	24	odds
4	black	25	owls
5	bronze	26	pass
6	browse	27	pipe
7	cheat	28	puff
8	choose	29	punt
9	curse	30	rear
10	feed	31	rind (rind)
11	flap	32	rode
12	gape	33	roe
13	good	34	scare
14	greek	35	shine
15	grudge	36	shove
16	high	37	sick
17	hill	38	sly
18	inch	39	solve
19	kid	40	thick
20	lend	41	thud
21	love	42	trade

PB-50 List 6

1	as	22	grope
2	badge	23	hitch
3	best	24	hull
4	bog	25	jag
5	chart	26	kept
6	cloth	27	leg
7	clothes	28	mash
8	cob	29	nigh
9	crib	30	ode
10	dad	31	prig
11	deep	32	prime
12	eat	33	pun
13	eyes	34	pus
14	fall	35	raise
15	fee	36	ray
16	flick	37	reap
17	flop	38	rooms
18	forge	39	rough
19	fowl	40	scan
20	gage	41	shank
21	gap	42	slouch

	PB-50 List 5				PB-50 List 6	
43 true		47 wink		43 sup		47 wait
44 tug		48 wrath		44 thigh		48 wasp
45 vase (vāce)		49 yawn		45 thus		49 wife
46 watch		50 zone		46 tongue		50 writ

	PB-50 List 7				PB-50 List 8	
1 act		26 off		1 ask		26 hum
2 aim		27 pent		2 bid		27 jell
3 am		28 phase		3 bind		28 kill
4 but		29 pig		4 bolt		29 left
5 by		30 plod		5 bored		30 lick
6 chop		31 pounce		6 calf		31 look
7 coast		32 quiz		7 catch		32 night
8 comes		33 raid		8 chant		33 pint
9 cook		34 range		9 chew		34 queen
10 cut		35 rash		10 clod		35 rest
11 dope		36 rice		11 cod		36 rhyme
12 dose		37 roar		12 crack		37 rod
13 dwarf		38 sag		13 day		38 roll
14 fake		39 scout		14 deuce		39 rope
15 fling		40 shaft		15 dumb		40 rot
16 fort		41 siege		16 each		41 shack
17 gasp		42 sin		17 ease		42 slide
18 grade		43 sledge		18 fad		43 spice
19 gun		44 sniff		19 flip		44 this
20 him		45 south		20 food		45 thread
21 jug		46 though		21 forth		46 till
22 knit		47 whiff		22 freak		47 us
23 mote		48 wire		23 frock		48 wheeze
24 mud		49 woe		24 front		49 wig
25 nine		50 woo		25 guess		50 yeast

C. Spondiac Word Lists

There are purposes for which it is desirable to use lists of words of homogeneous audibility, that is, lists in which each individual word is as difficult as each other word. Such words are most easily selected from those which have two syllables spoken with equal stress on both syllables. These words are called *spondees*. Examples: railroad, horseshoe.

The spondees have proved particularly useful in tests whose purpose is to establish accurately the amplification or power level at which speech can just be heard. These homogeneous words all reach the threshold of hearing within a narrow range of intensity and thereby serve to determine the threshold of hearing with precision.

Spondee List 1

1 airplane	12 coughdrop	23 headlight	34 shotgun
2 armchair	13 cowboy	24 hedgehog	35 sidewalk
3 backbone	14 cupcake	25 hothouse	36 stairway
4 bagpipe	15 doorstep	26 inkwell	37 sunset
5 baseball	16 dovetail	27 mousetrap	38 watchword
6 birthday	17 drawbridge	28 northwest	39 whitewash
7 blackboard	18 earthquake	29 oatmeal	40 wigwam
8 bloodhound	19 eggplant	30 outlaw	41 wildcat
9 bobwhite	20 eyebrow	31 playground	42 woodwork
10 bonbon	21 firefly	32 railroad	
11 buckwheat	22 hardware	33 shipwreck	

Spondee List 2

1 although	12 grandson	23 nutmeg	34 sundown
2 beehive	13 greyhound	24 outside	35 therefore
3 blackout	14 horseshoe	25 padlock	36 toothbrush
4 cargo	15 hotdog	26 pancake	37 vampire
5 cookbook	16 housework	27 pinball	38 washboard
6 daybreak	17 iceberg	28 platform	39 whizzband
7 doormat	18 jackknife	29 playmate	40 woodchuck
8 duckpond	19 lifeboat	30 scarecrow	41 workshop
9 eardrum	20 midway	31 schoolboy	42 yardstick
10 farewell	21 mishap	32 soybean	
11 footstool	22 mushroom	33 starlight	

D. Sentence Lists

In testing communication equipment, sentence articulation has only a limited use. As pointed out above, the intelligibility of sentences is favored to a considerable degree by the psychological factors of meaning, context, rhythm, motivated interest, etc. As a consequence, under most test conditions articulation scores obtained with lists of sentences are so high that communication systems must differ considerably before a substantial difference in the scores is obtained. The influence of these psychological factors on the scores makes the results difficult to analyze and to interpret. Furthermore, since the listeners easily remember the sentences, a very large number of sentences is required in an extensive testing program.

There are, nevertheless, special circumstances in which sentence lists are of value. For example, in testing the intelligibility of telephone talkers, the utterance of a sentence provides a sample of a more complex type of action than does speaking single words. Rate, inflection, stress pattern, and maintenance of loudness level can be tested adequately only with sentence material.

There are several forms of sentence tests. In one form of test the listener is required to respond to questions or commands by an appropriate word or phrase. Each sentence is then scored as either right or wrong, depending on whether or not it appears that the listener has understood the meaning. In another type of test the listener is required to record the sentence as read to him. The articulation score is then based upon the number of key words correctly recorded by the listener, this method providing a more objective measure of the words actually heard. In the following lists of 20 sentences each, the five key words to be scored in each sentence are italicized. An effort has been made to avoid clichés, proverbs, and other stereotyped constructions, as well as the too-frequent use of any one word.

List 1

1. The *birch canoe slid* on the *smooth planks*.
2. *Glue* the *sheet* to the *dark blue background*.
3. *It's easy* to *tell* the *depth* of a *well*.
4. These *days* a *chicken leg* is a *rare dish*.
5. *Rice* is *often served* in *round bowls*.
6. *John* is *just* a *dope* of *long standing*.
7. The *juice* of *lemons makes fine punch*.
8. The *chest* was *thrown beside* the *parked truck*.
9. The *hogs* were *fed chopped corn* and *garbage*.
10. A *cry* in the *night chills my marrow*.
11. *Blow high* or *low* but *follow* the *notes*.
12. *Four hours* of *steady work faced* us.
13. A *large size* in *stockings* is *hard* to *sell*.
14. *Many* are *taught* to *breathe through* the *nose*.
15. *Ten days' leave* is *coming up*.
16. The *Frenchman* was *shot when* the *sun rose*.
17. A *rod* is *used* to *catch pink salmon*.
18. He *smoked* a *pipe until* it *burned* his *tongue*.
19. The *light flashed* the *message* to the *eyes* of the *watchers*.
20. The *source* of the *huge river* is the *clear spring*.

List 2

1. *Death marks* the *end* of *our efforts*.
2. The *gift* of *speech* was *denied* the *poor child*.
3. *Never kill* a *snake* with your *bare hands*.
4. *Kick* the *ball straight* and *follow through*.
5. *Help* the *woman get back* to her *feet*.
6. *Put* a *dot* on the *i* and *sharpen* the *point*.
7. The *hum* of *bees made Jim sleepy*.

8. A *pint* of *tea helps* to *pass* the *evening.*
9. *Smoky fires lack flame* and *heat.*
10. The *soft cushion broke* the *man's fall.*
11. *While* he *spoke,* the *others took* their *leave.*
12. The *core* of the *apple housed* a *green worm.*
13. The *salt breeze came across* from the *sea.*
14. The *girl* at the *booth sold fifty bonds.*
15. The *purple pup gnawed* a *hole* in the *sock.*
16. The *fish twisted* and *turned* on the *bent hook.*
17. A *lot* of *fat slows* a *mile racer.*
18. *Press* the *pants* and *sew* a *button* on the *vest.*
19. The *swan dive* was *far short* of *perfect.*
20. *James tried* his *best* to *gain ground.*

List 3

1. For *quick cleaning, buy* a *hemp rug.*
2. The *beauty* of the *view stunned* the *young boy.*
3. *Two blue herring swam* in the *sink.*
4. *Her purse* was *full* of *useless trash.*
5. The *colt reared* and *threw* the *sick rider.*
6. It *snowed, rained,* and *hailed* the *same morning.*
7. An *eel tastes sweet* but *looks awful.*
8. *Read verse out loud* for *pleasure.*
9. *Hoist* the *load* to *your left shoulder.*
10. He was *bribed* to *cause* the *new motor* to *fail.*
11. *Take* the *winding path* to *reach* the *lake.*
12. *Red pencil* the *words spelled wrong.*
13. A *plump hen* is *well fitted* for *stew.*
14. The *tempo* was *slow* but *picked up soon.*
15. *Note closely* the *size* of the *gas tank.*
16. *Haste may cause* a *loss* of *power.*
17. The *coast* was *guarded* by *field guns* in the *hills.*
18. *Cold, damp rooms* are *bad* for *romance.*
19. A *true saint* is *lean* but *quite human.*
20. *Wipe* the *grease off* your *dirty face.*

List 4

1. *Mend* the *coat before* you *go out.*
2. The *wrist* was *badly strained* and *hung limp.*
3. The *stray cat bore green kittens.*
4. A *pest may be* a *man* or a *disease.*
5. The *coy girl gave* no *clear response.*
6. The *meal* was *cooked before* the *bell rang.*
7. *What joy there is* in *living.*
8. A *king ruled* the *state* in the *early days.*
9. The *ship* was *torn apart* on the *sharp reef.*
10. *Soldiers poured* through the *wide breach* in the *wall.*
11. The *deep cave wound left* then *straight.*
12. *He quoted* the *book by* the *hour.*

13. A *frog grunts loudly* if he *wants food.*
14. *Sickness kept* him *home* the *third week.*
15. *Give her* the *gun,* he *shouted then.*
16. The *broad road shimmered* in the *hot sun.*
17. The *lazy cow lay* in the *cool grass.*
18. *Joe blew* his *bass horn wildly.*
19. *Lift* the *square stone over* the *fence.*
20. The *rope* will *bind* the *seven mice* at *once.*

List 5

1. *Hop over* the *fence* and *plunge in.*
2. A *dead dog* is no *use* for *hunting ducks.*
3. This *soup tastes like stewed buzzard.*
4. The *ape grinned* and *gnashed* his *yellow teeth.*
5. The *friendly gang* is *gone* from the *drug store.*
6. *Mesh wire keeps chicks inside.*
7. *Sue* the *bank under* a *false name.*
8. The *frosty air passed through* the *coat.*
9. *He drank* a *coke* with *rum therein.*
10. The *crooked maze failed* to *fool* the *mouse.*
11. *Print* her *name beside* the *plain cross.*
12. *Adding fast leads* to *wrong sums.*
13. The *show* was a *huge flop* at the *very start.*
14. The *berry hung* and *swayed* on the *bare stem.*
15. *Sam loves* his *sour* and *grouchy wife.*
16. *Do* the *task quickly* or *you fail.*
17. A *saw* is a *tool used* for *making boards.*
18. *She horned* in *on* the *gossip* of the *girls.*
19. The *plague killed thirty cows* in a *week.*
20. *Weeds stop* the *plants* from *getting big.*

List 6

1. The *wagon moved* on *well oiled wheels.*
2. The *fleas hopped* on *both* the *cat* and the *chair.*
3. *Never buy* a *blind pig* in a *bag.*
4. *March* the *soldiers past* the *next hill.*
5. A *cup* of *sugar makes sweet fudge.*
6. *Place* a *rosebush near* the *porch steps.*
7. *George gave* his *sister* a *lot* of *coin.*
8. *Both lost* their *lives* in the *raging storm.*
9. *We talked* of the *side show* in the *circus.*
10. *Use* a *pencil* to *write* the *rough draft.*
11. He *ran half way* to the *hardware store.*
12. *Eight cops visit* the *new cook.*
13. A *cute baby* is *not shy* or *cross.*
14. The *clock struck* to *mark* the *third period.*
15. *College girls* are *full* of *zip* and *verve.*
16. A *small creek cut across* the *field.*
17. *Boys thrive* on *rough games* and *candy.*

18. *Cars* and *busses stalled* in *snow drifts.*
19. The *set* of *china hit* the *floor* with a *crash.*
20. *May* is a *grand season* for *hikes* on the *road.*

List 7

1. The *dune rose from* the *edge* of the *water.*
2. *Those words* were the *cue* for the *actor* to *leave.*
3. *Farmers hate* to *use* a *hoe* or *rake.*
4. A *yacht slid around* the *point* into the *bay.*
5. The *two met while playing* on the *sand.*
6. *It's foolish* to *make* a *pass* at *Jane.*
7. The *ink stain dried* on the *finished page.*
8. *Fail once* on this *job* and *be discharged.*
9. *Scotch can't* be *bought today* at *all.*
10. The *walled town* was *seized without* a *fight.*
11. The *lease ran out* in *sixteen weeks.*
12. *They pulled* a *fast one* on the *deacon.*
13. The *lewd face stared out* of the *window.*
14. A *fine starry night greets* the *pair.*
15. *I* am *speaking dumb* and *vain words.*
16. A *tame squirrel makes* a *nice pet.*
17. The *throb* of the *car woke* the *sleeping cop.*
18. *George* the *second* was *then queen* of the *May.*
19. *Great men are* the *worst husbands.*
20. The *heart beat strongly* and with *firm strokes.*

List 8

1. The *pearl* was *worn* in a *thin silver ring.*
2. The *fruit peel* was *cut* in *thick slices.*
3. The *Navy attacked* the *big task force.*
4. *See* the *cat glaring* at the *scared mouse.*
5. The *crest* of the *wave* was *eight feet below.*
6. *There* are *more* than *two factors here.*
7. *Breed dogs until* you *win* the *prize.*
8. The *climb* was *warm* and *done without water.*
9. *Ann tore* her *blonde hair* in *anger.*
10. The *hat brim* was *wide* and *too droopy.*
11. *Girls chat* and *gossip all day.*
12. The *lawyer tried* to *lose his case.*
13. The *lash curled around* the *fence post.*
14. *Cut* the *pie into large parts.*
15. *Put* a *big crawling bug* in her *ear.*
16. The *bait* was *snapped* and the *black fox captured.*
17. *Men strive* but *seldom get rich.*
18. *Always close* the *barn door tight.*
19. He *lay prone* and *hardly moved* a *limb.*
20. *Soothe* the *child* with *cocaine* and *cough drops.*

17·8 Scoring Tests

Neither listeners nor talkers should score the finished tests. The instructions to the graders should stress the fact that the words are to be scored for *sound*, not for *spelling*. Thus if "blue" was the word read, *blue, blew,* and *bloo* are all equally correct. On the other hand, "wear" is not correct for *where,* or "chose" for *choose.*

17·9 Analysis of Data

The most convenient form of analysis for data such as these is the statistical method known as *analysis of variance.*

When an attempt is made to repeat articulation tests under identical conditions, the articulation scores obtained are usually somewhat different. If a test is repeated a large number of times, scores of various magnitudes will be obtained. A frequency distribution of these scores typically shows that the scores occur most frequently around some central value, and that marked deviations from this central value are relatively infrequent. Unless the mean score is very high or very low the scores tend to be distributed according to the normal law of error.

Since different articulation scores are obtained even when the same communication system is tested over and over under the "same" conditions, it is obvious that an obtained difference between the mean (average) score of system A and the mean score of system B may be caused by "errors" of random sampling alone. The obtained scores constitute only a sample from a universe defined by the distribution of a very large number of scores all obtained under the "same" conditions of testing. The averages of successive samples drawn from this universe of scores will differ. Let us assume here a process of unlimited random selection of scores from an infinitely large set of data. The statistical problem then consists in determining the relative frequency with which the obtained differences between the means of the scores will occur. The detailed steps in the statistical procedure are those of the *analysis of variance,* and the fundamental notions involved in this type of analysis will now be discussed superficially.[2]

[2] A more complete discussion of this statistical method will be found in many of the standard advanced statistical texts: E. F. Lindquist, *Statistical analysis in educational research,* Houghton Mifflin (1940); R. A. Fisher, *Statistical methods for research workers,* Oliver and Boyd (1944). Modern computer programs are available for taking the drudgery out of "analysis of variance."

It can be demonstrated that the variance (square of the standard deviation) (see Chapter 10 for a definition of standard deviation) of a large sample which consists of a number of equal groups can be analyzed into two components. These components are: the mean of the variances within the groups, and the variance of the group means.

For example, suppose that we have a very large number of experimental points with a standard deviation σ_L and a mean M_L (see Fig. 17·2a). From this mass of data we select a number of subgroups of data. Each group will have a mean M_ν and a standard deviation σ_ν. Here, ν is assigned integral values; that is, M_1 and σ_1 are the mean and standard deviation for group 1, M_2 and σ_2 for group 2, etc. It will be more convenient in this discussion to deal with the square of the standard deviation (called *variance*) than with the standard deviation itself.

We can form a distribution curve from the variances of the subgroups and assign to it a mean M_{vs} and a variance $\sigma_{vs}{}^2$. We can form also a distribution curve from the means of the subgroups and assign to it a mean M_{Ms} and a variance $\sigma_{Ms}{}^2$. From M_{vs} and $\sigma_{Ms}{}^2$ we can obtain two independent estimates of the variance of the population from which the total sample was drawn, that is, $\sigma_L{}^2$.

The hypothesis to be tested is that all the subgroups of the total sample are drawn from the same population. If the hypothesis is true, the two estimates of the population variance should differ only by chance. For subgroups of a given size, tables are available which give the manner in which the *ratios* of the variances of two subgroups drawn from the same population are distributed. Consequently, for samples of a given size, it is known (from these tables) how frequently a given value of F (the ratio of the two variances) will be obtained by chance alone. In the detailed example described below the method is slightly more involved than that outlined above. However, the basic logic is the same.

The test papers, as they come from the graders, will show the number of words heard correctly by each listener out of the fifty read. Multiplying the average of the scores on a fifty-word test by 2 will give, of course, the average percentage score for that particular test. It will then be necessary to make up another table similar to Table 17·1 inserting in place of the test

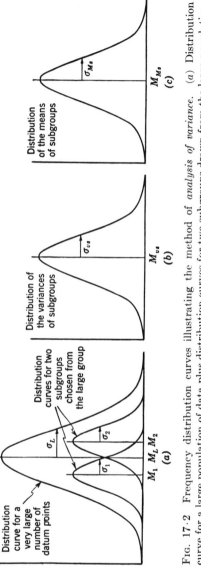

FIG. 17·2 Frequency distribution curves illustrating the method of *analysis of variance*. (*a*) Distribution curve for a large population of data plus distribution curves for two subgroups drawn from the large population. (*b*) Distribution curve of the variances (σ^2) of subgroups.   (*c*) Distribution curve of the means (μ_v) of subgroups.

numbers the average percentage scores obtained on those tests. When the table has been filled in, we may determine the relative standings of the three systems by averaging the percentage scores by horizontal row. If these averages are separated from one another by 20 or 30 percent, no further analysis need be made, since differences of that size among the means of eight or more tests are known to be extremely rare as a result of chance fluctuation only, provided the testing has been done carefully. Such unequivocal results are not to be expected most of the time, however. Thus, a more complex method of analysis must be used to determine whether the differences in the mean scores obtained on the different systems could be due to chance rather than actual differences between the communication systems.

Let us assume that one new system has been compared with the two standard systems in a series of three blocks of tests. The tests have been scored, the average percentage scores obtained, and the table filled in as described above. Table 17·2 is an example of such an array of data ready to be analyzed.

TABLE 17·2

Block	1				2				3			
Talker	A	B	C	D	A	B	C	D	A	B	C	D
System 1. High fidelity	98·7	90·7	86·7	86·0	90·0	87·3	76·0	78·0	90·7	83·3	77·3	82·0
2. Reference	60·7	61·3	52·7	64·0	51·3	60·0	54·7	63·3	58·7	68·7	40·7	54·0
3. New type	77·3	76·0	64·7	67·3	78·0	78·0	44·0	73·3	76·7	60·0	52·7	76·7

Averaging of the data of Table $17 \cdot 2$ by horizontal row gives the following average word articulation scores for the three systems.

System	Percent Word Articulation
1. High fidelity	85.6
2. Reference	57.5
3. New type	68.7

It is evident that the new system (3) is not as good as the high fidelity system (1), but is probably better than the reference system (2), and by only about 11 percent. Furthermore, examination of the scores obtained on these two systems shows that system 3 was not *always* better than system 2, nor was system 1 *always* better than system 3. Because of this overlapping of scores, it cannot be concluded without further analysis that the difference between systems 2 and 3 is due to significant differences in the effectiveness of the systems and not to the many irrelevant factors that become involved in this type of test.

For an adequate analysis of such data, a number of computations must be made and several new tables constructed from the table of scores (Table $17 \cdot 2$). Table $17 \cdot 3$ shows the computations needed, and Table $17 \cdot 4$ the values obtained when the data from Table $17 \cdot 2$ are substituted in Table $17 \cdot 3$.

TABLE 17·3

X	= any score in the table of scores
$X_{\text{No. 1}}$	= any score obtained on system 1
X_{A}	= any score obtained by talker A
X_1	= any score obtained in block 1
$X_{\text{No. 2C}}$	= any score made on system 2 by talker C
$X_{\text{No. 3B2}}$	= the score made on system 3 by talker B in block 2
$\sum$	= summation
(1) $\sum X$	= the sum of all the scores in the table of scores
(2) $\left(\sum X \right)^2$	= the square of (1)
(3) $\left(\sum X \right)^2 / 36$	= (2) divided by the number of scores in the table
(4) $\sum X^2$	= the sum of the squares of all the scores in the table of scores

TABLE 17·3 (Continued)

(5) Talker A   B   C   D $\sum$

System

	A	B	C	D	$\sum$
1	$\sum_{1}^{3} X_{\text{No. 1A}}{}^{*}$	$\sum_{1}^{3} X_{\text{No. 1B}}$	$\sum_{1}^{3} X_{\text{No. 1C}}$	$\sum_{1}^{3} X_{\text{No. 1D}}$	$\sum_{A}^{D}\sum_{1}^{3} X_{\text{No. 1}}$
2	$\sum_{1}^{3} X_{\text{No. 2A}}$	$\sum_{1}^{3} X_{\text{No. 2B}}$	$\sum_{1}^{3} X_{\text{No. 2C}}$	$\sum_{1}^{3} X_{\text{No. 2D}}$	$\sum_{A}^{D}\sum_{1}^{3} X_{\text{No. 2}}$
3	$\sum_{1}^{3} X_{\text{No. 3A}}$	$\sum_{1}^{3} X_{\text{No. 3B}}$	$\sum_{1}^{3} X_{\text{No. 3C}}$	$\sum_{1}^{3} X_{\text{No. 3D}}$	$\sum_{A}^{D}\sum_{1}^{3} X_{\text{No. 3}}$

$$\sum \quad \sum_{\text{No. 1}}^{\text{No. 3}}\sum_{1}^{3} X_A \quad \sum_{\text{No. 1}}^{\text{No. 3}}\sum_{1}^{3} X_B \quad \sum_{\text{No. 1}}^{\text{No. 3}}\sum_{1}^{3} X_C \quad \sum_{\text{No. 1}}^{\text{No. 3}}\sum_{1}^{3} X_D \quad \sum_{\text{No. 1}}^{\text{No. 3}}\sum_{A}^{D}\sum_{1}^{3} X$$

$$= (1) \text{ above}$$

(6) $\sum \overline{S \times T}^{2}$ = the sum of the squares of all the values in (5) within the box (See example of Table 17·4.)

(7) $\sum \overline{S \times T}^{2}/3$ = (6) divided by the number of scores summed for each entry in (5)

(8) Talker A   B   C   D $\sum$

Block

	A	B	C	D	$\sum$
1	$\sum_{\text{No. 1}}^{\text{No. 3}} X_{A1}\dagger$	$\sum_{\text{No. 1}}^{\text{No. 3}} X_{B1}$	$\sum_{\text{No. 1}}^{\text{No. 3}} X_{C1}$	$\sum_{\text{No. 1}}^{\text{No. 3}} X_{D1}$	$\sum_{A}^{D}\sum_{\text{No. 1}}^{\text{No. 3}} X_{1}$
2	$\sum_{\text{No. 1}}^{\text{No. 3}} X_{A2}$	$\sum_{\text{No. 1}}^{\text{No. 3}} X_{B2}$	$\sum_{\text{No. 1}}^{\text{No. 3}} X_{C2}$	$\sum_{\text{No. 1}}^{\text{No. 3}} X_{D2}$	$\sum_{A}^{D}\sum_{\text{No. 1}}^{\text{No. 3}} X_{2}$
3	$\sum_{\text{No. 1}}^{\text{No. 3}} X_{A3}$	$\sum_{\text{No. 1}}^{\text{No. 3}} X_{B3}$	$\sum_{\text{No. 1}}^{\text{No. 3}} X_{C3}$	$\sum_{\text{No. 1}}^{\text{No. 3}} X_{D3}$	$\sum_{A}^{D}\sum_{\text{No. 1}}^{\text{No. 3}} X_{3}$

$$\sum \quad \sum_{1}^{3}\sum_{\text{No. 1}}^{\text{No. 3}} X_A \quad \sum_{1}^{3}\sum_{\text{No. 1}}^{\text{No. 3}} X_B \quad \sum_{1}^{3}\sum_{\text{No. 1}}^{\text{No. 3}} X_C \quad \sum_{1}^{3}\sum_{\text{No. 1}}^{\text{No. 3}} X_D \quad \sum_{A}^{D}\sum_{1}^{3}\sum_{\text{No. 1}}^{\text{No. 3}} X$$

$$= (1) \text{ above}$$

(9) $\sum \overline{T \times B}^{2}$ = the sum of the squares of all the values in (8) within the box

* That is, the summation of the three scores made on system 1 by talker A.
† That is, the summation of the three scores made by talker A in block 1.

TABLE 17·3   (*Continued*)

(10) $\sum \overline{T \times B}^2/3$ = (9) divided by 3, the number of scores summed for each entry in (8)

(11) System   1   2   3 $\sum$

Block

	1	2	3	$\sum$
1	$\sum_{A}^{D} X_{1\,\text{No. 1}}\ddagger$	$\sum_{A}^{D} X_{1\,\text{No. 2}}$	$\sum_{A}^{D} X_{1\,\text{No. 3}}$	$\sum_{\text{No. 1}}^{\text{No. 3}} \sum_{A}^{D} X_1$
2	$\sum_{A}^{D} X_{2\,\text{No. 1}}$	$\sum_{A}^{D} X_{2\,\text{No. 2}}$	$\sum_{A}^{D} X_{2\,\text{No. 2}}$	$\sum_{\text{No. 1}}^{\text{No. 3}} \sum_{A}^{D} X_2$
3	$\sum_{A}^{D} X_{3\,\text{No. 1}}$	$\sum_{A}^{D} X_{3\,\text{No. 2}}$	$\sum_{A}^{D} X_{3\,\text{No. 3}}$	$\sum_{\text{No. 1}}^{\text{No. 3}} \sum_{A}^{D} X_3$

$$\sum \quad \sum_{1}^{3}\sum_{A}^{D} X_{\text{No. 1}} \quad \sum_{1}^{3}\sum_{A}^{D} X_{\text{No. 2}} \quad \sum_{1}^{3}\sum_{A}^{D} X_{\text{No. 3}} \quad \sum_{\text{No. 1}}^{\text{No. 3}}\sum_{1}^{3}\sum_{A}^{D} X = \text{(1) above}$$

(12) $\sum \overline{S \times B}^2$ = the sum of squares of all the values in (11) within the box

(13) $\sum \overline{S \times B}^2/4$ = (12) divided by 4, the number of scores summed for each entry in (11)

(14) $\sum S^2$ = the sum of the *squared* system totals found in (5) or (11);

i.e., $\left(\sum X_{\text{No. 1}}\right)^2 + \left(\sum X_{\text{No. 2}}\right)^2 + \left(\sum X_{\text{No. 3}}\right)^2$

(15) $\sum S^2/12$ = (14) divided by 12, the number of scores summed for each *system* total

(16) $\sum T^2$ = the sum of the squared *talker* totals found in (5) or (8);

i.e., $\left(\sum X_{\text{A}}\right)^2 + \left(\sum X_{\text{B}}\right)^2 + \left(\sum X_{\text{C}}\right)^2 + \left(\sum X_{\text{D}}\right)^2$

(17) $\sum T^2/9$ = (16) divided by 9, the number of scores summed for each *talker* total

(18) $\sum \bar{B}^2$ = the sum of the squared *block* totals found in (8) or (11); i.e., $\left(\sum X_1\right)^2 + \left(\sum X_2\right)^2 + \left(\sum X_3\right)^2$

(19) $\sum \bar{B}^2/12$ = (18) divided by 12, the number of scores summed for each *block* total

‡ That is, the summation of the four scores made on system 1 in block 1.

TABLE 17·3 (Continued)

(20) Analysis of variance

Source of Variance	Degrees of Freedom (df)	Sums of Squares (SS)	Mean Square (variance)	F	P§
Systems	(Number of systems) − 1	(15) − (3)	SS of Systems / df of Systems	Systems mean square / Error mean square	
Talkers	(Number of talkers) − 1	(17) − (3)	SS of Talkers / df of Talkers	Talkers mean square / Error mean square	
Blocks	(Number of blocks) − 1	(19) − (3)	(Similarly divide each sum of squares by its own degrees of freedom.)	(Similarly divide each mean square by the Error mean square.)	
S × T	(Systems df) × (talkers df)	(7) − (15) − (17) + (3)			
T × B	(Talkers df) × (blocks df)	(10) − (17) − (19) + (3)			
S × B	(Systems df) × (blocks df)	(13) − (15) − (19) + (3)			
Total	(Number of scores in the table) − 1	(4) − (3)	(Do not compute for Total)		
Error	(df of the Total) − (all df's above it)	(SS of the Total) − (SS of all above it)	SS of Error / df of Error		

§ P = probability.   See text.

TABLE 17·4

(Table 17·3 filled in with data from Table 17·2)

(1) ΣX = 2541.5   (3) $(\Sigma X)^2/36$ = 179 422.84

(2) $(\Sigma X)^2$ = 6 459 222.25   (4) ΣX^2 = 186 697.67

(5) Talker System

	A	B	C	D	Σ
1	279.4	261.3	240.0	246.0	1026.7
2	170.7	190.0	148.1	181.3	690.1
3	232.0	214.0	161.4	217.3	824.7
Σ	682.1	665.3	549.5	644.6	2541.5

(6) $\Sigma S \times T^2$ = 557 389.09   (7) $\Sigma S \times T^2/3$ = 185 796.36

(8) Talker Block

	A	B	C	D	Σ
1	236.7	228.0	204.1	217.3	886.1
2	219.3	225.3	174.7	214.6	833.9
3	226.1	212.0	170.7	212.7	821.5
Σ	682.1	665.3	549.5	644.6	2541.5

(9) $\Sigma T \times B^2$ = 542 757.81   (10) $\Sigma T \times B^2/3$ = 180 919.27

(11) System Block

	1	2	3	Σ
1	362.1	238.7	285.3	886.1
2	331.3	229.3	273.3	833.9
3	333.3	222.1	266.1	821.5
Σ	1026.7	690.1	824.7	2541.5

(12) $\Sigma S \times B^2$ = 737 747.77   (16) ΣT^2 = 1 625 343.91

(13) $\Sigma S \times B^2/4$ = 184 436.94   (17) $\Sigma T^2/9$ = 180 593.77

(14) ΣS^2 = 2 210 480.99   (18) ΣB^2 = 2 155 424.67

(15) $\Sigma S^2/12$ = 184 206.75   (19) $\Sigma B^2/12$ = 179 618.72

(20) Analysis of variance

Source	df	SS	Mean Square (variance)	F	Probability*
Systems	2	4783.91	2391.96	53.00	< 0.01
Talkers	3	1170.93	390.31	8.65	< 0.01
Blocks	2	195.88	97.94	2.17	> 0.05
$S \times T$	6	418.68	69.78	1.55	> 0.05
$T \times B$	6	129.62	21.60	< 1	> 0.05
$S \times B$	4	34.31	8.58	< 1	> 0.05
Total	35	7274.83			
Error	12	541.50	45.13	1	

* See text.

It must be pointed out that the numerical values of the divisors in steps (3), (7), (10), (13), (15), (17), and (19) and the number of degrees of freedom in step (20) are determined by the numbers of systems, talkers, and blocks in the test series. The divisors will change in accordance with changes in the numbers of systems, talkers, and blocks. An analysis of a series testing *four* systems using *five* talkers in *six* blocks would use as divisors:

Step	Divisor
(3)	120
(7)	6
(10)	4
(13)	5
(15)	30
(17)	24
(19)	20

The degrees of freedom in step (20) would then be as follows:

Source	Degrees of Freedom (df)
Systems	3
Talkers	4
Blocks	5
$S \times T$	12
$T \times B$	20
$S \times B$	15
Total	119
Error	60

The final step of the analysis after the F values have been computed, step (20), is to determine whether the variables involved (systems, talkers, blocks, and their interactions) have produced significant effects upon the scores obtained in the tests. To be considered statistically *significant,* a difference between two scores (or a ratio between two estimates of variance) must be of such magnitude that the probability of the occurrence, simply as the result of the fluctuations of random sampling of a difference (or ratio) as large as or larger than the one actually obtained, is very small. More rigorously we say that a score must have associated with it a relatively small probability of occurrence from errors due to random sampling alone. It is a statistical convention to assume that the occurrence of an event, expected only one time in a hundred by chance alone, is due to some factor other than chance. The occurrence of an event which is expected to occur only five times in a hundred by chance alone, although not usually considered statistically significant, is regarded as suggestive of significant factors. The values of the F ratio which will be exceeded only 1 percent of the time and those which will be exceeded only 5 percent of the time under a given set of conditions have been tabulated in standard statistical texts. An abbreviated form of such a table giving 1 percent and 5 percent values of the F ratio is shown in Table 17·5. In that table, the larger variance may have 2, 3, 4, or 6 degrees of freedom, whereas the smaller variance is restricted to 12 degrees of freedom. These values were chosen to satisfy our needs under (20) of Table 17·4. It is possible, therefore, by use of such F tables, with the appropriate numbers of degrees of freedom, to determine whether a given F ratio is likely or unlikely as a result of chance fluctuations only.

In step (20) in Table 17·4, the *Error* mean square or *Error* variance is arbitrarily taken to be the smaller variance in all cases (i.e., 45.13 is smaller than the first four variances above it). Because the $T \times B$ and $S \times B$ variances are smaller than 45, F ratios for them are smaller than unity and have not been computed. The critical values of the F ratio for this particular problem are therefore to be found in the row of a suitable F table in which the smaller variance has 12 degrees of freedom. Their location in that row is determined by the number of degrees of freedom in the larger variance.

When we compare the F ratios of Table 17·5 with the ratios computed in step (20), Table 17·4, we find that the F ratio for *Systems* (53.00) is much larger than the corresponding critical 1 percent value (6.93), and the F ratio for *Talkers* (8.65) is somewhat larger than its corresponding critical 1 percent value (5.95). Both F ratios are therefore significant at the 1 percent level or better; that is, differences of the sizes obtained would occur much less than 1 percent of the time because of chance alone. We may

TABLE 17·5 TABLE OF F RATIOS

df for Smaller Variance	P	*df* for Larger Variance			
		2	3	4	6
12	1%	6.93	5.95	5.41	4.82
	5%	3.88	3.49	3.26	3.00

feel confident in concluding that the systems and the voices were in fact significantly different as far as their effect on articulation is concerned. None of the four other F ratios of step (20) of Table 17·4 (the two computed and the two smaller than unity) is significant at even the 5 percent level. We are therefore adequately justified in concluding that the sources of variation corresponding to those ratios were not particularly effective in determining differences in the test scores.

Since the two standard systems introduced into the experiment differ so greatly in efficiency, a significant F ratio would be expected for *Systems*. One more step is necessary, therefore, to determine whether the new system is significantly better than the inferior system or significantly worse than the high fidelity system. With the aid of a t table, to be found in any standard statistical text, the significance of these differences can easily be tested. It is first necessary to find the 1 percent value of t associated with the number of degrees of freedom in the *Error* variance of step (20). If we substitute the appropriate values in the following formula we obtain a value for "d":

$$d \equiv t_{1\%} \sqrt{\frac{2 \times Error \text{ variance}}{\text{Number of scores obtained on any one system}}}$$

If we obtain scores from two systems and the difference between these scores is d, or greater, the test is significant at the 1 percent level. That is to say, when there is *no* real difference between two systems, a value as large as or larger than d will occur by chance only 1 percent of the time. This also means that the difference between two systems has to be at least as large as d to be detected reliably.

For the values in Table 17·4,

$$d = 3.055 \sqrt{\frac{2 \times 45.13}{12}} = 8.4$$

Since the difference obtained between system 2 (the reference system) and the new system, 3, was 11.2 percent (larger than the critical value of 8.4 percent), it may be concluded that the new system is significantly better than the reference system. Obviously, it is significantly worse than the high fidelity system.

Although the main purpose of the experiment and the statistical analysis has been achieved in the last calculation, a good deal of other important information can be derived from step (20) which will throw light on the adequacy of the whole testing procedure.

If the results obtained on the three systems are to have general validity, it is important that the talkers constitute a reasonably representative sample of the population that will ultimately use the equipment. Should the *Talkers* variance prove insignificant, all the data might almost as well have been obtained on a single talker. A single talker is obviously not a representative sample of a population within which significant differences have been shown to exist. Much previous experience with talkers indicates that it is very likely that a given group of them will show a significant variance. If this should not occur, however, the experiment should be repeated with a new group.

The variance due to *Blocks* should ordinarily not be significant. If it is, a comparison of the block means will show whether there were systematic changes in the scores from block to block. If the listening crew or the talkers were not over the learning period, the *Block means* will show a rising trend. A systematic drift in the characteristics of the noise may also produce a systematic trend in the *Block means*. If the different blocks are run on different days, irregular but significant differences in *Block means* may appear. Unless the differences among *Block means* are very large, however, (10 or 15 percent), they may be disregarded. If the differences are large, every effort should be made to determine the cause and eliminate it.

The *Systems* × *Talkers* interaction variance is a fairly important datum derived from the experiment. If significant, it indicates that the differences among the systems were not quite the same for different talkers; for example, the signal-to-noise ratio in the system might have been more favorable for one talker than for another as a result of a better fit of the mouthpiece of the microphone. Small, statistically insignificant differences may again be disregarded. Large differences call for further experimentation using more talkers, with a view to determining the factors producing the interaction and eliminating them if possible.

Should the *Talkers* × *Blocks* variance or the *Systems* × *Blocks* variance prove significant, further investigation of the various means is necessary in order to determine the exact source of the deviation. It is sometimes quite possible to account for deviant scores. One talker with laryngitis one day can easily produce a large $T \times B$ variance, as can an unstable talker or one inade-

quately trained. The noise leaking into a sound-powered system through an earphone accidentally exposed during several tests on the system will depress the scores for the system in that block of tests and produce a large $S \times B$ variance. If such simple explanations can be found for the observed deviations, it may be necessary to repeat only a single block of tests. It will not usually be possible, however, to account for the variations at a later time, and, if they are very large, the whole test series might better be repeated, with more careful checking of the possible extraneous sources of variability.

17·10 Simplified Articulation Test

There are times when the elaborate test procedure outlined in the previous sections of this chapter may prove too cumbersome and inefficient. Such instances occur when the investigation involves numerous permutations of experimental conditions. It is then expeditious to devise short-cut methods.

One simplified method which has proved successful[1] involves a single individual. The test words are recorded phonographically by means of high fidelity equipment. The person conducting the test has before him a written list of the words, which are also recorded on the phonograph record. These words are kept covered with a blank card. The subject listens to each word in turn, and *after* he has both heard the word and decided what he thinks it is, he moves the blank card so as to uncover the correct word. He then checks whether or not he has heard the word correctly. Good results have been obtained by employing a single list of test words used over and over. This procedure obviously requires care and honest judgment on the part of the experimenter, but observations have shown that the method can be made to yield valid results. Since the experimenter, instead of writing down the words he hears, merely checks his correct responses, he is able to work at a fast pace, and the speed-up in the articulation testing is considerable.

Although a single list of one hundred words, of which several recordings have been made in altered sequences, may prove adequate, the generality of the method can be extended by adding other recorded lists and by using a group of different announcers to record the words.

The adequacy of a single list is enhanced if the words are made to resemble one another as closely as possible and at the same time to sample the various sounds of speech. Two one-hundred-

word lists, in which fifteen vowels and diphthongs are represented by six words each, are given in Table 17·6. The different consonant sounds are distributed among these ninety words. The remaining ten words of each hundred are used to sample some of the compound consonants.

TABLE 17·6

R List 1

1 aisle	21 dame	41 jack	61 rack	81 still
2 barb	22 done	42 jam	62 ram	82 tale
3 barge	23 dub	43 law	63 ring	83 tame
4 bark	24 feed	44 lawn	64 rip	84 toil
5 baste	25 feet	45 lisle	65 rub	85 ton
6 bead	26 file	46 live	66 run	86 trill
7 beet	27 five	47 loon	67 sale	87 tub
8 beige	28 foil	48 loop	68 same	88 vouch
9 boil	29 fume	49 mess	69 shod	89 vow
10 choke	30 fuse	50 met	70 shop	90 whack
11 chore	31 get	51 neat	71 should	91 wham
12 cod	32 good	52 need	72 shrill	92 woe
13 coil	33 guess	53 oil	73 sing	93 woke
14 coon	34 hews	54 ouch	74 sip	94 would
15 coop	35 hive	55 paw	75 skill	95 yaw
16 cop	36 hod	56 pawn	76 soil	96 yawn
17 couch	37 hood	57 pews	77 soon	97 yes
18 could	38 hop	58 poke	78 soot	98 yet
19 cow	39 how	59 pour	79 soup	99 zing
20 dale	40 huge	60 pure	80 spill	100 zip

R List 2

1 ball	21 dial	41 hen	61 peeve	81 tap
2 bar	22 dig	42 huff	62 phase	82 them
3 bob	23 dine	43 hush	63 peep	83 then
4 bong	24 ditch	44 jar	64 pull	84 tile
5 book	25 doubt	45 job	65 put	85 tine
6 boot	26 dowel	46 joy	66 raid	86 tong
7 booth	27 drain	47 joys	67 raze	87 toot
8 bout	28 em	48 kirk	68 rich	88 tooth
9 bowel	29 en	49 leap	69 rig	89 tout
10 boy	30 fade	50 leave	70 roam	90 tont
11 boys	31 far	51 made	71 roe	91 toy
12 brain	32 foam	52 maize	72 root	92 toys
13 bull	33 fob	53 mew	73 rough	93 weave
14 crane	34 foe	54 muff	74 rush	94 weep
15 cue	35 foot	55 mush	75 ruth	95 while
16 curb	36 full	56 mute	76 sack	96 whine
17 curd	37 gall	57 new	77 sap	97 wig
18 curse	38 gong	58 newt	78 slain	98 witch
19 curt	39 grain	59 oh	79 tack	99 yak
20 cute	40 hem	60 ohm	80 tall	100 yap

18.

Measurement of the Acoustic Properties
of Rooms, Studios, and Auditoriums

18·1 Introduction

The most complex request that can be made of an acoustician is, "Explain the nature of sound propagation in an auditorium." In conception the mathematical problem posed is difficult, and in detail it admits of only approximate solutions. Professor F. R. Watson was hardly joking when he said, "Acoustics? That auditorium has plenty of them." Equally complex is an understanding of the psychophysical aspects of acoustics. Involved are not only the processes of hearing, but also habits of listening and the fact that musical compositions are intended to sound well in particular environments—usually highly reverberant auditoriums. These and other factors influence in a major way a listener's evaluation of an auditorium or studio as good or bad. However, not until all the significant physical variables are understood and controlled shall we be able to say that one design of studio or auditorium is superior to another.

18·2 Reverberation Time

A. The Definition and Concept of Reverberation Time

The least controversial of all physical criteria for use in rating the subjective listening quality of a room, of which several are necessary, is the reverberation time of the sound field measured as a function of frequency. Reverberation time T is defined as the length of time in seconds it takes for the energy in the steady-state sound field in a room to decay 60 dB after the source of sound excitation is suddenly turned off.[1,2] The simplicity of this definition vanishes when one begins the process of physically measuring T.

A sound source can excite any number of the thousands of modes of vibration that co-exist in a room, each of which has its own natural frequency f_n and rate of decay k_n.

When a pure tone source of sound, exciting any particular mode of vibration is turned off, the pressure will decrease according to the expression

$$p_n = p_n(x,y,z)e^{-k_n t}. \tag{18.1}$$

The reverberation time T_n for a single mode of vibration is given by

$$T_n = 6.91/k_n \quad \text{sec.} \tag{18.2}$$

If more than one characteristic vibration is excited, each will die out individually at its own rate of decay k_n and normal frequency f_n. Because these modes of vibration have different natural frequencies, beats caused by interference will occur.

Typical decay curves for (a) a single mode of vibration, (b) two modes of vibration, and (c) many modes of vibration are shown in Fig. 18·1. Both the instantaneous values of pressure and the logarithm of the time average of pressure are shown.

In cases in which one pair of walls is more highly damped than others definite double slopes appear in the decay curve. Typical examples of these are shown in Fig. 18·2.

We see from this general discussion that the reverberation time might be defined in any of the following ways: (1) the interval between the time when the source is turned off and the time when the instantaneous value of the pressure level first falls to 60 dB below its steady-state value, (2) as the lapsed time until the average value of the fluctuating pressure first falls to this value, (3) as the lapsed time until the average value of the fluctuating log p decay curve first falls to 60 dB below its steady-state value, or (4) the time required for the initial or final slopes of Fig. 18·2 to drop off 60 dB.

[1]W. C. Sabine, *Collected Papers on Acoustics*, prepared by T. J. Lyman, 1922 (Dover, New York, 1964). Ten papers are included, including "Architectural acoustics," published in seven parts in Am. Arch. Building News **68** (April–June 1900).

[2]L. L. Beranek, *Acoustics* (American Institute of Physics, New York, 1986).

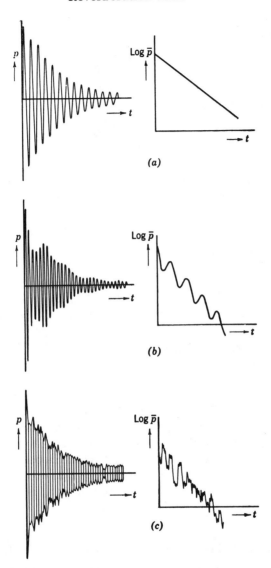

FIG. 18·1 Sound pressure decay curves for (a) a single mode of vibration, (b) two closely spaced modes of vibration, and (c) a number of closely spaced modes of vibration. The graphs on the left show the course of the instantaneous sound pressure; those on the right show the course of the envelope of the left graph plotted in a log $\bar{p}$ vs t coordinate system.

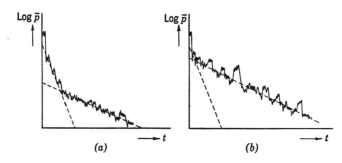

FIG. 18·2 Decay curves with double slopes produced by normal modes of vibration with different decay rates.

It is not appropriate here to choose among the different methods for determining reverberation time that are given above, although one can add other concepts for specifying reverberation time in a meaningful way. One concept is measure only the slope of the reverberation curve during the first 15 or 30 dB, on the theory that each subsequent tone in a musical composition tends to mask the tail of the preceding reverberating tone. Hence, the weaker part of the decay curve is not important.

Another concept is that the first few 50 or so msec of the decay curve should be disregarded in taking the slope of the curve because the early part of the curve is made up of the direct sound and the first reflections from surfaces in the room. It is generally agreed that these early components have a special significance to the listener in judging the quality of a listening space and should be handled separate from the reverberation of a room which contributes mostly to the "liveness" of the space.

B. The Sound Source Used in Measuring Reverberation Time

The definition of reverberation time speaks only of the energy in the sound field. In practice, the energy level of a sound field is not measured, but instead the sound pressure level is determined. When only a pure tone is used as the source, a small number of modes of vibration for the room may be excited, particularly at low frequencies, and the beats among them give rise to fluctuations that often make accurate determination of the reverberation time T impossible (see Fig. 18·4). It is common, therefore, to use sources of sound that, in a frequency band whose width is typically about one-third octave, contain a large number of frequency components. One simple way of generating a band of frequencies is to "warble" the pure tone by modulating it (today) about $\pm 10\%$ around the mean frequency at a rate of 6 to 10 Hz (see Fig. 18·3). This technique produces a number of sideband tones which, however, are of irregular amplitude.

One disadvantage of the warble-tone technique is that the results of different observers will be different because of their independent choices of the warble parameters. A procedure for obtaining a more uniform set of components in the "warble" band is to modulate the signal with a saw-tooth wave.

Two types of sound generators used in room acoustics measurements theoretically produce an infinite number of frequencies of equal amplitude in a given bandwidth. These are: (a) a gated random noise source and (b) an impulsive noise source, such as a pistol shot or an electrical discharge. When either of these is chosen, roughly equal energy is given to all modes of vibration in the frequency band used (see Fig. 18·4).

With continuous spectra noises, a filter set must be used. One-third-octave bands are often employed, located either at the signal generator or after the microphone amplifier. With the former, lower-power loudspeakers are necessary. With impulse noises, the filters are always in the receiving circuit. The

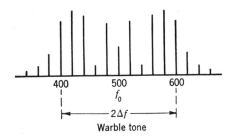

FIG. 18·3 Distribution and relative amplitudes of components in a warble tone with a mean frequency of 500 cps, a maximum frequency deviation of ± 100 cps, and a modulation frequency of 20 cps.

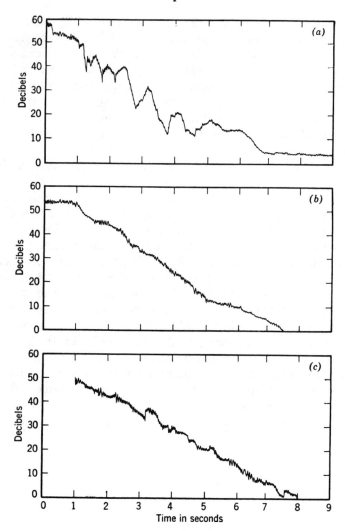

FIG. 18·4 Typical decay curves obtained with sources producing (a) pure
tones, (b) warble tones, and (c) random noise.

duplicability of random noise generators makes them a very desirable measuring tool. Measured reverberation times on many halls are given in Ref. 3.

In addition to the type of source chosen, its location in the room is important. A source located at the corner of a rectangular room will excite up to eight times as many modes of vibration, as will one located near the geometrical center of the room.[2] Although a random noise source of sufficient duration will excite all modes of vibration in a given frequency band uniformly, when such a source is turned off, the amplitude and phase of any one component have random values. By contrast, on repeated "firings," when an impulse source is used, the decay curves are uniformly started with a precisely defined phase and amplitude distribution for each component.

C. Other Factors Affecting Measured Reverberation Time

Irregularities in the decay curve can be reduced by several other techniques. The sound pressure measuring microphone can be mounted on the end of a boom that rotates circularly in a room. Or the source of sound can be mounted on a rotating boom. In laboratory situations, large rotating panels can be used to disturb the normal modes of vibration, thus causing the beats to occur much more rapidly, and to be averaged more easily.

The means for recording the decay curve is also important in averaging out the fluctuations. If a high-speed, graphic-level recorder is used, a succession of decay curves can be superimposed and the average taken visually (Fig. 18·5).

Obviously, the desire generally is to obtain an ensemble average of all possible decay curves for the frequency band under study. Techniques for obtaining by computer an ensemble average of all possible decay curves have been described by several experimenters[6–10] and their procedures are compared in Refs. 4 and 5.

[3]L. L. Beranek, *Music, Acoustics, and Architecture* (Wiley, New York, 1962).

[4]L. Cremer and H. Mueller, *Principles and Applications of Room Acoustics*, translated by T. J. Schultz (Applied Science Publishers, London, 1982).

[5]H. Kuttruff, *Room Acoustics* (Wiley, New York, 1973).

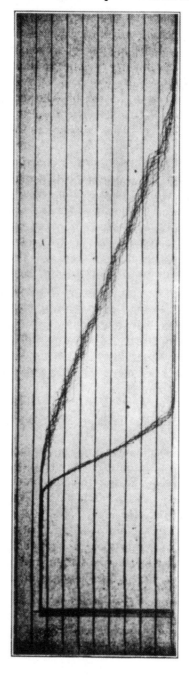

Fig. 18·5 Overlay of successive decay curves measured on a logarithmic graphic level recorder.

D. References

The best general discussion of the measurement of reverberation time is given in Ref. 4, Chaps. II.4 and II.5 on "Measurement of reverberation time" and "Measurement of sound absorption in the reverberant room." Two additional excellent references are: Kutruff,[5] a chapter on "Measuring techniques in room acoustics—Measurement of reverberation time," and Ginn,[6] chapters on "Measuring techniques" and "Suggested instrumentation—Reverberation time." The need for repeatable data by different experimenters in different laboratories is so important that a carefully crafted standard of measurement has been written: International Standards and ISO Recommendations, ISO 3382 1975, "Measurement of reverberation in auditoria."

18·3 Initial-Time-Delay Gap and the Succeeding Pattern of Early Reflections

In recent years the importance of the initial-time-delay gap to musical quality in a concert hall has been recognized widely.[3,10,11] The initial-time-delay gap is the time lapse at a listener's ears between the direct sound from a source in an auditorium and the first reflection from a surface in it. Also recognized as important is the sequence of reflections that follows. These early reflections can best be measured by modern computer techniques, or by proper display on a computer screen. Listener preference studies to determine the exact relationships are still in progress.[11]

18·4 Auto- and Cross-Correlation Measurement Techniques

A school of thought has begun to emerge in the field of concert hall acoustics which teaches that a listener may judge the

[6]K. B. Ginn, *Architectural Acoustics* (Bruel & Kjaer, Marlborough, MA, 1978).

[7]M. R. Schroeder, "New Method of Measuring Reverberation Time," J. Acoust. Soc. Am. **37**, 409–412 (1965).

[8]R. Kuerer, Archiwum Akustyki **2**, 153 (1968).

[9]R. Kuerer and U. Kurze, "Integrationsverfahren zur Nachhallauswertung," Acustica **19**, 313–322 (1967/68).

[10]H. Kuttruff and M. J. Jusofie, "Comments on Ref. 9," Acustica **19**, 56–58 (1967/68).

[11]V. Ando, *Concert Hall Acoustics* (Springer, New York, 1985).

acoustical quality of music in a concert hall by a process that can be related to several objective measurements.[11] These measurements are grouped under the words "sound-transfer function" which measures the arrival of music in a concert hall at the two ears of a listener in terms of (a) a number of early reflected sound components and (b) the reverberation that follows after the first few reflected components.

Ando[11] states that, "All independent objective parameters of acoustic information...[arriving] at the [basilar membranes of the] two ears may be reduced to: "...(i) the autocorrelation function of the source [he calls this autocorrelation function "temporal-monaural criterion" which comes under (a) above]; (ii) a set of transfer functions that "represent the initial-time-delay gap between the direct sound and the first reflection, as well as the structure of the early reflections, the subsequent reverberation, and the spectral changes due to reflections [this group also falls under (a) and is another "temporal-monaural criterion"]; and (iii) the cross-correlation function which relates to the directions from which the reflections arrive at the two ears and to their amplitudes. Criterion (iii) describes the diffuseness of the sound field. It is measured by the interaural cross-correlation between signals that arrive at the two basilar membranes [he calls this a "spacial–binaural criterion" and it corresponds to (b) above].

Ando makes reference to a number of papers published in technical journals which, besides a large number of his own that are referenced in his book, give added theoretical and experimental background necessary to understand the emerging use of correlation techniques to relate subjective judgments of musical quality to objective measurements in a hall.[12–16]

[12]E. V. Jannsson and J. Sunberg, "Long-Time-Average Spectra Applied to Analysis of Music," Acustica **34**, 15–19 (1975).

[13]P. Damaske, "Subjektive Untersuchung von Schallfeldern," Acustica **19**, 199–213 (1967/68).

[14]M. Baron, "Subjective Effects of First Reflections in Concert Halls," J. Sound Vibr. **15**, 475–494 (1971).

[15]M. R. Schroeder and B. S. Atal, "Computer Simulation of Sound Transmission in Rooms," IEEE International Conv. Rec., Part 7, 150–155 (1963).

[16]K. Yamaguchi, "Multivariate Analysis of Subjective and Physical Measures of Hall Acoustics," J. Acoust. Soc. Am. **52**, 1271–1279 (1972).

Digital electronic equipment is available from a number of manufacturers for measuring auto- and cross-correlation functions in the manner described by Ando[11] and others.

18·5 Measurement of Speech Intelligibility

Most auditoriums are used for speech as well as music. It is well known that for optimum listening conditions the reverberation times for speech and music are much different. Whether it is the primary purpose of the room or not, it seems reasonable that any room in which speeches will be given should be designed to provide adequate speech intelligibility. The suitability of existing auditoriums for speech intelligibility is determinable by a speech intelligibility test. The procedure can be used either for unamplified or for amplified speech. There it is a test for the adequacy of the sound reinforcement system. Many specialists have applied these techniques in auditoriums.

The procedure for conducting articulation tests does not differ from that given in Chap. 17. Usually, nonsense syllables are preferable as speech material, because the articulation scores may lie too near unity if words or sentences are used. In addition, the room should be occupied by a normal-sized audience when the tests are being conducted unless the seats absorb nearly the same amount whether occupied or not. If possible, the entire audience should record the syllables or words so that contours of percentage speech intelligibility can be plotted on the floor plan of the auditorium.

Data on speech intelligibility are costly and time consuming to take, but once obtained are very significant. In fact, there is no other psychophysical test for use in auditoriums whose validity has been as well established.

18.6 Objective Speech Transmission Meter[17]

A recently available objective speech transmission meter is described in Section 13.6 of Chap. 13. The result of a test using this method leads to a single number that has been related by Steenehan and Houtgast[18] to the intelligibility of phonetically-balanced (PB) lists. The instrument takes into account the reverberation in the room and the background noise.

[17]International Standard IEC Draft Publication 268, Part 16 (1987).

[18]H. J. M. Steeneken and T. Houtgast, "A Physical Method for Measuring Speech-Transmission Quality," J. Acoust. Soc. Am. **67**, 318–326 (1980), and Technical Review No. 3—1985, Bruel and Kjaer, Naerum, Denmark.

19.

Measurement of Noise Sources, Noise in Buildings, and Materials and Structures for Noise Control

19·1 Introductory Remarks

The measurement of noise produced by sound sources indoors and outdoors has received extensive attention in the past 30 years, especially following the introduction of worldwide noise control legislation.

Early attention was placed on noise control in buildings, including air conditioning systems. Next followed the introduction of jet aircraft operations at the major airports of the world with the attending need to control and measure jet engine noise. Since the early 1970s primary attention has been given to the control and measurement of noise from machinery and consumer products.

The literature on the subject of this chapter is so voluminous as to make comprehensive treatment impossible here. Instead, an extensive bibliography of books and standards is given. The July–August, 1987 issue of the *Noise Control Engineering Journal* (Vol. 29, No. 1) is entirely devoted to "Measurement Standards". In addition to discussing the historical development, a list of standards applicable to noise measurement issued since 1968 is given.[1-3] The presentation in Section 19.3, "Standards", below, is modeled after that in Ref. 2.

[1]W. W. Lang, "The Evolution of Noise Measurement and Standards," Noise Control Eng. J. **29**, 4–8 (1987).

[2]W. Melnick, "Noise Standards for the Work Place," Noise Control Eng. J. **29**, 13–17 (1987).

[3]R. K. Baade, "Standards and Test Codes for Measuring the Noise Emission of Stationary Sources," Noise Control Eng. J. **29**, 18–25 (1987).

19·2 Books Related to Noise Measurement

1. M. A. Cadoff, *Index to Noise Standards*, 3rd ed. (American Institute of Physics, New York, 1985).

2. James R. Ramsey, *Architectural, Building and Mechanical Systems Acoustics: A guide to technical literature. Volume I Applications; Volume II Technology* (R/T Books, P.O. Box 1833, La Crosse, WI 54602-1833, 1986).

3. Y. Ando, *Concert Hall Acoustics* (Springer, New York, 1985).

4. Anon., *Acoustics Testing Facility Survey of the United States* (Institute of Environmental Science, 1975).

5. L. L. Beranek, *Acoustics* (Acoustical Society of America, New York, 1986).

6. L. L. Beranek, *Noise Reduction* (McGraw–Hill, New York, 1960). Out of Print.

7. L. L. Beranek, *Noise and Vibration Control*, Revised Ed. (Institute of Noise Control Engineering, P. O. Box 3206, Poughkeepsie, NY 12603, 1988).

8. J. T. Broch, *Mechanical Vibration and Shock Measurements* (Bruel & Kjaer, Marlborough, MA, 1984).

9. L. Cremer and M. Heckl, *Structure-borne Sound* (Springer, New York, 1973).

10. L. Cremer and H. A. Mueller, *Principles and Applications of Room Acoustics*, 2 Vols., translated by T. J. Schultz (Applied Science, London, 1978).

11. M. J. Crocker and A. J. Price, *Noise and Noise Control* (CRC Press, Cleveland, 1975), Vol. I; M. J. Crocker and F. M. Kessler, *ibid.* (CRC Press, Cleveland, 1982), Vol. II.

12. F. J. Fahy, *Sound and Structural Vibration* (Academic, London, 1985).

13. K. B. Ginn, *Architectural Acoustics* (Bruel & Kjaer, Marlborough, MA, 1978).

14. C. M. Harris, *Handbook of Noise Control*, 2nd ed. (McGraw–Hill, New York, 1979).

15. R. S. Jones, *Noise and Vibration Control in Buildings* (McGraw–Hill, New York, 1984).

16. V. O. Knudsen and C. M. Harris, *Acoustical Designing in Architecture* (revised and reissued by Acoustical Society of America, New York, 1980).

17. H. Kutruff, *Room Acoustics*, 2nd ed. (Applied Science, London, 1983). [Distributed in USA by Update Publishing International, Englewood, NJ, 1979.]

18. G. Lord, W. S. Gatley, and H. A. Evensen, *Noise Control for Engineers* (McGraw–Hill, New York, 1980).
19. A. V. Nikonov and L. Z. Pajaernov, *Instruments for Sound Level Measurements* [in Russian] (Radio i Svyaz', Moscow, 1981).
20. L. G. Ospiov, D. Z. Lopashev, and E. N. Fedoseeva, *Acoustical Measurements in Construction* [in Russian] (Stroiizdat, Moscow, 1978).
21. A. P. G. Peterson, *Handbook of Noise Measurement* (GenRad, Concord, MA, 1980).

19·3 Standards

The standards listed below are placed in four groups: Underlying Acoustics, General Noise Measurement Methods, Measurement of Specific Types of Sources, and Measurement of Structures and Materials used in Noise Control. American National Standards only are listed where their international counterparts are nearly identical. (**R** in parenthesis means "Reaffirmed".)

Group I: Underlying Acoustical Standards

A. Vocabulary

> **ANSI S1. 1-1960 (R1976)**, Acoustical terminology.
> **ANSI S3.20-1973 (R1986)**, Psychoacoustical terminology.
> **SAE J1184**, Definitions of acoustical terms.

B. Symbols and Units

> **ISO R31/7-1978**, Quantities and units of acoustics.
> **ANSI/ASME, Y10.11-1084** Letter symbols for acoustics.

C. Reference Quantities and Preferred Frequencies

> **ANSI S1.6-1984**, Preferred frequencies, frequency levels and band numbers for acoustical measurements.
> **ANSI S1.8-1969 (R1974)**, Preferred reference quantities for acoustical levels.

Group II: General Noise Measurement Methods

ANSI S1.13-1971 (R1986), Methods for measuring sound pressure levels.

ANSI S1.23-1976 (R1983), Methods for the designation of sound power emitted by machinery and equipment.

ANSI S1.30-1979 (R1986), Guidelines for the use of sound power standards and for the preparation of noise test codes.

ANSI S1.31-1980 (R1986), Precision methods for the determination of sound power levels of broad-band noise sources in reverberation rooms.

ANSI S1.32-1980 (R1986), Precision methods for the determination of sound power levels of discrete-frequency and narrow-band noise sources in reverberation rooms.

ANSI S1.33-1982, Engineering methods for the determination of sound power levels of noise sources in a special reverberation test room.

ANSI S1.34-1980 (R1986), Engineering methods for the determination of sound power levels of noise sources for essentially free-field conditions over a reflecting plane.

ANSI S1.35-1979 (R1985), Precision methods for the determination of sound power levels of noise sources in anechoic and hemi-anechoic rooms.

ANSI S1.36-1979 (R1985), Survey methods for the determination of sound power levels of noise sources.

ANSI S12.37, 1988, Determination of sound power levels of sound sources—Methods for *in situ* measurement using a reference sound source.

ANSI S12.38-1988, Characteristics and methods of calibration of reference sound sources.

ANSI S12.1-1983, Guidelines for the preparation of standard procedures to determine the noise emission from sources.

ANSI/ASME PTC36-1985, Measurement of industrial sound.

ASTM E1014-84, Method for the measurement of outdoor A-weighted sound levels.

SAE J184-1980, Qualifying a sound data acquisition system.

SAE J247-1980, Instrumentation for measuring acoustic impulses within vehicles.

SAE J1242-1983, Acoustic emission test methods.

Group III: Measurement of Specific Types of Sources

A. Vehicles

The International Organization for Standardization (ISO) has promulgated about 100 standards in the fields of transportation and powered equipment. Lists are available from the American National Standards Institute (ANSI), 1430 Broadway, New York, NY 10018.

The Society of Automotive Engineers (SAE) has promulgated over 70 standards on noise measurement and rating in the fields of aerospace, engine test cells, all types of surface vehicles, construction, earth moving and farm machinery. Lists are available from SAE, 400 Commonwealth Dr., Warrendale, PA 15096.

ANSI Standards may be purchased from the Acoustical Society of America, 500 Sunnyside Blvd., Woodbury, NY 11797.

B. Powered Machines

ANSI/SAE J1074-1986, Engine sound level measurement procedures.

ANSI B56.11.5-1987, Measurement of sound emitted by lowlift, highlift and rough terrain powered industrial trucks.

ANSI B71.5-1984, Operator ear sound level measurements and rating procedure for powered lawn and garden and snow removal equipment.

ANSI S12.3-1985, Statistical methods for determining and verifying stated noise emission values of machinery and equipment.

ANSI S2.17-1980 (R1986), Techniques of machinery vibration measurement.

ANSI S10.1-1983, Measurement of sound emitted by portable electric power tools, stationary and fixed electrical power tools and gardening appliances.

ISO 2151-1972, Measurement of airborne noise emitted by compressor/primemover units intended for outdoor use NMBTA⋅ Technique-1976, Noise measurement technique.

ISO 2151-1972, Measurement of airborne noise emitted by compressor/primemover units intended for outdoor use NMBTA Technique-1976, Noise measurement technique.

C. Textile Machines

ATMA July 1973, Noise measurement technique for textile machinery.

D. Gear Noise

AGMA 295. 04-1977, Specification for measurement of sound on high speed helical gear units.
AGMA 299. 01, Section II-1980, Sources, specifications and levels of gear sound.

E. Air Conditioning Equipment

AMCE 210-1974 [ASHRAE 51-1975], Laboratory method of testing noise rating from fans.
ARI 575-1979, Method of measuring machinery sound within equipment rooms.
ASHRAE 36-72 (1972), Method of testing for sound rating heating, refrigerating, and air-conditioning equipment.
ASHRAE 68-1978, Method of testing in-duct sound power measurement procedure for fans.

F. Computer and Business Equipment

ANSI S12.10-1985, Methods for the measurement and designation of noise emitted by computer and business equipment.
ISO DIS 7779-1987, Measurement of airborne noise emitted by computer and business equipment.

G. Electrical Machinery

ANSI C37. 082-1982, Sound pressure levels of AC power circuit breakers, standard methods for the measurement of.

IEEE 85-1973 [NEMA MG1-12.49-1978], Airborne sound measurements on rotating electric machinery, test procedure for.

ISO/DP 1680, Test code for the measurement of airborne noise emitted by rotating electrical machinery.
Part 1: Engineering method for free-field conditions over a reflecting plane.
Part 2: Survey method.

NEMA TR-1-1980, Section 9-04, Audible sound tests of transformers, regulators and reactors.

Group IV: Structures and Materials Used in Noise Control

ANSI 12.5-1985, Requirements for the performance and calibration of reference sound sources.

ANSI S12.8-1987, Methods for the measurement of acoustical performance of outdoor noise barriers.

ASTM C384-1977, Impedance and absorption of acoustical materials by the impedance tube method.

ASTM C423-1984, Sound absorption coefficients by the reverberation method.

ASTM C522-1980, Airflow resistance of acoustical materials.

ASTM E90-1983, Laboratory measurement of airborne sound transmission loss of building partitions.

ASTM E336-1984, Measurement of airborne sound insulation in buildings.

ASTM E413-1973, Determination of sound transmission class.

ASTM E492-1977, Laboratory measurement of impact sound transmission through floor-ceiling assemblies using the tapping machine.

ASTM E596-1978, Laboratory measurement of the noise reduction of sound-isolating enclosures.

ASTM E597-1981, Determining single-number rating of airborne sound isolation for use in multi-unit building specifications.

ASTM E795-1983, Mounting test specimens during sound absorption tests.

ASTM E966-1984, Field measurements of airborne

sound insulation of building facades and facade elements.

ASTM E1007-1984, Method for field measurement of tapping machine impact sound transmission through floor-ceiling assemblies and associated support structures.

ASTM P-105, Proposed method for laboratory measurement of sound attenuation of partial height space dividers.

ASTM E1014-1984, Method for the measurement of outdoor A-weighted sound levels.

ISO-140-1978, Measurement of sound insulation in buildings and of building elements:

> Part 1: Requirements for laboratories.
> Part 2: Statement of precision requirements.
> Part 3: Laboratory measurements of airborne sound insulation of building elements.
> Part 4: Field measurements of airborne sound insulation between rooms.
> Part 5: Field measurements of airborne sound insulation of facade elements and facades.
> Part 6: Laboratory measurements of impact sound insulation of floors.
> Part 7: Field measurements of impact sound insulation of floors.
> Part 8: Laboratory measurements of the reduction of transmitted impact noise by floor coverings on a standard floor.
> Part 9 (1985): Laboratory measurement of room-to-room airborne sound insulation of a suspended ceiling with a plenum above it.

ISO 354-1985, Measurement of sound absorption in a reverberation room.

ISO 717-1982, Rating of sound insulation in buildings and of building elements:

> Part 1: Airborne sound insulation in buildings and of interior building elements.
> Part 2: Impact sound insulation.
> Part 3: Airborne sound insulation of facade elements and facades.

ISO 3382-1975, Measurement of reverberation time in auditoria.

20.

The Sound Level Meter

20·1 Introduction

The sound level meter is basic to all sound- and noise-level measurements, particularly those made outside the laboratory. In this chapter, the meter is considered in its broadest terms, as an overall level (single number) indicator, as a portable sound analyzer, and as an instrument that provides levels averaged over long periods of time. To assure a user that measured data from instruments of different manufacture and with different observers are comparable, national and international standards have been promulgated on the basic instrument,[1-3] on filter bands,[16] and on integrating characteristics.

In this chapter, primary reference will be made to USA National Standards. Corresponding International Standards will only be referenced. Because there are many variations, a user should familiarize himself with the Standards of his own country.

The performance of the human ear was discussed in some detail in Chap. 5 and was supplemented in Chap. 6. Originally, it was thought that the sound-level meter should have a frequency response that matched the equal loudness counters of Fig. 5·14 (Chap. 5). Thus if one were measuring relatively low sound levels (20–55 dB), the meter response should equal the

[1]American National Standard ANSI S1.4-1983, "Specification for sound level meters" and ANSI S1.13-1971, "Methods for the measurement of sound pressure levels," Acoustical Society of America.

[2]International Standard IEC 651-1979, "Sound level meters," International Electrotechnical Commission.

[3]American National Standard ANSI S1.42-1986 "Design response of weighting networks for acoustical measurements," Acoustical Society of America.

inverse of the 40-phon equal loudness contour, called the "*A*" weighting network. In the medium-level range (55–85 dB), the meter response should emulate the 70-phon curve, called the "*B*" weighting network. Finally for high sound levels (85–140 dB), the response should be flat, rounded off starting at 100 Hz at low frequencies and 2500 Hz at high frequencies, called the "*C*" weighting network.

The operator of the sound-level meter, according to early standards, had continually to shift among the weighting networks, and when a noise level was being measured near the change points (i.e., 55 or 85 dB) and two different levels were measured for the same noise on two different networks, the average of the readings was taken. During World War II, "speech interference levels" were established and are now standardized.[4,5] During the 1950s, methods for computing the "loudness level" of a continuous noise were developed, one by Stevens[6] in the USA and the other by Zwicker in West Germany.[7] These have been reduced to National and International Standards.[8,9] With the coming of the jet age, it was apparent that special methods had to be developed to relate jet engine exhaust and turbine noise to the annoyance they evoked in populated areas around airports. This led to a method for calculating "perceived noisiness levels." [10] Acceptable noise levels in indoor living spaces were also developed.[11–13]

[4]L. L. Beranek, "Airplane quieting II—specification of acceptable noise levels," Trans. ASME **67**, 97–100 (1947).

[5]American National Standard, ANSI S3.14-1977 "Rating noise with respect to speech interference," Acoustical Society of America.

[6]S. S. Stevens, "Procedure for predicting loudness: Mark VI," J. Acoust. Soc. Am. **33**, 1577–1585 (1961).

[7]E. Zwicker and R. Feldtkeller, *Das Ohr als Nachrichtenempfaenger* (Hirzel, Stuttgart, 1967).

[8]American National Standard, ANSI S3.4-1980 (ASA 37-1980), "Procedure for the computation of loudness of noise," Acoustical Society of America.

[9]ISO 532-1975, "Method for measuring loudness level."

[10]K. D. Kryter, *Effects of Noise on Man* (Academic, New York, 1970).

[11]L. L. Beranek, *Acoustics* (Reprinted by Acoustical Society of America, 1986).

[12]L. L. Beranek, W. E. Blazier, Jr., and J. J. Figwer, "Preferred noise criterion (PNC) curves and their application to rooms," J. Acoust. Soc. Am. **50**, 1223 (1971).

[13]L. L. Beranek, *Noise and Vibration Control* (McGraw–Hill, New York, 1971). [To be reprinted by the Institute of Noise Control Engineering in 1988.]

To the surprise of most investigators, and for reasons not completely understood, there is an impressive degree of correlation between A-weighted sound level, speech interference level, loudness level, noisiness level, and permissible room criteria.[11-15] Because human reactions to noise vary among individuals, and because the other noise ratings are so highly correlated among themselves, it has been argued that A-weighted sound levels are as good as other methods for obtaining a single number to rate noise. Thus, a number read from an instrument incorporating the A scale has become the most accepted way to rate human reaction to noise when a single number is required and when accuracy does not require a more precise procedure.

Notwithstanding the above, the USA Standard for sound level meters still requires that all three networks, A, B, and C, be incorporated.[3] Readings taken with those networks are designated as dB(A), dB(B), and dB(C), respectively. The IEC International Standard specifies only the A and C networks. Also, in most sound-level meters, there is one flat network, usually called "linear" (1–20 Hz at the low end of the spectrum and 12–20 kHZ at the high end) and, perhaps, one called "all-pass" (electrically, out to, say, 50 kHz).

20·2 Definitions—American Standard

Sound (Noise) level: The sound, or noise, level is the sound pressure level in decibels measured by use of the A, B, or C frequency weighting and fast (F), slow (S), or impulse (I), exponential-time-averaging, or peak (pK) time-related-characteristic as specified in the American Standard. The frequency weighting and exponential-time-averaging constant shall be specified, otherwise the A-frequency weighting and standardized fast (125 ms) exponential-time averaging are understood. The reference sound pressure is 20 μPa(0.0002 dyne/cm^2).

---

[14]R. W. Young, "Don't forget the simple sound level meter," Noise Control 3, 42–43 (1958).

[15]T. J. Schultz, "Technical background for noise abatement," BBN report 2005 (Sept. 1970).

Slow sound level: Sound level measured by use of the standardized slow (1000 ms) exponential-time averaging.

Impulse sound level: Sound level measured by use of the standard impulse (35 ms) exponential-time averaging for increasing portions of the signal and 1500-ms time constant for decreasing portions of the signal.

20·3 General Characteristics

A sound-level meter comprises a microphone, an amplifier with a standardized frequency weighting, a standardized exponential-time-averaging device, a logarithm taker, and a means to display the results in decibels. It may also embody a set of filters, special means for determining other types of sound level such as L_{eq} (A-weighted sound level averaged over the measurements period), SEL (sound exposure level), L_{max} (maximum peak or rms level in the measurements period), L_{min}, L_{dn} (A-weighted sound level averaged over 24 hours with increased emphasis on nighttime as compared to daytime levels), DOSE, and others.

Additional items that are necessary to meet any of the requirements of the specification (such as extension rods or cables or a special correction grid or cap on the microphone to approximate random-incidence response) are regarded as integral parts of a sound level meter.

20·4 Types of Sound Level Meter

The Standards provide for four types of sound level meter:
Type 0: The type 0 instrument or system is intended for use primarily in the *laboratory* as a reference standard. Type 1: The type 1 instrument, designated *Precision* is intended for accurate sound measurements in the field and the laboratory.
Type 2: The type 2 instrument, designated *General Purpose*, is intended for general field use, i.e., measurement of typical environmental sounds when high frequencies do not dominate.
Type S: The type S instrument, designated *Special Purpose*, may satisfy any one of the three grades in regard to accuracy and stability, but is not required to contain all the functions.
The requirement for each of the first three types that distinguishes one from another is accuracy of measurement. The expected total allowable error for a sound-level meter measuring

steady broadband noise in a reverberant sound field is approximately ± 1.5 dB for type 1 and ± 2.3 dB for a type 2 instrument.

For steady sinusoidal sounds in a diffuse field at a specific frequency in the range from 100 to 1250 Hz, the expected total allowable error based on most of the allowable tolerances is ± 1.6 dB for a type 1 and ± 2.3 dB for a type 2 instrument.

For a sinusoidal signal at the calibration frequency, incident on the microphone with random incidence (USA National Standard), the measurements, for each frequency weighting, must have an accuracy of ± 0.4, ± 0.7, and ± 1.0 dB for types 0, 1, and 2, respectively. The measurements must be corrected to the standard reference atmospheric pressure, and to 20 °C and 65% R.H.

The USA Standard intends that when sounds are being measured with significant spectral content above 3000 Hz (sound spectra that do not slope off above 3000 Hz when measured with a one-third-octave-band analyzer), or with rapidly varying temporal characteristics, or both, a type 0 or type 1 instrument may be required.

A sound-level meter that conforms to one of the four types above does not guarantee that the accuracy indicated will be achieved in the field. The procedures and precautions that the operator of the meter uses determine the accuracy of the measurement as much as the instrument. For this reason, the Standard requires that the manufacturer provide a comprehensive instruction book which contains extensive information on the capabilities, limitations, and recommended use procedures for the instrument.

20·5 Microphone and Instrument Case Characteristics

The microphone, or the microphone and instrument case together must, in the USA Standard, be designed to have the frequency-weighting characteristics and tolerance limits given in Sec. 20·6 for the measurement of sound at random incidence. The Standard allows laboratories to calculate the response to random-incidence sound from the instrument's responses to free-field sounds arriving from different directions. In the calculation, a sphere surrounding the acoustical center of the microphone is divided into seven equal areas. Because of symmetry, each area (except for the two at 0° and 180°) is approximately cylindrical and can be designated by an angle θ_n. The equal areas have the angles, respectively, of 31°0′, 55°9′, 73°24′, 90°0′, 106°36′, 124°51′, and 149°0′. (See Fig. 20·1.)

Let the relative response level (in dB) of the microphone, to a plane-wave sound arriving at the microphone from the angle θ_n and at frequency f, be equal to $R(\theta_n, f)$. The relative incremental contribution of energy arriving from that angle through its one-seventh area is given by the equation

$$\Delta K(\theta_n, f) = (1/7)10^{0.1R(\theta_n, f)}. \tag{20·1}$$

The relative response for random incidence, r, is then

$$R_{rf} = 10 \log \sum_n \Delta K(\theta_n; f). \tag{20·2}$$

The persons who drafted the Standard viewed any laboratory interested in checking the random-incidence response of the instrument as having the ability to produce a plane wave in a

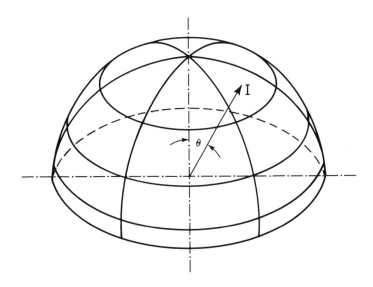

FIG. 20·1 Method for dividing a sphere into seven parts of equal area.

free field, but not necessarily having a truly random-incidence field available for the calibration. Furthermore, in practical measurements where the random-incidence sound is not found, the operator should hold the instrument at an angle relative to the direction of the sound wave that gives a response closest to the random-incidence sound response. Hence, they ask the manufacturer to state the angle θ at which the frequency response of the microphone (with instrument case and with the user present, if the instrument is normally to be hand-held) has a free-field response most closely approximating its random-incidence response. This is called the "calibration angle of incidence."

The free-field relative response of the microphone within $\pm$ 22.5° of the calibration angle of incidence shall not deviate more than the amount shown in Table 20·1.

When an extension rod or cable is required to meet the condition of Table 20·1, the manufacturer must so state in the manual.

Finally, the maximum allowable deviation of the free-field relative response level of the whole instrument—but primarily determined by the microphone—for sounds arriving at any angle of incidence with respect to the random-incidence relative response level is given in Table 20·2. The deviations shown there dictate the use of microphones at least as small as $\frac{1}{2}$ in., as

TABLE 20·1 MAXIMUM ALLOWABLE DEVIATION OF FREE-FIELD RELATIVE RESPONSE LEVEL WITH RESPECT TO THE RANDOM-INCIDENCE RELATIVE RESPONSE LEVEL WHEN THE ANGLE OF INCIDENCE IS VARIED BY $\pm$ 22.5° FROM THE CALIBRATION ANGLE OF INCIDENCE. (REF. 1).

Frequency range (Hz)	Type 0 (dB)	Type 1 (dB)	Type 2 (dB)
31.5 to 2 000	± 0.5	± 1	± 2
2 000 to 4 000	± 1	± 1.5, − 1	± 2.5
4 000 to 5 000	± 1	+ 2, − 1.5	± 3
5 000 to 6 300	± 1.5	+ 2.5, − 2	± 3.5
6 300 to 8 000	± 2	+ 3, − 2.5	± 4.5
8 000 to 10 000	± 2	+ 3.5, − 3.5	a
10 000 to 12 000	± 3	+ 4, − 6.5	a

ª None specified.

TABLE 20·2 MAXIMUM ALLOWABLE DEVIATION OF FREE-FIELD RELATIVE
RESPONSE LEVEL FOR SOUNDS ARRIVING AT ANY ANGLE OF INCIDENCE WITH
RESPECT TO THE RANDOM-INCIDENCE RELATIVE RESPONSE LEVEL. (REF. 1).

Frequency range (Hz)	Type 0 (dB)	Type 1 (dB)	Type 2 (dB)
31.5 to 2 000	± 1	+ 1.5, − 1	± 3
2 000 to 4 000	± 1.5	+ 2.5, − 2	+ 3, − 4
4 000 to 5 000	± 1.5	+ 3.5, − 3	+ 4, − 6
5 000 to 6 300	± 2	+ 4, − 4	+ 5, − 8
6 300 to 8 000	± 3	+ 5.5, − 5.5	+ 8, − 9
8 000 to 10 000	± 3.5	+ 7, − 8	a
10 000 to 12 000	± 4.5	+ 8, − 11	a

ᵃ None specified.

can be seen from the directivity curves of Chap. 5 for the various sizes of microphones.

The requirements on the stability of the microphone are included as part of the requirements on the stability of the sound level meter.

At this point we should state that the International Standard differs from the USA Standard in one very important way: IEC 651-1979 requires that the specifications given here be met in calibration by a free-field sound wave incident on the microphone at $\theta = 0°$, i.e., the wave front arrives parallel to the diaphragm of the instrument. In practice, this means that to obtain the same reading for a plane-wave free-field sound wave on ANSI and IEC instruments, the ANSI instrument must be held at the "calibration angle" (θ about equal to 70°) and the IEC instrument at $\theta = 0°$.

20·6 Frequency Weighting and Amplifier Characteristics

The random-incidence relative response levels as a function of frequency for each of the three networks, A, B, and C, are given in Fig. 20·2. The tolerance limits in design are shown in Table 20·3.

These weighting characteristics are realizable with passive resistor-capacitor circuits. Detailed formulas and parameters for network design are given in the ANSI Standard. Note that the IEC instrument would have to meet these specifications for a plane-wave incident at $\theta = 0°$.

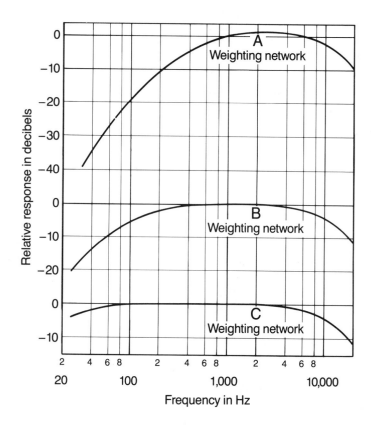

FIG. 20·2 *A*-, *B*-, and *C*-weighting network specifications. The tolerance on these curves are given in Table 20·3[3].

20·7 Exponential-Time-Averaging Characteristics

The subject of indicating and integrating instruments for the measurement of complex waves was treated in Chap. 11. We saw there that an exponential-time-averaging instrument, in which class the sound-level meter falls, consists of three parts, (1) a squaring circuit; (2) an exponential-time-averaging circuit; and (3) a logarithm taker and sound level display (meter or digital indicator). We showed that the squaring and exponential-time-averaging circuit could be combined in one circuit. (See Fig. 11·13.)

TABLE 20·3 TOLERANCE LIMITS ON RELATIVE RESPONSE LEVELS FOR SOUND AT RANDOM INCIDENCE MEASURED ON AN INSTRUMENT'S CALIBRATION RANGE.[a]

Nominal frequency (Hz)	Type 0 (dB)	Type 1 (dB)	Type 2 (dB)
10	+ 2, − 5	± 4	+ 5, − ∞
12.5	+ 2, − 4	± 3.5	+ 5, − ∞
16	+ 2, − 3	± 3	+ 5, − ∞
20	± 2	± 2.5	+ 3
25	± 1.5	± 2	± 3
31.5	± 1	± 1.5	± 3
40	± 1	± 1.5	± 2
50	± 1	± 1	± 2
63	± 1	± 1	± 2
80	± 1	± 1	± 2
100	± 0.7	± 1	± 1.5
125	± 0.7	± 1	± 1.5
160	± 0.7	± 1	± 1.5
200	± 0.7	± 1	± 1.5
250	± 0.7	± 1	± 1.5
315	± 0.7	± 1	± 1.5
400	± 0.7	± 1	± 1.5
500	± 0.7	± 1	± 1.5
630	± 0.7	± 1	± 1.5
800	± 0.7	± 1	± 1.5
1 000	± 0.7	± 1	± 1.5
1 250	± 0.7	± 1	± 1.5
1 600	± 0.7	± 1	± 2
2 000	± 0.7	± 1	± 2
2 500	± 0.7	± 1	± 2.5
3 150	± 0.7	± 1	± 2.5
4 000	± 0.7	± 1	± 3
5 000	± 1	± 1.5	± 3.5
6 300	+ 1, − 1.5	+ 1.5, − 2	± 4.5
8 000	+ 1, − 2	+ 1.5, − 3	± 5
10 000	+ 2, − 3	+ 2, − 4	+ 5, − ∞
12 500	+ 2, − 3	+ 3, − 6	+ 5, − ∞
16 000	+ 2, − 3	+ 3, − ∞	+ 5, − ∞
20 000	+ 2, − 3	+ 3, − ∞	+ 5, − ∞

[a] American National Standard, ANSI S1.42-1986, "Design response of weighting networks for acoustical measurement," Acoustical Society of America. Included are accurate analytical expressions for the theoretically ideal frequency-domain and time-domain responses of the A-, B-, and C-weighting networks. Similar expressions for the D (aircraft noise weighting) and E (Stevens[6] "loudness level" weighting) networks are included in the Appendix.

The Standard for the sound-level meter reads, "The indication of the sound level meter...shall be the exponential-time-average sound level, the averaging being done by dividing the time integral of the (analog of) exponentially time weighted, squared, frequency-weighted sound pressure by the applicable time constant." Let us take this statement apart. First, frequency-weighted sound pressure is the output of the electrical circuit in the sound level meter. Let us call it $p(t)$. It has in it any necessary corrections for the response of the microphone and the appropriate A, B, or C network weighting. This output is squared, yielding $p^2(t)$, using a circuit like that of Fig. 11·12. The squared quantity is fed to an RC averaging (weighting) network like that of Fig. 11·12. The remainder of the statement says that

$$X^2_{\text{rms}}(t) = (1/RC) \int_{-\infty}^{\tau} f(\tau)e^{[\,-(t-\tau)/RC]} \, d\tau \,, \qquad (20·3)$$

where $f(\tau)$ equals $p^2(t)$ and $X_{\text{rms}}(t)$ is the quantity that provides the meter indication, after the logarithm of it is taken.

Equation (20·3) is simply the exponential-time-average operation that an RC circuit performs.

The "fast (F)" sound level is taken with a time constant, RC, equal to 125 ms. The "slow (S)" requires a time constant of 1000 ms. "Impulse (I)" sound level requires a time constant of 35 ms for a sound pressure that increases with increasing time. For a sound pressure that decreases with increasing time, the peak detector introduces a decay time constant of 1500 ms.

20·8 Other Sound Level Meter Specifications

There are other tables in the Standard relating to (a) the maximum allowable error in decibels for various crest factors, (b) maximum overshoot for fast and slow weighting, (c) tone-burst response and tolerance limits for fast and slow weighting, (d) single tone-burst response and tolerance for impulse weighting, (e) response and tolerance limits of impulse weighting for a sequence of 5-ms duration bursts of 2000-Hz signals, and (f) tolerance limits on differential level linearity over the principal frequency range for each type. It is the combination of all the variations allowed under these tolerances, plus the tolerances of Fig. 20·2, Table 20·3, and the basic circuit stability, that yield the "total allowable error for a sound-level meter" given in Sec. 20·4.

The Standard for sound level meters also gives details of the tests used to verify the basic characteristics of the different types of sound level meters covered by the specification.

20·9 Octave- and One-Third-Octave-Band Filter Sets

Many acoustical measurements require frequency analyses of continuous noise spectra using fractional-octave-band band-pass filter sets. The two most common types for use in the field have 10 octave-band filters and 30 one-third-octave-band filters contained in one or two units. Laboratory filter sets contain 40 or so one-third-octave-band filters with midfrequencies from 1.6–20 kHz and 14 octave-band filters from 2–16 kHz.

An American Standard recently issued covers performance requirements on both laboratory and field fractional-band filter sets.[16] In the Standard, filter designs are described by an Order number which is equal to the number of pole pairs in the analog prototype bandpass filter. The overall accuracy of the filter is specified by Type and Sub-Type numbers, which are determined by the accuracy of measurement of random-noise signals with flat and with sloping spectra. Thus a filter-set might be marked "One-Third-Octave-Band Filter Set, Order 3, Type 3C, Extended Range per ANSI S1.11-1986."

The corresponding International Standard on bandpass filters is IECR225 (1966).[17]

A. Standard Frequencies for Filter Bands

Analog filters are designed according to the Butterworth Theory, which specifies the number of poles in the analog prototype low-pass filter, or the number of pole pairs or resonant circuits in the analog prototype bandpass filter. A common design for acoustics is Order 3.

---

[16]American National Standard ANSI S1.11-1986, "Specification for octave-band and fractional-octave-band analog and digital filters," Acoustical Society of America.

[17]International Electrotechnical Commission Recommendation, Publication 225 (1966), "Octave, half-octave, and third-octave-band filters intended for the analysis of sounds and vibrations."

The standard midband (geometric-mean) frequencies f_m for octave-band and one-third-octave-band filters are shown in Table 20·4. The reference frequency, for acoustic measurements, is 1000 Hz. The lower and upper bandedge frequencies f_1 and f_2 for Order 3 octave-band and one-third-octave-band filters are given in Table 20·5. The reference bandwidth is $B_r = (f_2 - f_1)$. The reference bandwidth ratio B_r/f_m is shown. Let us define a reference bandwidth quotient,

$$Q_r = f_m/B_r = f_m/(f_2 - f_1) \, . \qquad (20\cdot4)$$

An ideal (vertical skirts) bandpass filter would be Order infinity. For a maximally flat (in passband) Butterworth design bandpass filter to transmit the same white-noise power as an ideal bandpass filter, the actual bandwidth of the filter needs to be smaller than the reference bandwidth. The value of the design bandwidth quotient Q_d, which is larger than the reference quotient Q_r, is given by

$$Q_d = [(\pi/2n)/\sin(\pi/2n)]Q_r \, . \qquad (20\cdot5)$$

For Order 3 ($n = 3$) Butterworth filters, Q_d is given in Table 20·5.

B. Attenuation Characteristics of Individual Filters

The attenuation characteristics for a practical bandpass filter can be discussed in three parts: Part one is the attenuation in the pass band. The attenuation there is flat, rounded, or has ripples. Part two includes the upper and lower transition bands (sometimes called the "skirts"). Part three describes the stopbands, the ultimate attenuations reached below and above the transitions bands. The stopbands may be smooth or have ripples. If there are ripples, the stopband attenuation is the minimum attenuation (peak of ripples) [see (b) and (c) of Fig. 20.3].

Reference design attenuation. The reference design attenuation A_d in decibels, for any frequency and any filter order, is chosen as that for a maximally flat Butterworth characteristic,

$$A_d = 10 \log\left[1 + Q_d^{2n}\left(\frac{f}{f_m} - \frac{f_m}{f}\right)^{2n}\right], \qquad (20\cdot6)$$

where n is the Order and Q_d is given in Eq. (20·5).

TABLE 20·4 LISTING OF FILTER BANDS TO BE PROVIDED BY A SET OF FILTERS FOR MEASUREMENT OF THE SPECTRAL CONTENT OF SIGNALS OVER THE FREQUENCY RANGE OF THE AUDIO FREQUENCY BAND. (REF. 16).

Band number, N	Preferred frequency (Hz)	Octave-band range: Restricted	Extended	One-third-octave-band range: Restricted	Extended	Optional range
14	25				x	
15	31.5		x		x	
16	40				x	
17	50				x	
18	63		x		x	
19	80				x	A S
20	100			x	x	
21	125	x	x	x	x	S
22	160			x	x	P E
23	200			x	x	C
24	250	x	x	x	x	I
25	315			x	x	F I
26	400			x	x	E
27	500	x	x	x	x	D
28	630			x	x	B
29	800			x	x	Y
30	1 000	x	x	x	x	
31	1 250			x	x	M A
32	1 600			x	x	N
33	2 000	x	x	x	x	U
34	2 500			x	x	F A
35	3 150			x	x	C
36	4 000	x	x	x	x	T
37	5 000			x	x	U R
38	6 300				x	E
39	8 000		x		x	R
40	10 000				x	
41	12 500				x	
42	16 000		x		x	
43	20 000				x	

TABLE 20·5 NOMINAL BANDEDGE FREQUENCY RATIOS AND FILTER BAND-
WIDTH RATIOS FOR ORDER 3 OCTAVE-BAND AND ONE-THIRD-OCTAVE-BAND
FILTERS. (FROM REF. 16).

Formula	Octave-band Base 2 or Base 10	One-third-octave-band Base 2 or Base 10
f_1/f_m	$2^{-1/2}$	$2^{-1/6}$
f_2/f_m	$2^{1/2}$	$2^{1/6}$
Numerical value		
f_1/f_m	0.707 11	0.890 90
f_2/f_m	1.414 21	1.122 46
Reference bandwidth ratio B_r/f_m		
$(f_2 - f_1)/f_m$	0.707 11	0.231 56
Reference quotient, Q_r		
f_m/B_r	1.414 21	4.318 47
Butterworth design		
Q_d *for* $n = 3$	1.480 96	4.522 29

Tolerance values. The Standard says that the actual measured attenuations must lie between two tolerance curves
which are calculated from Butterworth design curves with Q_d's
that lie on either side of the design Q_d of Eq. (20·5) as follows:

$$1.023Q_d > Q_d > 0.977Q_d \quad \text{for Type 0-}X,$$

$$1.059Q_d > Q_d > 0.944Q_d \quad \text{for Type 1-}X,$$

$$1.100Q_d > Q_d > 0.900Q_d \quad \text{for Type 2-}X \text{ and 3-}X.$$

For the significance of X see Sub-Type later.

The Standard specifies that the design attenuations for practical (non-Butterworth) filters, at any frequency in the transition bands, less than f_1 and greater than f_2, must be equal to or
greater than the attenuation of a Butterworth filter of the
same Order and Type designation, calculated with the lower
value of the allowable range of Q_d given above.

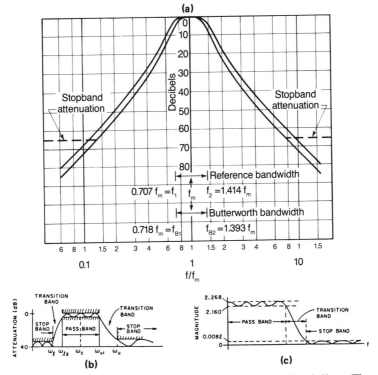

FIG. 20·3 (a) Design tolerances permitted for an octave-band filter. The reference bandwidth is shown for a perfect filter with vertical sides, $(f_2 - f_1)/f_m = 0.7071$. The Butterworth bandwidth is narrower because some power gets through the filter's transition bands $(f_{B2} - f_{B1})/f_m = 0.6752$. (b) Attenuation characteristics of a typical bandpass filter showing passband, stopbands, and transition bands. (c) Magnitude characteristic of a typical filter showing its ripple characteristics. (From Ref. 16)

The Butterworth attenuation A in decibels, for the standard-required tolerance curves of practical filters, using the ranges of Q_d given above, are given in Table 20·6.

Five values of attenuations in Table 20·6 are given, first for Q_d of Eq. (20·5), i.e., the design bandwidth quotient, and then for the external values of Q_{max} and Q_{min} for Type 1-X and 2-X filters (X is the Sub-Type letter to be discussed below). These values give the limits within which the transition band attenuations must fall. (See Fig. 20·3.)

In the passband, the attenuation at the mean frequency is 0 dB. Separately, the Standard prescribes that the stopband attenuation shall be not less than 65 dB.

The Sound Level Meter

TABLE 20·6 ATTENUATION A FOR ORDER 3 TYPE 1-X AND TYPE 2-X OCTAVE-BAND AND ONE-THIRD-OCTAVE-BAND BUTTERWORTH FILTERS. (REF. 16).

Octave-band attenuation (dB)						One-third-octave-band attenuation (dB)					
f/f_m or f_m/f	Q_d	Type 1-X		Type 2-X		f/f_m or f_m/f	Q_d	Type 1X		Type 2-X	
		Q_{max}	Q_{min}	Q_{max}	Q_{min}			Q_{max}	Q_{min}	Q_{max}	Q_{min}
1.00	0.00	0.00	0.00	0.00	0.00	1.00	0.00	0.00	0.00	0.00	0.00
1.20	0.11	0.16	0.08	0.19	0.06	1.08	0.47	0.65	0.33	0.80	0.26
1.26	0.45	0.62	0.31	0.76	0.24	1.10	1.50	2.01	1.09	2.39	0.86
1.41	3.52	4.43	2.70	5.07	2.21	1.12	3.37	4.26	2.58	4.89	2.11
1.60	10.03	11.42	8.60	12.32	7.65	1.16	8.44	9.77	7.10	10.64	6.21
1.80	16.04	17.53	14.48	18.48	13.39	1.18	10.99	12.41	9.53	13.32	8.54
2.00	20.83	22.34	19.24	23.30	18.12	1.22	15.59	17.07	14.03	18.02	12.95
2.25	25.64	27.16	24.03	28.12	22.91	1.26	19.49	21.00	17.90	21.96	16.79
2.50	29.57	31.09	27.96	32.05	26.83	1.33	25.06	26.57	23.45	27.53	22.32
3.15	37.36	38.88	35.75	39.85	34.62	1.41	30.06	31.58	28.45	32.54	27.32
3.35	39.30	40.82	37.69	41.79	36.56	1.50	34.57	36.09	32.96	37.06	31.83
4.00	44.67	46.19	43.06	47.16	41.93	1.65	40.44	41.96	38.83	42.93	37.70
5.00	51.11	52.63	49.49	53.59	48.36	1.80	42.02	46.54	43.41	47.50	42.27
5.60	54.28	55.80	52.67	56.76	51.53	2.00	49.89	51.41	48.27	52.37	47.14
6.30	57.53	59.05	55.92	60.01	54.78	2.25	54.72	56.24	53.11	57.20	51.97
7.10	60.79	62.30	59.17	63.27	58.04	2.60	60.05	61.57	58.44	62.53	57.30
8.00	64.01	65.53	62.40	66.49	61.26	3.00	64.88	66.40	63.27	67.36	62.13
10.00	69.97	71.49	68.36	72.45	67.23	3.50	69.75	71.26	68.13	72.23	67.00
12.50	75.88	77.40	74.27	78.36	73.13	4.25	75.54	77.06	73.93	78.02	72.80
16.00	82.38	83.90	80.77	84.86	79.63	5.00	80.20	81.71	78.58	82.68	77.45

The reference passband attenuation (defined as minimum attenuation) of any filter band in a set shall not differ from the reference passband attenuation of any other filter band in the set by more than 0.1 dB for Type 0, 0.3 dB for Type 1, 1.0 dB for Type 2, and 2.0 dB for Type 3 filters.

Selection of Type and Sub-Type numbers. The main Type number is determined by the difference (in decibels) between the white noise power passed by the filter and that which would be passed by an ideal filter (vertical sidebands). The criteria for selection are given in Table 20·7.

The peak-to-valley ripple within the passband of each filter in the set, whether by design choice or effect of component tolerance, must not exceed 0.1 dB for Type 0 filters, 0.25 dB for Type 1 filters, and 0.5 dB for Type 2 filters. Filters having 0.6 to 2.0 dB peak-to-valley ripple shall be designated as Type 3-X filters.

The Sub-Type ("X") number is determined by the difference (in decibels) between the power passed by the filter using a composite set of calculations for either of two cases of three different sloping spectrum powers (0, − 15, and + 9, dB/Octave and 0, − 36, + 30 dB/Octave) and that which would be passed by an ideal filter for the same cases. The details of calculation are given in the Standard. Composite errors of 1.0 dB, give a rating of C, and composite errors greater than 1.0 dB, a rating of D. An A rating would require a composite error of less than 0.25 dB.

The method of calculation is tedious and reference should be made to the Standard[16] for details.

C. Integrating Characteristics

Sound-level meters can be obtained which contain a large range of integrating characteristics. These are tailored to various standards for measuring quantities in decibels that are related to the effects of noise on communities, damage to hearing, speech communication, annoyance, office personnel, and so on. Further details are given in Ref. 13, Chap. 18. A few are listed here:

TABLE 20·7 CRITERIA FOR SELECTING TYPE NUMBER. (REF. 16).

White noise bandwidth error (dB)	Type number
= or < than 0.1	0
= or < than 0.25	1
= or < than 0.41	2 or 3[a]

[a] Depends on passband ripple.

L_{max} = maximum sound level since last reset. This time period is generally controlled by the personnel or a clock mechanism, or the life of the batteries.

L_{min} = minimum sound level since last reset.

L_{eq} = level of the average mean-square sound signal measured since the last reset. The time interval must be specified. [Some observers believe the value of L_{eq} would better be found from the formula $L_{eq} = (L_{10} - 3)$ dB, where L_{10} is the instantaneous noise level exceeded 10% of the time.[15]]

SEL = A-weighted level equal to the constant level which, if maintained for one second, would have the same acoustic energy as the measured A-weighted level of the mean-square sound signal since the last reset.

L_{dn} = L_{eq} measured throughout a 24-hour period, except that the levels at night (2200 to 0700 hours) are increased by 10 dB before they are averaged in.

20·10 Techniques, Precautions, and Calibrations

The USA National Standard[1] requires that a fully informative instruction book be issued by the instrument maker that covers proper usage of the instrument. In addition, the professional should be fully aware of the standard methods for measurement of sound pressure levels.[18]

Effects of meter case and observer. The reading of a sound-level meter, whether hand-held or simply mounted on a tripod, is different from a microphone on the end of a small diameter extension tube. Two manufacturers have published data on the effect of the readings of the instrument case and of a person holding the meter.[18,19]

---

[18]A. P. G. Peterson, *Handbook of Noise Measurement* (GenRad, 300 Baker Avenue, Concord, MA 01742).

[19]P. Hedegaard, "Free field calibration of a sound level meter," Technical Review, No. 2, 1969. Bruel & Kjaer, 185 Forest Street, Marlborough, MA 01752.

The effect of a person standing and facing the source of a plane-wave free-field pure-tone sound wave on the readings of a microphone on an extension cable located at distances of a few centimeters to 1.25 m is shown in Fig. 20·4. The graph shows the difference in readings before and after entry of the person at 400, 1600, and 6300 Hz.[19] Because the International Standard requires that the diaphragm of the microphone on a sound level meter face the source, the meter would normally be between the person and the source. If the distance from the diaphragm of the microphone, when the

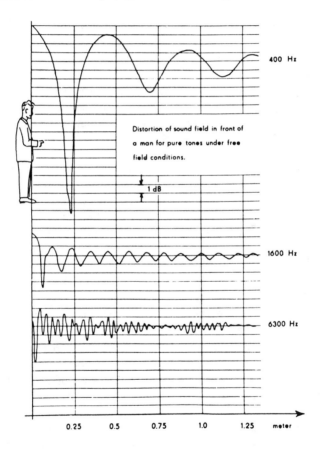

Distortion of sound field in front of
a man for pure tones under free
field conditions.

1 dB

400 Hz

1600 Hz

6300 Hz

0.25   0.5   0.75   1.0   1.25   meter

FIG. 20·4 Distortion of sound field of an average size man.
(Courtesy of Bruel & Kjaer)

instrument is hand-held under this condition, is 0.8 m, the effect on the readings will be ± 2 dB at most frequencies between 200 and 10,000 Hz, and ± 1 dB above and below. If a 20-cm extension tube is added between the microphone and the instrument case, this variation is reduced to ± 1 dB.

To keep errors within ± 0.5 dB, the microphone should be used with a tripod. With the microphone diaphragm facing the sound source, i.e., according to the International Standard, a 20-cm extension tube should be placed between the microphone and the clip that attaches to the tripod rod. The tripod rod is 40 cm long and goes between the clip and the tripod. Finally, the tripod rod should be tilted so that the angle formed between (a) a line between the source and microphone and along the extension tube and (b) the rod is about 60°.

Peterson[18] shows a configuration that uses the USA Standard reference microphone angle (70°) relative to the source position, mounted on a pair of 23-cm extension rods, hinged at a 20° angle. The variations are about ± 0.5 dB with the instrument mounted on a tripod, and ± 1.2 dB with the instrument and observer present (Fig. 20·5). Note that under the USA Standard, it is logical for the observer to be facing 90° to the direction of travel of the sound wave.

Reading of fluctuating meter needle. When the sound-level meter is on "fast," the meter needle may fluctuate. If the fluctuations are less than 6 dB, the average of the maximum and minimum readings are taken. If the fluctuations are greater than 6 dB, the reading is taken at 3 dB down from the maximum. Infrequent higher peaks are disregarded. Usually, it is best to use the "slow" meter if the readings fluctuate more than 4 dB.

Calibration of the Sound-Level Meter. Certain USA Government regulations, promulgated in connection with government contracts require that "calibration of the sound-level meter measuring system will be conducted at the beginning of a series of measurements and every 5 to 15 minutes thereafter until the system has not drifted from its established level. At that point calibrations are required every hour."

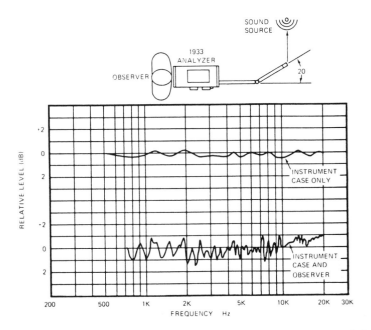

FIG. 20·5 Error introduced by the presence of the instrument case and observer with microphone extended from the case and body. On the precision sound-level meter shown, the microphones fit atop the telescoping 18-in. extension to reduce the effects of the instrument and operator on the source field. (Courtesy of GenRad Co.)

Each manufacturer of sound-level meters merchandizes a portable sound-level calibrator that fits standard-size microphones. A small pocket-size calibrator will be accurate to within about ± 0.3 to ± 0.5 dB, the lower spread being associated with calibration at room temperature and at the principal frequency. Half these variations will be achieved with a precision portable calibrator, provided correction is made for changes in atmospheric pressure. Obviously, highly accurate laboratory calibrations can be made by reciprocity techniques described in Chap. 4.

APPENDIX

Bibliography for Further Study

This bibliography supplements the references in the footnotes of each chapter. The entries cover material published in book form since 1968 which has not been condensed and added to the chapters herein. In particular, no material on signal analysis or digital filter design is contained in this text, simply because this is a second edition and not a complete rewrite.

Digital filters, properly designed and used with suitable low-pass filtering to avoid aliasing, obey the same physical laws as analog filters. Even if the practicing engineer uses digital filters and Fast Fourier Transforms exclusively, a clear understanding of the techniques of analog measurement is extremely helpful in interpreting digitally measured results.

Compared to analog analysis, digital processing primarily offers greater accuracy, better phase control, and wider dynamic ranges. Similarly, the availability of high-speed computation and large computer memories primarily serve to speed up the processing of signals and to make processing more flexible.

Acoustical measurements must be tailored to the task at hand. The articles published in technical periodicals demonstrate ways in which the principles of measurement are adapted to the particular problems of current experimenters. Periodicals include:

Journal of the Acoustical Society of America, published monthly by the Acoustical Society of America. Address: 500 Sunnyside Blvd., Woodbury, NY 11797.

Noise Control Engineering Journal, published bi-monthly by the Institute of Noise Control Engineering (INCE). Address: P. O. Box 3206, Arlington Branch, Poughkeepsie, NY 12603.

Acustica, a Europhysics Journal, published monthly. Address: S. Hirzel Verlag, Stuttgart, Germany.
Journal of Sound and Vibration, published semi-monthly by Academic Press, London. Address: 111 5th Avenue, New York, NY 10003.
Applied Acoustics, published eight times per year by Elsevier Applied Science Publishers. Address: Crown House, Linton Road, Barking Essex IG118JU, England.
Soviet Physics Acoustics, English translation published bimonthly by the American Institute of Physics. Address: 335 East 45th Street, New York, NY 10017.
Acoustics, Speech and Signal Processing, published monthly by the ASSP Society of the IEEE. Address: 345 East 47th Street, New York, NY 10017.
Sound and Vibration, published monthly by Acoustical Publications. Address: P. O. Box 40416, Bay Village, OH 44140.
Proceedings of NOISE-CON, collected papers from annual USA conferences of INCE. Same address as INCE, except P. O. Box 3469.
Proceedings of INTER-NOISE, collected papers from annual International INCE conferences. Address as above.

A.1 General References

1. L. L. Beranek, *Noise and Vibration Control,* Revised Ed. (Institute of Noise Control Engineering, P. O. Box 3206, Poughkeepsie, NY, 1988).
2. R. S. Jones, *Noise and Vibration Control in Buildings* (McGraw-Hill, New York, 1984).
3. E. Zwicker and M. Zollner, *Electroakustic* (Springer, New York, 1984).
4. A. P. Dowling and J. E. Ffowcs-Williams, *Sound and Sources of Sound* (Wiley, New York, 1983).
5. *Acoustical Measurements: Methods and Instrumentation,* edited by H. B. Miller (Benchmark papers in acoustics/16, Academic Press, New York, 1982).
6. T. J. Schultz, *Community Noise Rating,* 2nd Edition (Applied Science Publishers, New York, 1982).
7. L. E. Kinsler, A. R. Frey, A. B. Coppens, and J. V. Sanders,

Fundamentals of Acoustics, 3rd Edition (Wiley, New York, 1982).

8. M. Rossi, *Acoustics and Electracoustics* (Artech House, 685 Canton St., Norwood, MA, 1988).

9. *Noise and Acoustic Vibration Control*, edited by B. D. Tartakovski [in Russian] (Moscow, 1982).

10. J. D. Irwin and E. R. Graf, *Industrial Noise and Vibration Control* (Prentice-Hall, Englewood Cliffs, NJ, 1979).

11. P. H. Parkin, H. R. Humphreys, and J. R. Cowell, *Acoustics, Noise and Buildings*, 4th Edition (Faber & Faber, London, 1979).

12. *Handbook of Noise Assessment*, edited by D. N. May (Van Nostrand Reinhold, New York, 1978).

13. D. R. Flynn, W. A. Leasure, Jr., A. I. Rubin, and M. A. Cadoff, *Noise Emission Standards for Regulatory Purposes*, Handbook 122 (National Bureau of Standards, Washington, DC, 1977, order from U. S. Government Printing Office).

14. R. H. Lyon, *Statistical Energy Analysis of Dynamical Systems: Theory and Applications* (MIT Press, Cambridge, MA, 1977).

15. P. Lienard, *Decibels et Indices de Bruit (Noise)* [in French] (Masson et Cie, Paris, 1974).

16. A. V. Rimskii-Korsakov, *Electroacoustics* [in Russian] (Svyaz', Moscow, 1973).

17. M. C. Yunger and D. Feit, *Sound, Structures and Their Interaction* (MIT Press, Cambridge, MA, 1972).

18. *Aerodynamic Noise*, edited by H. S. Ribner (Univ. of Toronto Press, Toronto, 1969).

19. *Physics of Aerodynamic Noise*, edited by E. Rudoe and P. E. Doak (Boston Spa, Yorkshire, 1969).

20. P. M. Morse and K. U. Ingard, *Theoretical Acoustics* (McGraw-Hill, New York, 1968; reprinted by Princeton University, 1987).

21. E. Skudrzyk, *Simple and Complex Vibratory Systems* (Penn State University Press, State College, PA, 1968).

A.2 Microphones and Loudspeakers

22. E. Frederiksen, O. Schultz, M. Pil, and M. Brock, "Microphones for intensity probes," Tech. Rev. No. 4 (Bruel & Kjaer, Naerum, Denmark, 1986).

23. L. L. Beranek, *Acoustics* (1954). (Reprinted with changes by the Acoustical Society of America, New York, 1986).
24. R. C. Seippel, *Transducers, Sensors and Detectors* (Prentice-Hall, Englewood Cliffs, NJ, 1983).
25. *Piezoelectric and Acoustoelectronic Devices*, edited by A. F. Plonskii [in Russian] (Polytechnic Institute, Omsk, 1982).
26. H. N. Norton, *Sensor and Analyzer Handbook* (Prentice-Hall, Englewood Cliffs, NJ, 1982).
27. Anon, *Condenser Microphones*, Data Handbook (Bruel & Kjaer, Naerum, Denmark, 1982).
28. N. Pawera, *Microphones, Technique and Technology*, 2nd edition (ARSIS, Dachau, West Germany, 1981).
29. M. Colloms, *High Performance Loudspeakers* (Halsted/Wiley, 1978).
30. S. Guilford, *The Evaluation and Calibration of Ultrasonic Transducers* (I. P. C. Science and Technology Press, 1978).
31. A. A. Kharkevich, *Theory of Electroacoustic Transducers, Vols. I, II, and III* (in Russian, Nauka, Moscow, 1973).
32. G. Rasmussen, P. V. Bruel, F. Skode, and E. Frederiksen, *Measuring Microphones* (Bruel & Kjaer, Naerum, Denmark, 1972).

A.3 Audiometers, Hearing Aids and Earphones

33. *Hearing Measurement*, 2nd Edition, edited by J. B. Chaiklin, I. M. Ventry, and R. S. Dixon (Addison-Wesley, Reading, MA, 1982).
34. L. B. Beck, *Handbook of Hearing Aid Measurement* (Dep. Med. Surg., Veterans Admin., Washington, DC, 1979). PB82-117235 (No. 2 1982).
35. *Hearing Measurement*, edited by W. F. Rintelmann (University Park Press, Baltimore, MD, 1979).
36. W. J. Staab, *Hearing Aid Handbook* (Tab Books, Blue Ridge Summit, PA, 1978).
37. M. E. Bryan and W. Tempest, *Industrial Audiometry* (Bryan and Tempest, 4 Belmont Close, Brinscall, Nr. Chorley, Lancs., England, 1976).
38. J. Jerger, *Audiology*, 2nd edition (Academic Press, New York, 1973).

A.4 Measurement of Sound

39. S. J. Yang and A. J. Ellison, *Machinery Noise Measurement* (Clarendon, Oxford, England, 1985).
40. G. Rasmussen, *Intensity Measurement*, Publication BA-7196-11 (Bruel & Kjaer, Naerum, Denmark, 1985).
41. J. R. Mathews, *Acoustic Emission* (Gordon & Breach Science Publishers, New York, 1984).
42. S. Gade, *Sound Intensity: Theory*. Technical Notes, Part 1 (Bruel & Kjaer, Naerum, Denmark, 1982).
43. A. V. Nikonov and L. Z. Papernov, *Instruments for Sound Level Measurements* [in Russian] (Radio i Svyaz', Moscow, 1981).
44. *Mechanics of Sound Generation in Flows*, edited by E. A. Mueller (Springer, Berlin, 1979).
45. A. Hassall and K. Zaveru, *Acoustic Noise Measurements*, 4th Edition (Bruel & Kjaer, Naerum, Denmark, 1979).
46. L. G. Ospinov, D. Z. Lopashev, and E. N. Fedoseeva, *Acoustical Measurements in Construction* [in Russian] (Stroiizdat, Moscow, 1978).
47. K. B. Ginn, *Architectural Acoustics*, 2nd Edition (Bruel & Kjaer, Naerum, Denmark, 1978).
48. S. Singh, *Measurement Procedures in Speech, Hearing and Language* (University Park Press, Baltimore, MD, 1975).
49. A. P. G. Peterson, *Handbook of Noise Measurement* (Gen-Rad, Concord, MA, 1974).
50. H. Kutruff, *Room Acoustics* (Wiley, New York, 1973).

A.5 Signal Processing and Transforms

The first six of the following references are recommended as first reading for engineers not familiar with the theory of signal processing:

51. D. W. Steele, "Data Analysis," Chap. 5 in *Noise and Vibration Control*, edited by L. L. Beranek, Revised Ed. (Institute of Noise Control Engineering, P. O. Box 3206, Poughkeepsie, NY, 1988).
52. R. B. Randall, *Frequency Analysis*, 3rd Ed. (Bruel & Kjaer, Naerum, Denmark, 1987).
53. M. Bellanger, *Digital Processing of Signals: Theory and Practice* (Wiley, New York, 1985).

54. A. V. Oppenheim and R. W. Schafer, *Digital Signal Processing* (Prentice-Hall, Englewood Cliffs, NJ, 1975).
55. L. R. Rabiner and B. Gold, *Theory and Application of Digital Signal Processing* (Prentice-Hall, Englewood Cliffs, NJ, 1975).
56. R. N. Bracewell, *Fourier Transform and its Applications*, 2nd Edition (McGraw-Hill, New York, 1986).
57. S. J. Orfanidis, *Optimum Signal Processing: An Introduction* (Macmillan, New York, 1985).
58. B. Widrow and S. D. Stearns, *Adaptive Signal Processing* (Prentice-Hall, Englewood Cliffs, NJ, 1985).
59. H. Biering and O. Z. Pederson, "Time delay spectrometry," Tech. Rep., Part I in No. 1 and Part II in No. 2 (Bruel & Kjaer, Naerum, Denmark, 1983).
60. D. F. Elliott and K. R. Rao, *Fast Transforms: Algorithms, Analysis and Applications* (Academic Press, New York, 1983).
61. N. C. Geckinli and D. Yavuz, *Discrete Fourier Transformation and its Applications to Power Spectra Estimation* (North Holland, Amsterdam, 1983).
62. J. S. Bendat and A. G. Piersol, *Engineering Applications of Correlation and Spectral Analysis* (Wiley, New York, 1980).
63. L. B. Rabiner and R. W. Schafer, *Digital Processing of Speech Signals* (Prentice-Hall, Englewood Cliffs, NJ, 1979).
64. R. K. Otnes and L. Enochson, *Applied Time Series Analysis* (Wiley, New York, 1978).
65. A. Papoulis, *Signal Analysis* (McGraw-Hill, New York, 1977).
66. E. O. Brigham, *Fast Fourier Transform* (Prentice-Hall, Englewood Cliffs, NJ, 1974).
67. E. B. Magrab and D. S. Blomquist, *Measurement of Time-Varying Phenomen* (Wiley-Interscience, 1971).

A.6 Frequency Analysis

68. R. B. Randall, *Frequency Analysis*, 3rd Edition (Bruel & Kjaer, Naerum, Denmark, 1987).
69. R. S. Rothschild, "The second revolution in real-time spectrum analysers," Sound and Vibration, 21, 14–22 (March 1987).

70. L. B. Jackson, *Digital Filters and Signal Processing* (Kluwer Academic Publishers, Boston, 1986).
71. H. Honig and D. Messerschmidt, *Adaptive Filters: Structures, Algorithms and Applications* (Kluwer Academic Publishers, Boston, 1986).
72. R. E. Crochiere and L. R. Rabiner, *Multirate Digital Processing* (Prentice-Hall, Englewood Cliffs, NJ, 1983).
73. E. Christian, *LC Filter Design, Test & Manufacturing* (Wiley, New York, 1983).
74. H. N. Norton, *Sensor and Analyzer Handbook* (Prentice-Hall, Englewood Cliffs, NJ, 1982).
75. J. T. Broche, *Principles of Analog and Digital Frequency Analysis* (Tapir, Norwegian Institute of Technology, Trondheim, 1981).
76. A. Antoniou, *Digital Filters: Analysis and Design* (McGraw-Hill, New York, 1979).
77. H. Larson, "Measurement of effective bandwidth of filters," Tech. Rep. No. 2, pp. 21–36 (Bruel & Kjaer, Naerum, Denmark, 1978).
78. *Digital Filters and the Fast Fourier Transform*, edited by B. Liu (Halsted Press/Wiley, 1975).
79. R. W. Daniels, *Approximation Methods for Electronic Filter Design* (McGraw-Hill, New York, 1974).

Subject Index

A

A-weighted sound levels
definition of, 800–803
frequency curve, 807,809
A-weighting network, 807,808
anechoic chamber
definition, 16
early, 14
absorption coefficient *(see also*
non-linearity in gases and
attenuation of sound)
chamber, 15
definitions, 15
free-wave, 15
sabin, 16
absorption of sound
definition, 15
gases, 44,45,64
water, 51,75,76
acoustic calibration
earphones, 718–738
hearing aids, 741–748
loudspeakers, 649–694
microphones, absolute, 111–175
microphones, 624–648,695–718
acoustic compliance, 18
acoustic constants
air, 41,46–48
gases, 46,49
liquids, 51–53
solids, 54
water, 51,52
acoustic impedance *(see* impedance)
acoustic inertance, 28
acoustic intensity, 25,26,261–265
acoustic mass, 28
acoustic ohm, 16
acoustic reactance, 31
acoustic resistance, 31
acoustic wave *(see* wave)

actuator, electrostatic, 173–176
air, properties of, 39,50,64–71
air conduction, 354–364,369,370
American National Standards
absorption by atmosphere, 64
acoustical calibrators, 172
acoustical terminology 794
acoustical quantities, preferred, 794
analog and digital filters, 811
audiometers, 354,355,364
barriers, outdoors, 798
bone vibrators, 364–369
business machines, 797
calibration of earphones, 728
calibration of microphones, 114
hearing aid specifications, 745
calibrators, 172
ear simulator, 728
earphones, 728
filters, 811
hearing aid tests, 744
laboratory microphones, 208
loudness calculation, 512
machinery noise, 796
manikin specification, 740
microphones, 114,172,208
network, weighting, 800
noise from business machines, 797
noise from machinery and equipment,
796
noise measurement, 546,795–798
noise rating, 504
occluded ear simulator, 728
outdoor noise barriers, 798
preferred acoustical
quantities, 794
procedures for determination of noise
emission, 795
psychoacoustical terminology, 794
reference sound sources, 795,798
sound level meters, 800
sound pressure level measurements, 795

B

baffles, loudspeaker
definition, 18
diffraction around, 106–110
finite, 106–110
infinite, 107,656
Ballantine meter, 476,477
band levels, conversion, 562–567
bandwidth, filters, 526–529,
550–560, 812–817
bar microphone
directivity pattern, 253
equations, 256–258
barium titanate transducers
properties, 248,249
sensitivity, 249,250
structure, 249
basilar membrane, 192–194
Bel, 18
Bessel functions, 57–61
bone conduction
artificial mastoid, 364–366,738,739
audiometer tests, 368,369
definition, 18,364
tests of hearing, 364–369
threshold force levels, 367
vibrator, 364–366
bridge
acoustic impedance, 328–342
capacitance, 138
electroacoustic, 340–342
frequency, 286–288
Wien, 286–288

C

calibration of analyzers
conversion to spectrum levels, 562–567
cutoff frequencies, 557–560
dynamic characteristics, 573,574
filter band response, 548–557
mean frequency, 560–562
non-pass attenuation, 568–573
overload point, 568
rectifier characteristics, 573,574
residual noise, 567

calibration of microphones
American standards, 114,172,208
artificial voice testing,
387–397,704–718
complex signal fidelity, 625
directional characteristic, 624,635–639
diffuse-field response, 633–635,
668–672
distortion characteristic,
425–429,625,643–645,715–717
dynamic range, 625,647,648
electrical impedance, 140,215
625,645,646
free-field response, 592, 631–633
frequency response, 624, 626–635.
open-circuit voltage, 589–592
pistonphone, 172–173
power efficiency, 625,639–642
pressure response, 584–589,592
primary calibration
American standard, 114
electrostatic actuator, 173–176
particle amplitude, 159–161
Rayleigh disk, 148–158
reciprocity, 113–148
free-field, 116–122
coupler, 123–148
thermophone, 161–171
real-voice testing, 695–704
transient response, 646,647
capacitance bridge, 138
carbon microphone
breathing, 207
distortion, 206,700,715–717
electrical current, 206,717,718
non-linearity, 206
position, 717,718
thermal effects, 207
testing, 704–718
vibration, 704,710
cardiod microphone
directivity, 251,252
structure, 251
cavity resonance
closed chambers, 140–148
microphones, 180,181,225
cent, 18,272
chambers
anechoic, 14,16,632,656,657